H
Microcontrollers

Handbook of Microcontrollers

Myke Predko

McGraw-Hill

New York   San Francisco   Washington, D.C.   Auckland   Bogotá
Caracas   Lisbon   London   Madrid   Mexico City   Milan
Montreal   New Delhi   San Juan   Singapore
Sydney   Tokyo   Toronto

Library of Congress Cataloging-in-Publication Data

Predko, Michael.
    Handbook of microcontrollers / Myke Predko.
       p. cm.
    Includes index.
      ISBN 0-07-913717-2 (hardcover). — ISBN 0-07-913716-4 (softcover)
      1. Programmable controllers—Handbooks, manuals, etc. I. Title.
    TJ223.P76P73   1998
    629.8'95416—dc21
                                           98-16890
                                            CIP

McGraw-Hill

*A Division of The **McGraw·Hill** Companies*

Copyright © 1999 by The McGraw-Hill Companies, Inc. All rights reserved. Printed in the United States of America. Except as permitted under the United States Copyright Act of 1976, no part of this publication may be reproduced or distributed in any form or by any means, or stored in a data base or retrieval system, without the prior written permission of the publisher.

2 3 4 5 6 7 8 9 0 DOC/DOC   0 3 2 1 0

P/N 052708-3
Part of
ISBN 0-07-913717-2 (hc)

P/N 052707-5
Part of
ISBN 0-07-913716-4 (pbk)

The sponsoring editor of this book was Scott Grillo. The editing supervisor was Sally Glover, and the production supervisor was Clare Stanley. It was set in Palatino per the TAB4 Design by Joanne Morbit of McGraw-Hill's Professional Book Group composition unit, Hightstown, New Jersey.

Printed and bound by R. R. Donnelley & Sons Company.

This book is printed on recycled, acid-free paper containing a minimum of 50% recycled, de-inked fiber.

McGraw-Hill books are available at special quantity discounts to use as premiums and sales promotions, or for use in corporate training programs. For more information, please write to the Director of Special Sales, McGraw-Hill, Professional Publishing, Two Penn Plaza, New York, NY 10121-2298. Or contact your local bookstore.

CONTENTS

ACKNOWLEDGMENTS

Although this is only my second book, I feel like I have been able to start to develop a strong network of people who can help me with getting the information and sample products that make writing about electronics a lot easier. There are a number of people I would like to recognize and thank for their help and enthusiasm for this project.

The first thank you is to Scott Grillo, my editor at McGraw-Hill. It was his idea for this book, and it really was the right book for me at this time. Writing this book really has been an educational experience for me and I appreciate the opportunity to do it. Scott's patient help on this and my previous book, as well as guiding me through the publishing process, is really appreciated.

One of the truly great ideas on the Internet is the listserver. For each of the microcontrollers presented here, I have provided pointers to listservers and instructions for joining them. For everyone who helps others by answering questions, helping "newbies" figure out why their applications won't run or sharing the occasional joke, you really deserve a hearty pat on the back.

In my first book, I was able to get a lot of help from Dave Cochran of Pipe-Thompson (my local manufacturer's rep). With this book, I was able to continue working with Dave as well as Greg Anderson and Al Loverich of Microchip. Guys, thanks for your help and guideance with the PICMicro.

I would like to thank Jim Farrell of Motorola SPS and Derek Klotz of the Toronto sales office. I was really impressed with your enthusiasm for the 68HC05 and your help in getting information and samples. As I was writing this book, Motorola announced that it has built more than 2 billion 68HC05s; this is not surprising, with the strong support that I received and the enthusiasm I saw from them.

Frank Taylor of Dallas Semiconductor spent time with me going through the Dallas Semiconductor's 8051 compatible (and enhanced product line). I would also like to recognize my local rep, Arun Zarabi of Intelletech, for being available to answer questions and provide samples. I really appreciate your help.

One of the newest microcontrollers on the market is the AVR. I want to recognize Chris Heyden and Joe Young of Atmel for spending the time to help me find all the information that I needed.

Parallax, Inc. has set a standard for supporting its products. This is seen in Parallax providing numerous example applications and tools and setting up listservers its their engineers monitor. Thank you for making superior support from all your employees business as usual.

Thanks goes to everyone at Celestica, Inc., my regular employer, for their enthusiasm for this project and my previous book. It's the best place in the world to work.

Special thanks to Phillipe Techer of Virtual Micro Design and Don McKenzie of Dontronics for their help in understanding and providing me with samples of their products.

Both UMPS and the SimmStick are wonderful products that help in the development of applications, and both of you have to be commended for your efforts in developing and supporting these products.

A thank you goes to Ben Wirz for listening to my ideas, hearing about how I'm doing on the book, and basically caring. "Ben Tiger" is still a favourite at our house.

At home, my children—Joel, Elliot, and Marya—while not always quiet enough to do proofreading, have been a great help in their enthusiasm and interest in this book. Sorry I used examples from this book to help you with your homework.

1997 was a very difficult year for my wife, Patience, and me. Without her love and support, I never would have been able to finish this book. We never got to the beach after the last book. Hopefully we will after this one.

Myke Predko
Toronto, Ontario, Canada
December, 1997

INTRODUCTION

Many people regard the "computer revolution" to be the automation of many tasks requiring intensive or repetitive numerical calculation such as billing, complex scientific investigations, and control of highly complex operations and equipment such as in factories. Lately, the "computer revolution" has been expanded to include the Internet and digital communication.

But there has been a second revolution, probably having a much more substantial effect on our individual lives. This is the automation of almost literally everything around us using cheap and powerful microcontrollers.

For example, if you lived in what you considered a fairly unsophisticated home, how many microcontrollers do you think would be in it? Looking around my house, I was able to identify at least twenty. This included eight for our TV/stereo (the remote control, transmitters, and receivers each contain microcontrollers), three in our kitchen appliances, three for heating/cooling and thermostats, another three in phones and answering machines, a couple of light timers, and a baby monitor that senses movement. And I'm probably missing a few, either in devices that I wouldn't expect microcontrollers to be used in or in devices that use more than one microcontroller for complex/independent functions.

Cars use a surprising number of these devices. Most modern cars can have well over twenty microcontrollers not only controlling and monitoring the engine's status, but also providing antilock braking control, airbag and other safety systems control, external lighting control and monitoring, passenger compartment temperature control, and radio/stereo control. Using dedicated networks inside the car, each door or external light may have a microcontroller that is unique to the part.

Your PC has at least four microcontrollers built in—two for the keyboard/mouse, one for the hard disk drive, one for the power supply, and probably many more for hardware peripherals like controlling the CRT, modem (or network card), and the printer.

If you've never been exposed to microcontrollers, you might think that they are very standard devices. Nothing could be further from the truth. The term "microcontroller" is a very loose term, often being left up to a manufacturer to define.

I once saw a definition for poetry as "prose in which each line doesn't take up a whole line of space."

While my definition for a microcontroller isn't quite so Zen, it is not as specific as how other devices are defined: "A microcontroller is a self-contained computer system in which the processor, support, memory, and input/output are all contained in a single package." (Figure I.1.)

This definition actually holds quite well for the smaller devices which can only process data 8 bits at a time, but breaks down as the devices get larger (i.e., able to process 16 and 32 bits of data at a time).

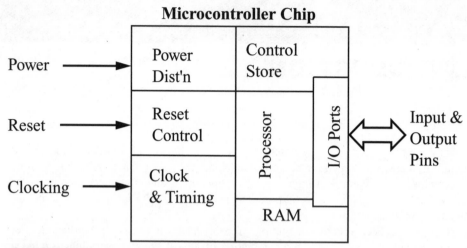

Figure I.1. Microcontroller block diagram.

When microcontrollers are used in applications, they are used to interpret input (user and environmental), communicate with other devices, and output data to a variety of different devices. In this capacity, they can reduce the "BOM" (bill of material) cost of a product significantly by reducing the number of components required to carry out complex functions, add a great deal of "user friendliness" to a product for very little additional cost, or allow flexibility in the product development process by giving the designers the opportunity to use the same hardware design for a variety of applications (each with unique software). When developing a new product or project that is used to control hardware, using a microcontroller can bring about significant advantages in the final design.

Differences lie not only in different architectures and features, but also in operation and packaging. Many microcontroller designs have taken a microprocessor and packaged it with memory and input/output ("I/O") hardware. Some microcontrollers are not physical devices but are VHDL macros that are designed to be placed in an ASIC design, allowing the design engineer to specify a microcontroller with exactly the memory and input/output required for the application. Another variable to consider is the fact that all microcontrollers are actually members of families, in which many of the hardware features available are presented in different combinations.

The myriad of different variables available in choosing a microcontroller can make choosing the "best" device for an application very difficult.

As I began to research this book, I was disappointed by the difficulty of finding good introductory information, both in the field of microcontrollers for beginners as well as the different devices available for use in an application. I consider myself to be reasonably well versed in computer systems, and I found it very frustrating to easily understand the different features of the various microcontroller designs and to be able to compare the different products to determine which would be the best device for a specific project. As I was gathering information, I felt that beginners would probably give up and look toward the first device that seemed to meet their requirements and that they could easily get information on or the device that they are already familiar with.

The purpose of this book is to try to relieve some of this confusion and provide a reference to some of the more popular 8-bit fully self-contained (or "embedded") microcontrollers currently available.

In the first section of this book, the microcontroller reference is kept at a reasonably high level, explaining the most important aspects of different microcontroller designs, software, and application considerations. As part of this section of the book, I discuss different types of microcontrollers, some standard methods of input/output to user's external hardware, as well as some techniques I've discovered for ensuring that high-quality software is created for the devices.

Each of the subsequent sections of the book are devoted to introducing you to a different microcontroller family, explaining the architecture, hardware features, and application-specific interfaces, and going through example applications. The different applications are used to show how the devices work, point out some aspects of the device, and illustrate points I make elsewhere in the book. I try to point out some specific pros and cons of the different devices and add any additional comments that I think are relevant. At the end of each microcontroller section, I give manufacturer and resource information for the family of devices.

Obviously, it would be impossible to explain every microcontroller family along with every constituent member (and even if it were possible, new devices on the market would make such a book obsolete within three or four months). Instead, the purpose of this book is to introduce the most popular 8-bit microcontroller architectures, along with an explanation of what is available in terms of features, how to program them (both developing software and burning the code into the device), and where to get additional information.

Additional Information and Resources

While the purpose of this book is to introduce you to microcontrollers, it is not a vehicle for teaching electrical engineering and computer science basics. It is assumed that you will have some experience in electronics and assembly language and high-level language programming techniques. Without a basic understanding of how microprocessors work, you may find this book to be confusing and difficult to understand.

Included with this book is a CD-ROM containing the code used to provide the applications presented in the book for each different microcontroller, along with a set of datasheets in adobe ".PDF" format for various members of the device family.

This CD-ROM should not be considered the ultimate resource for the various microcontrollers. Chip manufacturers often work at a breakneck pace, with new products and errata sheets released on a weekly basis. When doing any type of application using a microcontroller (or any other type of part for that matter), you should always make sure the information you are using is the most current possible.

I am a great believer in the Internet and its ability to help the engineer get technical information. For all the products presented in this book, this is very true. Along with Web sites, where updated information can be found, I have also included information on listservers, user groups, and information on contacting the part manufacturers directly.

Conventions Used in This Book:

K—1,000 ohms

uF—microfarads

ms—milliseconds

us—microseconds

0x0nn, $nn, 0nnh and H'nn'—Hex numbers

0b0nnn, %nnn, 0nnnb and B'nnn'—Binary number

nnn and 0nnnd—Decimal number

AND and &—Bitwise "AND"

OR and ¦—Bitwise "OR"

XOR and ^—Bitwise "XOR"

_Label—Negative active pin. In some manufacturer's data sheets, this is represented with a leading "!" character or with a bar over the entire label.

INTRODUCTION TO
MICROCONTROLLERS

MICROCONTROLLERS

CONTENTS AT A GLANCE

Different Types of Microcontrollers
EMBEDDED MICROCONTROLLERS
EXTERNAL MEMORY MICROCONTROLLERS
DIGITAL SIGNAL PROCESSORS

Processor Architectures
CISC VERSUS RISC
HARVARD VERSUS PRINCETON

Microcontroller Memory Types
CONTROL STORE
VARIABLE AREA
STACKS
HARDWARE INTERFACE REGISTERS
 ("I/O SPACE")

There really is one thing that I should make clear. When you are developing a microcontroller application, not only are you developing an application and wiring the microcontroller up to the external hardware, but you are also going to be responsible for creating many of the systems operations traditionally left to operating systems and microprocessor support chips.

Personally, I really enjoy this. It gives me a chance to optimize a design (both in terms of hardware and software) for a given application and experiment with different ways of doing things. Throughout this book, I will give you some of my thoughts on how this should be done.

As part of this chapter, I will briefly introduce you to some of the larger devices also called microcontrollers to show the differences between them and the 8-bit devices. These larger devices tend to provide more "subsystem"-type tasks, rather than the simple, stand-alone applications of the 8-bit embedded microcontrollers written about in this book.

Differences in processor architecture can make very significant performance differences in different applications. Discussions of different computer architectures can take on the intensity of a World War I trench battle (with a similar number of casualties). To avoid getting into philosophical discussions, I will present an overview of the most important issues of different architectures and what types of applications they may be best suited for.

Memory functions and different types of memory are also discussed in this chapter. If you have worked on just about any other types of computers, you may be surprised at how memory is used and allocated in a microcontroller.

Different Types of Microcontrollers

If you were to investigate all the different types of microcontrollers, you would probably be amazed at the number of different ones available. The different types of devices break down as:

- Embedded (self-contained) 8-bit microcontrollers
- 16–32-bit microcontrollers
- Digital signal processors

EMBEDDED MICROCONTROLLERS

There is quite a wide range of self-contained devices available. The term "embedded" is usually substituted for "self contained." In an embedded microcontroller, all the necessary resources (memory, I/O, etc.) are available on the chip; all you have to do is provide power and clocking. These microcontrollers can be based on an established microprocessor core or use a design specific to microcontroller functions. This means that there is a great deal of variability of operation, even in devices that are doing the same tasks.

The primary role of these microcontrollers is to provide inexpensive, programmable logic control and interfacing to external devices. This means that they typically are not required to provide highly complex functions. But they are capable of providing surprisingly sophisticated control of different applications.

When I say that the devices are inexpensive, this is to say they range from $1.00 to $20.00 apiece (with cost depending on complexity, which is a function of internal features and external pin count, and quantity bought).

Generally, these devices have the following characteristics that allow them to be simply wired into a circuit with very little support requirements. The following list will give you an idea of what's generally available in an embedded microcontroller:

- Processor reset
- Device clocking
- Central processor
- Control store (E(E)P)ROM and programming interface
- Variable RAM

- I/O pins
- Instruction cycle timers

The original microcontroller diagram shown in Figure 1.1 will give you an idea of how an embedded microcontroller chip could be laid out and interfaced to the outside world.

The basic requirements for a computer system may be added to the features list for more sophisticated embedded microcontrollers:

- Built-in monitor/debugger program
- Built-in control store programming from a direct host connectionn
- Interrupt capability (from a variety of sources)
- Analog I/O (both PWM and variable D.C. I/O)
- Serial I/O (synchronous and asynchronous data transfers)
- Parallel I/O (including directly interfacing to a master processor)
- External memory interfaces ("microprocessor mode")

All these features increase the flexibility of the device considerably and not only make developing applications easier, but possible in some cases. Note that most of these options enhance the I/O pins' function.

Early microcontrollers were manufactured using bipolar or NMOS technologies. All modern devices are fabricated using CMOS technology, which decreases the current chip size and the power requirements considerably.

Maximum speeds for the different devices are typically in the low tens of megahertz. The primary limiting factor is the access time of the memory used in the microcontrollers. For the typical applications carried that use these devices, this is generally not an issue.

EXTERNAL MEMORY MICROCONTROLLERS

Some microcontrollers (most notably devices with 16-or 32-bit data paths) rely completely on external memory. This external memory contains the Control Store as well as any RAM required for the application. Figure 1.1 can be updated to include external memory as shown in Figure 1.2.

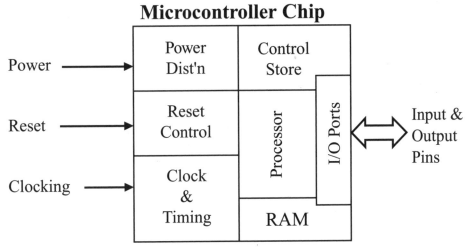

Figure1-1 Microcontroller block diagram.

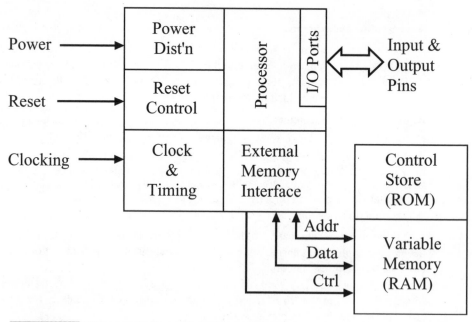

Figure1-2 Microcontroller with external memory.

The classic example of this type of microcontroller is the Intel 80188. This was essentially an 8088 (used in the IBM PC and compatibles), but with additional circuitry to provide many of the "standard" functions needed to run applications (i.e. Interrupt and DMA Controllers) added to the chip. The purpose of the 80188 was to provide an integrated package containing all the necessary circuitry for the development engineer to simply create an 8088 application.

To avoid getting lots of letters later, yes, I know the 8088 was an 8-bit external and 16-bit internal Data Path version of the 8086 (which has a 16-bit external and internal 16-bit Data Path) and there is also an 80186 that follows the same pattern (it works like the 80188 but has a 16-bit external Data Path).

I decided not to include any references to any external memory microcontrollers except as options on some devices in this book because I felt that they are designed for different applications than the embedded devices. These applications generally require large amounts of RAM and few I/O pin functions (other than serial or bus interfaces). In an application well suited to an external-memory microcontroller, the critical resource is RAM, as opposed to general-purpose I/O pins, as is the case with embedded microcontrollers.

A typical application for an external memory microcontroller is as a hard disk cache/buffer that buffers and distributes large amounts of data (usually measured in megabytes). The external memory allows the device to run at higher speeds than what an embedded microcontroller's memory would run at.

DIGITAL SIGNAL PROCESSORS

Digital signal processors ("DSPs") are a relatively new category of processor. The purpose of a DSP is to take sample data of an analog system and calculate an appropriate response. DSPs and their ALUs ("arithmetic logic units"—the hardware that performs calculations) run at very high speeds to allow this control in real time. DSPs are often used in applications like active noise-canceling microphones in aircraft (a second, ambient noise microphone provides a signal that is subtracted from the primary microphone signal, allowing canceling out of the ambient noise, leaving just the pilot's voice) or eliminating "ghosting" in broadcast television signals.

Developing DSP algorithms is a science unto itself and is a sub-branch of "control theory." The science of control theory requires very advanced mathematics and is really beyond the scope of this book (although later I will discuss "fuzzy logic," which is a non-traditional method of producing computer control of systems). DSPs come in a variety of designs that use features found in the embedded microcontrollers and external-memory microcontrollers. While typically not designed for stand-alone applications, they can be used for controlling external digital hardware as well as processing the input signals and formulating appropriate output signals.

Processor Architectures

As I mentioned above, I don't want to begin an argument between the proponents of CISC or RISC processors using Harvard or Princeton architectures. As I go through these sections, I will try to explain the differences between these processor design philosophies and how they relate to microcontroller design and applications.

CISC VERSUS RISC

Currently, many processors are called "RISC" ("Reduced Instruct Set Computers") because there is a perception that RISC is faster than "CISC" (or "Complex Instruction Set Computers"). This can be confusing because there are many processors available that are identified as "RISC-like," but are in fact "CISC" processors. And, in some applications, "CISC" processors will execute code faster than RISC processors or execute applications that RISC processors cannot.

What is the real difference between RISC and CISC? In CISC processors, there tends to be a large number of instructions, each carrying out a different permutation of the same operation (accessing data directly, through index registers, etc.) with instructions perceived to be useful by the processor's designer.

In a RISC system, the instructions are at as bare minimum as possible to allow the users to design their own operations, rather than let the designer do it for them. Below, I show how a stack "push" and "pop" would be done by RISC system in two instructions which allow the two simple constituent instructions to be used for different operations (or "compound instructions" such as this).

This ability to write to all the registers in the processor as if they were the same is known as "orthogonality" or "symmetry" of the processor. This allows some operations to be unexpectedly powerful and flexible. This can be seen in conditional jumping. In a CISC system, a conditional jump is usually based on status register bits. In a RISC system, a conditional jump may be based on a bit anywhere in memory. This greatly simplifies the operation of flags and executing code based on their state.

But for a RISC system to be successful, more than just reducing the number of things that are done in an instruction has to be done. By careful design of the processor's architecture, the flexibility can be increased to the point to where a very small instruction set, able to execute in very few instruction cycles, can be used to provide extremely complex functions in a most efficient manner.

HARVARD VERSUS PRINCETON

Many years ago, the U.S. government asked Harvard and Princeton universities to come up with a computer architecture to be used in computing tables of Naval Artillery shell distances for varying elevations and environmental conditions.

Princeton's response was a computer that had common memory for storing the control program as well as variables and other data structures. It was best known by the chief scientist's name, "Von Neumann." (Figure 1.3.)

The "memory interface unit" is responsible for arbitrating access to the memory space between reading instructions (based upon the current program counter) and passing data back and forth with the processor and its internal registers.

It may at first seem that the memory interface unit is a bottleneck between the processor and the variable/RAM space (especially with the requirement for fetching instructions at the same time), but in many Princeton-architected processors, this is not the case because the time required to execute a given instruction can be used to fetch the next instruction (this is known as "prefetching") and is a feature on many Princeton-architected processors.

In contrast, Harvard's response was a design that used separate memory banks for program storage, the processor stack, and variable RAM. (Figure 1.4.)

The Princeton architecture won the competition because it was better suited to the technology of the time. Using one memory was preferable because of the unreliability of

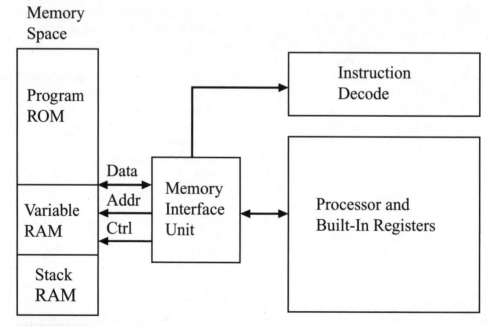

Figure1-3 Princeton architecture block diagram.

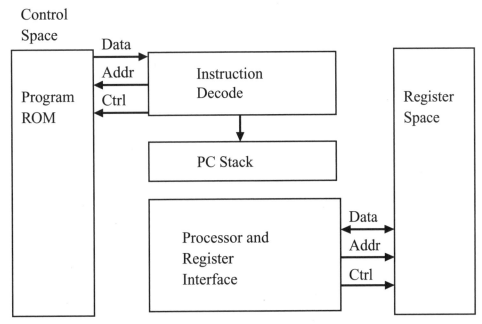

Figure1-4 **Harvard architecture block diagram.**

electronics at the time (this was before transistors were in widespread use); a single memory would have fewer things that could go wrong.

The Harvard architecture was largely ignored until the late 1970s when microcontroller manufacturers realized that the architecture had advantages for the devices they were currently designing.

The Von Neumann architecture's largest advantage is that it simplifies the microcontroller chip design because only one memory is accessed. For microcontrollers, its biggest asset is that the contents of "RAM" ("random access memory") can be used for both variable (data) storage as well as program instruction storage. An advantage for some applications is the program counter stack contents that are available for access by the program. This allows greater flexibility in developing software, primarily in the area of real time operating systems (which will be discussed at greater length elsewhere in the book).

The Harvard architecture executes instructions in fewer instruction cycles than the Von Neumann architecture. This is because a much greater amount of instruction "parallelism" is possible in the Harvard architecture. "Parallelism" means that instruction fetches can take place during previous instruction execution and not wait for either a "dead" cycle of the instruction's execution or have to stop the processor's operation while the next instruction is being fetched.

For example, if a Princeton-architected processor were to execute a read byte and store it in the accumulator instruction, it would carry out the instruction sequence shown in Figure 1.5.

In the first cycle of the instruction execution, the instruction is read in from the memory space; in the next cycle, the data to be put in the accumulator is read from the memory space.

The Harvard architecture, because of its increased parallelism, would be able to carry out the instruction while the next instruction is being fetched from memory (the current instruction was fetched during the previous instruction's execution). (Figure 1.6.)

Executing this instruction in the Harvard architecture also takes place over two instructions, but the instruction read takes place while the previous instruction is carried out. This allows the instruction to execute in only one instruction cycle (while the next instruction is being read in).

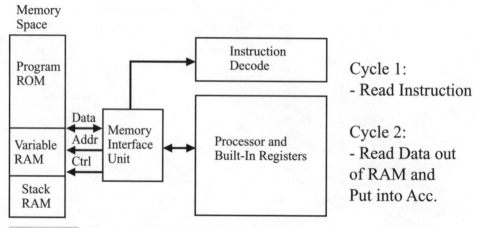

Cycle 1:
- Read Instruction

Cycle 2:
- Read Data out of RAM and Put into Acc.

Figure1-5 mov Acc, Reg in Princeton architecture.

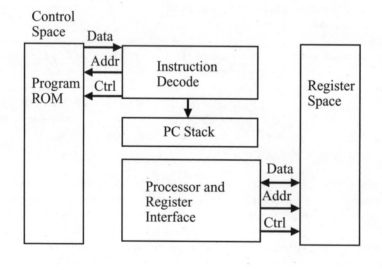

Cycle -1:
- Complete Previous Instruction
- Read the "move Acc, Reg" Instruction

Cycle 1:
- Execute "move Acc, Reg" Instruction
- Read next Instruction

Figure1-6 mov Acc, Reg in Harvard architecture.

This method of execution ("parallelism"), like RISC instructions, also helps instructions take the same number of cycles for easier timing of loops and critical code. This point, while seemingly made in passing, is probably the most important aspect that I would consider in choosing a microcontroller for a timing-sensitive application.

For example, the Microchip PIC executes every instruction, except ones that modify the program counter in four clock cycles (one "instruction cycle"). This makes critical timing operations much easier to do than say an Intel 8051, which can take anywhere from 16 clock cycles to 64 clock cycles to complete an instruction. Often, a simulator or a hardware emulator will be required to accurately time a function rather than trying to figure out manually how many cycles will be used from the code.

I should caution you (I will continue to do so throughout the book) and note that these types of performance comparisons may not be representative of all the processors and microcontrollers using these two types of architectures. The comparison that matters is the actual application, and different architectures and devices will offer unique features that may make it easier to do a different application. In some cases, certain applications can only be done by specific architectures and features.

This is especially true in the case shown above. After reading this section, you probably feel that a Harvard-architected microcontroller is the only way to go. But the Harvard architecture lacks the flexibility of the Princeton in software operations required for some applications. Examples of this will be shown later in this book.

So rather than trying to point you into thinking that one architecture is better than another, I want to educate you on what the different architectures look like and what the advantages/disadvantages of the different architectures are in different situations.

Microcontroller Memory Types

I tend to break up microcontroller memory into three basic types. "Control store" (or "program storage") is read only memory used for storing software and table data that doesn't change during execution. The "variable area" is used for storing temporary values or parameters for use during program execution. "Hardware interface registers" are both the internal processor's registers as well as the registers used to control the operation and peripheral interfaces.

As a word of warning, you'll probably be surprised at how little memory is available in microcontrollers. As you will see, this is not a major limitation, but it will be surprising the first time that you see the different devices' specifications (especially when you consider modern PCs, which have tens of megabytes of RAM storage).

CONTROL STORE

The program memory is usually made up of four different types of memory: PROM, EPROM, EEPROM (also known as "flash"), or ROM. All three types of memory are "non-volatile," which means that the content of the memory is retained even when power has been removed from the microcontroller. This is because the microcontroller doesn't have any mass storage (i.e., disk) to load programs from upon boot (like a PC does). This means that the application code is resident at all times.

During execution, the program instructions are read from this memory, and the processor's instruction decode unit executes the coded instruction. This memory cannot be reprogrammed during program execution, which means that a microcontroller is dedicated to an application until this memory is erased (if possible) and programmed with a new set of instructions.

One aspect that should be noted with different microcontrollers is that the bus width specification (i.e., 8, 16, or 32 bits) is for the data bus. For Harvard architectures, the control store may be wider to allow a full instruction (with imbedded data) to be read in at one time. For example, the PIC microcontrollers can have control store widths of 12, 14, or 16 bits, depending on the part used. In the AVR, the instruction is always 16 bits wide. Regardless of the control store width, in both microcontrollers the data bus width is always 8 bits.

In Princeton-architected devices, the bus width is often also the data path size. In the Motorola 68HC05, a 24-bit instruction is stored in three 8-bit control store locations and requires three byte reads before it can be executed.

So, to avoid confusion, when I refer to a device as 8 bit, I am referring to the size of a data word that the microcontroller can process.

Read only memory ("ROM") is the term used when the application code is literally built into the microcontroller during chip manufacturing. To create this type of memory, once the application program is tested and "qualified" (deemed to be ready for mass production), it is given to the chip manufacturer, who then converts the program into an optical "mask." This mask is used to provide interconnect information for the chip control store. Because of this process, "ROM" is also known as "mask programmed ROM."

"ROM" control store programming, while being the cheapest method of programming parts for high volume applications, has some significant downsides that have put it out of favor in the past few years. These downsides are primarily related to the up-front costs required to have the manufacturer develop custom masks for the part and the time required to build parts with this mask; the whole process typically takes ten weeks and requires on the order of ten thousand parts to break even with a field-programmable ROM (which typically is E(E)PROM). But there are additional costs, primarily in the area of inventory and handling (the microcontroller stock cannot be used for other applications if the need arises).

Erasable programmable memory ("EPROM") consists of the program memory cells that are electrically programmable and erasable using an ultraviolet light. "PROM" can only be programmed once. PROM memory usually consists of fuses that can be electrically "blown" at programming time. I have not seen PROM parts for a very long time (over ten years). While there still may be some manufacturers building PROM memories, they have really fallen out of favor.

An EPROM cell is actually a MOS transistor with the gate left floating, surrounded by silicon dioxide ("SiO2"), and the drain connected to ground and a pull-up attached to the source. When an EPROM cell is "erased" or "cleared," the "floating gate" ("Float" in Figure 1.7) doesn't contain any charge, which means the transistor is "off" (and the Source is being pulled up). At this time a "1" is read from the cell (which is the voltage level at the Source). This means that "programming" (or "burning") a program into EPROM memory simply consists of programming "0"s into the memory.

Programming is accomplished by putting a high voltage on the "Control Gate" ("Control" in Figure 1.7). This voltage is high enough to break down the insulating layer of the SiO2 between the two gates, and a charge is transferred from the Control Gate to the Floating Gate. This causes the MOS transistor to actually turn on, pulling down the source to ground (and returning a "0" when the cell is read).

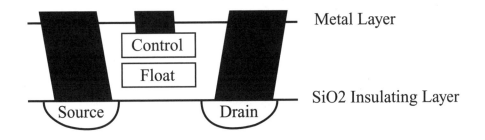

Metal Layer

Control

Float

SiO2 Insulating Layer

Source

Drain

Silicon Substrate

Figure1-7 EPROM memory cell.

To clear a cell (erase a bit), ultraviolet light is shined on the chip, giving the charge trapped in the insulated Floating Gate enough energy to escape and leave the Floating Gate with no charge (causing a "1" to be read again from the cell). This process can take anywhere from seconds to minutes to erase an entire device.

Typically, EPROM chips are distributed in ceramic packages with a quartz window to allow the chip inside to be erased by ultraviolet light. This package is actually quite expensive and drives up the cost of the device considerably. To reduce this cost, often an EPROM-based chip will be encased in a windowless plastic part and is known as a "one time programmable" ("OTP") package and is often used to reduce the price of the EPROM part. This cost reduction can be so significant that often a ROM-based part cannot be cost competitive with it for many applications. This is especially true when the "extra" costs of the ROM part (extra inventory and special handling) are taken into account in the total cost of the application manufacturing process.

Early microcontrollers could only be programmed using complex parallel protocols. As will be seen later in the book, this has changed significantly with some of the latest device's EPROM (and EEPROM) programming specifications, which allow microcontrollers to be programmed "in-system" (often known as "in-system programming" or "ISP"). ISP microcontrollers can be programmed after being soldered to a board at Incircuit Testing, which can be a saving to the board manufacturer, who now doesn't have to worry about keeping special, preprogrammed parts in stock and doesn't have to invest in specialized programming equipment.

The last type of control store is "electrically erasable programmable memory" (EEPROM). This can be thought of as the next generation of EPROM memory, in which the memory cell is not cleared by ultraviolet light, but by providing a switch that connects the floating gate to ground, allowing the trapped charge to escape.

EEPROM allows a microcontroller to be cleared and reprogrammed without having to remove the device from a board and exposing it to ultraviolet light. This allows periodic updates of microcontroller code and even if the device is in an "OTP" package. EEPROM tends to be somewhat more expensive than EPROM (about two times EPROM OTP costs), and devices using EEPROM can be somewhat slower than EPROM.

The biggest advantage to EEPROM is its ability to be reprogrammed repeatedly without having to be pulled out of a circuit and be cleared before it's reprogrammed. This can be a terrific advantage coupled with ISP when you are first developing applications or learning about a microcontroller. I can't count the number of hours I've lost over the years looking for reasons why something won't run after an erase/program cycle, only to find a device misplugged, an adjacent circuit broken, or a leg bent underneath the part and not making proper contact.

As a note of caution, right now there is a lot of confusion (especially where microcontrollers are concerned) over whether or not parts are EEPROM or "flash." "Flash" memory is similar to EEPROM, but differs primarily in the area of how the cells are erased. In "EEPROM," the erasing circuits are unique to each memory cell, but in "flash," these circuits are common to a block of memory cells. If you want to change one location in flash, you will have to reprogram a number of locations (or the whole control store), but with EEPROM this isn't true. In EEPROM-based microcontrollers (and memory chips), code "patches" can be put into isolated areas of a program without reprogramming an entire device.

Often, microcontrollers will be described as having "flash" memory, when in fact they actually have EEPROM. At this point in time, there is little practical difference between the two; the two terms are being used interchangeably.

VARIABLE AREA

When you first look at a data sheet for a microcontroller, the first thing that probably jumps out at you is how little RAM is available. This memory can range from tens of bytes to hundreds of bytes. If EEPROM memory is available for data storage, this may also be somewhere in the order of tens of bytes as well.

If you're used to writing PC applications, you're probably wondering how anybody can do anything with so little memory. If you're like me, you've probably done PC applications where the nonarray variables can be measured in the kilobytes. With arrays, the amount of memory required can be in the hundreds of kilobytes. So how does anybody do anything with as little as 25 bytes?

The answer is, and this will probably surprise you, it's easy. This is not to say that you can code for a microcontroller in exactly the same manner as you did with a PC application, but with some simple rules, you will be amazed at what you can do with such small amounts of RAM.

Wherever possible, nonchanging data is not stored in variables, and hardware features (such as timers, index registers) are used to avoid using up valuable RAM. This means that when preparing to develop an application, care must be taken with how the memory resources are used in an application. The applications should also be designed so large arrays are not required.

STACKS

What I wanted to discuss here is how the RAM is arranged in the microcontroller for use in branching to subroutines and handling interrupts. During these operations, the program counter and context registers (the registers that contain the current execution status (i.e., the accumulators, status register, index registers, etc.) are saved and restored upon return.

This is typically done with a "stack." A *stack* is an electronic data construct that works very similarly to a physical counterpart. When something is put onto a stack ("pushed"), it stays there, in that position, until it is pulled off ("popped").

If you were to imagine sheets of paper, each of a different color put down one by one onto a stack, when the sheets were removed, they would come off in the reverse order they were put on. For this reason, stacks are often described as "LIFO" queues (where "LIFO" stands for "last in, first out").

With Princeton architectures, RAM is used for a number of hardware functions (most notably stack and context register storage), which decreases the performance of the device because access to different memory requires multiple accesses, which can't be carried out concurrently. The reason for this is the same reason why a Princeton architecture tends to require more cycles per instruction than a Harvard architecture.

Harvard-architected processors may have three data areas that can be addressed in parallel (at the same time): control store, variable and I/O space, and stack space.

In a Harvard architecture, such operations as program counter stack storage can be done in a separate memory dedicated to the task. This means that when a "call" is executed in a Harvard-architected processor, several functions are done in parallel. In the Princeton architecture, the "call" operation is complicated by the fact that the program counter has to be put onto the stack in the variable area before the next instruction can be retrieved from memory.

It is important to remember that for microcontrollers, in both types of architectures, there is only a finite amount of space available for saving data. Going beyond this limit can cause problems in program execution.

If a unique stack area is defined in the processor, if the stack limit is exceeded, then the pointer "wraps" around to another, already-used stack element. This means that after too many calls have been made, when the processor begins to execute "return" statements, an incorrect return address (which had been written over the correct value) is retrieved from the stack.

If a device uses the same memory space for variable and stack space, there is a danger that a stack overrun will write over memory used for variable storage or try to retrieve data pushed into ROM space.

Now, what I haven't discussed is saving registers on a stack. In some architectures, there isn't an explicit "push" or "pop" instruction. In fact, in the four microcontroller families presented in this book, only two of them have "push" and "pop" instructions.

The "push" and "pop" instructions can be simulated very easily by using an index register explicitly pointing to a stack area. Each "push" and "pop" instruction would use two instructions as shown below:

```
Push                              ;  "Push" Data onto the Stack
   move          [index], acc     ;  Save contents of accumulator on Stack
   decrement     index            ;  Point to the Next location in the Stack

Pop                               ;  "Pop" Data from the Stack
   increment     index            ;  Point to previous location on the Stack
   move          acc, [index]     ;  Move contents of Stack into Accumulator
```

While this may seem to be less efficient than a separate "push" and "pop" instruction and uses an index register that may be required elsewhere in the software, it is effective for simulating a stack in a processor that doesn't have one.

There is one problem with the example instructions above. What happens if an interrupt request is serviced after the first instruction of the two simulating the "push" and "pop"? If the interrupt handler uses the "stack," data will be lost. To prevent this, you may want to mask (disable) interrupts before executing the instructions or re-order them to:

```
Push                           ;   "Push" Data onto the Stack
  decrement    index           ;   Point to the Next location in the Stack
  move         [index], acc     ;   Save contents of accumulator on Stack

Pop                            ;   "Pop" Data from the Stack
  move         acc, [index]     ;   Move contents of Stack into Accumulator
  increment    index           ;   Point to previous location on the Stack
```

If the first instruction of the re-ordered "push" and "pop" is interrupted and a handler that updates the stack is executed, the stack address will be updated without modifying the contents of the stack.

HARDWARE INTERFACE REGISTERS ("I/O SPACE")

Like all computer systems, microcontrollers have a number of registers that are used for controlling the hardware attached to the processor. These registers can be the "typical" processor registers (accumulators, status registers, index registers), execution control registers (interrupt control registers, timer control registers), or input/output ("I/O") control registers (parallel I/O control registers, serial I/O control registers, analog I/O control registers, and data registers). These registers can be accessed a number of different ways.

The actual method of accessing the registers can mean a lot in terms of performance of one device compared to another. Therefore, it is important to understand how registers are accessed before you can successfully write software for a microcontroller.

In "RISC"-architected processors, all registers (often including the accumulators) are given an explicit address. This allows much greater flexibility in the operation of the processor and can allow some funky operations.

For example, say you wanted to branch to another address if a bit in an I/O port register is set. This can be written out in pseudo-code for a "CISC" processor as:

```
Accumulator = IOPort                        ;   Get the Value in the IOPort
                                            ;   Register
Accumulator = Accumulator & ( 1 << Bit )    ;   Mask all but Bit
if ZeroFlag != 0                            ;   If Zero, then the Bit is Set
  goto Address
```

Ideally, this operation would compile into:

```
if IOPort.Bit == 1
  goto Address
```

In the Microchip PIC, it can be done exactly this way:

```
btfsc    IOPort, Bit    ;  Skip Next if the Bit is Low
  goto    Address
```

And even done more efficiently in the Intel 8051:

```
jb       IOPort.Bit, Address    ;  Jump if the Bit is Set
```

Obviously, having a processor that can operate directly on any register in the microcontroller can be of advantage in developing simple applications (in the PIC example, the accumulator and status register aren't changed during the jump on the IOPort bit being set).

Another aspect of register accessing is to understand where registers are located. In some processors, all the registers and RAM are located in the same memory space. This means that program space is intermingled with the registers and is typically known as "memory mapped I/O."

I/O can also be in a separate memory map, which is referred to as the "I/O space" and is separate from the program (and variable) memory.

The primary advantage of this method of placing the I/O registers in a separate memory map is that it allows much simpler wiring of the program (and variable) memory. I/O functions tend to require small blocks of register addresses, which can make decoding awkward when present with large blocks of program and variable memory. A separate I/O space also offers some advantages for Princeton-architected processors in that it allows instruction fetches while the I/O registers are being accessed.

Now, having said this, you probably are under the impression that I think that a Harvard architecture with the registers and variables put into one memory space is the most efficient. And you would be right. But that doesn't mean that there are other reasons why a Princeton-architected microcontroller with memory-mapped I/O may not be the appropriate device for some applications.

EXTERNAL MEMORY

Despite the tremendous advantages that a microcontroller has with built-in program storage and internal variable RAM, there are times (and applications) where you will want to add external (both program and variable) memory to your microcontroller.

There are two basic ways of doing this. The first is to add a memory device to the microcontroller as if it were a microprocessor. Many microcontrollers are designed with built-in hardware to allow this.

The second way is to add an interface-bussed memory device to the microcontroller and control the bus I/O in software. This will allow simple I/O devices without complex bus interfaces.

As you consider the two methods, you're probably wondering which method is best. Like most other things, it depends on the application.

HARDWARE FEATURES

CONTENTS AT A GLANCE

CONTENTS AT A GLANCE

In the previous chapter, I introduced microcontrollers and talked a bit about architectures and accessing programs, variables, and I/O. In this chapter I would like to discuss many of the more practical aspects of microcontrollers in terms of their internal features and introduce interfacing them to external devices.

If you've looked at the table of contents, you'll probably feel like I explain every aspect of interfacing the microcontrollers. To be honest, I've only scratched the surface. Many different devices use slightly different interfaces, different protocols, and interfaces that I haven't even discussed here yet.

Device Packaging

When I use the term "device packaging," I am describing the material (known as "encapsulant") that is used to protect the chip and the interconnect technology used to connect the chip electrically to the printed circuit card (which I call the "raw card"). There are quite a few options in this area, and selecting the appropriate ones to use can have a significant impact on the final application's cost, size, and quality.

There are two primary types of encapsulation used to protect chips: plastic and ceramic. Plastic encapsulants are the most prevalent and use an epoxy "potting compound" that is injected around a chip after it has been wired to a "lead frame."

The lead frame becomes the pins used on the package and is wired to the chip via very thin aluminum wires ultrasonically bonded to both the chip and the lead frame. Some chips are attached to the lead frame using "C4" technology, which is described later.

Once the encapsulant has hardened, the chip is protected from light, moisture, and physical damage from the outside world. EPROM microcontrollers come in a plastic package, and they are generally referred to as "one time programmable" ("OTP") packages. Once the EPROM has been programmed, the device cannot be loaded with another application. (Figure 2.1.)

The primary purpose of putting a microcontroller into a ceramic package is that a quartz window can be built into the package for the purpose of erasing the EPROM control store. (Figure 2.2.)

When a ceramic package is used, the chip is glued to the bottom half and is wired to the lead frame. Ceramic packaging is typically only available as a PTH device, where plastic devices can be a very wide range.

Ceramic packaging can drive up the cost of a single chip dramatically (as much as ten times more than the price of a plastic OTP-packaged device). This makes this type of packaging only suitable for such uses as application debug, where the advantage of the window for erasing outweighs the extra cost of the package.

The technology used to attach the chip to the board has changed dramatically over the past ten years. In the 1980s, pretty much all devices were only available in "pin through hole" technology, in which the lead frame pins are soldered into holes in the raw card. (Figure 2.3.)

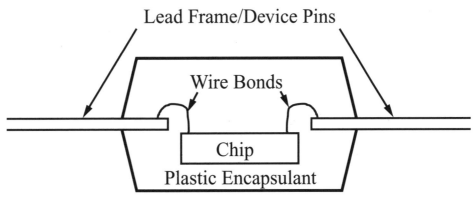

Figure 2.1 OTP plastic package.

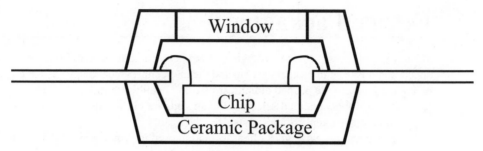

Figure 2.2 Windowed ceramic package.

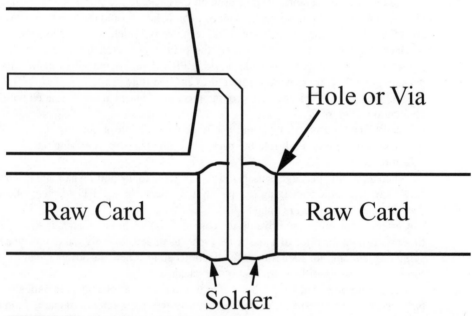

Figure 2.3 Pin through hole connection.

This type of attach technology has the advantage that they are very easy to work with (very little specialized knowledge or equipment is required to manufacture or rework boards built with PTH chips). The disadvantages of PTH are the amount of space required to put the hole in the card, and requirements for space around each hole make the spacing between lead centres quite large in comparison to SMT technology, in which the pins are soldered to the surface of the card. (Figure 2.4.)

There are two primary types of SMT leads used. (Figure 2.5.) The two different types of packages offer advantages in certain situations. The "gull wing" package allows for hand assembly of parts and easier inspection of the solder joints. The "J" leaded parts reduce the size of the overall footprint. Right now, "gull wing" parts are significantly more popular because this style of pin allows easier manufacturing and rework of very small leads (with lead centres down to 0.016").

The smaller size and lead centres of the SMT devices have resulted in significantly higher board densities (measured in chips per square inch) than PTH. Typical PTH lead centres are 0.100" (with the minimum for "interstitial pins" being 0.071"), while SMT starts at 0.050" and can go as low as 0.16". The SMT parts with small lead centres are known as "fine pitch" parts.

To give an idea of what this means in terms of board density, let's look at a PTH package that has pins at 0.100" lead centres and an SMT package with pins at 0.050" lead centres. With the smaller lead sizes, the SMT package can be about half the size of the PTH part in each dimension (which means that four SMT parts can be placed in the same space as one PTH part). As well, without holes through the card, components can be put on both sides of the card meaning that in the raw card space required for one PTH part, up to eight SMT parts can be soldered to the card.

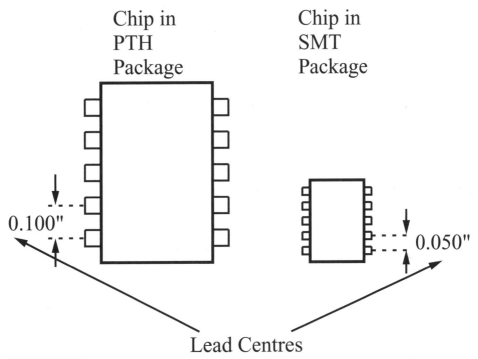

Figure 2.4 PTH package size versus SMT.

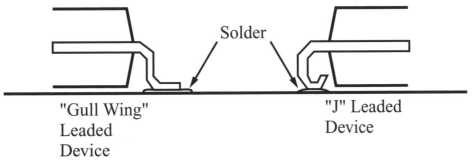

Figure 2.5 Surface mount technology packages.

To both increase the board density and support chips with more pins, SMT pin lead centres have shrunk to the point where 0.020" lead centre dimensions are not unusual. But, as these pin counts go up, new packaging technologies have been invented to make board assembly easier.

Assembly and rework of SMT parts is actually easier in a manufacturing setting than PTH. Raw cards have a solder/flux mixture (called "solder paste") put on the SMT pads and then run through an oven to melt the solder paste, soldering the parts to the board. To rework a component, hot air (or nitrogen gas) is flowed over the solder joints to melt the solder, allowing the part to be pulled off. While SMT is easier to work with in a manufacturing setting, it is a lot more difficult for the hobbyist or developers to work with (especially if parts have to be pulled off a board to be reprogrammed).

For very high pin counts (300+) the PTH part is usually impractical because of its size, and SMT parts will have problems because of the difficulty in making sure all the pins stay "co-planar" (which is a fancy way of saying "undamaged" and all still bent the same way). For very high pin count devices, three technologies—"ball grid array" ("BGA"), "chip on board ("COB"), and "tape automated bonding" (TAB)—are available.

In BGA technology, a two-dimensional array of solder balls is surface mounted to the chip package and is then soldered to the raw card in the same way as an SMT part. (Figure 2.6.)

BGA offers some significant advantages over traditional SMT for very high pin count chips. Let's take a 304-pin device, for example. Typically for SMT, this high a pin count is packaged in an SMT package called a "quad flat pack" ("QFP"), which is a square package with pins on all four sides with lead centres of 0.020". A BGA package would consist of a 16-by-19 array of balls on 0.050" centres. The minimum SMT package size is 1.540" on each size (for 2.372 square inches), while the minimum BGA package size is 0.850" by 1.000" (for 0.850 square inches). For this example, the BGA package takes up about a third of the space of the QFP and has an additional bonus that is not obvious. Because the ball centres are 0.050", it is much easier for the card assembler to place and solder onto a board than a component that has leads in the X and Y dimensions on 0.020 centres.

As noted before, the QFP pins would be very fragile (lead size for 0.020" lead centres is typically 0.012", about twice the size of a human hair)) while the BGA part, having solid solder balls, is a lot more robust. Because of the fragility of small SMT leads, manufacturers typically try to place and solder these parts totally by machine without a human ever touching the parts. This level of concern is not necessary for BGA packages.

While placing and replacing a BGA part only requires the same tools as SMT parts, inspection usually requires more sophisticated tools, including X-Ray machines. But BGA parts

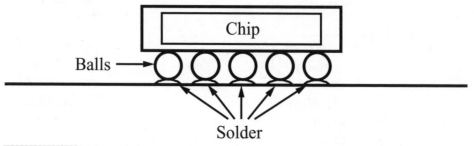

Figure 2.6 Ball grid array package.

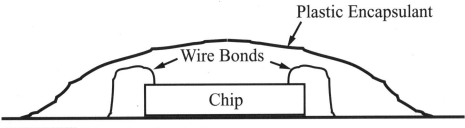

Figure 2.7 Chip-on-board packaging.

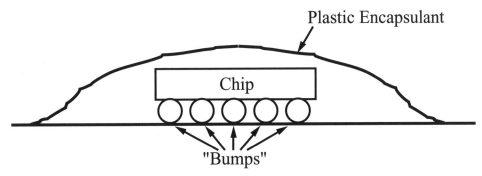

Figure 2.8 C4 chip-on-board packaging.

have significantly higher quality than their SMT counterparts (an SMT part typically has a 20–50-PPM lead defect rate, while a BGA can have as low as 1–2 PPM lead defect rate).

"Chip on board" ("COB") packaging is very descriptive because in this type of packaging, a chip is literally placed on the raw card.

There are two methods of COB attachment that are currently in use. The first method is to place the chip on the card and wire the pads of the chip to the pads on the card using the same technology as wiring a chip inside a package (using small aluminum wires ultrasonically welded to the chip and raw card). (Figure 2.7.)

The chip itself can either be glued or soldered to the raw card. Soldering the chip to the raw card is used in applications where the raw card is to be used as a heat sink for the chip (which reduces the overall cost of the assembly).

The other method of COB is known as "C4" and is actually very similar to the BGA process described previously. The solder balls used in this process are called "bumps" (because they are so much smaller than BGA balls). (See Figure 2.8.) This technology was originally developed by IBM for attaching chips to ceramic packages (without having to go through a wire bonding step).

The C4 attach requires a very significant investment in tools for placement and a very specialized process. (Because of the small distance between the chip and the card, water used for washing the card can be trapped with flux residue, causing reliability problems later.) C4 attachment is really in the experimental stage at this point, both because of the difficulty in reliability in putting the chip down onto a raw card and the opportunity for fatigue failure in the bumps, caused by the chip and raw card expanding and contracting at a different rate due to heating and cooling.

Chip-on-board packaging is best for very high volume applications, where a very short space is available for the chip (such as in telephone "smart cards"), or there are special heatsinking requirements.

There is one last type of packaging that's a combination of SMT and COB that's called "TAB" (for "tape automated bonding"). In this type of packaging, the chip is bonded to a copper and kapton tape lead frame that is then soldered to the raw card. (Figure 2.9.)

TAB first came out in the mid-1980s as a method of providing very high pin counts for chips. With improvements in SMT packages (i.e., smaller lead centres) and the invention of BGA, TAB has largely been made obsolete (although some chip manufacturers are still working with TAB). The problems with TAB centred around the need for specialized equipment for placing and soldering TAB components and the difficulty in inspecting the solder joints.

When choosing a device package for an application, the choice you make can affect the size of the finished product, its cost, the quality of the solder joints, and which card assembly sites can build and rework it.

I know I've thrown out a lot of information (and going with that, more TLAs ("Three Letter Acronyms") than in any other part of the book. To be honest, I've just scratched the surface in explaining all the issues regarding device packaging. When you are selecting the chip packaging for an application, please research all the options thoroughly and talk to the engineers at the manufacturing site you are planning on using. (When it comes right down to it, they are the experts in their process and know what are the best packaging technologies to use.)

Chip Technologies

Microcontrollers, like all other electronic products, are growing smaller, running faster, requiring less power, and are cheaper. This is primarily due to improvements in the manufacturing processes and technologies used (and not the adoption of different computer architectures).

Virtually all microcontrollers built today use "CMOS" ("complementary metal oxide semiconductor") logic technology to provide the computing functions and electronic interfaces. "CMOS" is a "push-pull" technology in which a "PMOS" and "NMOS" transistor are paired together. (Figure 2.10.)

Figure 2.10 is a diagram of a CMOS inverter or "NOT" gate. When the input signal is low, the PMOS transistor will be conducting (or "on"), and the NMOS transistor will

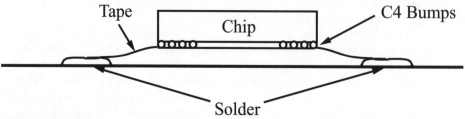

Figure 2.9 Tape automated bonding package.

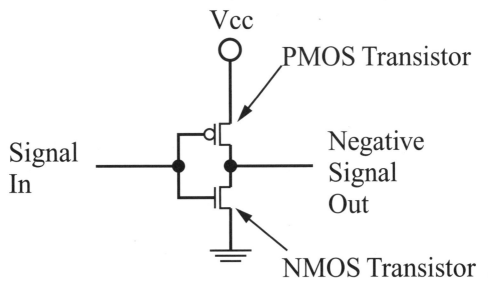

Figure 2.10 CMOS NOT gate.

be "off." This means that the "switch" (or transistor) at Vcc will be on, providing Vcc at the signal out. If a high voltage is input to the gate, then the PMOS transistor will be turned off and the NMOS transistor will be turned on, pulling the output line to ground.

During a state transition, a very small amount of current will flow through the transistors. As the frequency of operation increases, current will flow more often in a given period of time. (Put another way, the average current will be going up.) This increased current flow will result in increased power consumption by the device. Therefore, a CMOS device should be driven at the slowest possible speed, to minimize power consumption.

"Sleep" mode can dramatically reduce a microcontroller's power consumption during inactive periods because if no gates are switching, there is no current flow in the device.

An important point with all logic families is understanding the switching point of the input signal. For CMOS devices, this is typically 1.4-volt to one-half of Vcc. But it can be at different levels for different devices. Before using any device, it is important to understand what the input threshold level is. (This will be discussed in greater detail below with regards of "level conversion.")

CMOS can interface directly with most positive logic technologies, although you must be careful of low-voltage logic, to make sure that a "high" can be differentiated from a low in all circumstances (i.e., a "high" input is always above the voltage switching threshold level).

There are many more issues to be considered with different logic families, but I think I have brought up the major considerations. Each device is built with different technologies, so these issues are different for different devices.

Just to give you an idea of how microcontroller technology has improved over the years, here is a comparison of two devices. The first is a mid-1980s vintage 8748, which is similar to the original IBM PC's keyboard controller with the PIC 17C44, a modern PIC device. Both are 40-pin 0.600" devices, and both cost approximately the same to buy.

Technology	8748H	PIC17C44
EPROM/Logic Technology	HMOS	CMOS
EPROM Memory	2K	8K
RAM Registers	128 Bytes	454 Bytes
Max Clock Speed	11 MHz	33 MHz
Current Required	100 mA	38 mA
Sleep Current Req'd	N/A	1 uA
Built-in Functions	27 I/O Pins	33 I/O Pins
	8-Bit Timer	3x 16-Bit Timers
	Async/Synch I/O	PWM I/O
		Asynch/Synch I/O

Power

Many microcontroller applications are powered by batteries and may even rely on "super-capacitors" for staying operational during power outages. For this reason, minimizing power consumption in microcontrollers is an important issue.

As noted above, virtually all microcontrollers today are built using CMOS technology, which requires significantly less power than older, bipolar or NMOS-based devices. But there are some considerations in ensuring that the application only uses as much power as it requires.

Because of the wide variety of different applications and power sources microcontrollers are designed for, their power-handling circuitry is often designed as robustly as possible to ensure that the device will run under a variety of conditions.

One important point to note on power is all the different terms that can be used to describe it. For different devices, you'll see "Vcc" and "Vdd" to indicate power (typically +5 volts, although in some devices it can be as low as +2 volts). Similarly, "Vss" and "Gnd" is used to indicate Ground. In this book, I will use "Vcc" to indicate power (even when the manufacturer uses "Vdd") and "Gnd" to indicate ground.

POWER CONSUMPTION

There are three conditions that have to be considered when planning for a microcontroller's power consumption in an application. The first is what I call "intrinsic power," which is the power required just to run the microcontroller. Next, there is the "I/O drive power," which takes into account the power consumed when the microcontroller is sinking/sourcing current to external I/O devices. The third is the power consumed when the microcontroller is in "sleep" or "standby" mode and is waiting with clocks on or off for a specific external event. Taking these three conditions into account when planning an application can change an application that will only run for a few hours to literally several months.

"Intrinsic power" is the power consumed by the microcontroller when it is running and nothing is connected to the I/O pins. This consumption of power is largely a function of the CMOS switching current, which in itself is a function of the speed of the microcontroller.

By decreasing the system clock frequency, the intrinsic power can be reduced significantly. For example, the chart below shows the current requirements ("Idd") for a PICMicro 16C73A running at different frequencies with 5 volts power input.

FREQUENCY	CURRENT
1.0 MHz	550 uA
2.0 MHz	750 uA
3.0 MHz	1 mA
4.0 MHz	1.25 mA

By lowering the clock speed used in an application, the power required (which is simply the product of input voltage and current) will be reduced. This may mean that the application software may have to be written "tighter," but the gains in product life for a given set of batteries may be an important advantage for the application.

Obviously, the intrinsic power consumption can be further reduced by supplying a lower voltage input to the microcontroller (which may or may not be possible, depending on the circuitry attached to the microcontroller and the microcontroller itself). Many devices are designed to run on as little as 2.0 volts.

The I/O drive power is a measurement of how much power is sourced/sunk by the microcontroller to external devices and is unique to the application. In many applications, the microcontroller is the only active device in the circuit (i.e., it is getting input from switches and outputting information via LEDs). If the microcontroller is driving devices continually at times when they are not required, more current (which means more power) than is absolutely necessary is being consumed by the application.

The last aspect of power consumption to consider when developing an application is "sleep"/"standby" mode. This is usually entered by executing a special instruction and after executing this instruction, the microcontroller shuts down its oscillator and waits for some event to happen (such as a watchdog timer to count down or an input to change state).

Using this mode can reduce the power consumption of a microcontroller from milliwatts to microwatts. An excellent example of what this means is taken from the Parallax BASIC Stamp manual in a question-and-answer section:

How long can the BASIC Stamp run on a 9-volt battery?

This depends on what you're doing with the BASIC Stamp. If your program never uses sleep mode and has several LEDs connected to I/O lines, then the BASIC Stamp may only run for several hours. If, however, sleep mode is used and I/O current draw is minimal, then the BASIC Stamp can run for weeks.

Using the sleep mode in a microcontroller will allow the use of a virtual "on/off" switch that is connected directly to the microcontroller. This provides several advantages. The first is cost and reliability; a simple momentary on/off switch is much cheaper and much less prone to failure than a slide or toggle switch. Second is operational; while sleep mode is active, the contents of the variable RAM will not be lost or changed. And the last advantage is purely aesthetic; I like applications that use a push-button switch for on/off.

There is one potential disadvantage of sleep mode for some applications, and that is the time required for the microcontroller to "wake up" and restart its oscillator. This can be as long as ten milliseconds, which will be too long for many applications. Actually, I would probably qualify it to say that it's probably too slow for interfacing with other computer equipment. If the main thing the microcontroller is interfacing to is a human, this wake-up time will not be an issue at all.

One thing to remember with sleep mode is to make sure there is no current draw when it is active. A microcontroller sinking current from an LED connected to the power rail while in sleep mode will result in extra power being consumed.

CONNECTING POWER

A microcontroller is often put into applications in which its power may be less than optimal. Application power sources can include radio battery power, rectified and roughly filtered AC, or generator output. This means that microcontrollers will run with a variety of voltage inputs and interface to devices running at different logic levels. Microcontrollers are designed to run in environments that can be described as inhospitable and impossible for many other electronic devices.

Fortunately, most microcontrollers will take these variances in stride and work without complaint. The only issue to be considered when doing a microcontroller application is the decoupling of the power voltage. Typically, I use a 0.1-uF tantalum capacitor as physically close as possible to the Vcc (or "Vdd") input pin. This will allow the device to handle much greater I/O current transients without causing inadvertent resets or data corruption. This simple capacitor will hide a multitude of sins.

Reset

Ensuring that a microcontroller runs only during valid environmental conditions is usally critically important to an application. Looking back over what I've written here, it is very apparent that reset can only take place when you are sure power to the microcontroller is valid.

Typically, microcontroller applications begin to operate when power is applied to the device. To ensure that power has stabilized, I like to use the circuit shown in Figure 2.11.

With this circuit, reset becomes active approximately 22 msecs (using the approximation of the time delay = 2.2 RC) after power comes up. This gives lots of time for power and the device's oscillator to stabilize before the microcontroller begins operation.

The "momentary on push button" ("manual reset") is used to allow resetting the application during application development. When you are debugging an application, you will find that it is useful to control reset and be able to restart the microcontroller (to help characterize a problem). The 100-ohm resistor in series with the capacitor will limit current from the capacitor during reset (a charged capacitor will behave like a high current source when shorted to ground). This circuit can be used with microcontrollers which have a positive active reset (such as the 8051) by inverting the voltage at the capacitor (using something like a 7404).

In some microcontrollers, the RC network can be deleted because of internal circuitry within the device that puts in a delay before allowing the microcontroller to become active (i.e., start the oscillator and begin to execute the instruction at the reset address).

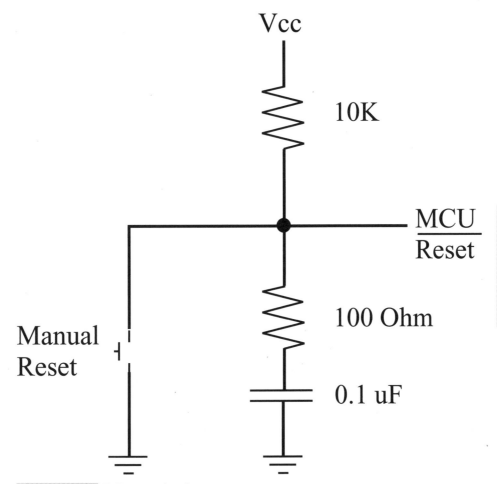

Figure 2.11 Full reset circuit.

This means the circuit can be simplified to what is shown in Figure 2.12. Looking at this, you are probably thinking that the circuit can be further simplified to just a connection between the reset pin and Vcc. This is true, but should only be done when the circuit is complete and debugged (and even then, I would like to see a current-limiting resistor put in place to allow resetting of the device by shorting reset to ground).

These reset circuits are best used in applications where the power voltage (Vcc) can be guaranteed to be within operating limits. Many microcontroller applications rely on batteries, which produce lower voltage over time. As the voltage drops, this may make the application run erratically, as some devices' cut-off voltage is reached before others.

To eliminate this as a problem, there are devices (known as "brown-Out" circuits) designed to monitor the Vcc/Vdd level and if it drops below a predetermined point (usually 4.5 volts), reset will be asserted actively. Typically, these voltage-monitoring circuits include a delay to operate similarly to the RC reset circuit above and monitor the incoming voltage level and are packaged similarly to a three-leaded transistor.

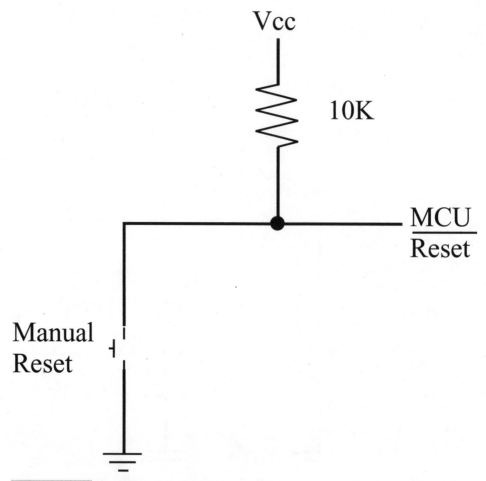

Figure 2.12 Modified reset circuit.

System Clock/Oscillators

If you've worked with designing clock circuits for microprocessors, you will find yourself in a pleasant surprise when designing the clock circuitry for a microcontroller circuit. Microcontrollers are designed for requiring the minimum amount of external circuitry for their system clocks.

Most microcontrollers are designed to be able to run at a very wide range of frequencies: from literally DC (no clock transistions at all) to tens of megahertz. This is accomplished by the use of fully static logic and memory designs internal to the microcontrollers. While I have not done this personally, I have known of people who have run applications at 1 Hz or less to single-step through their designs to debug the software. This extreme frequency range allows the application designer to better tailor the microcontroller appropriately to the application.

There are three different methods used for providing a clock in a microcontroller, and each has unique advantages and disadvantages. The first method of providing a clock to a microcontroller is by using a crystal, wired as shown in Figure 2.13.

This allows a crystal with a very precisely specified frequency (typically with an error rate of 100s of parts per million) to be used to drive the microcontroller. This level of precision is required for interfacing with other devices (or ensuring that a real-time clock is accurate).

The values of the capacitors used are specified by the microcontroller manufacturer for a specific crystal frequency. Sometimes a very large (on the order of megohms) resistor across Clk0 and Clk1 is required for the clock to run stably. Often, a manufacturer will specify that a variable capacitor is attached to Clk1 to allow the oscillator to be "tuned" to the exact frequency.

I, personally, hate to have any tunable parts in any application that I design, and I have never designed a microcontroller clock circuit that required a tunable part. If frequency tolerance is a problem, I will use another clocking circuit that won't have this problem.

As a rule of thumb, less capacitance will give you a better waveform. If you put on capacitances that are too large, your clock will degrade to the point where the microcontroller won't start up. If you aren't sure about the capacitance values you are using, take a look at the clock waveforms using a high-impedance probe with an oscilloscope. You should see the upper waveform shown in Figure 2.14.

If you have overloaded your circuit with too much capacitance, you will see something like the lower waveform, if the microcontroller runs at all (if it doesn't, the signal will be a DC voltage at approximately Vdd/2).

The two major disadvantages of this clocking method are the number of components that are required and the fragility of quartz crystals. Both of these problems can be eliminated by using a ceramic resonator. A ceramic resonator is much more resistant to physical shocks, and many are available with built-in capacitors, reducing the parts count from three devices to one. Ceramic resonators typically have a frequency accuracy of several thousand PPM (roughly 0.5%).

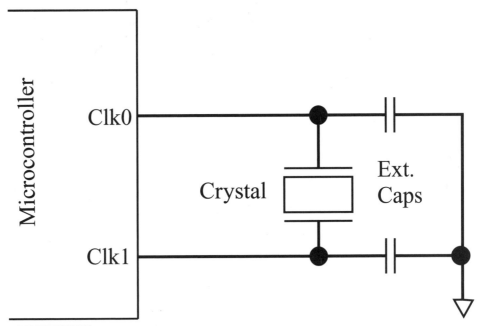

Figure 2.13 Crystal-based microcontroller clock.

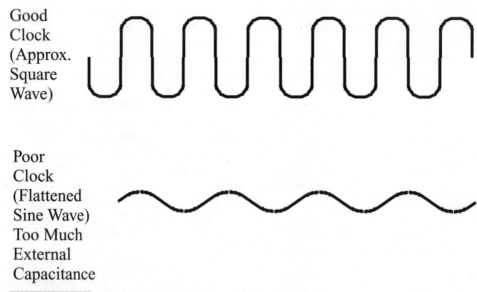

Good Clock (Approx. Square Wave)

Poor Clock (Flattened Sine Wave) Too Much External Capacitance

Figure 2.14 Good and bad PICMicro clock waveforms.

The next type of system clock is the "RC oscillator." This method of clocking uses the characteristic rise/fall time of an RC network to provide a repeatable delay as a clock. (Figure 2.15.)

This is the cheapest method of providing a clock to a microcontroller—unfortunately, it's also the least accurate. Whereas a crystal provides an error of only tens of PPM, and a ceramic resonator in the thousands of PPM, the RC network is only accurate to hundreds of thousands of PPM.

In some limited experimentation with the PIC, I have found that the accuracy of an RC oscillator is up to 20% (or 200,000 PPM). While this is obviously unacceptable for many applications where timing is critical, this may not be an issue for other applications.

There is no general formula for calculating the resistor or capacitor values for this type of oscillator. This is because of the internal parts of the microcontroller which nonlinearly sink current. Values for R and C to oscillate at an approximate frequency can be found in the microcontroller's data sheets.

The great advantage of this method is the low cost of this solution; the external circuitry for an RC oscillator can be less than one cent! Looking at the circuit, you are probably feeling that it can be tuned to a precise frequency by using a variable resistor or capacitor. Yes, this is true, but the complexity (and the cost) of the oscillator scheme is increased.

Another type of oscillator isn't one at all; it's bringing in an external clock signal. As I have said, microcontrollers are capable of running at an extremely wide range of frequencies. An external clock can be almost literally any frequency possible.

Some microcontrollers have internal RC or "ring" oscillators which can be used to run the device without any external parts for the oscillators. The internal oscillators are usually enabled by a configuration register that is programmed with the control store.

INSTRUCTION CYCLES

If you are new to processors in general and microcontrollers specifically, one thing that you will be surprised to find out is that an instruction cycle is not the same as a clock cycle. An "instruction cycle" is usually defined as the number of clock cycles that are required by the processor to do a useful piece of work. In Figure 2.16, the instruction cycle is four clock cycles long.

The instruction cycle is usually executed within the processor/microcontroller as a minimal operation, using the clock cycles to provide timing for each event within the instruction cycle.

Some instructions in all microcontrollers take more than one instruction cycle to execute. This can make timing operations within the microcontroller difficult and often a manual exercise with a data book or using a simulator/debugger to time program execution. In the example applications chapters later in this book, I show some of the practical aspects of setting up precise timing loops.

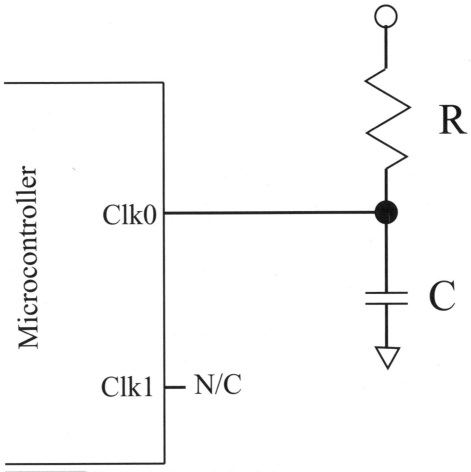

Figure 2.15 RC network microcontroller clock.

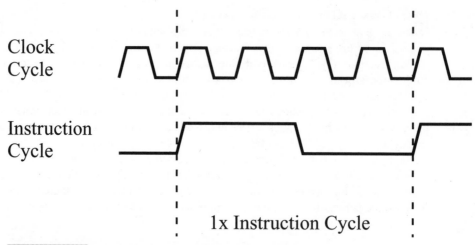

Clock Cycle

Instruction Cycle

1x Instruction Cycle

Figure 2.16 Instruction cycle versus clock cycle.

Program Counter

The program counter ("PC") is used to keep track of where the program is currently executing. This function is made more complex by having to save the current value during interrupts and subroutine calls as well as just simply to branching to a new location. Figure 2.17, while showing some of the complexity of the PC, really doesn't show all the different things that the program counter is responsible for.

The PC is really a parallel input/output counter. The diagram shows how a program counter would be implemented in a Princeton-architected machine. In this type of processor, the value of the PC is read and sent through the data bus to the memory controller to provide an address to read (often the program counter will be part of the memory controller to eliminate the overhead of passing the current address through the data bus). The important features of the counter are the parallel load (which updates the program counter from the data bus), the reset (which resets the PC to reset address of the microcontroller), and the increment (or clock) line (which is toggled after each instruction is read in). These lines are controlled by the instruction decode unit, which sequences how the microcontroller executes.

The "parallel load" option is used to load in "goto" (or "jump") or "call" (subroutine) addresses. In Princeton-architected machines, this address has to come through the data bus. While I describe these devices as having 8-bit processors, they're usually a hybrid because the program counter is usually larger than 8 bits (which would only allow addressing 256 memory locations). When the address is being updated, the new address has to come through the data bus 8 bits at a time (which takes extra cycles). To reduce this address load overhead, some processors have "branch" instructions in which only the least 8 bits of the new address are loaded into the program counter (the other, more significant bits are left unchanged). Executing a "branch" instruction means that only one byte has to be loaded through the data bus as opposed to at least two for the full "jump" instruction if a 16-bit address space is provided.

The reset value for the microcontroller's processor can be any value. While beginning execution at address 0x000 might seem to be the most obvious value, different microcontrollers will begin execution at different addresses. There is also a similar value (or "vector") for interrupts. Interrupts usually load the PC with a specific value which is different from the reset address, but may use the same hardware.

After each instruction is read in, the program counter is incremented. This is done to make sure it is loaded with the next address, so if a subroutine call or an interrupt is executed, the return address (which is the next instruction) can be saved on the stack, without having to execute additional cycles to increment the program counter.

There are some important things to note about the increment function of the program counter. In Princeton-architected microcontrollers, care must be taken in the software to make sure the program counter doesn't leave the program area (i.e., increment outside of it). If this happens, you can literally be executing data (which obviously will have unpredictable results) as the PC strays outside of the control store area.

Another issue to consider is, what happens when the program counter reaches the end of the memory space? In some devices, it wraps around to address 0x000, but in others it continues to increment with the instruction decode circuitry, executing indeterminate instructions.

Arithmetic Logic Unit

The arithmetic logic unit ("ALU") of a processor is used to carry out all the mathematical operations of a program. These operations include addition, subtraction, ANDing, ORing,

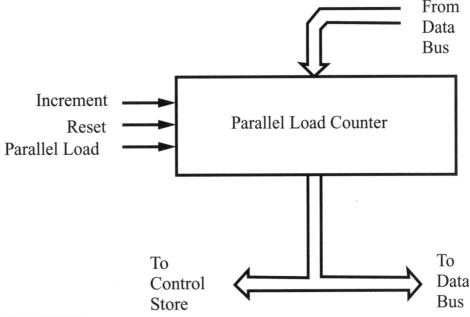

Figure 2.17 Program counter.

shifting registers and values, and passing the status of these operations to the status Register. The ALU is not used to read or save data or instructions, nor is it used to execute instructions.

The ALU is probably best presented as hardware that combines two words of data and stores the result. (See Figure 2.18.) How this data is brought in and stored is a major consideration of different microcontrollers (and is one of the major differenciators between processors and instruction sets). Some designs will take source from an accumulator (along with another word) and put the result back in the accumulator. Others will allow you to specify the two different sources and the destination.

ALUs typically only work with positive integers. However, "twos complement" negative numbers are usually produced as a matter of course when a number is subtracted from a smaller number. This can lead to some confusion with how the ALU works and what kind of result is to be expected.

In the Microchip PIC, this can be shown in how the subtraction instructions work. Instead of actually subtracting one number from another, it actually adds the negative. You're probably thinking to yourself, what difference does this make? In grade school, you were probably taught that:

$$A - B = A + (- B)$$

In binary systems, the equation above is actually not true. It makes a lot of difference whether you are subtracting or adding the negative. To get the twos complement negative of a number, it is complemented and then incremented:

$$- B = (B \wedge 0x0FF) + 1$$

By providing circuitry to do this negation, a subtractor doesn't have to be designed into an ALU, just an Adder. Through substitution:

$$A - B = A + (B \wedge 0x0FF) + 1$$

This method of handling a subtraction can be confusing when the carry flag is used for both addition and subtraction. In "typical" ALUs (which have an adder and subtractor) the carry bit is often referred to as a "carry/borrow" flag. In this case, the bit is set when the result of addition is greater than 0x0FF or the result of subtraction is less than zero. In both cases, the bit is

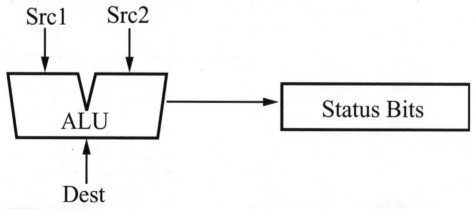

Figure 2.18 Arithmetic logic unit block diagram.

used to indicate when upper 8 bits of the number are affected by the operations on the lower 8 bits. In the case where the ALU doesn't have a subtractor (as in the example above), the carry flag is still checked after addition or subtraction, but it works differently.

To understand what happens, let's go through a couple of examples. The first example is to show what happens when a number is subtracted from a value larger than itself (resulting in a positive number):

$$0x077 - 0x055 = 0x077 + (- 0x055)$$
$$= 0x077 + (0x055 \wedge 0x0FF) + 1$$
$$= 0x077 + 0x0AA + 1$$
$$= 0x0125$$

The result is greater than 0x0FF, which causes the carry flag to be set (which is not expected in the case of a carry/borrow flag). The least significant 8 bits are 0x022, which is what will be transferred to the destination, which is the answer that we expect.

Next, consider the case where a number is subtracted from a smaller one, which results in a negative result:

$$0x055 - 0x077 = 0x055 + (- 0x077)$$
$$= 0x055 + (0x077 \wedge 0x0FF) + 1$$
$$= 0x055 + 0x088 + 1$$
$$= 0x0DE$$

In this case, in a "normal" ALU, we would expect the result 0x0DE and the carry/borrow flag to be set. Again, the least significant 8 bits are as expected and the most significant bit (which will be loaded into the carry flag) is not.

Trying to understand this situation, you can see that the carry flag is set when the subtraction result is positive and reset when the result is negative. In this situation, I think of the carry flag as the "carry/positive" flag. After going through these examples, you can see that this actually is quite easy to understand, but when you first see the operation of the instructions and the status flag results, it's easy to become confused and unable to understand exactly what is happening.

One last thing to consider with ALUs is that when you look at a family of devices, some have features which you would expect in the ALU (multiplication is a classic example of this). It would be wrong to assume that the ALU is different between the different members of the family.

Instead, the extra function is probably added as extra hardware to the silicon-like enhanced peripheral functions and doesn't affect the ALU at all. This means that the new features use registers that are unrelated to the ALU status register and accumulator(s). For example, looking through different members of the Motorola 6800-based microcontroller family, I found this to be the case.

After reading this section, you'll probably realize that the ALU is as complicated as the microcontroller as a whole. Often, manufacturers have whole teams working on the ALU that are equal in size to the teams that are designing the rest of the microprocessor or microcontroller (probably more when something like a PC processor is being designed). How the ALU works affects the operation of the processor within the microcontroller, and the operation of the microcontroller as well.

2

INTRODUCTION

Watch Dog Timers

Often in electrically "noisy" environments, induced signals and currents will cause a microcontroller to jump to an unexpected memory location unexpectedly and run in an unexpected manner (this is usually referred to as the microcontroller "running amok" or has taken a "branch to the boonies"). To monitor this, an aptly named device called the "watch dog timer" is often implemented in the silicon of the microcontroller.

This device causes a reset of the microcontroller if it is not updated within a predetermined amount of time (usually tens of milliseconds to several seconds). If a microcontroller's instruction pointer is inadvertently changed, then chances are, it will not re-acquire the watch dog timer update code and be reset by the watch dog timer and placed back in a known state.

I, personally, have never enabled a watch dog timer in an application. This is because I have never felt that it has been required from the electrical "noise" point of view (i.e., putting a microcontroller in a CRT display, close to the flyback transformer or close to an automobile's ignition coil). This may sound a bit facetious, but I feel that with modern electronics, the chance of an electrical upset is remote—although it would be very real in situations similar to the ones above.

I would also recommend against using the watch dog timer for masking software problems. While this may reduce the chances that the code will cause something bad to happen, I don't feel that it will eliminate all possible instances of this, and rather than relying on the hardware to prevent software-induced upsets, testing of the software under all situations should be carried out.

Subroutines and Functions

I realize that typically subroutines and functions are discussed in many books and courses as programming constructs and techniques. What I wanted to do here is discuss the hardware used to implement the calling subroutines and passing parameters back and forth.

Calling a subroutine involves saving the current program counter so that the "return" operation knows where to restore the program counter. This can be accomplished by automatically (as part of the "call" instruction) pushing the return address onto a "program counter stack," then when a "return" instruction is executed, this address is popped off the stack and put into the program counter.

But what about devices that don't have stacks? One example that will probably surprise you is the IBM 370 mainframe architecture; it doesn't have a stack for storing the program counter or any register contents. In these types of architectures, a return value is stored in a register any time a "goto" is executed. This leaves it up to the software developer to determine what is the most efficient way to save the return address. The best way of implementing a "call" may be simply leaving the return address in the register if the subroutine doesn't call any "nested" routines (and then to return from the subroutine, putting the contents of the register into the program counter).

Along with stacks, saving the return address following a goto instruction in a register may not even be available in some devices. So to implement a subroutine call, the return address has to be saved in a variable.

This could be implemented by the code:

```
  .
  :
  ReturnVar = AfterGoto       ;  Save the Return Address
  goto Subroutine             ;  "Call" the Subroutine
AfterGoto
  .
  :
Subroutine                    ;  Start of the Subroutine
  .
  :
  ProgramCounter = ReturnVar  ;  Return to Instruction AFTER goto
```

Complicating subroutines are functions. I define a function as a subroutine with parameters passed to it and returned from it. For example, a "C" function could be declared as:

```
int Func( int i, char far * Ptr );
```

In this example, "Func" is defined as a function that requires two input parameters, an integer and a pointer, and returns an integer. One of the most efficient (and most-often implemented) methods of passing parameters to a function is to put them on the (program counter) stack before the subroutine/function is called. Once in the subroutine, the index register can be given the current stack value and can reference these values. This method of handling parameters has one significant advantage over other methods and that is the memory used for storing the parameters is completely resuable. Variables declared within a function (and this includes the input parameters) are often called "local" or "automatic" because they are only usable locally in the function, and the space for them is created automatically.

While it appears that this type of function calling can only be accomplished by having a stack built into the processor, it can be accomplished by using an index register to simulate a stack. If a program counter stack is not available for pushing data, the simulated stack can also be used to store the return address of the calling routine.

The other methods of passing parameters are putting the input parameters into the processor's registers or into special variables. While passing input parameters in processor registers is possible in some cases, it will cut down on the number of registers available in the function. Storing input parameters in special variables is also possible but reduces the amount of memory available in the program (and memory is often at a premium in a microcontroller).

Returning a parameter can be done in any of the three ways discussed for passing parameters into the function. But the returned value is typically returned in the processor's registers because this is the most efficient (fastest) method of transferring the data, and register space is available.

Interrupts

For most people, interrupts are in the class of hardware best left alone because it requires godlike knowledge of the processor to develop interrupt handler code for an application (lest the system freezes up or runs amok when an interrupt is encountered). This feeling usually comes from experiences trying to program interrupts for the PC. The PC has many issues which complicate the development of an interrupt handler that are not relevant in a microcontroller environment. Actually, using interrupts in a microcontroller environment can simplify applications and make their development easier.

If you've never been exposed to interrupts, you may wonder exactly what they are. In a computer system, an interrupt is a special subroutine (called an "interrupt handler" or "interrupt service routine") that is requested by a hardware event, to be executed after suspending the execution of the currently running program. The term "interrupt request" is used because sometimes the software will refuse to acknowledge the interrupt and execute the interrupt handler immediately. (Figure 2.19.)

Interrupts in a computer system are exactly analogous to interrupts that you may encounter in your everyday life. The classic example of real-life interrupts (at least for me) is what happens when the phone rings while you are watching TV.

When the phone rings, you have three possible responses. The first is to ignore the phone and let the answering machine take a message that you'll deal with after the show is finished. The second response is to answer the phone, but take a message and say you'll call back later. The last possible response is to record the remainder of the show on your VCR while you take the call and then watch the taped show when the call is complete.

In a computer system, there are three similar responses that can be used to respond to the external hardware event. The first possible response (not responding to the interrupt at all until the current task is complete) could be accomplished by disabling (or "masking") the interrupt sources and when the task is complete, either "unmasking" the interrupt sources (which causes the interrupt handler to be executed and the event will be handled) or by looking at (also known as "polling") the interrupt request bits and executing the response code directly, without having to deal with the interrupt handler. This method of handling interrupts is used when the mainline code is critically timed and any interruptions can cause it to fail to interface properly.

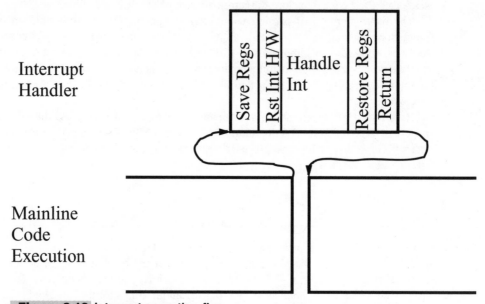

Figure 2.19 Interrupt execution flow.

Masking interrupts for long periods of time is not recommended because of the danger of having multiple events lumped together and only being recognized as one. Defining "long periods of time" is dependent on the application and the type and frequency of events and the interrupt. As a rule of thumb, interrupts should not be masked for more than half of the shortest period between the expected period between interrupt requesting events.

An interrupt handler always takes the form:

1. **Save** the "context registers."
2. **Reset** the interrupt controller hardware and reset the requesting hardware.
3. **Handle** the data from the interrupt.
4. **Restore** the "context registers."
5. **Return** to the previously executing code.

The "context registers" are the registers used to determine the current execution state of the mainline code. Typically, these registers are: the program counter, the status registers, and accumulator(s). Other processor registers, such as the index registers, may be used in the interrupt handler, so these should be saved at this time as well. These other registers are device and application specific.

Next, the processor's interrupt controller is reset, ready to accept another interrupt, and the hardware that generated the interrupt is reset, also ready to accept again the conditions which caused the original interrupt. I like to do this at this point because another interrupt request may be received by the interrupt controller. If everything is reset and ready for another interrupt, the processor's interrupt mask register will prevent the interrupt request from being handled, but the interrupt status register will record the event so pending interrupt requests can be handled when the current interrupt has completed and interrupts are unmasked.

Nested interrupts may not be easily implemented in some microcontrollers (these devices typically don't have a data stack) or may cause potential stack overflow problems. The issue of the stack overflowing is a concern in microcontrollers because of their limited RAM and stack; allowing nested interrupts may cause more data to be put on the stack than was expected or available.

Finally, the interrupt is processed. In the second TV example, the interrupt was handled as quickly as possible and then the data received was used to carry out the requested task. In a microcontroller, this would be the same as putting the incoming data on an array and then dealing with it when the primary task has been completed. This is a good compromise between fully handling the interrupt (which may take a long time) and ignoring it (which may result in events being lost).

Restoring the context registers and executing the interrupt return instruction puts the processor back in the exact state it was in when the interrupt handler was invoked.

You may be wondering what happens to the various registers during interrupts. I have discussed a number of things that happen, but I thought it would be a good idea to summarize what actually happens. The status register is often saved along with the program counter when an interrupt begins executing. This eliminates the effort required to move it to and from the area used to save it without changing it before returning to the previously executing code. This does not happen in all architectures, so care must be taken when handling interrupts (this will be shown in the application section of each microcontroller). If

2

INTRODUCTION

the status register is saved at the start of interrupt execution, the interrupt return instruction will restore it as well.

If other registers within the processor are changed within the interrupt handler, these too should be saved before they are changed and restored before returning to the mainline. I find that I typically save all the processor's registers, with the feeling that it's better safe than sorry (and sorry in this case will probably be debugging a microcontroller working unpredictably at difficult-to-reproduce intervals or circumstances).

The address that the program counter jumps to on acceptance of an interrupt request is known as a "vector." (There are several types of vectors; the address the program counter is set to after reset is called the "reset vector.") There may be multiple vectors for different interrupts, which eliminates the code required for determining which interrupt caused the handler to execute. Different interrupts sharing the same vector are usually not a serious problem in microcontrollers because the application is the only program running in the processor. This is different from the PC, where multiple interrupt sources can be added at different times. (If you've ever set up two devices on the COM1 and COM3 ports, you'll know exactly what I am talking about.) In a microcontroller application, where the hardware is well known, there shouldn't be any problems if interrupt vectors are shared.

The last point I want to make about interrupts is the use of "software interrupts." These are processor instructions that can be used to simulate a hardware interrupt. The most obvious use for these instructions is to "call" system subroutines that have arbitrary locations in memory or require "long calls" to access. This feature is built into the Intel i86 and is used in the IBM PC's BIOS (basic input/output system) and PC-DOS to provide system subroutines without having to place entry points at specific locations in memory. Instead, the different interrupt vectors point to the code to be executed when the interrupt is "called" in software.

After reading this section, I don't know if interrupts will seem easier to you or if I've scared you away from them even more. As I introduce each microcontroller, I will show how interrupts are implemented and how they can simplify an application.

Timers

If you're familiar with microprocessors, you'll probably think that they are only used for providing a constant delay. In microcontrollers, timers are used for a lot more applications.

Being used as a straight timer usually involves setting the timer to use the instruction clock as an input (as opposed to an external signal). By loading in an initial count, a specific time interval can be timed, the overflow indicating when the interval has been reached.

Often, a "prescaler" is put in front of the timer to allow longer intervals to be measured. This hardware will only allow the timer itself to be incremented when a specific count is reached. (Figure 2.20.)

If you wanted to get a 10-msec (1/100 sec) delay in a system that had a 10-MHz clock, you could use the circuit shown in Figure 2.20 in the following manner.

First, a prescaler value would have to be determined. At 10 MHz, this means the timer would have to count 10,000 times, which is impossible for an 8-bit counter.

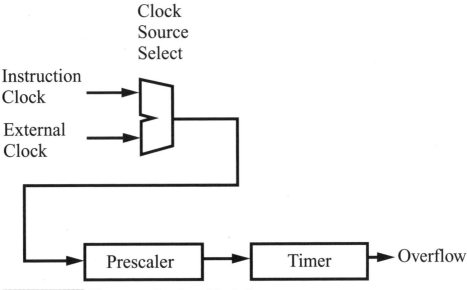

Figure 2.20 Microcontroller timer block diagram.

So a prescaler value has to be chosen to get a good count value. Typically, a prescaler value is simply a power of two (i.e., 1, 2, 4, 8,...256). If a prescaler value of 64 is chosen, that means the timer has to count to 156 (64 × 156 = 9,984, which is a close approximation and can be nailed down exactly by adding "nop"s or other time-wasting instructions).

Now, to wait for this interval, the timer could be cleared and the value in the timer continually compared against 156. Or a more efficient way is to load the timer with 256-156 and wait for the timer overflow interrupt flag to be set.

With the latter method, a simple multitasking program could be written, with a task switch taking place when the timer counts down the 10-msec delay.

While this method can be used to provide a real-time clock function for a microcontroller, it is not recommended. Often, when a timer is reloaded, the prescaler is at an unknown value (and is not deterministic) and is reset when a value is put into the timer registers. Instead, letting the timer run continuously is best (the prescaler is never reset), and when the timer overflow is indicated, the bit is simply reset and a real-time clock counter is incremented. This means that when the program wants to know the current time, it simply takes the real-time clock counter value and manipulates it to get the correct time. This is the method used by the IBM PC and is the reason why each real-time clock "tick" occurs 18.2 times per second.

With the circuit above, you can see that the clock can also be used to count events external to the microcontroller. This is accomplished by simply selecting the Timer input source from "Instruction Clock" to "External Clock" in the circuit above.

If the microcontroller had two timers, a simple tachometer (event per unit time counter) could be easily created. (Figure 2.21.) The tachometer code would first clear TMR2 and then set up TMR1 to wait for some interval. Once this interval had passed (i.e., the TMR1 Overflow bit was set), the value in TMR2 would be read out.

Timers in microcontrollers are often used for "pulse width modulated" ("PWM") I/O. A PWM signal is often used to pass analog data to and from digital systems. The signal

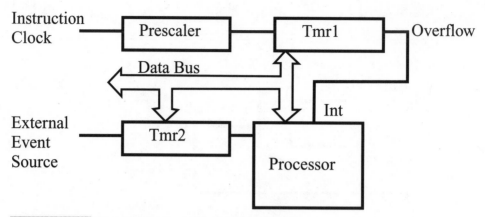

Figure 2.21 Microcontroller tachometer application.

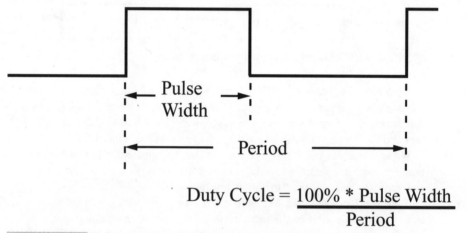

$$\text{Duty Cycle} = \frac{100\% * \text{Pulse Width}}{\text{Period}}$$

Figure 2.22 Pulse wave modulated signal waveform.

consists of a repetitive waveform which uses a pulse to indicate the analog signal by its width. (Figure 2.22.)

The pulse width is proportional to the analog value. PWM is often used for electric motor control (for speed or servo position) and can be output from a microcontroller using the following built-in circuitry shown in Figure 2.23.

In this circuit, as long as the "Pulse Width" value is greater than the timer value, the output will be high (the pulse). When the timer value is equal to or greater than the "Period," the timer is reset back to zero and the process repeats. This method of outputting a PWM waveform requires a minimum amount of processor support (just making sure the pulse width and period is correct) and the pulse width value can be updated by the processor at any time without having to stop the timer's PWM output.

If a square wave of a specific frequency has to be output from a microcontroller, the same circuitry can be used with the period value being twice that of the pulse width value.

Measuring the pulse width of an input PWM waveform can be accomplished very simply. (See Figure 2.24.) This circuit keeps the timer reset until the input signal goes high and then stops it, latches the timer value into the "pulse width" register and then resets the timer (and disables it's clock input) until the next pulse comes in. To make the circuit easier to read and understand, I haven't included some built-in circuit delays to make sure that the timer value is latched into the "duty cycle" register before the timer is reset.

Digital I/O

The basic external interface between a microcontroller and the outside world is via the digital input/output ("I/O") pins. While in many devices, these pins can be reprogrammed for different set functions (such as serial and analog I/O), they are useful for providing digital I/O. When first learning about a microcontroller, understanding how the I/O pins work (especially with different instructions) should be a very high priority.

In most devices, the pins are selectable between input and output. The typical circuit design for each pin is shown in Figure 2.25. The most important thing to note about this circuit is that reading in the bit takes the pin value, not the contents of the "data F/F". This means that if other devices connected to the pin are capable of overpowering the pins O/P driver, the "readback" value will be what is actually at the pin, not what is expected. In some microcontrollers, you have the option between reading the value at the output driver or at the actual pin.

Hardware that reads the pin can cause some problems with microcontrollers that have processor instructions that can read/write I/O pins in one operation. Reading in a wrong value will cause the data F/F to be written with an incorrect state at the end of the read/write instruction.

Another common type of common I/O pin type is the "open collector" (really "open drain") output. (See Figure 2.26.) In this type of pin, the pin remains at the bus state unless

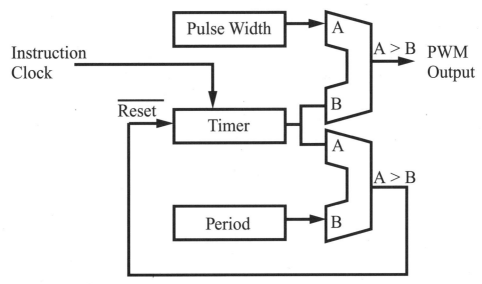

Figure 2.23 PWM generator circuit.

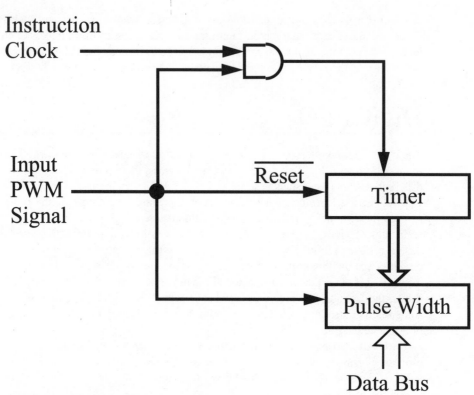

Figure 2.24 PWM pulse read circuit.

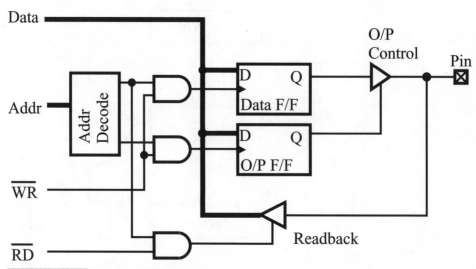

Figure 2.25 Standard I/O pin hardware.

it is set to "output" and the bit value is "0". When this happens, the pin is pulled to ground by the FET transistor ANDED with the output of the data F/F and O/P (output) F/F.

This type of digital I/O pin is useful for creating "dotted AND" busses which consist of a pull up to Vcc and a number of switches or transistors able to pull the bus down. An example application that would use this type of bus is in a single medium bidirectional bus with multiple transmitters (each of which can put data on the bus by pulling it down).

A "typical" I/O pin can simulate the "open collector" output by remaining in input mode except when a "0" is to be asserted. When a "0" is to be asserted on the bus, the data F/F would be loaded with a "0" and then, using the O/P F/F, the pin would pull the line low.

The "O/P F/F" (or "output flip-flop") is used to control the ability of an I/O pin to drive an output value. As I have shown in the diagrams, the Data F/F and O/P F/F load clocks are individually selectable (through the use of the address bus). In some older devices, this is not the case; often groups of 4 and 8 bits are lumped together for input/output selection. These devices may require some more planning in the circuit and software to make sure the pins work as desired.

The last aspect of I/O pins that you should be aware of is that external inputs can be used to generate interrupt requests. This typically (but not always) only happens when the pins are in input mode (this is to prevent changing the output state and causing an interrupt request).

Level Conversion

Often when working with microcontrollers you will have to interface devices of different logic families together. For standard positive logic families (i.e., TTL to CMOS), this is not a problem; the devices can be connected directly. But interfacing a negative logic to a positive logic family (i.e., ECL to CMOS) can cause some problems.

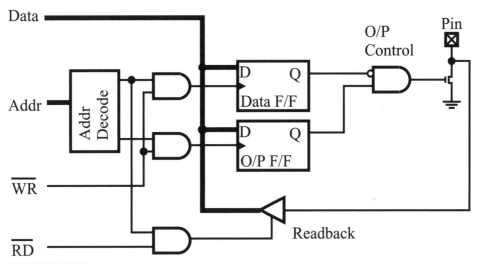

Figure 2.26 Open collector I/O pin hardware.

While there are usually chips available for providing this interface function (for both input and output), typically they only work in only one direction (which precludes bidirectional busses, even if the logic family allows it) and the chips can add a significant cost to the application.

The most typical method of providing level conversion is to match the switching threshold voltage levels of the two logic families. As shown in Figure 2.27, the "ground" level for the COMS microcontroller has been shifted below ground (the microcontroller's "ground" is actually the "CMOS "0"" level) so that the point where the microcontroller's input logic switches between a "0" and a "1" (known as the "input logic threshold" voltage) is the same as the ECL logic. The resistor (which is between 1K and 10K) is used to limit the current flow due to the different logic swings of the two different families.

Looking at the circuit block diagram, you're probably thinking that the cost of shifting the microcontroller power supply is much greater than just a few interface chips. Actually, this isn't a big concern because of the low power requirements of modern CMOS microcontrollers. In the example above, the ECL logic's -5V reference can be produced by placing a silicon diode (which has a 0.7 voltage drop across it) from the microcontroller's ground to the ECL's -2-volt power supply negative output (and the -5-volt supply is referenced from "ground" of the -2-volt supply) to balance the logic thresholds. This example may seem simplistic, but it would provide the ability to connect a CMOS 0 to +5-volt microcontroller to ECL logic (and allow signals to be sent bidirectionally) at a very low cost.

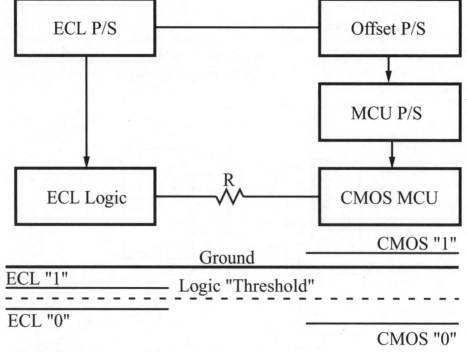

Figure 2.27 ECL to CMOS logic level conversion.

Serial I/O

Most intersystem (or intercomputer) communications are done serially. This means that a byte of data is sent over a single wire, one bit at a time with the timing coordinated between the sender and the receiver. The obvious advantage of transmitting data serially is that fewer connections are required.

There are a number of common serial communication protocols that are used by microcontrollers. In some devices, these protocols are built into the chip itself, to simplify the effort required to develop software for the application.

ASYNCHRONOUS SERIAL COMMUNICATIONS

The most common form of serial communications is "asynchronous," in which a data byte is sent as a "packet" along with data start and stop information and error detection information.

The first bit sent isn't a data bit at all, but it's a "start bit" indicating that a data packet is being sent and is following. This is used by the receiver to synchronize the reading of the data which follows (least significant bit first).

A "parity bit" can optionally be sent after the data to ensure that the receiver has received the correct data. There are typically two types of parity sent. "Odd parity" means that if the number of set (or "1") bits and the parity bit are totaled, the sum would be an odd number (i.e., 0x055 would have a parity bit of "1" to make the total number of bits sent equal to 5, which is odd). "Even parity" is the opposite (for the example of sending 0x055, the parity bit would be "0").

In some microcontrollers, the parity has to be calculated manually and then entered into a register. A simple algorithm for doing this is to take the byte to be transmitted and XOR all the bits together, as the following 8051 code shows:

```
    mov    Count, 8      ;  Do all 8 Bits
    mov    A, 0          ;  Start Out With Nothing in "A"
P_Loop                   ;  Come Back Here for Each Bit
    xrl    A, Char       ;  XOR the LSB with LSB in "A"
    rrc    A             ;  Rotate Char Over to Put the Next Bit in Position
    djnz   Count, P_Loop ;  Repeat 8x
```

The value in the least significant bit of "A" will be the "even" parity value for "Char." That is to say, if all the bits are totaled and added to the least significant of "A," the sum will be even. To get "odd" parity, the least significant bit of "A" should be XORed with 1.

After the parity bit, there is a "stop bit" that is used by the receiver to store and process the data byte just read in from the packet.

An asynchronous data packet (with 5 bits of data) looks like Figure 2.28. There are a number of options that you should be aware of. The number of bits that are sent is application definable. In Figure 2.28, I only show 5 bits (which was the original number used in teletypes), but as many as 8 bits can be sent in the data packet.

Along with "odd" and "even" parity, there is also "no," "mark," and "space" parity. "No" parity means that no parity bit is transmitted with the data in the packet. "Mark" or "space" parity means that a "1" or "0," respectively, is always sent after the data in the packet. This type of parity is very rarely used, and when it is used, the reason for its use is to allow the receiver time to process the data before the next data byte comes along.

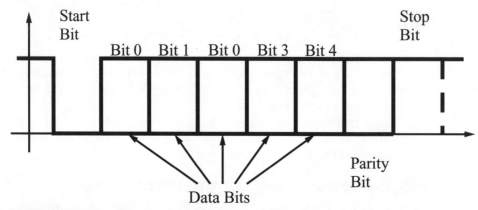

Figure 2.28 Asynchronous serial data stream.

The number of stop bits is also an option, for the same reasons as mark and space parity. A second stop bit can be inserted in the data packet to give the receiver more time to process the received byte before preparing to receive the next one.

In virtually all modern asynchronous communications, the data format is "8-N-1," which means 8 data bits, no parity, and one stop bit as the packet format. The parity and additional end interval are generally not required for serial communications.

The most popular type of asynchronous serial communication is known as "RS-232," which is now an EIA standard. This is a very old standard used to connect different computers. I discuss interfacing to RS-232 in the "Common Microcontroller Interfaces" chapter.

The asynchronous receiver hardware waits for the "start bit." When the input line goes low (indicating a start bit), the input line is polled one-half bit later (which is timed by an over-speed clock). If the line is still low (if it's not, then the receiver assumes that the low was a "glitch" and data bits won't be received), then the receiver waits one bit period and reads in the data. (See Figure 2.29.) This method is used for both hardware and software asynchronous data receiving (in software receivers, a timed loop is used for the half bit and full bit delays).

Another common method of serially transmitting data asynchronously is to use the "manchester" encoding format. In this type of data transfer, each bit is synchronized to a pulse and the type of bit is dependent on the length of time until the next pulse. (Figure 2.30.) In this type of data transmission, the data size is known so the "stop pulse" is recognized and the space afterward is not treated as incoming data.

Manchester encoding is unique in that the "start bit" of a packet is quantitatively different from a "1" or a "0." This allows a receiver to determine whether or not the data packet being received is actually at the start of the packet or somewhere in the middle (and should be ignored until a start bit is encountered).

Manchester encoding is well suited for situations where data can be easily interrupted. Because of this, it is the primary method of data transmission for infrared control (such as used in your TV's remote control).

Synchronous Serial Communications

For synchronous data communications in a microcontroller, a clock signal is sent along with serial data. (Figure 2.31.) This clock signal is used by the receiver to strobe in the data.

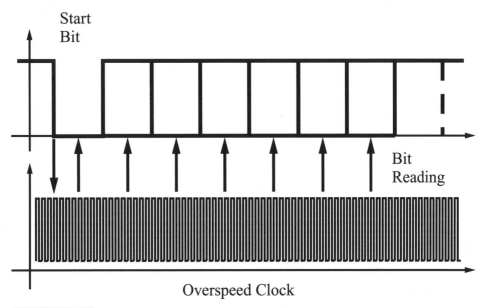

Figure 2.29 Reading an asynchronous serial data stream.

2

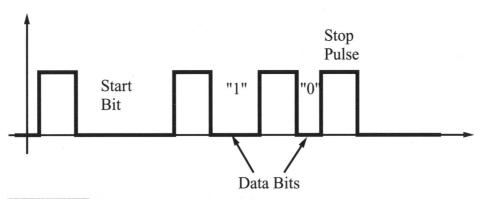

Figure 2.30 Manchester encoded serial data.

Figure 2.31 Synchronous data waveform.

A typical circuit, using discrete devices, is shown in Figure 2.32. This circuit converts serial data into eight digital outputs, which all are available at the same time (when the "O/P latch" is strobed). For most applications, the second '374 providing the parallel data is not required. This serial-to-parallel conversion can also be accomplished using serial-to-parallel chips, but I prefer using 8-bit registers because they are generally easier to find than other TTL parts.

There are two very common synchronous data protocols: Microwire and SPI. These methods of interfacing are used in a number of chips (such as the serial EEPROMs used in the BASIC Stamps). While the Microwire and SPI standards are quite similar, there are a number of differences that should be noted.

I consider these protocols to be methods of transferring synchronous serial data rather than microcontroller network protocols because each device is individually addressed (even though the clock/data lines can be common between multiple devices). If the chip select for the device is not asserted, the device ignores the clock and data lines. With these protocols, only a single "master" can be on the bus. (Figure 2.33.)

If a synchronous serial port is built into the microcontroller, the transmit circuitry might look like Figure 2.34. This circuit will shift out 8 bits of data. For protocols like microwire where a "start bit" is initially sent, the "start bit" is sent using direct reads and writes to the I/O pins. To receive data, a similar circuit would be used, but data would be shifted into the shift register and then read by the microcontroller.

MICROWIRE

The Microwire protocol is capable of transferring data at up to one megabit per second. Sixteen bits are transferred at a time.

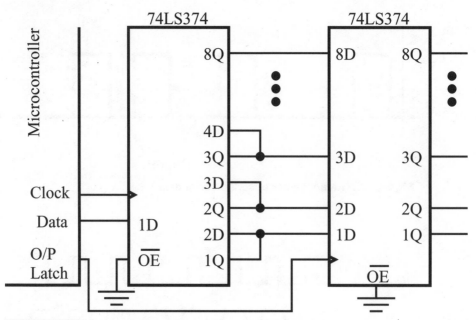

Figure 2.32 Synchronous serial-to-parallel output circuit.

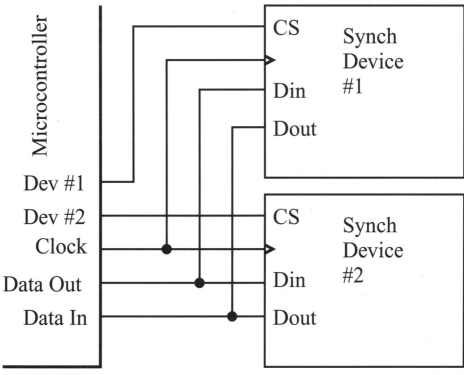

Figure 2.33 Synchronous serial device bus.

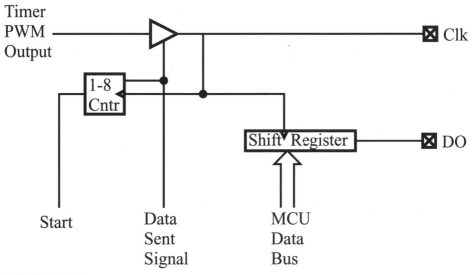

Figure 2.34 Synchronous output circuit.

To read 16 bits of data, the waveform would look like Figure 2.35. After selecting a chip and sending a start bit, the clock strobes out an 8-bit command byte (labelled "OP1," "OP2," "A5" to "A0" in Figure 2.35), followed by (optionally) a 16-bit address word transmitted and then another 16-bit word either written or read by the microcontroller.

With a one megabit per second maximum speed, the clock is both high and low for 500 nsecs. Transmitted bits should be sent 100 nsecs before the rising edge of the clock. When reading a bit, it should be checked 100 nsecs before the falling edge of the clock. While these timings will work for most devices, you should make sure you understand the requirements of the device being interfaced to.

SPI

The SPI protocol is similar to Microwire, but with a few differences.

1. **SPI** is capable of up to 3 megabits per second data transfer rate.
2. **The** SPI data "word" size is 8 bits.
3. **SPI** has a "hold" which allows the transmitter to suspend data transfer.
4. **Data** in SPI can be transfered as multiple bytes known as "blocks" or "pages."

Like Microwire, SPI first sends a byte instruction to the receiving device. After the byte is sent, a 16-bit address is optionally sent, followed by 8 bits of I/O. As noted above, SPI does allow for multiple byte transfers. (Figure 2.36.)

The SPI clock is symmetrical (an equal low and high time). Output data should be available at least 30 nsecs before the clock line goes high and read 30 nsecs before the falling edge of the clock.

When wiring up a Microwire or SPI device, the one trick that you can do to simplify the microcontroller connection is to combine the "DI" and "DO" lines into one pin. (Figure 2.37.)

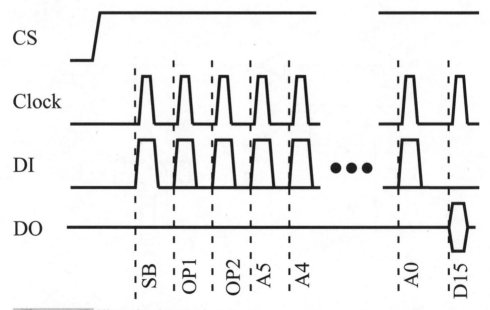

Figure 2.35 Microwire data read.

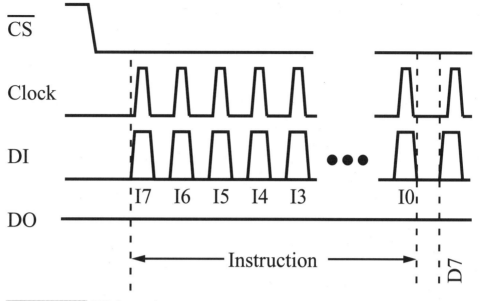

Figure 2.36 SPI data write.

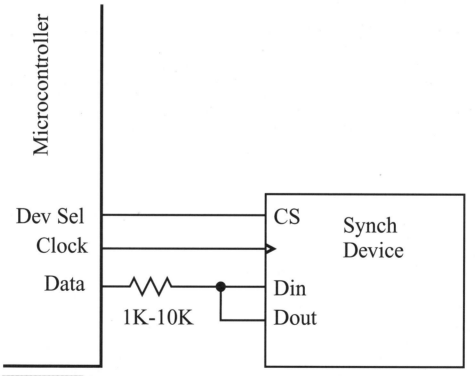

Figure 2.37 Combining DO and DI from a synchronous serial device.

2

In this method of connecting the two devices, when the data pin on the microcontroller has completed sending the serial data, the output driver can be turned off and the microcontroller can read the data coming from the device. The current-limiting resistor between the "data" pin and "DI"/"DO" limits any current flows when both the microcontroller and device are driving the line.

Network Communications

When I discuss networking with regards to microcontrollers, I'm generally talking about busses used to connect additional hardware devices to the microcontrollers and allowing communications between microcontrollers. (This is opposed to "local area networks" ("LANs"), like "Ethernet" that you were probably thinking about when you saw the word "networks.")

There are a variety of standards (which can be broadened to include Microwire and SPI discussed in the previous subsection), which leads to some confusion over what is and what isn't a network. I personally define a microcontroller network as a single communications medium (i.e., wire) and multiple devices connected to this medium which can initiate message transfers and respond to messages directed towards them.

In these types of networks, a "master" is an intelligent device which can initiate data transfers. Devices which respond to requests (and can't initiate them) are known as "slaves." Microcontroller networks can have multiple masters, which means the network protocol requires an arbitration scheme which allows multiple masters to transmit without ruining each other's messages.

Typically, microcontroller networks transmit very little data, so the bandwidth required is quite modest when compared to something like an ethernet-connected PC that has an owner who is a Web surfer. It's not unusual to have a microcontroller network that is transferring bytes per second (compared to a PC network that may transfer megabytes per second).

I will introduce you to two of the most popular microcontroller networks, and while what I have written is quite complete, it's not sufficient to use as a reference for developing network applications. If you are planning on using these network protocols, you will have to get more information, in the form of device datasheets or standards specifications. What I have done is given you enough information to understand the basics of the protocols and evaluate them for an application, to decide which is the most appropriate.

I2C

The most popular form of a microcontroller network is "I2C," which stands for "inter-intercomputer communicaitons." This standard was originally developed by Philips in the late 1970s as a method to provide an interface between microprocessors and peripheral devices without wiring full address, data, and control busses between devices. I2C also allows sharing of network resources between processors (which is known as "multimastering").

The I2C bus consists of two lines: a clock line ("SCL") which is used to strobe data (from the "SDA" line) from or to the master that currently has control over the bus. Both these bus lines are pulled up (to allow multiple devices to drive them).

A I2C controlled stereo system might be wired as shown in Figure 2.38. The two bus lines are used to indicate that a data transmisstion is about to begin as well as pass the data on the bus.

To begin a data transfer, a "start condition" is put on the bus. Normally, (when the bus is in the "idle state," both the clock and data lines are not being driven (and are pulled high). To initiate a data transfer, the master requesting the bus pulls down the SDA bus line followed by the SCL bus line. During data transmission, this is an invalid condition (because the data line is changing while the clock line is active/high).

To end data transmission, the reverse is executed: the clock line is allowed to go high, which is followed by the data line. (Figure 2.39.)

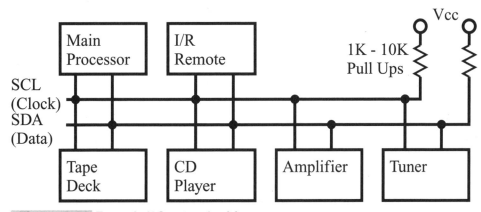

Figure 2.38 Example I2C network wiring.

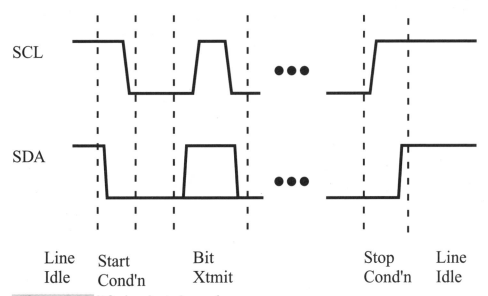

Figure 2.39 I2C signals and waveforms.

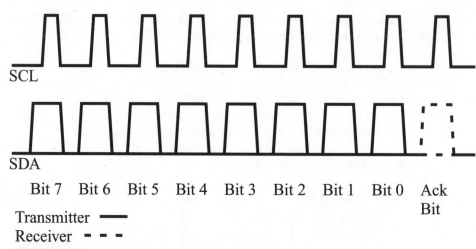

SCL

SDA

Bit 7   Bit 6   Bit 5   Bit 4   Bit 3   Bit 2   Bit 1   Bit 0   Ack
                                                                Bit
Transmitter ——
Receiver — — —

Figure 2.40 I2C data byte transmission.

Data is transmitted in a synchronous fashion, with the most significant bit sent first and after 8 bits are sent, the master allows the data line to float (it doesn't drive it low) while strobing the clock to allow the receiving device to pull the data line low as an acknowledgment that the data was received. After the acknowledge bit, both the clock and data lines are pulled low in preparation for the next byte to be transmitted, or a stop/start condition is put on the bus. (Figure 2.40.)

Sometimes the acknowledge bit will be allowed to float high, even though the data transfer has completed successfully. This is done to indicate that the data transfer has completed and the receiver (which is usually a "slave device" or a "master" which is unable to initate data transfer) can prepare for the next data request.

There are two maximum speeds for I2C (because the clock is produced by a master, there really is no minimum speed); "standard mode" runs at up to 100 kbps and "fast mode" can transfer data at up to 400 kbps. (Figure 2.41.)

A command is sent from the master to the receiver in the format shown in Figure 2.42. The "receiver address" is 7 bits long and is the bus address of the receiver. There is a loose standard, which is the most significant four bits are used to identify the type of device, while the next three bits are used to specify one of eight devices of this type (or further specify the device type).

As I said above, this is a "loose standard." Some devices require certain patterns for the second three bits, while others (such as some large serial EEPROMS) use these bits to specify an address inside the device. There is also a 10-bit address standard in which the first 4 bits are all set, the next bit is reset, the last 2 bits are the most significant of the address, and the final 8 bits are sent in a following byte. All this means is that it is very important to map out the devices to be put on the bus and all their addresses.

The following first four bit patterns generally follow the following convention for different devices:

0000 - Reserved address
0010 - Voice synthesizer
0011 - PCM audio interface
0100 - Audible tone generation

0111 - LCD/LED displays
1000 - Video interface
1001 - A/D and D/A interfaces
1010 - Serial memory
1100 - RF tuning/control
1101 - Clock/calendar
1111 - Reserved/10-bit address

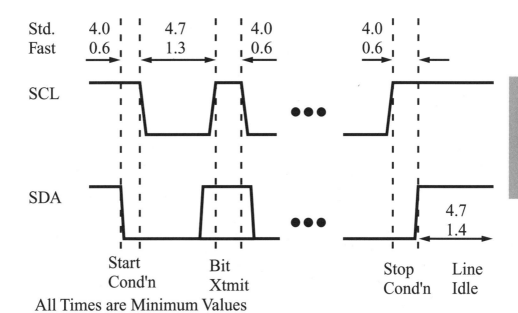

All Times are Minimum Values
All Times in uSeconds

Figure 2.41 I2C signal timing.

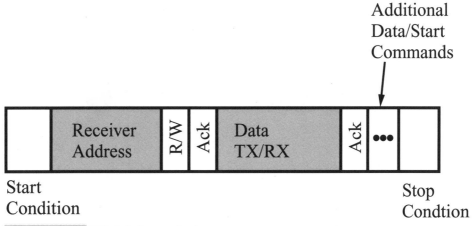

Figure 2.42 I2C data transmission.

This is really all there is to I2C communication, except for a few points. In some devices, a start bit has to be resent to reset the receiving device for the next command (i.e., in a serial EEPROM read, the first command sends the address to read from, the second reads the data at that address).

The last point to note about I2C is that it's "multimastering," which is to say that multiple microcontrollers can initiate data transfers on the bus. This obviously results in possible collisions on the bus (which is when two devices attempt to drive the bus at the same time). Obviously, if one microcontroller takes the bus (sends a "start condition") before another one attempts to do so, there is no problem. The problem arises when multiple devices initiate the "start condition" at the same time.

Actually, arbitration in this case is really quite simple. During the data transmission, hardware (or software) in both transmitters synchronize the clock pulses so they match each other exactly. During the address transmission, if a bit that is expected to be a "1" by a master is actually a "0," then it drops off the bus because another master is on the bus. The master that drops off will wait until the "stop condition" and then re-initiate the message.

I realize that this is hard to understand with just a written description. In the next subsection, "CAN," I will show how this is done with an asynchronous bus, which is very analogous to this situation.

I2C can be implemented in software quite easily. But, due to software overhead, the "fast mode" probably cannot be implemented; even the "standard mode's" 100 kbps will be a stretch for most devices. I find that implementing I2C in software to be best as the single master in a network. That way it doesn't have to be synchronized to any other devices or accept messages from any other devices which are masters and are running a hardware implementation of I2C that may be too fast for the software slave.

CAN

The "controller area network" (CAN) protocol was originally developed by Bosch a number of years ago as a networking scheme that could be used to interconnect the computing systems used within automobiles. At the time, there was no single standard for linking digital devices in automobiles. I read an interesting statistic when researching this book; before the advent of CAN (and J1850, which is a similar North American standard) cars could have up to three miles of wiring weighing 200 pounds interconnecting the various electronic systems within the car.

"CAN" was designed to be:

1. **Fast** (1 Mbit/second).
2. **Insensitive** to electromagnetic interference.
3. **Simple,** with few pins in connectors for mechanical reliability.
4. **Devices** could be added or deleted from the network easily (and during manufacturing).

While CAN is similar to J1850 and does rely on the same first two layers of the OSI seven-layer communications model, the two standards are electrically incompatible. CAN was the first standard and is thoroughly entrenched in European and Japanese cars and is rapidly making inroads (please excuse the pun) with North American automotive manufacturers.

CAN is built from a "dotted AND" bus that is similar to that used in I2C. Electrically, RS-485 drivers are used to provide a differential voltage network that will work even if one of the two conductors is shorted or disconnected (giving the network high reliability inside the very extreme environment of the automobile). This "dotted AND" bus allows arbitration between different devices. (When the device's "drivers" are active, the bus is pulled down—like in I2C.)

An example of how this method of arbitration works is shown in Figure 2.43. In this example, when a driver has a miscompare with what it is actually on the network (i.e., when it is sending a "1" and a "0" shows up on the bus) then that driver stops sending data until the current message (which is known as a "frame") has completed. This is a very simple and effective way to arbitrate multiple signals without having to retransmit all of the "colliding" messages over again.

The frame is transmitted as an asynchronous serial stream (which means there is no clocking data transmitted). This means that both the transmitter and receiver must be working at the same speed (typical data rates are in the range of 200 kbps to 1 Mbps). A frame is shown in Figure 2.44:

In CAN, a "0" is known as a "dominant" bit and a "1" is known as a "recessive" bit.

The different fields of the frame are defined as:

SOF. Start of frame, a single dominant bit.
Identifier. 11- or 19-bit message identifier.
RTR. This bit is set if the transmitter is also Tx'ing data.
r1/r0. Reserved bits. Should always be dominant.
DLC. 4 bits indicating the number of bytes that follow.

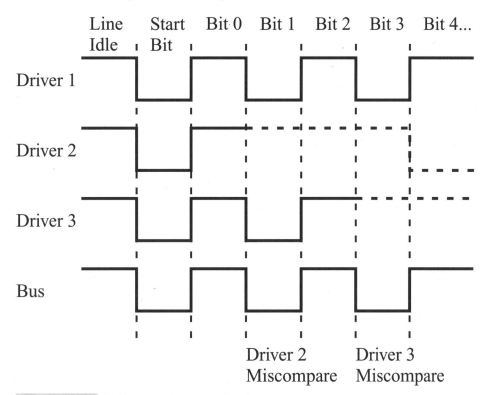

Figure 2.43 CAN transmission arbitration.

Data. 0 to 8 bytes of data, sent MSB first.
CRC. 15 bits of CRC data followed by a recessive bit.
Ack. 2-bit field, dominant/recessive bits.
EOF. End of frame, at least 7 recessive bits/.

The last important note about CAN is that devices are not given specific names or addresses. Instead, the message is identified (using the 11- or 19-bit message identifier). This method of addressing can provide you with very flexible messaging (which is what CAN is all about).

The CAN "frame" is very complex, as is the checking that has to be done, both for receiving a message and transmitting a message. While it can be done using a microcontroller and programming the functions in software, I would recommend only implementing CAN using hardware interfaces. There are several microcontroller vendors which provide CAN interfaces as part of the devices, and there are quite a few different "standard" chips (the Intel 82527 is a very popular device) available which will carry out CAN interface functions for you effectively and cheaply.

Analog I/O

The world outside the microcontroller is not all black and white (or ones and zeros); it is really varying shades of grey (or values between zero and one). Often a microcontroller will have to interface with analog signals (between Vcc and ground), both receiving them (and interpreting the value) as well as outputting them. In many models of the different microcontroller families there are analog-to-digital convertors ("ADCs") and digital-to-analog convertors ("DACs"). In this subsection, I will introduce you to analog voltage I/O, not analog data communication, which is discussed in the "Timer" section of this chapter (which describes sending and receiving PWM data).

There are three types of analog voltage input for microcontrollers. The first is a physical positional control sensor in which the microcontroller determines the position of a potentiometer. Next, an analog voltage comparator can be used to determine whether or not an input voltage is greater than or less than a reference voltage. The last type of ADC used in microcontrollers is known as an "integrating ADC," which can determine a voltage level independently. Each of these different types of ADCs are best suited for different applications.

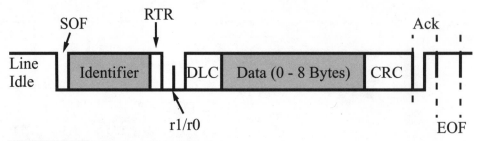

Figure 2.44 CAN 11-bit identifier frame.

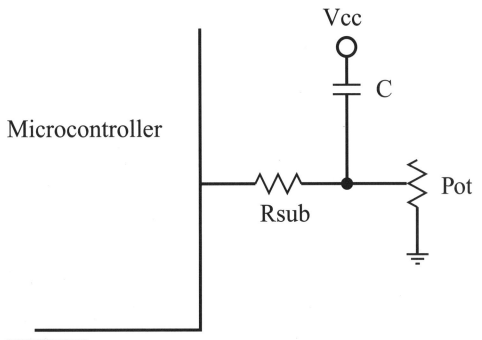

Figure 2.45 Using digital I/O pins to read a potentiometer.

The first type of ADC isn't really an ADC at all, but a method of reading a potentiometer's current resistance using digital I/O pins. To read the resistance, a simple RC network is attached to a microcontroller I/O pin. (Figure 2.45.)

The potentiometer resistance is read by measuring how long the voltage of the current flowing from the charged capacitor through the potentiometer is above the digital threshold level. The higher the resistance, the longer the input is read as a "1." (Figure 2.46.)

To measure the discharge cycle, the I/O pin is enabled as an output and set to a "1." The cap is allowed to charge to Vcc (through "Rsub," which limits current to prevent short circuit currents when the cap is initially charged). Once the cap is fully charged, the pin output driver is disabled and the cap is allowed to discharge through the potentiometer. The measurement ends when the voltage goes below "Vthreshold." Typically, a timer is used to time how long the voltage is above threshold.

If you were to look at this operation on an oscilloscope, you would see the waveform shown in Figure 2.46. To determine the values for R & C (Rsub is usually in the range of 100 to 200 Ohms), you can use the approximation:

$$t = 2.2 \times R \times C$$

Where "t" is the time for the time required to discharge the capacitor.

When I say that this will give you the "approximate" time, I mean to say that it will really only get you in the ballpark. This is generally not a precision circuit because of the tolerances of the resistor and capacitor and the nonlinear behaviour of the CMOS input bit. You can get more exact values by specifying a precision capacitor (which is often hard to find and expensive), but for the circuit, the application shouldn't really require it.

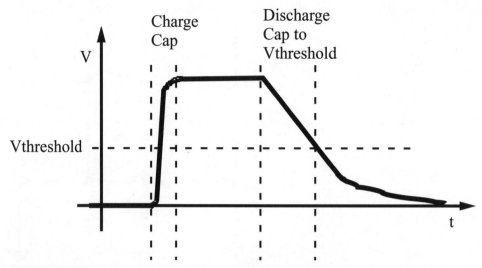

Figure 2.46 Electrical waveform for reading a potentiometer.

Now you're probably asking yourself, if this is a very imprecise method of reading a potentiometer, where and why is it used? It's used in circuits that simply provide a relative value for the potentiometer's position. For example, the IBM PC uses this type of circuit to read the current joystick postion. This imprecision is often reflected in the games where the user is asked to move the joystick to extremes to "train" the program in how the capacitor and joystick resistors interact.

Typically, I use a 0.1-uF tantalum cap and a 10K potentiometer for this circuit. This gives me an approximate maximum time delay of 22 msecs, which is long enough for a microcontroller to accurately read the time delay and is fast enough that the user won't be aware that the resistance measurement is taking place. I use a 0.1 tantalum cap because I use them for decoupling Vcc and ground in devices, and I always have a bunch of them around. The problem with using tantalum caps is that they can often be out by as much as 100% from their rated value. This means that I usually have the microcontroller "calibrate" the extreme values of the potentiometer before the application is usable.

The next type of ADC commonly available in microcontrollers is the analog voltage comparator. A comparator is a simple circuit which compares two voltages and returns a "1" when the input signal voltage is greater than the reference voltage ("Vref"). (Figure 2.47.) This circuit is best used for applications like thermostats, where something happens at specific input voltage points.

Often, in microcontrollers that use comparators for ADCs, the reference voltage ("Vref") is generated internally using a resistor ladder and an analog multiplexer to select the desired voltage to output. (Figure 2.48.)

This circuit can actually give some modicum of voltage specification. A simple algorithm could be used to run through each of the different voltages until the comparator output changes. The point of change is the actual input voltage. The reason why I say this gives a "modicum" of voltage determination is because typically the Vref circuit has a fairly wide range between each voltage step (this is also known as a large "granularity"). If the resistor ladder/analog multiplexer had 8 voltage levels, in a 5-volt system, the granularity between voltage steps is over 700 mvolts.

Another method of creating an ADC using comparators is to arrange them in a "flash" configuration. (Figure 2.49.) The reason why this is known as a "flash" ADC is because it is very fast when compared with other types of ADCs. The time delay to get an analog voltage measurement is limited by the delay through the comparators and priority encoder. This type of ADC tends to be very expensive because of the chip real estate required for multiple ADCs (for example, to get 8-bit precision, 256 comparators would be required, which would require special buffers to deal with internal signal "fan out").

The last type of ADC also uses a comparator, but it uses an analog voltage source which starts at zero volts and runs linearly up to Vcc (this is known as a "sweep generator"). (Figure 2.50.)

In this circuit (known as an "integrating ADC") when the conversion is to start, the timer is reset and the sweep generator is set to zero volts. Then the timer clock and sweep generator are enabled. When the sweep generator output is greater than "Vin," the clock is turned off to the timer and an "ADC stop" signal is asserted (which can cause an interrupt). At the end of the comparison, the timer will contain a value proportional to Vin.

This method, while being quite accurate, has a few issues associated with it. The first is the time required to do the conversion. The higher Vin is, the longer it will take to complete the conversion. Some microcontrollers have sweep generators built in their ADCs that can run at different speeds (although running at a faster speed will decrease the accuracy of the measurement).

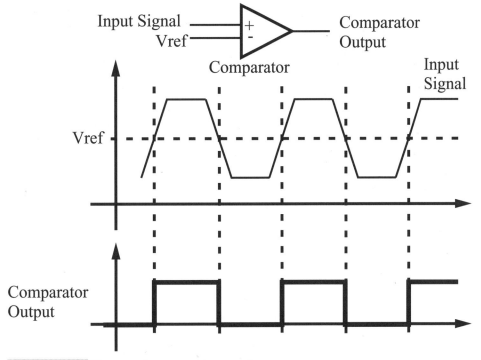

Figure 2.47 Comparator response waveforms.

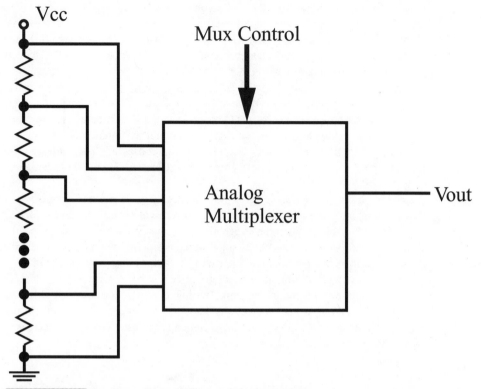

Figure 2.48 Analog voltages from a resistor ladder.

Another problem is what happens if the input signal changes during the sample. This problem is avoided by allowing a capacitor to charge very quickly and then sampling the voltage level on the capacitor.

The last issue to be considered with integrating ADCs is the time required with regards to the sampling of very fast input waveforms. For the example in Figure 2.51, a completely different waveform will be read than what is actually present at the microcontroller's ADC pin. Understanding what is the correct sample frequency goes beyond this book, but explanations of determining the correct sample frequency can be found in DSP textbooks.

When you look at microcontroller specifications, you will find very few devices with analog voltage output. Of the ones that do, the output is typically generated from the comparator Vref resistor ladder circuit. The reason for this is the many different circuits an analog voltage would be required to drive. If these circuits are not properly interfaced to the microcontroller output, the device drivers may be overloaded (which will cause an incorrect voltage output), or rapidly changing outputs may cause "reflections" which will appear as an incorrect output waveform.

So, to generate analog output voltages, external DACs, digital potentiometers (wired as voltage dividers) or PWM signals filtered by an RC network are usually used in applications. These devices offer very good voltage granularity (often in the range of millivolts).

But, there is a simple circuit that can be used on a microcontroller to provide an analog voltage output. In the circuit in Figure 2.52, by enabling different pin outputs (and out-

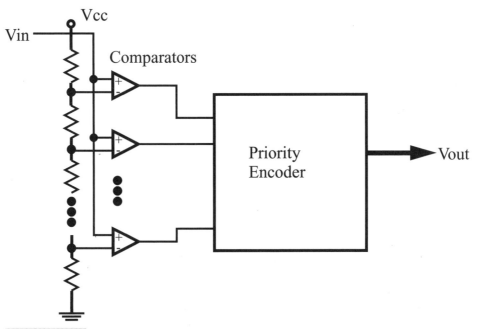

Figure 2.49 Flash analog-to-digital converter.

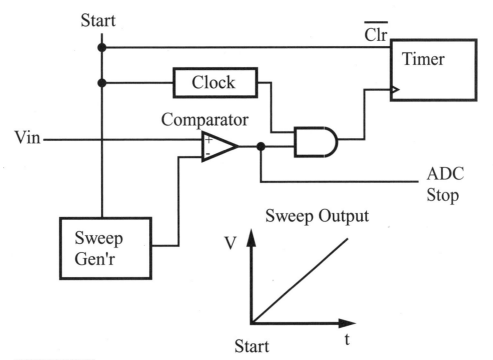

Figure 2.50 Integrating analog-to-digital converter.

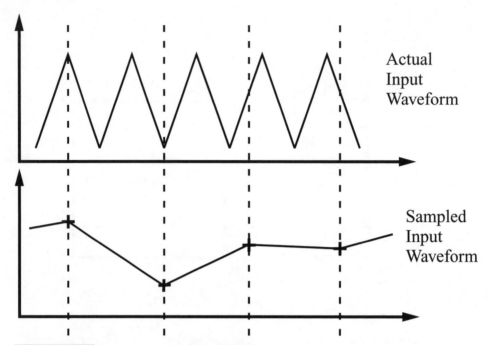

Figure 2.51 **Missed sample read waveforms.**

putting a "0" on the I/O pin), different voltages will be available at the input of the op amp. The op amp is used to isolate the resistor ladder from the load circuit. The resistor values are dependent on the number of pins used to control the output.

Looking at this circuit, you may be thinking that it can be used to provide greater than Vcc voltages (by providing higher than Vcc at the top of the resistor ladder). This will probably not work because of clamping diodes placed on the I/O pins to prevent overvoltage conditions which could damage the device. Instead, the op amp should be provided with a voltage-amplifying resistor network.

There are a lot of different options with analog I/O. The good news is that most devices are designed to make Analog I/O quite simple (often doing a sample with an integrating ADC is simply setting a "start" bit in a register and waiting for a "complete" bit to become set) as long as the analog voltage changes fairly slowly. If a high-frequency signal is input, then external flash ADCs coupled to DSPs should be used to process the input.

Slaved Devices

One of the most interesting and potentially useful operating modes available in some microcontrollers is the "Slave Mode," in which the microcontroller is wired to another processor as if it were a peripheral device. (Figure 2.53.)

In this mode, a number of the microcontroller's I/O lines are dedicated to interfacing with the "master" processor's bus. In this mode, the "slave" device is really behaving as an intelligent ASIC in the "master's" system.

The first application where I saw this mode used was in the IBM PC/AT. An Intel 8042 is used as the keyboard interface (along with some other features) to allow the central processor to simply read and write data, rather than having to interface directly with the serial keyboard (and having to execute the keyboard serial protocol).

Not shown in Figure 2.53, the microcontroller can interrupt the "master" by using one of its I/O pins to drive one of the master's interrupt request lines. I should point out that some devices can work in a "microprocessor" mode where the microcontroller is driving the buses.

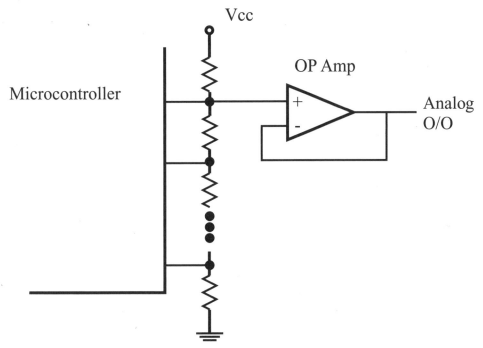

Figure 2.52 Analog voltage output circuit.

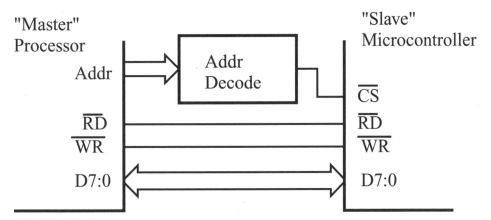

Figure 2.53 Microcontroller slaved to master.

Device Programming

Often you will use E(E)PROM-based microcontrollers for developing your applications as well as shipping in your product. Elsewhere in the book, I have discussed the advantages of this type of device over ROM-based programming. The disadvantage of this type of microcontroller is that you have to program it.

This is usually done by loading a holding register with the value you want to program into a location, then triggering a circuit for burning the contents of the holding location at a specific address, waiting some period of time for the programming to complete, and then verifying what you have written. Programming a full device can take anywhere from a few seconds to a few minutes, depending on the size of the device and the algorithms used for programming.

Often the programming equipment is very expensive (especially for the hobbyist/small business) and can be controller (i.e., PC or workstation) specific. But there are cases where the programming equipment is quite reasonable and simple. For example, when I discuss the PIC and AVR, I know you'll be amazed at how simple a device can be used to program some versions of them. There are also devices where no programming equipment is required (such as the Basic STAMP) or has built-in hardware and software which eliminates the need for external hardware other than supplying power to the device to be programmed (the 68HC05).

A very important aspect of the programming of a device is whether or not it can be "in system" programmed ("ISP"). If a microcontroller is said to be ISP capable, it means that a blank device can be soldered into a circuit and then have it programmed without affecting any of the other devices in the circuit. This can be an important consideration when choosing a device; implementing an ISP device in a circuit can eliminate the requirement to buy a unique programmer, allow software updates without having to pull stock, and allow the manufacturer to carry stock that is not unique to a specific product.

CONTROL STORE SECURITY

For many applications it may be desirable to protect the code burned into the microcontroller. To help aid in this, most devices provide some method of preventing the program being read from the device. Often this is done by setting a configuration bit during programming.

This bit is usually designed to be only cleared after the information in the rest of the chip is cleared (i.e., by ultraviolet light in the case of an EPROM-based part).

The built-in code protection will not prevent a really determined effort to read the code contained within it. This can be done in many chip failure analysis labs (and in a surprisingly short time). To try and make this operation less effective, some companies scramble the instructions loaded into the control store and then provide hardware on the chip for converting the scrambled data back into instructions for the processor.

I'm not trying to scare you or tell you not to use the control store protect bit, but rather caution you to the pitfalls of setting the bit as well as warning you that it is probably not the ultimate protection of the code in the device (which is where a significant amount of development effort has gone for the application/product).

Debug Interfaces

Most of the devices presented here have in circuit emulators ("ICEs") available for application debug. These devices physically replace the microcontroller in the circuit and provide an interface into the operation of the device, both from a hardware and a software point of view. Often, ICE developers will provide an integrated interface between the software development system (editor and compiler) and the emulator, allowing real-time debug of the software and application without time-consuming erasure and reprogramming, or setting up of serial I/O (or even LEDs) to determine the operation of the microcontroller. The only issue with these devices is the cost, which can be in the thousands of dollars.

Some microcontrollers do provide serial interfaces as part of hardware that is specific to debugging an application. These interfaces allow uploading and downloading of programs, data, and register contents as well as provide an execution interface to allow the user to start or stop the microcontroller remotely (and then download the variables/RAM content to see how the program executed). When coupled with a comprehensive control/interface program, this type of interface can replace an ICE for program development or manufacturing debug (and at a considerable cost savings over the ICE). Often, this type of interface is only available in high-pin-count and high-function microcontrollers, but it is available in some of the lower cost/function devices.

The last type of debugging interface is actually using specialized software to control the execution of the application software. A "monitor program" is actually a very simple execution control program that will allow you to start, stop, and modify ("patch") the application code, read and modify variable and register contents, and single-step or stop on breakpoint the application. In very small devices, this is probably not an option, but as devices are available with more memory, this is becoming more possible, and there are some devices which have monitor programs built in.

2

INTRODUCTION

SOFTWARE

3

The best microcontroller applications are a perfect marriage of hardware and software. Often hardware designers are reluctant to get involved with the development of software because it is something that they are not as comfortable with as designing and debugging hardware. But having a good understanding of how the device to be used is programmed is at least as important as understanding how the hardware interfaces will work. As you go through this chapter, I hope that you will discover that from both the hardware and software avenues, microcontrollers all work in similar ways and have similar tools available.

Development Tools/Environments

The idea of synergy between hardware and software is something that I feel is very important. And I believe that integrating software development tools with the hardware development tools can be an important advantage in an application. For microcontrollers, there are five different tools that are used for developing applications, and combining these functions into one package can make application development much easier.

The five development tools used for microcontroller application development are the source code editor, the compiler/assembler, a software simulator, a hardware emulator, and a device programmer. While not all of these tools are required and can be run as stand-alone applications, you'll find that when they are integrated, you will be able to develop and debug the applications much easier.

The editor is used to create the source code. There is almost an unlimited variety of editors to choose from, ranging from simply copying keyboard input directly into a file to highly configurable (or programmable) editors that will allow you to program specific responses to certain keyboard entries.

For example, the editor I use for developing "C" programs actually executes a "REXX" program after each keystroke. This program handles what happens after different keystrokes and provides special responses to different situations. I have customized this program to make "C" code development easier for me.

For example, after keying in "if," the editor responds with:

```
if ()
   {
   }
else
   {
   }  /*  endif  */
```

Which is the format of the "C" "if" statement that I am most comfortable with. With this entered into the program, the structure for the "if" statement is already entered into the program and I can be less concerned about forgetting to add something that is syntactically critical.

This editor works directly from the DOS command line, which makes it less useful in GUI environments (such as Windows) because data cannot be cut and pasted between files in a standard fashion.

But, for developing "C" applications, it is the method with which I am most comfortable and this is the point; the editor that you use should be the one that makes you feel the most comfortable.

The compiler/assembler is used to convert the source code into assembler instructions for the microcontroller and then translate this into a data format that can be downloaded into the device's control store. In the next subsection of this chapter, I will cover assembler and high-level languages and their implications, but here I want to talk about the compiler/assembler interface.

The interface I'm concerned about here is the interface between the editor and the compiler/assembler more than anything else. Having the ability to pass error information between the compiler/assembler and display the invalid lines on the editor can make program development much simpler and efficient. Now, with the editor I described above, I have written

REXX code that, when I want to compile, saves the current source, executes the "C" compiler, and if there are any errors, loads in the listing file, searches for the error string, and pulls up the failing line in the source file (the REXX program is actually very complex).

Simulators are programs that take compiled code and execute them on a host system as if they were running on the "target" system or processor. This allows you to monitor the software and microcontroller's response to different conditions. A simulator can be an invaluable tool during the development and qualification of software, allowing specific situations to be investigated that may be difficult to reproduce in actual hardware.

To provide these external conditions or situations, a stimulus file is typically used. This file provides a series of inputs to the simulated device from a source file. They typically look like:

```
Step    Bit0   Bit1    ;   Define the Input Bits
   1      1      1      ;   Initial Conditions - Everything High
 100      0      1      ;   Simulate Shifting In Data
 101      0      0
 102      0      1
 105      1      1      ;   Do the Next Bit
 106      1      0
 107      1      1
   .                    ;   And So On...
   :
```

If you are looking at this for the first time, you're probably thinking that developing a stimulus file can be a real pain (and you'd be right). But, in understanding how the microcontroller and the software work in a specific (and repeatable) situation, using a simulator and a stimulus file is hands down the best method. As well as this, stimulus files often cannot be used to simulate analog inputs.

I am a firm believer in stimulus files and I feel that before going to the trouble of burning a component, you should simulate what you expect is going to happen very closely. And, if the application doesn't work as expected, then you should look at the actual situation on an oscilloscope, modify the stimulus file, and try to understand what is happening with the simulator, where you can look at how the program is executing, rather than on the hardware, where all you can see is the high-level responses.

Avoiding explicit "bit wiggling" of the stimulus file, the "UMPS" integrated development system (which is presented later in the book) uses a graphical simulator that simulates the attachment of hardware to the microcontroller. With this circuit, you can "operate" your source code as if it were attached to hardware. This simulator can actually save hours in developing stimulus files and allow you to quickly try out specific inputs to try and find problems.

There is a readily available, real-time interface for microcontrollers, and that's known as an "emulator" which is short for "in circuit emulator" (or "ICE"). An emulator uses an actual microcontroller chip, hooked up to RAM (rather than ROM) control store, and runs the application at full speed. Many emulators can be used to record the sequence of instructions the processor executes at a specific time. This can help with understanding how the processor responds to a given situation (rather than single stepping to a certain condition).

But, an emulator has two significant disadvantages. The first is cost. A "true" ICE will cost a thousand dollars and up. The second disadvantage is regarding the actual electrical interconnections. They tend to be fragile and easily damaged, especially considering that they will be pushed in and pulled out of sockets repeatedly. But this is really a minor concern; a well-designed emulator can be a very powerful tool in developing an application.

3

INTRODUCTION

But even with the real-time capability, I prefer a simulator and spending some extra time developing stimulus files that I can run through the simulator to truly understand what is happening, without having to hook up hardware. With both the simulator and emulator, the need for having correct data to execute should be obvious; what may be less obvious are the advantages of having all the source information to allow the developer to debug the software using the actual source code, rather than compiler-generated files. This is known as "symbolic information," and being able to monitor the execution of a program while looking at the source is much easier than trying to follow the object code's execution.

The last development tool is a microcontroller programmer. While some microcontroller manufacturers primarily provide mask-programmable parts, they often provide an E(E)PROM version for application development. This means there must be some way of programming the part directly from the source code while developing the application.

For some devices, this is done using commercial device programmers, but more recently the trend has been toward simple programmers using ISP features in the devices. This means that the programmer hardware is part of the application.

There is one very important point for programmers, and that is to make sure the correct data is used for programming the part. This can be very important in parts with programmable configuration information, and setting bits incorrectly will mean that the part won't begin executing as expected.

Some programmers provide a simple emulator interface (i.e., a microcontroller on the programmer that can be used as an emulator or a platform to interface programmed parts to the circuit).

Assembly Language

Understanding assembly language programming is critical before beginning a microcontroller application (or even beginning to learn about a microcontroller). I find that if you are familiar with even one type of assembly language and understand the thought process used to develop the code, you shouldn't have any problems figuring out how to write code for another processor. I find this is true even if you want to develop the application in a high-level language (you may have to look at the actual processor instructions to understand what the code is actually doing).

Assembly language programming is typically taught in school as something to be endured because you can't graduate without passing the course. After the course, nothing is ever thought about it, other than how awful it was. Well, when developing microcontroller applications, you not only have to think about it, but you also have to understand it well enough to step through your application step-by-step and understand what is happening.

To make learning, writing, and debugging assembler easier and more intuitive, I use a couple of tricks. The first is to visualize how an instruction executes within a processor. The other is to apply structured language techniques to the code, which will make the code easier to read and understand.

I find that visualizing the instructions is best done by creating a block diagram of a processor/microcontroller and marking it up with the data flows for each instruction. This will result in a good visual understanding of how the instruction executes. For all the processors presented in this book, I have described each instruction's execution using this technique.

For example, here's what I did to understand the 68HC05's "ADC" (Add with Carry) instruction. First I created my own block diagram of the architecture. (Figure 3.1.)

Next, I drew on the data flows for the instruction. (Figure 3.2.)

Note that I broke up the data flow for the source and destination. This gives me a pretty good idea of what has to be done and how it is accomplished. Fully understanding the instruction is important because there may be status bits or other registers affected that don't seem obvious on the surface. I find that long after I have created these architecture drawings, I am able to remember how the instruction works without having to reference the databook.

Stating that using structured language techniques on assembly language probably seemed like an oxymoron to you when you first read it above, but I think you'll agree that some of the techniques will enhance the readability of your assembly language code.

The first technique is to separate functional blocks of code by blank lines or "white space."

For example, if I needed to read in 8 bits from a PIC I/O port and then respond with 0x07F on another port if the input were equal to zero, and repeat this eight times, I could use the code:

```
     movlw    8              ;  Loop 8x
     movwf    Count
Loop                         ;  Come Here for Each Loop
     movlw    0              ;  Is PortB == 0?
     iorwf    PORTB, w
     btfss    STATUS, Z
     goto     Skip           ;  No, Skip Over the Instruction
```

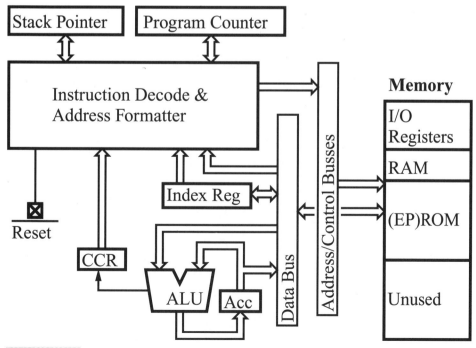

Figure 3.1 68HC05 architecture with stack and reset.

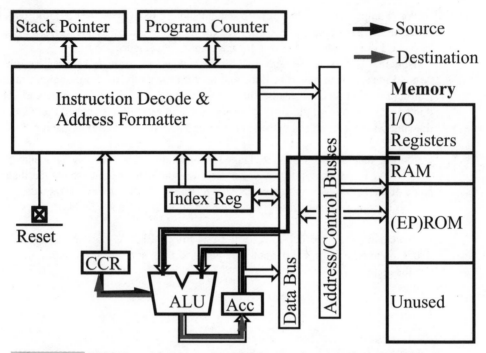

Figure 3.2 68HC05 architecture with ADC instruction data paths identified.

```
      movlw    0x07F          ;  Yes, Output the 0x07F Response
      movwf    PORTC
Skip
    decfsz    Count          ;  Decrement Count and if != 0 Loop Again
    goto      Loop
```

By adding blank lines to separate the functional blocks, I end up with:

```
      movlw    8              ;  Loop 8x
      movwf    Count

Loop                         ;  Come Here for Each Loop

      movlw    0              ;  Is PortB == 0?
      iorwf    PORTB, w
      btfss    STATUS, Z
      goto     Skip           ;  No, Skip Over the Instruction

      movlw    0x07F          ;  Yes, Output the 0x07F Response
      movwf    PORTC

Skip

    decfsz    Count          ;  Decrement Count and if != 0 Loop Again
    goto      Loop
```

Which has the blocks of code visually separated and more obvious.

Now, I can also indent conditional code, which I find improves the readability as well.

```
      movlw    8              ;  Loop 8x
      movwf    Count

Loop                         ;  Come Here for Each Loop

      movlw    0              ;  Is PortB == 0?
      iorwf    PORTB, w
      btfss    STATUS, Z
        goto   Skip           ;  No, Skip Over the Instruction
```

```
    movlw    0x07F          ;  Yes, Output the 0x07F Response
    movwf    PORTC
Skip

  decfsz  Count            ;  Decrement Count and if != 0 Loop Again
    goto   Loop
```

I find the code most readable when I eliminate all the unnecessary and redundant comments; I end up with something that's pretty good and easy to understand.

```
    movlw    8
    movwf    Count

Loop                       ;  Sample PortB 8x

    movlw    0             ;  If PortB == 0 then PortC = 0x07F
    iorlw    PORTB, w
    btfss    STATUS, Z
    goto     Skip

    movlw    0x07F
    movwf    PORTC
Skip

  decfsz   Count
    goto   Loop
```

When I go through the instruction sets and example applications for each of the different microcontrollers, I will explain how the instructions work, point out things to watch for, and give some hints on how to make the code more efficient.

Interpreters

If you are like me and remember back to the deep, dark days of personal computing, you probably have not-so-fond recollections of programming an Apple II or IBM PC in Microsoft BASIC. The source code was executed directly in the PC without an intermediate compilation step. The program that parses each line (to figure out what each line of the source is doing) and then executes it is known as an "interpreter." The name simply comes from the idea that each line is interpreted and then executed.

Interpreted code is usually the least efficient manner of program execution (although I'm sure I would get an argument from "Forth" aficionados). Before the purpose of the line can be executed, the source has to be fetched from memory, parsed, and then executed. Even if it took zero time to parse and execute the source code, interpreted code would always take longer to run than compiled code because the source code is always larger than the resulting compiled code and to execute the code, the source has to be read from memory and appropriate subroutines have to be called and executed, rather than running the compiled code directly from the application program.

Many interpreters work as simple compilers to first convert all the instruction statements into "tokens." These tokens are used by the interpreter to execute the desired functions without having to plough through each line. Interpreters that compile the source code first into tokens run the programs much faster than ones that don't.

If you know anything about the Parallax BASIC Stamp (which is described later in this book), you'd probably think that the device is a "PBASIC" (the Stamp's BASIC) interpreter. Actually, the Stamp consists of a PC host that compiles code into tokens and downloads them into an on-board EEPROM. Once in the EEPROM, the tokens are used to select subroutines to execute the program.

There are some microcontrollers that contain true interpreters on board (there is an Intel 8052 that has a version of BASIC built in and the source is loaded into an integrated RAM), but these devices do not tokenize the code. This means they run slower and have less program space available for program statements (because source code takes up more space than tokenized code). But the source code can be used to debug the application directly inside the microcontroller.

High-Level Languages

There are a large number of high-level languages available for microcontrollers. The term "high-level language" is used to describe languages in which easy-to-read statements written in a "language" are converted ("compiled") into assembly language and then object code (bits and bytes) for executing in the microcontroller.

These languages are typically general-purpose languages converted or "ported" to create code that will run on the processors built into the microcrontrollers and provide built-in functions specific to the microcontroller's features. There is a wide range of compilers available for microcontrollers, and the efficiency of code that they generate range from very poor to very good, the best requiring the fewest of the microcontroller's resources.

As I discuss a lot throughout this book, efficiency in microcontroller code is measured by the amount of control store used to load the program into, the amount of variable space required for storing temporary variables, and the resources used to support the compiled code.

The most popular languages available include "C," "BASIC," and "Forth." These are available for most of the microcontrollers discussed in this book. There are also a number of languages that are more device specific and are not available as universally. Microcontroller languages, even though they use the names, can be very nonstandard (as seen in the device explanations later in this book).

High-level language features normally include:

- Built-in functions (i.e., console I/O) with linked libraries.
- Numerous data types (8-, 16-, 32-bit integers and floating point).
- Stack-based arithmetic operation execution.
- "Automatic" and "global" variables.
- Data pointers and data structures.
- Data storage allocation.
- Hardware register access.
- Simulator/emulator symbolic data.

While these features are needed in a standard programming and execution environment (i.e., a PC or a workstation), supporting these features may lead to problems in an embedded microcontroller that has the following characteristics:

- Limited control store ROM space.
- Limited variable and stack RAM.
- No BIOS or operating system.
- Redefinable I/O (i.e., pins that can be digital/analog/serial I/O).

These characteristics can limit the usefulness and appropriateness of developing an application using a "standard" high-level language and built-in libraries.

For example, functions built into libraries, while useful in some applications, may not be appropriate in all cases. In the "C" language, the standard libraries contain functions for console input/output, data transfer, mathematical operations, data conversion, etc. While all the routines may be useful in different situations, I would be surprised if an application used all of the functions at the same time. This means that when the program is linked with the library, there will be functions stored in the program that are not required.

In a PC, which has essentially unlimited memory (segments of an application program can be moved in and out when required), this is not a problem. But in embedded microcontrollers this is a big problem.

Another problem with canned libraries is that different microcontrollers have different features, which can affect what is required when the source is compiled (i.e., some versions of a microcontroller processor may have a built-in serial port while others do not). Often, in cases like this, the function will first test for the hardware being present (or its versions and features) and then execute the correct code. This cuts down on the efficiency of the overall code (more control store is used up by the function and it takes longer than necessary to execute).

Both these function/library problems are fairly easy to overcome by looking at the usage of the built-in functions and only linking in the ones that are required and are specific to the microcontroller that the code is being created for. Often in microcontrollers, linking in separate object files (which libraries really are) is not done. Instead, all the code is compiled at the same time as part of the total program and, using conditional compiling/assembly, only the routines and features that are required are compiled with the rest of the source.

Too many different data types can cause space problems with a processor that can only handle data at 8 bits at a time (all the microcontrollers described in this book have 8-bit processors). When handling larger data types requiring more than 8 bits, additional code must be written to handle the operations.

For example, the "C" assignment:

```
FirstVar = FirstVar + SecondVar;
```

Could be done simply in a 8051 as:

```
mov   A, FirstVar       ;  Get the First Variable Value
add   A, SecondVar      ;  Add the Contents of Second to First
mov   FirstVar, A
```

If the variables are both 8-bit integers. If they are 16-bit integers, the code becomes a bit more complex:

```
mov   A, FirstVar           ;  Do the Addition on the first 8 bits
add   A, SecondVar
mov   FirstVar, A
mov   A, FirstVar + 1       ;  Do the Addition on the high 8 Bits
addc  A, SecondVar + 1      ;   Note that it's an Add with Carry
mov   FirstVar + 1, A
```

This code is actually simpler because of the add with carry instruction ("addc"); in devices without an add with carry, this code becomes more complex:

3

INTRODUCTION

```
mov   A, FirstVar           ;  Do the Addition on the First 8 bits
add   A, SecondVar
mov   FirstVar, A
jnc   Skip                  ;  If Carry Not Set, Skip Over Increment
inc   FirstVar + 1          ;    Increment High 8 Bits of the Destination
Skip
mov   A, FirstVar + 1
add   A, SecondVar + 1
mov   FirstVar + 1, A
```

The preceding example is only a single case to be considered. As operations get more and more complex (for example, "FirstVar = SecondVar + (ThirdVar * FourthVar)"), the resulting instructions become exponentially more complex and larger. When compounded by using larger data types, the operations may take an unacceptably long time to execute or more space than is available in the microcontroller.

Often, larger than base number operations are put into libraries, which increases the cycle count and the amount of memory needed to support the operations.

In the applications that I have done, I have found 16-bit integers to be very useful, but I have been successful in avoiding larger data format numbers. Sixteen-bit numbers require very little extra code or temporary variables, while giving a good range of numbers to work with. With some prior thought and planning, virtually all embedded 8-bit microcontroller applications can be implemented with just 8- and 16-bit integers.

In complex operations (such as the "FirstVar = SecondVar + (ThirdVar * FourthVar);" example above), the code can be compiled into a series of stack operations.

```
push      SecondVar
push      ThirdVar
push      FourthVar
mul
add
pop       FirstVar
```

These stack operations are not processor instructions, but instead are a series of instructions that carry out the operation. The compiler will often try to optimize this series of operations before converting them to processor instructions. With some processors, these operations are designed to be executed easily and the code can be very efficient.

Depending on the sophistication of the compiler, the instructions generated can be as efficient as hand-assembled code or as much as 100x (in terms of the number of instructions generated and the number of cycles required to execute) less efficient.

For some compilers, rather than integrating everything into one line, having several lines may be much more efficient.

```
FirstVar = SecondVar + ( ThirdVar * FourthVar );
```

May be more efficiently compiled as:

```
Temp = ThirdVar * FourthVar;
FirstVar = SecondVar + Temp;
```

Another important consideration for how a compiler converts a number is how temporary values are handled. In the example above, if "FirstVar" were actually defined as not an I/O port, the code example above could be converted into:

```
FirstVar = ThirdVar * FourthVar;
FirstVar = FirstVar + SecondVar;
```

This is an optimization because the compiler notes that "FirstVar" is not used in the operators and can be used in the place of a temporary value. There may be problems because if "FirstVar" is an I/O register, using it as an intermediate value may be incorrectly picked up by external hardware and used instead of the correct, final value.

In many high-level languages, there are two types of variables that can be specified. "Global" variables are defined throughout the program and as such cannot be redefined. Global variables are best suited for values which are either accessed inside of many different routines (and passing the value as a parameter is inefficient because it may be updated in the routine) or from the program mainline. Global variables are the only type of variable available in assembly language (unless you are willing to write automatic variable stack operations and variables manually).

"Automatic" variables are local to a routine and defined when the routine is called in a high-level language. Defining an automatic variable in two routines that are never nested means that only one variable is actually allocated by the compiler. Typically, automatic variables are pushed on the data stack when a routine is called and popped off when execution returns to the calling program. Because the memory used by an automatic variable is written over when another routine is called, you can never depend on it being available later in the program. When passing parameters to a routine, the parameters are usually (but not always) automatic variables, which means they can be modified without modifying the original values passed to the routine.

I find data pointers and structuring data invaluable programming techniques when I program devices with large memories. Pointers are primarily used within systems where memory is a manageable resource. This is not the case in a microcontroller where there is a very small and finite amount of memory, which means data cannot be saved on a disk when more memory space is required (when this is possible, the start of data is referenced by a pointer). For this reason, I really haven't found a compelling use for pointers in a microcontroller application that can't be satisfied using other techniques.

The primary method of replacing pointers in a high-level language is to create an array at the start of the memory you want to use. Then, to access arbitrary points within this memory, the index of the required memory is pointed to.

Data structures are something that I find very useful in microcontrollers. Just so we are talking in the same terms, I define a data structure as a block of memory used to define a standard data record.

If I wanted to make a structure in "C" of a processor instruction in memory, I could define it as:

```
struct instruct {      //  Instruction Data Format
   int   address;       //  Address of the Instruction
   char instruct;       //  Instruction
   int   value;         //  16 Bit Data Value
};
```

Normally, this is referenced in a block of memory by a pointer, but it can be placed inside an array of 16-bit words ("C" data type "int") and referenced by an index to the array. To access a specific element in the data area, the index of the element start plus the offset within the structure is taken, along with a data type override.

This is a real mouthful; instead, it would probably be easier to show what I mean by showing the code. If I wanted to return the "value" from the data area, if I were using a pointer I would use the code:

```
struct instruct * Ptr;      //  Declare Pointer to the Structure
   .
   :
 i = Ptr -> value;          //  Read "value" from current Element
```

With an array, this could be implemented with:

```
struct instruct Array[ 100 ];      //  Define Array of Structure
   .
   :
 i = Array[ Index ].value;
```

Which isn't a lot more complex than the pointer statement above it and has the added bonus that there is not a pointer that has to be kept track of, making sure that it is always pointing to the correct "instruct" element.

Another data structure that should be considered is the table. A table can be thought of as a single index array representing a data string that doesn't change. Typically, this string is a state machine or a message that is output to the user. Declaring it in "C," it could be:

```
char Greeting[13] = "Hello there!";
```

The language compiler should be able to place these types of tables into read-only control store ("ROM") to free up memory and save the RAM that is required to place the values within it and initialize the array elements. This table information would be accessible as an array and be identical to RAM arrays (in terms of the language operation) when an element is read.

In a microcontroller, it should be obvious that the code should be able to access hardware registers. Typically, this is done in one of two ways. The first is to allow assembler statements to be inserted in line in the code. The second is to allow the user to define variables at specific locations within the variable space (which includes registers). Either method is typically a departure from a language standard (or at least how it applies to PC/workstation standard languages), but both are usually supported by high-level languages ported to a microcontroller.

The last feature to consider with a high-level language is how symbolic information is passed to a simulator/emulator. Symbolic information is the references to lines, labels, and variables and where they are located in control and variable store. This information is used by simulators and emulators to display source code as it is running to allow you to debug the code without having to work only with assembler code and cross-reference addresses with the compiler's output listing.

Don't assume that all languages output the same symbolic information (or even output it at all). You may find that you really like to use a certain language but cannot find a version that passes useable symbolic information to a specific simulator.

These are the major considerations (or the most important features) of a high-level language I would have when choosing a compiler for a microcontroller. The comments I have placed here concern both the design of software and the operation of the microcontroller. Paying attention to these points will help make choosing a compiler more effective than simply a shot in the dark.

What I haven't discussed is why you'd actually want to use a high-level language. There are a number of reasons why you'd want to use one.

The first is code portability. By using a high-level language, there are many code examples and algorithms available to draw upon and even cut and paste directly into your application. You also may wish to transfer software between devices (both different members of the same family or to a completely different device). Using a high-level language will make this much easier.

One of the best reasons to choose developing applications in a high-level language is to avoid a lot of the "scut" work of assembly language programming. This includes having to code highly complex operations efficiently and simple syntax errors (because assembly language is often a lot more syntax dependent than high-level languages and this syntax is less intuitive than the syntax of a high-level language). Having to create very complex operations may result in less efficient code than a compiler because of the difficulty of following through the code and seeing "the big picture" the same way as a compiler can.

The last and probably most important reason for using a high-level language is application support. Often, you will find yourself having to modify or debug code that you have written months or years before. Developing the code in a high-level language will make this task a lot easier.

Fuzzy Logic

If you've ever taken (or suffered through) a course in control theory, you probably remember how difficult it was to understand and how "unnatural" it seemed. (I was never really able to visualize what exactly what was going on with the imaginary polar drawings.)

A modern solution to controlling processes is to use a digital signal processor to implement the control theory algorithms in a floating-point processor. This solution is as just as bad as trying to understand classical control theory and requires a lot of effort on the part of the person designing the system to come up with a correct response algorithm.

Visualizing a problem or a situation is very important for humans to be able to understand what is happening and enables us to come up with a solution. Traditional control theory taught in third and fourth years of electrical engineering at university only offers very mathematically intensive solutions that are very hard to visualize.

There is one interesting nontraditional method of controlling systems, and this is known as "fuzzy logic." Fuzzy logic can be considered a superset of Boolean logic, where values between "1" and "0" are input into the system and a nonbinary result is output.

The input values are manipulated in a manner similar to Boolean logic. Most people consider fuzzy logic to be a recent invention, but as I was researching this book, I was amazed to discover that fuzzy logic was first described in 1965—more than 30 years ago! The main reason for fuzzy logic seeming to be very new is the almost total disdain shown for it in North America. In Asia (especially Japan), fuzzy logic has become an important technology used in many applications, ranging from air conditioner thermostats to determining when and how much to feed infants.

Professor Lofti Zadeh of UC Berkeley, inventor of fuzzy logic, defined the following characteristics of fuzzy systems:

1. **In** fuzzy logic, exact reasoning is viewed as a limiting case of approximate reasoning.
2. **In** fuzzy logic, everything is a matter of degree.
3. **Any** logical system can be "fuzzified."
4. **In** fuzzy logic, knowledge is interpreted as a collection of elastic or equivalently fuzzy constraints on a collection of variables.
5. **Inference** is viewed as a process of propagation of elastic constraints.

To explain how to define a fuzzy logic system, I will use the classic control system example of the inverted pendulum. (Figure 3.3.) The purpose of this exercise is to keep the weight at the end of the pendulum vertical by moving the truck back and forth, using inertia to keep the weight upright. If you're not familiar with this example, take a pencil and balance it vertically with the point down on one of your fingers. See how long you can keep it upright. (The best I could do was about five seconds; this experiment will definitely give you more appreciation of what a trained seal can do.)

In developing a fuzzy control system, the first thing to be done is "fuzzification" of the system. This is done by specifying the different outputs relative to the different inputs. In this example, the output is the speed and direction of the truck. The inputs are the angle of the pendulum and its angular velocity.

A "fuzzy set" is defined for each input, which is a collection of "patches" defining different conditions. One of the parameters that I wanted for my system was to keep the truck in the centre of the system (so it could react to changes in the pendulum without running out of track to respond with). So I defined the position as five different patches defining whether or not the truck was at the "centre," "near," or "far" away. The "patches" should cover every part of the base variable ("X"- axis). (Figure 3.4.) This is to be repeated for the angle of the pendulum as well as its angular velocity.

Once the inputs are fuzzified, a set of rules is developed. These rules specify what the output response is for given conditions. As you can see in Figure 3.4, the position could be in both the "centre" and "near," which means that multiple rules could be valid for a given condition.

This may seem unusual, but in fuzzy systems, this is normal. Multiple rule intersection helps define what the response should be.

Some rules for this system could be:

1. if Angle = Vertical AND Angular_Speed = Stopped AND Pos = Centre
then Speed = 0

2. if Angle = -Lean AND Angular_Speed = -Slow AND Pos = Centre
then Speed = -Slow

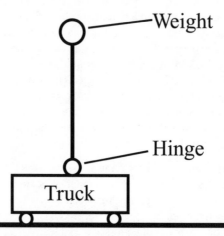

Figure 3.3 Inverted pendulum control system problem.

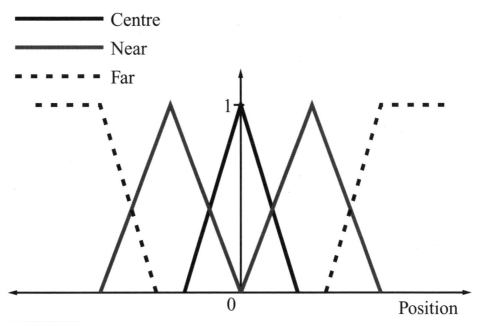

Figure 3.4 Inverted pendulum fuzzy logic position patch diagram.

and so on for each different case. This can be defined several different ways (such as if-then as shown above or using a modified Carnot map).

With the rules in place, the inputs are run through them. If we were to look at the second rule above, we may have a negative angle that maps out to Figure 3.5.

This angle returns a fuzzy value of 0.4. Now, to use this with the other fuzzy operations in rule number 2, we are ANDing this value with the "Angular_Speed" and the "Pos" to get a final result. In fuzzy Boolean operations, the mapped value (0.4 for the angle in this example) is compared to the other mapped values, and the lowest value is passed along.

ORing and NOTing can be done as well. For ORing, the maximum mapped value is passed along. For NOTing, the current value is subtracted from 1. All Boolean transformations and laws (i.e., associativity) apply to fuzzy logic, so the result can be computed easily.

This value is then used to create a weighting for the output value. This weighting is important because if multiple rules are satisfied, the output of each is combined and a final output is produced.

These different outputs are weighted together to get the actual output response. In the inverted pendulum example, Figure 3.6 shows what happens when two rules are satisfied and two weighted outputs are combined.

The output could be anywhere in the shaded area, but a centre of mass is taken and used as the actual output. This response is balanced between the output of the two rules by taking the centre of mass of both the responses.

This is really all there is to fuzzy logic. I realize that running through this example and explanation of executing a fuzzy control system with one example with one condition doesn't really explain how it works. But it is a lot simpler than explaining how a classic control system would operate (which would probably take up the whole book).

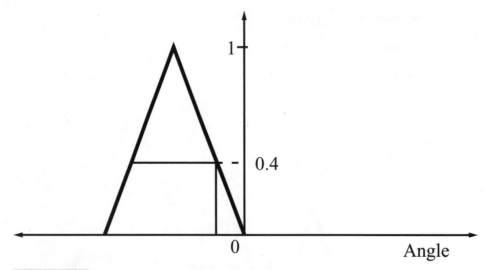

Figure 3.5 Inverted pendulum fuzzy logic angle value.

Software Development

As I introduce you to microcontroller software development, please note that I am discussing my way of doing things. Is my way the best for you or the best for a given application? Probably not. This subchapter is intended to introduce you to a number of different aspects of microcontroller software development.

When developing application software, I usually use a "bottoms-up" approach with the peripheral interface code developed first, followed by the application's logic functions. The "logic functions" determine how each peripheral element is used in the application.

Your own application programming style may be a "top-down" approach or something in between. I remember being told about a programming style known as "easy first," which does just that. The important thing to realize is that you should try different approaches until you have a method of software development that is good for you.

RESOURCE ALLOCATION

If you've programmed for a PC or other type of workstation before, you'll probably think of resource allocation in a way other than how I use it in terms of microcontrollers. In a PC or workstation, resource usage is probably minimized to end up with an efficient (fast and small) final application.

In the microcontroller world, there is only a finite amount of resources. When I say resources I am talking primarily about variable RAM and hardware features. In a PC or workstation, variable space is virtually unlimited (especially if disk spooling is used), and hardware resources are usually accessed using BIOS or operating system routines, which means that there is little source in the application devoted to accessing this hardware.

When developing microcontroller applications, there are a few rules I follow to make sure that I don't use more resources than what I have available.

1. **Only** use one interface to hardware resources. Multiple interfaces can cause problems if the hardware can be set differently at different times.
2. **Identify** global variables specific to routines and don't use them anywhere else in the code.
3. **Use** automatic variables wherever possible (this is only available in high-level languages).
4. **If** temporary variables are to be used, make sure the code can use them universally.

Following these rules when you develop an application will save you the grief of a difficult-to-find, intermittent software bug later on.

TIME-CRITICAL CODE

While there are many hardware features built into microcontrollers for performing precisely timed operations, there will be occasions when you have to create code that performs I/O operations on a precise schedule. A good example of this is handling asynchronous serial communications without using serial hardware. This means that the interval between sending bits or checking the input bits must be precisely timed.

At first, you may think that using a timer and interrupts will solve this problem, but this often won't give good enough accuracy for the application. In this section, I will go through the example of creating code to read/write serial data at 9600 bps using an microcontroller running with a 1.0-usec instruction cycle period. To illustrate some of the problems timing code, let's assume that all instructions take one instruction cycle to execute, except for jumps, which take three.

The 9600-bps bit rate results in a 104.167-msec bit period. This means the timing loop should take exactly 104 cycles to read and write data (which will leave an error of 0.16%).

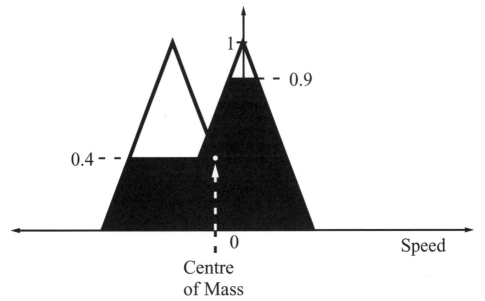

Figure 3.6 Inverted pendulum fuzzy logic result for current angle.

To read the data, let's assume the code to be used is:

```
mov    Count, 8
Loop                          ;  Get 8 Bits and store in "Char"
  mov  A, Dlay                 ;  Delay so loop takes 104 cycles
DlayLoop
  dec  A
  jnz  DlayLoop
  rr   Char                    ;  Rotate "Char" to Right
                               ;   - Last Read bit Now in Bit 6
  mov  A, Port                 ;  Get the I/O Port with the Data Bit
  and  A, 0x001                ;  Check Bit 0 (I/P Bit)
  jz   Skip
  or   Char, 0x080             ;  Set Bit in Char for High Bit
Skip
  dec  Count                   ;  Have we Read 8 Bits?
  jnz  Loop                    ;  If Not Zero, then "No"
```

Now, we have to figure out what "Dlay" should be.

The first thing I do is figure out the "intrinsic" loop delay, which is the time it takes to go through the loop once, with a delay value equal to 1 (which will cause the code to fall through). As I look at the loop, I see a problem: there's a one-cycle difference in the section of code that sets the bit in "Char" if the incoming bit is set.

If the input bit is reset, then the "jz" instruction will execute, requiring three instructions. If the bit is set, then only two instructions will be required for the no jump and "or" instruction. To make sure that the loop always take the same path, I will add two "nops" after the "or Char, 0x080" instruction.

With this done, I can see that the intrinsic loop delay is 14 cycles. This leaves 90 cycles for the delay loop. Four cycles are required for each loop (one for the "dec A" and three for the "jnz DlayLoop" instructions). So, for a "Dlay" value of 23 (which causes the loop to execute 22 times), I get a loop time of 88, which when added to the 13, gives a total of 101 cycles for the loop (which gives a timing error of 2.98%). Adding three "nops" or one jump to the next instruction will bring the timing to exactly 104 cycles.

Deciding what level of error is acceptable requires going back and understanding what the code is doing. For an asynchronous interface, this error is multiplied by at least ten (the eight data bits, start and stop bits). So a bit error of 0.86% results in an 8.6% error at the end of the packet (which is ten bits long); this is probably acceptable. A bit error of 2.98% results in almost a 30% error at the end of the byte, which probably isn't acceptable.

Creating precisely timed code for writing data is similar to reading it, but with one important twist; each event, whether it is a "1" or a "0" being output, must happen at the same time (or the receiver may miss the data).

For the example above, the code for transmitting the byte at 9600 bps would be:

```
mov    Char, 8
Loop                          ;  Output 8 Bits
  mov  A, Dlay                 ;  Delay so the Loop is 104 usecs/cycles
DlayLoop
  dec  A
  jnz  DlayLoop
  mov  A, Char                 ;  Figure whether to Output a 1 or a 0
  and  A, 1                    ;  Send the LSB First
  jz   SendZero                ;    Send a 0 Out
  or   Port, 2                 ;  Use Bit 1 for the Output
  jz   SentBit
```

```
SendZero                    ;  Send a Zero out
  and    Port, 0x0FD
SentBit
  rr     Char               ;  Put the Next Bit in the LSB Position
  dec    Count              ;  Do 8x
  jnz    Loop
```

In the data read example, the incoming data is only polled once, but in the write example, the data is output at two different points. A "1" being sent out will happen 3 cycles before the zero is sent out. This can be easily fixed by adding two nops before executing the "or Port, 2" instruction. Similarly, if a "0" is sent, the "SentBit" label will be reached three instructions before it will be if a "1" is sent, so after the "and Port, 0x0FD" instruction, a "goto SentBit" instruction should be put in after "and Port0, 0x0FD" and the data will be output to the port at the same number of cycles after the start of "Loop."

Once every possible path has been scoped out and all I/O events happen at the same point in the loop, the value for "Dlay" can be calculated the same way as was done in the data read example.

This example probably seems a bit contrived and needlessly complex, but in actuality, it may be very simple, compared to how the microcontroller's instruction set actually executes in terms of cycles and different conditions. Some processors have a much greater range of instruction execution cycle requirements than what is shown here.

This is one area where a RISC instruction set and Harvard architecture can really make a difference. In this case, instructions are loaded in one cycle (typically while the previous instruction is executing), the instruction is typically executed in the next cycle, the instruction timing variability is greatly reduced, and developing code for timing loops such as this is quite easy.

MACROS AND CONDITIONAL CODE

The purpose of macros and conditional code is to ease the work of developing and reading (which really means "understanding") code. These tools allow code to be written for general devices and applications to be used in more specific cases without having to rely on specific code.

A macro can be considered a function that replaces the "call statement" as opposed to being a subroutine located outside the mainline code. For example, if you were programming an LCD interface, which requires an "E" clock (which is bit 0 of "Port") pulse, you might use the code:

```
push  A            ;  Don't want to change contents of Accumulator
mov   A, 0x0001    ;  Make "E" high
or    Port, A
xor   Port, A      ;  Drop "E" Back Down
pop   A            ;  Restore the Accumulator
```

If this had to be used repeatedly, the source would become cluttered and harder to understand. So, to simplify the source, the code above could be put into a macro:

```
pulse_E macro      ;  Pulse the "E" Line
  push A           ;  Save Accumulator
  mov   A, 0x0001  ;  "E" High
  or    Port, A
  xor   Port, A    ;  "E" Low
  pop   A
  macroend
```

Now each time the "E" clock has to be pulsed, the code above will be inserted in the source just by putting in the line:

```
pulse_E
```

The code inside the macro will be placed in the line of the source.

Macros can also have parameters passed to them. If, in the example above, I wanted to make "pulse" work with an arbitrary bit, I would redefine the macro as:

```
pulse macro bit          ;  Pulse the "E" Line
  push  A                ;  Save Accumulator
  mov   A, 1 << bit      ;  Calculate the Bit
  or    Port, A          ;  Bit HIGH
  xor   Port, A          ;  Bit is low
  pop   A
  macroend
```

Now, rather than having a macro that's specific to the application with the "E" clock on bit 0 of port, "pulse" can be specified with the appropriate bit number.

For example,

```
pulse 2
```

This will insert the "pulse" macro code, which will pulse bit 2 of "Port."

Along with macros is the idea of conditionally compiling code (usually referred to as "conditional code"). Conditional code uses compile time variables to determine whether or not certain code is to be executed.

The "compile time variables" are only used at compile time and are used to control whether or not code is to be added to the source or not.

Going back to the original example, we may want to use a macro variable called "debug" that will allow specific code to execute during application debug. In our LCD "E" clock example, we may wish to invert an output pin (which is connected to an LED) every time the "E" clock is pulsed. This will give a visual indication when the LCD is being written to.

In most macro processors, there is a facility which processes these conditions before allowing the file to be compiled. In assemblers, these conditional statements are typically in the structured language form of "If (Cond)/else/end" with the added condition "ifdef (Variable)" which is used to allow the following code to be compiled if the macro variable is defined. In high-level languages, which use the "If (Cond)/else/end" format, slightly different conditional code operators are used (for example, in "C," "%if" is used for the conditional "if").

Now we want to modify the macro above so that if "Debug" is defined, we will toggle bit 7 of "Port," which has the LED attached to it during debug. The macro now becomes:

```
pulse macro bit          ;  Pulse the "E" Line
  push  A                ;  Save Accumulator
  mov   A, 1 << bit      ;  Calculate the Bit
  or    Port, A          ;  Bit HIGH
  xor   Port, A          ;  Bit is low
ifdef Debug              ;    If "Debug" is defined
  mov   A, 0x080         ;    Flip bit 7
  xor   Port, A
endif
  pop   A
  macroend
```

Conditional code does not only have to be placed within macros. It can also be put into the mainline code. It's just run at the same time as the macro processor, which is why it is usually discussed with macros (as I've done here). Even if you have never been exposed to assembler code before, you're probably aware of macros and conditional code. What you might not be aware of is that macros and conditional code are often available in high-level languages as well. The "#define" statements in "C" are actually macros and "#if/#else/#end" are used as conditional code.

In the "Common Assembler Commands" appendix, I go through conditional code and macros in more detail with other examples.

Resident Monitor and Debugger Programs

In some microcontrollers, "Monitor" (or "Debugger," as they are sometimes known) programs are loaded into the control store of the device to give the application developer the opportunity to load, execute, and debug applications on the actual hardware. The addition of this program can greatly speed up the debug of an application and eliminate the requirement for buying an in-circuit emulator for doing application debug. The idea of loading in a program to be used for debugging a microcontroller application may seem very unorthodox to you, but if you've ever developed code for a PC or workstation, chances are you used a resident debugger (or even a monitor) for making sure the program runs properly.

I use the terms "monitor" and "debugger" interchangeably to describe the same piece of software. The monitor is a program designed to control the execution of a program in a device as well as allow updating of the program memory or registers to modify how the program works.

Typical features for a monitor program include:

- Program load.
- Program execute.
- Stop on breakpoint.
- Single step.
- Program modification/"patch."
- Memory/register read/write.

If you have worked with a resident debugger (i.e., MS-DOS's "debug" program), you will probably recognize many of these features. I was going to suggest that if you aren't familiar with these concepts, you should get an old copy of MS-DOS and try out "debug" for yourself. A much better idea would be to skip along to the "8051 Example Application" chapter and see how the UMPS GUI IDE is used.

Now, applications are debugged using graphical interfaces with symbolic links to the source code. So rather than debugging compiled code, you can watch the actual source lines execute. These GUI interfaces, while seemingly light-years ahead of a command-line program, actually use the same concepts and operations to debug a program.

There is one very important point that I have to make about monitors/debuggers; they reside on the same processor and use the same memory space as the application they are debugging. This is an important point; the application's processor is used for both executing the program as well as the debug software. While it should be easy to visualize a PC's processor doing this job, it may be more difficult to see this happening in a microcontroller, which has much less memory to load both the application and the monitor program. I have seen monitors written that require as few as 512 bytes, so while space is an issue for microcontrollers, you can see that a monitor program can be linked in with the application with very little difference in the required control store.

Another issue is this: because the monitor is running in the microcontroller, if the program screws up a hardware resource of variables used by the monitor, you may not be able to regain control of the application or the monitor.

To run the features listed above for a monitor program, the microcontroller must have a number of hardware features built into it. The microcontroller's processor must be able to read/write the control store and be able to write to control store from an executing program, or a monitor program cannot be used to debug an application.

The Princeton architecture, as discussed earlier, has only one memory space, which is used for control store, variables, and the stack. In this case, the code to be debugged may be put into RAM to allow easy updating.

While it might seem obvious when I say it, having some I/O pins for the monitor to communicate with a host system (or terminal) is just as critical. If a very small pin-count device is to be used for the application, there may not be enough pins available for communicating with a host. Also, the host data receive pin should be interrupt driven to allow the host to interrupt an executing program, or the host system should be able to reset the microcontroller and the monitor will boot up rather than the application.

Loading the program into the device through the monitor is an important issue to consider. Not that it's necessarily hard writing code to receive data from a host—the issue is whether or not the microcontroller can write to its own control store. This feature is required for updating programs and putting breakpoints into the code.

One point that I should have probably made clear earlier before discussing application loading and updating is to explain what a monitor actually is. From the language of the text above, you probably think that a monitor is a stand-alone program that has the ability to load and execute another program. This is true to some extent, but I like to think of a monitor program as a specialized interrupt handler. The monitor is only invoked when certain input conditions have been met. To make sure this can happen at any time, this is best implemented as an interrupt handler, which stops the application from running when the user wants to interface with the monitor. In a microcontroller (or any other computer), the monitor is only active when the application has been interrupted by the user. This allows the application to run at full speed without any instruction overhead for supporting the monitor.

While most interrupt handlers are simple, dedicated to a specific piece of hardware, and run very quickly, the monitor is a very elaborate piece of software that not only controls how the application is to execute, but also interfaces with the user. Often this interface is a "dumb" terminal, which means the monitor must be able to parse commands from the user. Controlling the execution of an application is primarily done by manipulating the application's program counter, stored on the stack while the monitor is active.

This manipulation consists of monitoring and updating the return address on the stack. For example, if you wanted the program to start running at a specific point in the program, the monitor would "push" that address onto the stack so that when the monitor is ready to let the program run, a return from interrupt instruction is executed, which causes the desired address to be popped off the stack and stored in the program counter.

Breakpoints and single stepping also require the ability to modify the memory that contains the application code. In many processors, there is a single byte instruction for causing a "software" interrupt (in the i86, used in the IBM PC, this instruction is "int 3" which has an op-code of 0x0CC). To implement a breakpoint, this instruction is substituted for the byte at the start of the instruction (all instructions are at least one byte long). When the software interrupt instruction is encountered, the program counter stack is decremented (to point to the beginning of the instruction again), and the first byte of the instruction is restored (replacing the software interrupt instruction).

Single stepping can be handled in an analogous fashion (i.e., a jump to the monitor is at the start of the next instruction), but some processors' interrupt controllers have a mode that causes an interrupt after executing a single instruction.

Being able to read and write registers is often carried out by instruction from user input. This can be done after the command is received or can wait until the program has resumed executing.

Both methods have advantages. If the registers are updated immediately, then you can play "what if" with the hardware, to understand how the microcontroller and its different features work. If the registers are updated before the code resumes execution, then there is the opportunity to change the state of the microcontroller in such a way that the monitor can no longer be accessed (if, for example, the interrupt controller masked the host interface interrupt). This is not an issue if the registers are updated only before execution is resumed.

The last feature of a monitor that you should be aware of is the ability to assemble/disassemble instructions. This obviously takes up a lot of space (and, just as obviously, is not included in the 512-byte monitor software that I mentioned at the start of this section) and may not be available when the size of the microcontroller's control store and application requirements are considered.

If the assembler/disassembler features are not available in a built-in monitor, you will need a printout of the application's assembler listing (which contains the instructions, along with their hex op-codes and the address where they are located) to be able to specify correct breakpoint addresses and understand what is happening at a specific address.

Monitor/debugger programs are excellent tools for debugging applications even if there are significant limitations due to resource constraints. They can be powerful tools (and a lot less costly than an in-circuit emulator).

While monitor programs are available for many microcontrollers, they are not typically possible for Harvard-architected processors. As noted in the chapter titled "Microcontrollers," there are some applications that Harvard architectures cannot implement. A monitor/debugger is one of them.

The reasons why should be quite obvious. The control store is usually not available to the processor to write to (and even if it were, the instruction size is probably different than the word size and would make the task of updating the instruction much more difficult). This shortcoming in the Harvard architecture does not completely prevent a program being written that will act as a monitor, but without special control store interface capabilities, implementing monitor functions (even a reduced number of features) can be very difficult, if not impossible.

Real-Time Operating Systems

Before writing this section, I debated a lot on whether or not I wanted to include a discussion about "real time operating systems" ("RTOS") in this book. An RTOS is really meant for computer systems that are capable of doing multiple tasks at the same time. For example, the PC that I'm currently writing this on has "Coral Draw" in the background, is playing a music CD, is connected to the Internet, and I'm displaying a Web page using Netscape. I can load the computer with even more tasks. A typical microcontroller application, such as the microcontroller that reads the keyboard and sends data to a PC, is really doing only one task.

Each one of the "tasks" (as different programs running concurrently are known) that I have running in the PC are completely independent of each other, except for some inter-task communications features and resource management (i.e., arbitrating all the requests to access the disk drive so that data can be pulled out logically).

A real time operating system consists of a multitasking operating system that has been optimized for controlling processes. A "typical" multitasking operating system gives each task an equal "time share" to give the impression to the user that each program is running continuously. An RTOS is designed to respond to external events very quickly and gives the impression of many processors, each dedicated to controlling a single device. In your house, a single processor RTOS could be controlling heating and cooling, turning on external lights at night, monitoring fire and burglar alarms, and controlling the phone's answering machine. Each of these tasks has to be executed in such a way to make it look like a processor is dedicated to a specific task.

This is done by giving the processor a small "time slice" to devote to each of these functions (basically poll the input device and respond). Note that I say "devote to" and not "execute." In a multitasking operating system, tasks are run to completion, while in an RTOS, input to a task is checked and if there is input to be responded to, the task is executed. If there is nothing to respond to, then the task does not execute and the operating system jumps to the next task to see if there is anything waiting for a response.

In an RTOS, interrupts are used to receive input and indicate that a task is ready to execute. This is usually done by moving a task from a "waiting" queue to an "executable" queue.

In both the multitasking and real-time operating systems, a messaging function is provided to pass data between tasks. This means that each task has a queue for incoming messages and will only be allowed to execute during its time slice, or when an interrupt has been requested. If the response takes too long, the task will be put back on the "executable" queue and the next task waiting to execute will begin to run.

System resources (such as disks, timers, I/O devices, etc.) are typically only accessed through a specific task. This naturally queues requests to the resources and ensures that multiple tasks are not using the same resources at the same time.

This description of how multitasking operating systems (of which real-time operating systems are a specific type) is quite simplistic. There are a number of other features, including task priority and semaphore flags that I haven't touched upon that are quite important. What I wanted to do was give a flavor for how a multitasker generally works (and an RTOS more specifically).

Even with this simple explanation, you're probably not comfortable with how a real-time operating system works, so let's go through an example.

A good example would be the central control system for a space station. To save weight, volume, and power (all-important considerations in spacecraft), a single computer would be used to monitor and control all the nonscientific operations on board the station.

These include:

- Environmental control.
- Atmosphere quality and pressure.
  - Heating and cooling.
  - Lighting (dimming the lighting when it's "night").

- Power distribution.
  - Keep solar cells pointing towards the sun.
  - Charge/discharge batteries.
  - Monitor current draw from experiments.

- Communications.
  - Keep antennas pointing at receiving stations.
  - Multiplex communications from the intercom and experiments.
  - "Spool" messages.

- Attitude and position control.
  - Monitor station orbit and attitude.
  - Control thrusters.

With these basic functions, the processor would have a central hard file for logging communications and providing maintenance and repair instructions for the astronauts, a central display console for I/O, and a real-time clock to allow the different functions to be synchronized.

A block diagram for this system is shown in Figure 3.7. Now, what you're probably asking yourself is, is this the block diagram for the hardware or the software?

The answer is both. I feel that in a true RTOS, the system diagram is exactly the same as the software task block diagram. This means that at least one task is used for each hardware function. Note that some of the arrows are only in one direction; this is for data flow and indicates the direction information or commands are moving in. I should also point out that each block may contain more than one task. Often it is easier to code some functions as multiple tasks as opposed to just one (and allow the messaging functions to serialize the data requests and commands).

Looking at this example, you're probably thinking that the computer system used to control a real space station is a thousand times more complex, and an embedded microcontroller couldn't control a system like this.

If you did think this, you're wrong on both counts; the computer system for a real space station would probably be a million times more complex than this example, and an embedded microcontroller could control it.

You're probably shaking your head at the last one, but you have to think about the amount of computing power that is available in these simple 8-bit devices. The two "Voyager" probes, the first spacecraft to map the outer planets, were controlled by a

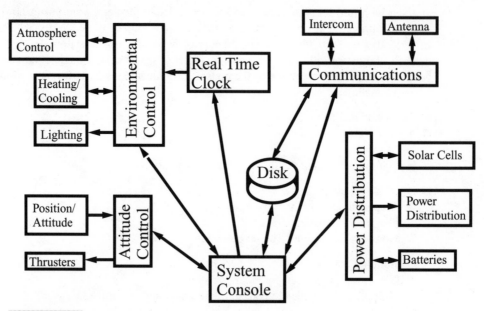

Figure 3.7 Space station RTOS application block diagram.

single microprocessor considerably less advanced (and running at a tenth of the speed) than the processors contained in the microcontrollers presented in this book. The processors only had 2K of control store available to them (parts of which had to be updated from Earth to keep the spacecraft computer current with the current mission status). The message is, "real-time" isn't all that fast for a computer, and events that seem fast to humans can be easily handled by a modest computer system.

If you are going to control a highly complex system with a single processor, I do recommend using one of the many real-time operating systems available to coordinate the different tasks required. Purchasing an RTOS will allow you to develop the application while only worrying about how the application works. In the 68HC05 section, I have provided an example RTOS.

COMMON MICROCONTROLLER INTERFACES

There are quite a number of common interface devices that are used with microcontrollers. This chapter is devoted to introducing them to you and providing a few pointers in how they should be used.

Switch Debounce

When a switch is opened or closed, there is a great deal of "noise" (which is known as "bouncing") at the moment of change. This is a concern in microcontrollers where buttons are often used for input (and the bouncing can register as multiple button presses). (See Figure 4.1.) This "bounce" is literally caused by the switch contacts bouncing on and off each other as contact is being made or broken.

In microcontroller applications, this bounce can be interpreted as several switch openings and closings. If the switch is used as a button for controlling the application, this will be processed by the microcontroller as multiple button presses (this will make the application very difficult to use). To eliminate this, special circuits or software are used to filter out the "bounce."

One of the simplest methods of eliminating bounce in a circuit is to add a RC network to the switch circuit. (Figure 4.2.) In this circuit, the time required to charge/discharge the capacitor to the point where the microcontroller's input pin threshold voltage is reached should mask the switch bouncing. A "Schmidt" triggered buffer could also be put between the switch circuit and the microcontroller to improve the debouncing carried out by the circuit.

The disadvantages of this method are the extra costs of the components, the board real estate to put them on, and the rise/fall time of the RC network. This may make the application awkward to use (for some very noisy switches, you may have to delay as much as a tenth of a second to get a positive input).

A much better way to perform switch debouncing is to do it in software. As a rule of thumb, if a switch hasn't changed state for 20 msec, then it has been debounced (and no more transitions can be expected).

So, a software function to carry out debouncing could be implemented in "C" as:

```
DBounce:                              //  Start Here while switch high
   while (( Port & SW ) != 0 );       //  Wait for Switch Bit to go Low
   TMR = 0;                           //  Reset Timer for 20msec check
   while ((( Port & SW ) == 0 ) && ( TMR < Twenty_msec ));
   if ( TMR < Twenty_msec )
     goto DBounce;                    //  Still Bouncing, Try Again
```

This code can be tailored to a specific application and simplified by the use of interrupts to handle the timer and button press.

LED Output

The most common form of output from a microcontroller is the ubiquitous light emitting diode ("LED"). As an output device, it is cheap and easy to wire to a microcontroller.

Generally, LEDs require more than 16 mA of current to light (which is often within the output sink/source specification for most microcontrollers). But remember that LEDs are diodes, which means current flows in one direction only.

The typical circuit that I use to attach an LED to a microcontroller I/O pin is shown in Figure 4.3. With this circuit, the LED will light when the microcontroller's output pin is set to "0" (low voltage). When the pin is set to input or outputs a "1," the LED will be turned off.

INTRODUCTION

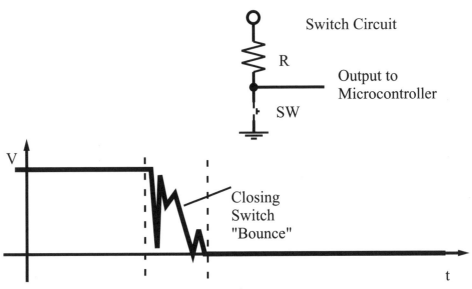

Figure 4.1 Switch bounce.

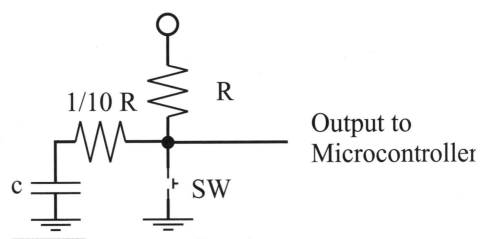

Figure 4.2 Switch debounce with capacitor.

The 220-ohm resistor is used for "current limiting" and will prevent excessive current, which can damage the microcontroller and the LED. Some microcontrollers already have current-limiting output pins, which lessens the need for the current limiting resistor. But I prefer to always put in the resistor to guarantee that a short (either to ground or Vcc) cannot ever damage the microcontroller of the circuit it's connected to (including the power supply).

7-Segment LED Display

Probably the easiest way to output numeric (both decimal and hex) data is via 7-segment LED displays. These displays were very popular in the 1970s (if you're old enough, your

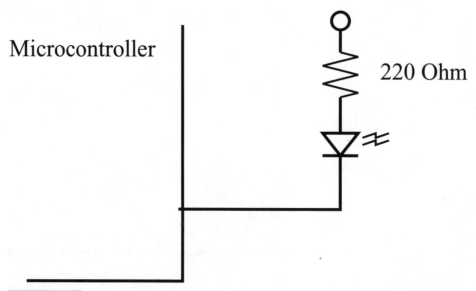

Microcontroller

220 Ohm

LED connected to a microcontroller I/O pin.

first digital watch probably had 7-segment LED displays), but these have been largely replaced by LCDs.

But 7-segment LED displays are still useful devices that can be added to a circuit without a lot of software effort. By turning on specific LEDs (which light up a "segment"), the display can be used to output decimal numbers. (Figure 4.4.)

Each one of the LEDs in the display is given an identifier, and a single pin of the LED is brought out of the package. The other LED pins are connected and wired to a common pin. This common LED pin is used to identify the type of 7-segment display (as either "common cathode" or "common anode").

Wiring one display to a micrcontroller is quite easy; it is typically wired as seven (or eight if the decimal point ("DP") is used) LEDs wired to individual pins.

The most important piece of work you'll do when setting up 7-segment LED displays is matching and documenting the microcontroller bits to the LEDs. Spending a few moments at the start of a project will simplify wiring and debugging of the display later.

The typical method of wiring multiple 7-segment LEDs together is to wire them all in parallel and then control the current flow through the common pin. Because the current is generally too high for a single microcontroller pin, a transistor is used to pass the current to ground (which selects which display is active).

In Figure 4.5, four 7-segment displays are connected to a microcontroller.

In this circuit, the microcontroller will shift between the displays showing each digit in a very short "time slice." This is usually done in a timer interrupt handler:

```
Int
    - Save Context Registers
    - Reset Timer and Interrupt
    - LED_Display = 0                    ;   Turn Off all the LEDs
    - LED_Output = Display[ ++Cur mod #LEDs ]
    - LED_Display = 1 << Cur             ;   Display LED for Current Display
    - Restore Context Registers
    - Return from Interrupt
```

This code will cycle through each of the digits (and displays), having current go through the transistors for each one. To avoid flicker, I generally run the code so that each digit is turned on/off at least 50 times per second. The more digits you have, the faster you have to cycle the interrupt handler (i.e., eight 7-segment displays must cycle at least 400 digits per second, which is twice as fast as four displays).

You may feel that assigning a microcontroller bit to each display LED to be somewhat wasteful (at least I do). I have used high-current TTL demultiplexer (i.e., 74S138) outputs as the cathode path to ground (instead of discrete transistors). When the output is selected from the demultiplexer it goes low, allowing current to flow through the LEDs of that display (and turning it on). This actually simplifies the wiring of the final application as well. The only issue is to make sure the demultiplexer output can sink the maximum of 140 mA of current that will come through the common cathode connection.

Along with 7-segment displays, there are 14- and 16-segment LED displays available which can be used to display alphanumeric characters ("A"–"Z" and "0"–"9"). By following the same rules as used when wiring up a seven-segment display, you shouldn't

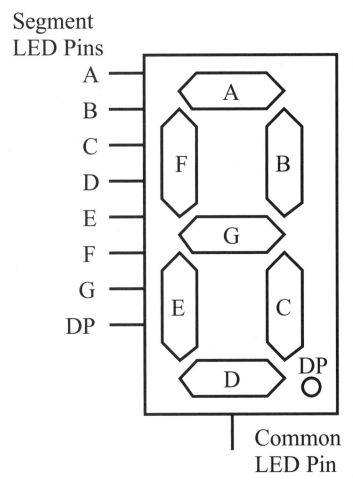

Figure 4.4 7 Segment LED display.

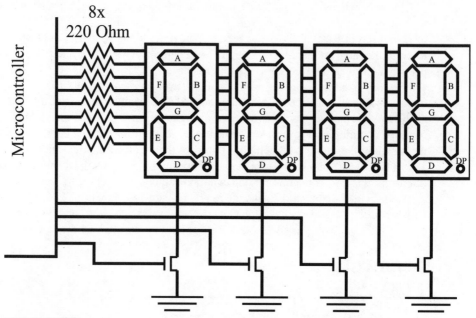

Figure 4.5 Wiring four 7-segment LED displays to a microcontroller.

have any problems with wiring the display to a microcontroller. In the "8051 Example Application" chapter, I show how a 16-segment LED can be used to display letters and numbers.

Switch Matrix Keypad Input

In many applications, button input is required for controlling the execution of the software. This can be accomplished using individual buttons as shown above, but this is wasteful in terms of I/O pins and code. Instead, a switch matrix keypad is a much better solution to the problem.

A switch matrix keypad is a collection of switches (which look like buttons or "keys" on a keyboard) wired in a row/column format. (Figure 4.6.)

To read a specific key, which means to see if a specific switch is closed, a signal is put on the column and then the rows are read in to see if the signal shows up in any of them. The easiest way of doing this is to pull up the rows and then tie one of the columns to ground. When the rows are scanned, if a row is low, then the switch at that row/column is assumed to be closed. (Figure 4.7.)

Figure 4.7 shows two FET transistors to pull the columns down to ground. As discussed in "Hardware Features," microcontroller pins can be used to simulate the "open-drain" operation of these transistors. The two transistors shown in Figure 4.7 are not needed, but I put them in to give you a better understanding of how the circuit works.

The matrix of switches can be expanded to virtually any size using very few additional microcontroller pins (a 104 PC keyboard is really a matrix of 13 by 8 switches) and the

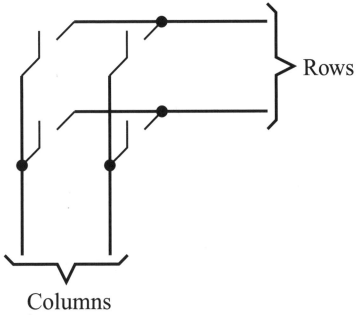

Figure 4.6 Matrix switch internal wiring.

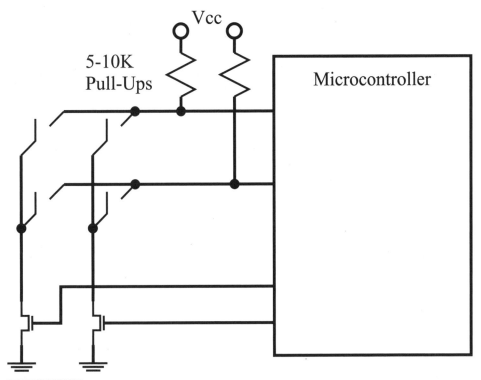

Figure 4.7 Wiring a matrix switch to a microcontroller.

software required to drive it doesn't change (except for row/column character constants) to support different-sized switch arrays.

You may simply not want to write the software or maybe not enough bits are available to implement this in the application. There are chips that will carry out this function and notify you when the data is available.

In Figure 4.8, the 74C922 is used to interface a four-by-four switch matrix keypad to the BASIC Stamp. In software, the Stamp continuously polls the "data avail" pin, and when it is asserted, the four bits containing the address are read into the Stamp and displayed on the LCD.

The 10K resistors coming from the 74C922 (and leading to the Stamp and LCD) are used to eliminate "bus contention" (which is defined as two or more drivers on a single bus attempting to drive different logic levels) at the Stamp and LCD. If a 74C922 pin is driving a line at a different level than the Stamp, there will be a voltage drop across the resistor (along with an associated current flow), eliminating the possibility of an indeterminate voltage at the Stamp and LCD.

When the Stamp pins are in input mode, the 74C922's pins are the only drivers on the buses; there is very little voltage drop across the 10K resistors allowing the Stamp to check the logic's status.

This method of putting different devices on the same bus is not one that I would recommend if you are uncertain how it works. Different devices have different I/O characteristics (i.e., internal pull-ups, voltage clamping, etc.) which can spell trouble for applications that have multiple driving devices. You'll never go wrong with developing applications where only one device can drive a net or bus at a time.

LCD Control

While LEDs are useful in indicating that an application is running, is connected, or is waiting for input, LEDs are not capable of providing the range of output options of a liquid crystal display ("LCD"). An LCD allows your application to output a very specific message (or prompt) to the user, making it much more "user friendly." I also find LCDs to be invaluable for displaying status messages and information during application debug.

ASCII-input LCDs, even though they have these advantages, have a reputation of being difficult to hook up and get to work. To show you that it isn't that difficult, in this subchapter I want to go through how LCDs work and how they can be wired to the microcontroller.

Most alphanumeric LCDs use a common controller chip, the Hitachi 44780, and a common connector interface. Both of these factors have resulted in alphanumeric LCDs that range in size from 8 characters to 80 (arranged as 40 by 2 or 20 by 4) and are all interchangeable, without requiring hardware or software changes.

The most common connector used for the 44780-based LCDs is 14 pins in a row, with pin centres 0.100" apart. The pins are wired as:

Pin 1. Ground.
Pin 2. Vcc.
Pin 3. Contrast voltage.

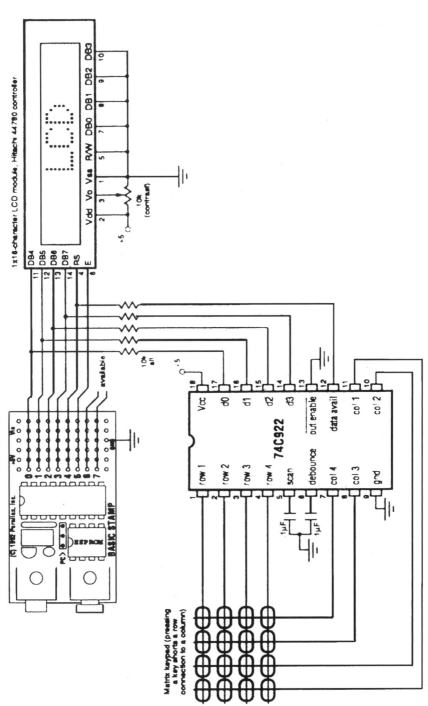

Figure 4.8 74C922 keyboard interface to a BASIC Stamp.

Pin 4. "R/S" instruction/register select.
Pin 5. "R/W" read/write select.
Pin 6. "E" clock.
Pin 7–14. Data I/O pins.

As you would probably guess from this description, the interface is a parallel bus, allowing simple and fast reading and writing of data to and from the LCD. (Figure 4.9.)

This waveform will write an ASCII byte out to the LCD's screen. The ASCII code to be displayed is eight bits long and is sent to the LCD either four or eight bits at a time. If 4-bit mode is used, 2 "nybbles" of data (sent high 4 bits and then low 4 bits with an "E" clock pulse with each nybble) are sent to make up a full 8-bit transfer. The "E" clock is used to initiate the data transfer within the LCD.

Sending parallel data as either 4 or 8 bits are the two primary modes of operation. While there are secondary considerations and modes, deciding how to send the data to the LCD is the most crucial decision to be made for an LCD interface application.

Eight-bit mode is best used when speed is required in an application and at least 10 I/O pins are available. Four-bit mode requires a minimum of 6 bits. To wire a microcontroller to an LCD in 4-bit mode, just the top 4 bits (DB4-7) are written to. (Figure 4.10.)

This can be further reduced by using a shift register so that a minimum of three I/O pins is required. (Figure 4.11.)

For this type of application, I use something like a 74x174 (where "x" is "HC" or "LS") wired up as a shift register. Eight-bit mode could be used with a shift register, but a ninth bit (which will be used as "R/S") will be required.

The "R/S" bit is used to select whether data or an instruction is being transferred between the microcontroller and the LCD. If the bit is set, then the byte at the current LCD "cursor" position can be read or written. When the bit is reset, either an instruction is being sent to the LCD or the execution status of the last instruction is read back (whether or not it has completed).

The character set available in the 44780 is basically ASCII. I say "basically" because some characters do not follow the ASCII convention fully (probably the most significant difference is 0x05B or "\" is not available). The ASCII control characters (0x008 to 0x01F) do not respond as control characters and may display Japanese characters.

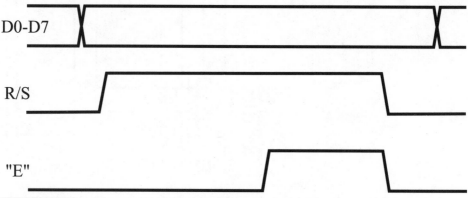

Figure 4.9 Waveform for writing a character to an LCD.

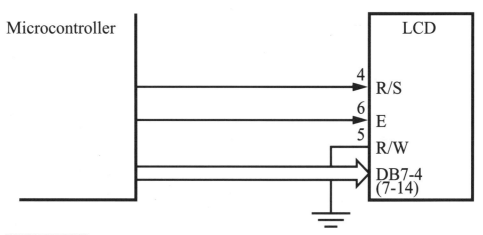

Figure 4.10 LCD 4-bit microcontroller interface wiring.

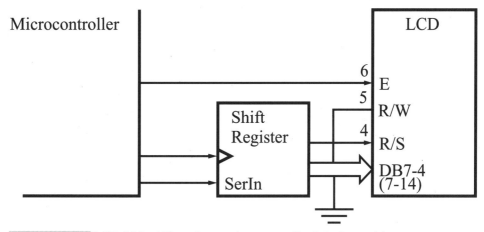

Figure 4.11 LCD 4-bit shift register microcontroller interface wiring.

Eight programmable characters are available and use codes 0x000 to 0x007. They are programmed by pointing the LCD's "cursor" to the character generator RAM ("CGRAM") area at eight times the character address. The next eight characters written to the RAM are each line of the programmable character, starting at the top.

The easiest way to list the different instructions is to use the following table:

R/S	R/W	D7	D6	D5	D4	D3	D2	D1	D0	Instruction/Description
0	0	0	0	0	0	0	0	0	1	Clear Display
0	0	0	0	0	0	0	0	1	*	Return Cursor to Home
0	0	0	0	0	0	0	1	ID	S	Set Cursor Move Direction
0	0	0	0	0	0	1	D	C	B	Enable Display/Cursor
0	0	0	0	0	1	SC	RL	*	*	Move Cursor/Shift Display
0	0	0	0	1	DL	N	F	*	*	Set Interface Length
0	0	0	1	A	A	A	A	A	A	Move Cursor to CGRAM

0	0	1	A	A	A	A	A	A	A	Move Cursor to Display
0	0	BF	*	*	*	*	*	*	*	Read the "Busy Flag"
1	1	D	D	D	D	D	D	D	D	Write ASCII to the Display
1	1	D	D	D	D	D	D	D	D	Read ASCII from the Display

Optional Bit Descriptions:
Set Cursor Move Direction:
  ID - Increment the Cursor After Each Byte Written to Display if Set
  S - Shift Display when Byte Written to Display
Enable Display/Cursor
  D - Turn Display On(1)/Off(0)
  C - Turn Cursor On(1)/Off(0)
  B - Cursor Blink On(1)/Off(0)
Move Cursor/Shift Display
  SC - Display Shift On(1)/Off(0)
  RL - Direction of Shift Right(1)/Left(0)
Set Interface Length
  DL - Set Data Interface Length 8(1)/4(0)
  N - Number of Display Lines 1(0)/2(1)
  F - Character Font 5x10(1)/5x7(0)
Move Cursor to CGRAM/Display
  A - Address
Read/Write ASCII to the Display
  D - Data

Note that the instruction type is determined by the number of leading zeros.

The "busy flag" is set as long as the instruction is executing within the LCD. For creating an application that runs as quickly as possible, this line can be polled (eliminating the requirement to delay the worst-case amount of time). This is typically not a big point because putting in an explicit software delay is not that difficult; all instructions take a maximum of 160 usecs except for "clear display" and "return cursor to home," which take a maximum of 4.1 msecs (although I always delay 5 msecs just to be on the safe side).

Different LCDs execute instructions at different rates. As I've pointed out, the delays quoted above are maximums; some LCDs will execute in less time. But, unless the busy flag is polled, I recommend that the maximum delay is always waited.

Reading data back is best used in applications that require data to be moved back and forth on the LCD (such as in applications that scroll data between lines). In most applications, I just tie the "R/W" line to ground because I don't read anything back. This greatly simplifies the application because when data is read back, the microcontroller I/O pins have to be alternated between input and output modes.

For most applications, there really is no reason to read from the LCD. I usually tie "R/W" to ground and just wait the maximum amount of time for each instruction. As well as making my application software simpler, it also frees up a pin for my use.

In terms of options, I have never seen a 5x10 LCD display. This means that the "F" bit in the "set interface instruction" should always be reset (equal to "0").

Before you can send commands or data to the LCD module, the module must be initialized. This is done using the following series of operations:

For 8-bit mode:

1. **Wait** more than 15 msecs after power is applied.
2. **Write** 0x030 to LCD and wait 5 msecs for the instruction to complete.
3. **Write** 0x030 to LCD and wait 160 usecs for instruction to complete.
4. **Write** 0x030 AGAIN to LCD and wait 160 usecs or poll the busy flag.
5. **Set** the operating characteristics of the LCD.
   - Write "Set Interface Length."
   - Write 0x010 to turn off the display.
   - Write 0x001 to clear the display.
   - Write "set cursor move direction" setting cursor behavior bits.
   - Write "enable display/cursor" and enable display and optional cursor.

In describing how the LCD should be initialized in 4-bit mode, I will specify writing to the LCD in terms of nybbles. This is because initially, just single nybbles are sent (and not two, which make up a byte and a full instruction). As I mentioned above, when a byte is sent, the high nybble is sent before the low nybble, and the "E" pin is toggled each time four bits is sent to the LCD.

1. **Wait** more than 15 msecs after power is applied.
2. **Write** 0x03 to LCD and wait 5 msecs for the instruction to complete.
3. **Write** 0x03 to LCD and wait 160 usecs for instruction to complete.
4. **Write** 0x03 again to LCD and wait 160 usecs (or poll the Busy Flag).
5. **Set** the operating characteristics of the LCD.
   - Write 0x02 to the LCD to enable 4-bit mode.
   - All following instruction/data writes require two nybble writes.
   - Write "set interface length."
   - Write 0x01/0x00 to turn off the display.
   - Write 0x00/0x01 to clear the display.
   - Write "set cursor move direction" setting cursor behavior bits.
   - Write "enable display/cursor" and enable display and optional cursor.

Once the initialization is complete, the LCD can be written to with data or instructions as required.

The last aspect of the LCD to discuss is how to specify a contrast value for the display. I typically use a potentiometer wired as a voltage divider. (Figure 4.12.)

This will provide an easily variable voltage between ground and Vcc, which will be used to specify the contrast (or "darkness") of the characters on the LCD screen.

At the start of this subsection, I said that LCDs have a reputation for being hard to get working. The biggest problem with using LCDs is not properly initializing them. If you follow the instructions given above, you shouldn't have any problems. Also, the minimum "E" pulse width is 450 nsec; if this pulse is shorter in duration, you may have intermittent problems with the LCD.

Looking back over this subchapter, I think I have given a pretty good explanation of how Hitachi 44780-based alphanumeric LCDs work. It's not complete by any stretch of the imagination, but what I have given here will at least get you up, running and comfortable enough to experiment with an LCD connected to a microcontroller. There are some interesting effects you can do with LCDs (especially if the programmable characters are used).

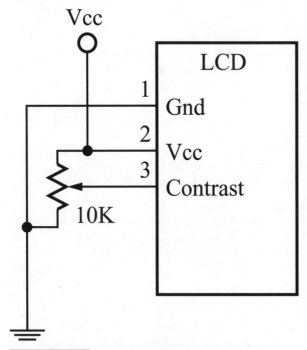

Figure 4.12 LCD contrast control.

Many of the different applications in this book use LCDs, and you can use this code for examples or code sources. But, as you can see, they really aren't that hard to wire up or to program.

Motor/Relay Control

Some real-life devices that you may have to control by a microcontroller are electromagnetic-like relays and motors. These devices cannot be driven directly by a microcontroller because of the current required and the "noise" generated by them. This means that special interfaces must be used to control electromagnetic devices.

The simplest method of controlling these devices is to just switch them on and off. In Figure 4.13, the microcontroller turns on the Darlington transistor pair, causing current to pass through the relay coil, closing the contacts. To open the relay, the output is turned off (or a "0" is output). The "shunt" diode across the coil is used as a "kickback" suppressor; when the current is turned off, the magnetic flux in the coil will induce a large back EMF (voltage), which has to be absorbed by the circuit or there may be a voltage spike that can damage the relay power supply and even the microcontroller. This diode must never be forgotten in a circuit that controls an electromagnetic device. The kickback voltage is usually on the order of several hundred volts for a few nanoseconds. This voltage causes the diode to break down and allows current to flow, attenuating the induced voltage.

Rather than designing discrete circuits to carry out this function, I like to use integrated chips for the task. One of the most useful devices is the ULN200x series of chips, which have Darlington transistor pairs and shunt diodes built in for multiple drivers.

Motors can be controlled by exactly the same hardware. The circuit shown in Figure 4.14 can be used if the motor only has to turn in one direction. A network of switches (transistors) can be used to control turning a motor in either direction; this is known as an "H-Bridge." (Figure 4.15.)

In the circuit shown in Figure 4.15, if all the switches are open, no current will flow and the motor won't turn. If switches "1" and "4" are closed, the motor will turn in one direction. If switches "2" and "3" are closed, the motor will turn in the other direction. If both switches on one side of the bridge are closed at the same time, the motor power supply will burn out or a fuse will blow because there is a short between motor power and ground.

Controlling a motor's speed is normally done by "pulsing" the control signals in the form of a pulse wave modulated ("PWM") signal. The frequency of the PWM signal should be greater than 20 kHz to prevent the PWM from producing an audible signal in the motors (which can be very annoying).

Like the ULN2003A simplified the wiring of a relay control, the 293D chip can be used for controlling a motor. (Figure 4.16.) The 293D can control two motors (one on each side), connected to the buffer outputs (pins 3, 6, 11, and 14). Pins 2, 7, 10, and 15 are used to control the voltage level (the "switches" in the H-bridge shown in Figure 4.15) of the buffer outputs. Pin 1 and pin 9 are used to control whether or not the buffers are enabled. These can be PWM inputs, which makes control of the motor speed very easy to implement.

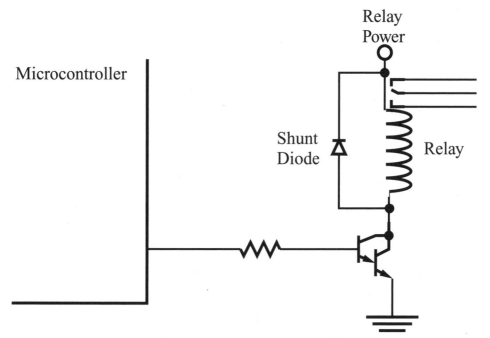

Figure 4.13 Microcontroller relay control.

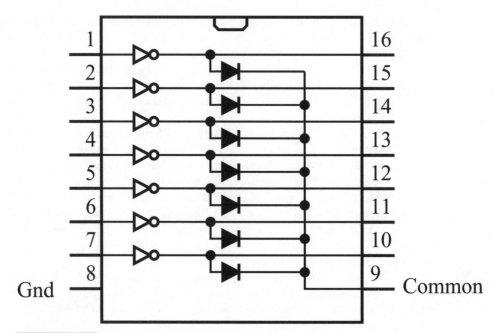

Figure 4.14 ULN2003A driver array.

"Vs" is +5V used to power the logic in the chip and "Vss" is the power supplied to the motors and can be anywhere from 4.5 to 36 volts. A maximum of 500 mA can be supplied to the motors. Like the ULN2003A, the 293D contains integral shunt diodes. This means that to attach a motor to the 293D, no external shunt diodes are required. (Figure 4.17.)

In Figure 4.17, you'll notice that I've included an optional "snubber" resistor and capacitor. These two components, wired across the brush contacts of the motor, will help reduce electromagnetic emissions and noise "spikes" from the motor. In the motor control circuits that I have built, I have never found them to be necessary, but if you find erratic operation from the microcontroller (especially when the motors are running), you may want to put in the 0.1-uF capacitor and 5-ohm (2-watt) resistor snubber across the motor's brushes as shown in Figure 4.17.

The 293D can also be used to control a four-pole stepper motor (each of the buffer outputs is used to control a pole of the stepper motor). In this application, both pin 1 and pin 9 should be tied high because the PWM speed control input is not required.

Stepper Motors

Stepper motors are much simpler to develop control software for than a regular DC motor. This is because the motor is turned one step at a time or can turn at a specific rate (specified by the speed in which the "steps" are executed). In terms of the hardware interface, stepper motors are a bit more complex to wire and require more current (meaning that they are less efficient), but these are offset by the advantages in software control.

A "bipolar" stepper motor consists of a permanent magnet on the motor's shaft, which has its position specified by a pair of coils. (Figure 4.18.)

To move the magnet and the shafts, the coils are energized in different patterns to attract the magnet. For Figure 4.18, the following sequence would be used to turn the magnet (and the shaft) clockwise.

Step	Angle	Coil "A"	Coil "B"
1	0	S	
2	90		N
3	180	N	
4	270		S
5	360/0	S	

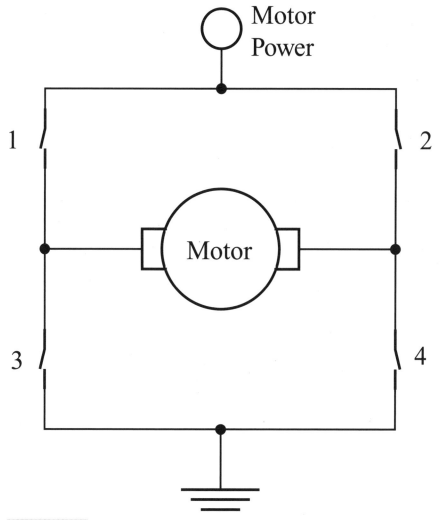

Figure 4.15 H-bridge motor driver.

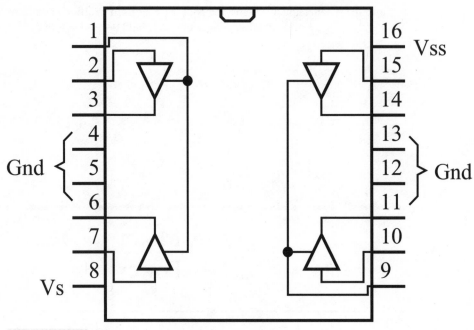

Figure 4.16 293D H-bridge motor driver chip.

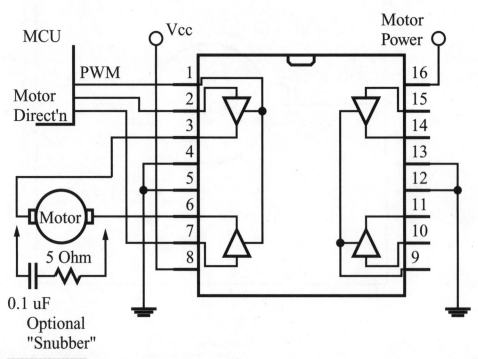

Figure 4.17 Wiring a motor to the 293D.

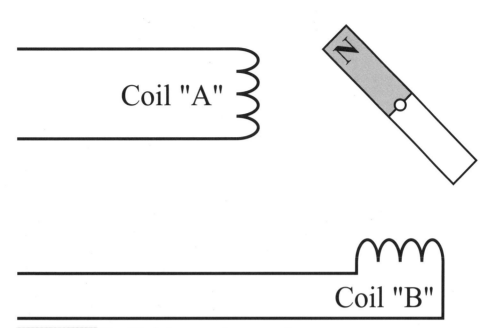

Figure 4.18 Simplified stepper motor connections.

In this sequence, coil "A" attracts the north pole of the magnet to put the magnet in an initial position. Then coil "B" attracts the south pole, turning the magnet 90 degrees. This continues on to turn the motor, 90 degrees for each "step."

The output shaft of a stepper motor is often geared down so that each step causes a very small angular deflection (a couple of degrees at most rather than the 90 degrees in the example above). This provides more torque output from the motor and greater positional control of the output shaft.

A stepper motor can be controlled by something like a 293D (each side driving one coil). But there are also stepper motor controller chips, like the UC1517. (Figure 4.19.)

In this chip, a step pulse is sent from the microcontroller along with a specified direction. The "INH" pin will turn off the output drivers and allow the stepper shaft to be moved manually. The UC1517 is capable of outputting "bilevel" coil levels (which improves efficiency and reduces induced noise) as well as "half stepping" the motor (which involves energizing both coils to move the magnet/shaft by 45 degrees and not just 90 degrees). These options are specific to the motor/controller used (a "bipolar" stepper motor can have four to eight wires coming out of it) and before deciding on features to be used, a thorough understanding of the motor and its operation is required.

R/C Servo Control

Servos designed for use in radio-controlled airplanes, cars, and boats can be easily interfaced to a microcontroller. They are often used for robots and applications where simple mechanical movement is required. This may be surprising to you because a positional servo is considered to be an analog device.

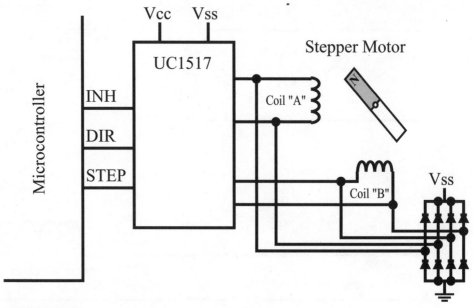

Figure 4.19 UC1517 control of a stepper motor.

The output of an R/C servo is usually a wheel, which can be rotated from 0 to 90 degrees. (There are also servos available that can turn from 0 to 180 degrees, as well as servos with very high torque outputs for special applications.) Typically, they only require +5V, ground, and an input signal.

An R/C servo is indeed an analog device; the input is a PWM signal at digital voltage levels. This pulse is between 1.0 and 2.0 msecs long and repeats every 20 msecs. (Figure 4.20.)

The length of the PWM Pulse determines the position of the servo's wheel. A 1.0-msec pulse will cause the wheel to go to 0 degrees while a 2.0-msec pulse will cause the wheel to go to 90 degrees.

With microcontrollers that have built-in hardware that is capable of outputting a PWM signal, controlling a servo is very easy, although they may not give you the positional accuracy that you will want.

For other microcontrollers that don't have PWM outputs, servo PWM signals (and PWM signals in general) can be output as follows:

```
Interrupt                              ;  This is done within an Interrupt Handler
   Save Context Registers
   Output a "1" on the PWM Line
   Wait for 1 msec
   Loop for 1 msec                     ;  Output the PWM Signal
      if Loop_Counter > Specified_ServoPos
        Output a 0                      ;  Finished with the PWM Signal
   Reset the Timer to Interrupt again in 18 msec
   Restore Context Registers
   Return from Interrupt
```

This code can be easily expanded to control more than one servo (by adding more output lines and "Specified_ServoPos" variables). This method of controlling servos is also nice because the "Specified_ServoPos" variables can be updated without affecting the operation of the interrupt handler.

The interrupt handler takes 2 milliseconds out of every 20. This means that there is a 10 percent cycle overhead for providing the PWM function (and this doesn't change even if more servo outputs are added to the device).

RS-232 Level Conversion

The most common application for level conversion is in RS-232 serial communication applications, when a microcontroller has to communicate with a host via RS-232. This can be done with a variety of chips, but there are some tricks that can be done to simplify (and lesson the cost) of a microcontroller-to-RS-232 interface.

RS-232 voltage and logic levels are a bit unusual. (Figure 4.21.) The first aspect that may cause some problems is the high voltage swings, but as we saw in the "Hardware Features" chapter, any unusual voltages and current flows can be attenuated by placing a current-limiting resistor in line between the receiving pin on the microcontroller and the RS-232 connector. This resistor will prevent any clamping diodes in the microcontroller from causing any large current flows and also keep the voltage levels at the microcontroller within specified levels and not drive the microcontroller into an invalid hardware state.

This works well because the negative voltages (RS-232 logic "1") will be sensed as "0" volts in the microcontroller, and positive voltages (RS-232 logic "0"), even when "clamped" to 5 volts, will be above the "switching region" (which is -3 volts to +3 volts) and a good read will be made.

This solution only works for receiving RS-232 signals. If data is to be sent to an RS-232 host, the negative voltage levels for a "1" cannot be output with this circuit (only zero volts will be available, which is within the "switching region" of an RS-232 receiver). Often, this will be ignored (just a resistor will be put in to make sure current limits are not

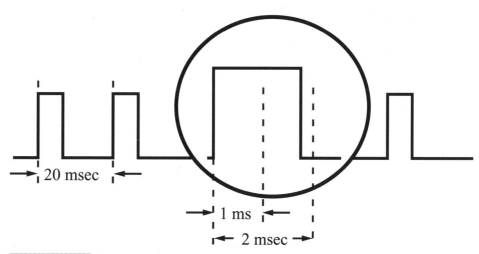

Figure 4.20 Servo PWM waveform.

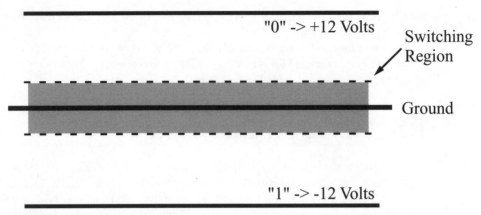

Figure 4.21 RS-232 voltage levels.

exceeded) and the microcontroller will be connected to the "true" RS-232 receiver and it will work. Transmitting to an RS-232 device just using a resistor is very application and device specific, and I really don't recommend it.

Instead, a popular method of creating negative voltages for transmission is to "steal" the negative voltage from the receiver (which is negative most of the time anyway). (Figure 4.22.)

In Figure 4.22, received data will be passed to the microcontroller through the 10K resistor (as was discussed above). When transmitting, normally the line will be negative (sending a "1") from the received line and when transmitting a "0" (a positive voltage), the output voltage will be at Vcc. This is a very cheap and elegant method of creating an RS-232 transmit and receive interface (basically a "3-Wire RS-232" interface, with the third wire being "ground").

This method, while it does work, has some issues to be considered before specifying it as part of an application. The receive and transmit data will be inverted from "positive" logic levels meaning that the microcontroller will have to invert them before they are usable. This may be a problem in some devices that have serial interfaces that cannot invert the data.

This interface is only acceptable for three-wire RS-232. If RS-232 "handshaking" is required by the host, then another interface will have to be used or the handshaking lines from the host will have to be shorted together (i.e., DTR to DSR and CTS to RTS).

Another concern of using this method is that data transmitted to the microcontroller will be sent right back to the transmitter. This is because when the receive voltage is positive (i.e., when a "0" is sent), the transmitted voltage will also be positive and the data being received will be sent right back out. This may not be a problem and may eliminate the need for you to write code to "echo" back what has been received, but it may cause some problems with some applications that aren't expecting data to be echoed back. This echoing means that data cannot be transmitted in a "duplex" manner, in which data is sent simultaneously in two directions.

If any of these issues is a problem for the application, you will have to use a solution like the Maxim MAX232 chip, which has an onboard negative voltage generator.

Random Numbers

One of the most difficult tasks in working with computers is to generate random numbers. There has been more than one Ph.D. thesis written on the subject. The problem is that computers, by nature, are deterministic and very repeatable. This means that they are designed specifically to run the same way, every time, with no facility for creating random information.

In some languages and computer systems, there are functions that create random numbers to a specification, but to calculate this random number, one or more "seed" values are required. This "seed" value, however, should be a random number, or the value produced from the function will always be the same.

There are three ways in microcontrollers to create a random number, and all require external input. The first way is if the microcontroller is connected to a real time clock. If fractions of a second can be read, then reading them at power-up will give you a basically random number. The chances of being able to repeatedly power up to the same hundredth or thousandth of a second is, for all practical purposes, just about infinitesimal.

The next method relies on a random number to be programmed in the control store as a constant. While this doesn't seem very random, for some applications (notably networking), this is adequate. This method does, however, usually require some way of modifying the object code to be put into a chip (and putting in a random value at that time).

The last method is to time some kind of external event. A common method is to connect the microcontroller to a reversed biased diode or to the output of a radio tuned to a frequency where there are no carriers and recording the number of noise "spikes" coming in a set period of time.

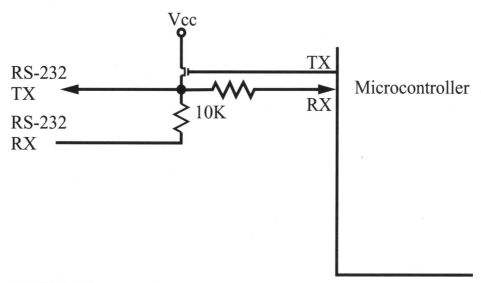

Figure 4.22 RS-232 to CMOS microcontroller interface.

Personal Computers

Probably the single device you will want to interface most with is an IBM compatible personal computer. There are four primary interfaces that a microcontroller has with a PC: the serial (RS-232) ports, the parallel ("printer" or "centronics") ports, the keyboard and mouse interface, and the ISA bus. While there are other methods of interfacing to the PC, these four are the most common. Books are available about connecting devices to each of these different interfaces. Obviously, I won't try to reproduce complete instructions here (especially for the ISA bus which has interrupt and DMA interfaces), but I will give an introduction to the different interfaces and an explanation of how a microcontroller can be wired to them.

In many ways, a PC is a very difficult device to interface with. The reason for this is the unpredictable nature of different PCs and their configuration (which results in somewhat unpredictable operation at the bits and bytes level). This might seem like a surprising statement, considering that the PC was first developed over 15 years ago. But, as the PC has evolved, functions that were once built out of discrete logic are now buried deep in ASICs, and microprocessors that once had very predictable instruction cycles have given way to devices that provide functions and capabilities that not that long ago would be considered only available in a mainframe.

All this means that functions that seem very easy to understand and design circuits for can operate very differently in different PCs or may not be available at all. This can cause a nightmare when trying to support an application, especially if it interfaces with a variety of different PCs using a nonstandard hardware interface.

The operating systems that run on the PC can also make a huge impact on whether or not an application will work. Right now, applications and projects that are designed to run on PCs must run under MS-DOS, Windows 3.1, and Windows/95 (and, to a lesser extent: OS/2, Windows NT, and various MS-DOS simulators running under different operating systems). Each of these operating systems uses different resources (such as timers and interrupt vectors) that will complicate the software required for an application interfacing with a microcontroller.

After all this, you're probably wondering why anybody would want to design hardware to interface with the PC, except in the case of it being a product that will be made in the millions, or they're going to develop the application for specifically a '286 in a PC running MS-DOS 3.3. In trying to work through many of the problems listed above, I can honestly say that I have asked this very question more than once.

In my regular job (as a test engineer), I have fought long and hard trying to get hardware that works in one PC to work in other PCs. In dealing with these struggles, I have come up with a philosophy that has allowed me to develop hardware for the PC with a high probability of success. This philosophy can be summarized as these two rules:

1. **Use** interfaces that will always work in different PCs running under different operating systems.
2. **The** hardware interfacing to the PC has to be intelligent and capable of handling blocks of data and instructions, rather than simple bits and bytes.

As I go through this subsection, I'll outline how these philosophical statements fare with the different interfaces.

The serial ("RS-232") ports are the interfaces that best conform to the philosophy above. The interface will not change over time either in terms of electrical or timing specifications. The PC can have either 9- or 25-pin "d-shell" connectors, which are wired as RS-232 "data terminal equipment" ("DTE").

The connectors are wired as:

DB-25M		D-9M
Pin 1 - N/C	Pin 14 - N/C	Pin 1 - I DCD
Pin 2 - O TX Data	Pin 15 - N/C	Pin 2 - I RX Data
Pin 3 - I RX Data	Pin 16 - N/C	Pin 3 - O TX Data
Pin 4 - O RTS	Pin 17 - N/C	Pin 4 - O DTR
Pin 5 - I CTS	Pin 18 - N/C	Pin 5 - Ground
Pin 6 - I DSR	Pin 19 - N/C	Pin 6 - I DSR
Pin 7 - Ground	Pin 20 - O DTR	Pin 7 - O RTC
Pin 8 - I DCD	Pin 21 - N/C	Pin 8 - I CTS
Pin 9 - N/C	Pin 22 - I RI	Pin 9 - I RI
Pin 10 - N/C	Pin 23 - N/C	
Pin 11 - N/C	Pin 24 - N/C	
Pin 12 - N/C	Pin 25 - N/C	
Pin 13 - N/C		

I usually bring these signals out to the microcontroller using a straight-through cable (not a null modem), and I always work with a 9-pin d-shell, rather than a 25-pin (because the connector is smaller).

The "RTS," "CTS," "DSR," "DCD," "DTR," and "RI" lines are all known as "handshaking" lines and are used during some types of communication to ensure that the status of the ability to sending data to the RS-232 interface is known. I should say "Unfortunately these lines are used in some types of communication" because one of the types of communication is the "BIOS" ("basic I/O subsystem") serial functions of some PCs. To ensure that there won't be any problems with the handshaking lines, I connect "DSR" to "DTR" and "CTS" to "RTS." This will "fool" the hardware and software into being able to send and receive data at any time.

These lines were originally built into the RS-232 standard when computers were a lot less capable than they are now. Their purpose is to stop a transmitter from sending data if the receiver isn't ready for it (as well as inform the transmitter of the status of a modem). In virtually every application and product that interfaces to an RS-232 device that you can buy on the market, the handshaking lines are wired together (as described in the paragraph above) and just the transmit and receive lines along with a common ground are used, for a "three-wire RS-232."

Through the use of "BIOS" functions, RS-232 ports have standard software interfaces, which will allow applications to run over different PCs and operating systems with very few problems. As an added bonus, when debugging an application, using the RS-232 terminal emulation programs available with the operating system can help debug your application.

This is a big advantage in developing applications that interface to the PC. When debugging the application, a terminal emulator can be used, rather than a partially debugged user interface. This is the reason for the second point of the philosophy statement above. By using human-readable commands, the terminal emulator can be used when developing the application, the commands can be typed in directly, and the responses can be read easily.

You may be of the opinion that the use of human-readable instructions is less efficient than using binary instructions (i.e., just sending the appropriate bits rather than full bytes). My reply to this is, "Who cares?" At 9600 bps, if two bytes are needed where only one could be used, the data will be sent in two msecs rather than one. Most microcontroller interfaces will not be transferring a significant amount of data, so this extra overhead will not be noticed by the user, and I think there will be huge advantages to you in the ease of debugging the application.

If huge amounts of data (on the order of tens of kbytes per minute or more) had to be transferred, then I wouldn't be looking at RS-232; instead I would be attaching directly to the PC's bus or using a network interface.

One last point on RS-232. The serial ports can be accessed using the file system by "opening" "COM1" to "COM4" (for the standard four serial ports in the PC). This also brings up a compatibility issue you should be aware of; if your PC has a Super-VGA graphics card, you will find that "COM4" cannot be attached to the system. This is because the "COM4" I/O space addresses are used by the graphics adapter (to be IBM 8514/A compatible).

Using the PC's parallel (or "printer") port is also a very popular method of communicating between a microcontroller and a PC. One of the interesting aspects of this interface is the many different ways it is used.

Operating as it is traditionally designed (as a "centronics" printer interface) data is sent from the PC to the receiver, as shown in Figure 4.23.

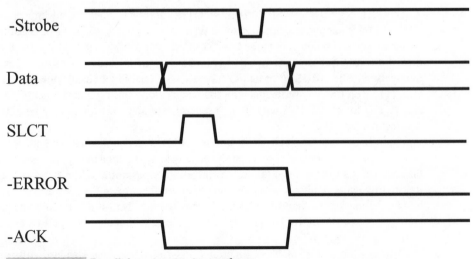

Figure 4.23 Parallel port output waveform.

This method checks the numerous handshaking lines for proper status before strobing the data out (which is done by the "strobe" bit) and can only send data out from the PC. In most applications I have seen that use the printer port, the data bus is used bidirectionally, with the handshaking lines just used to indicate the direction the data is being sent in without checking the status of the external device. In most new PCs, the eight data lines are capable of transferring data bidirectionally, but in many older PCs, the printer port data lines are only capable of sending data out.

The connector used for the printer port is a 25-pin female D-Shell with the following pin out:

```
DB-25F

Pin  1 -  O -Strobe        Pin 14 - O  -AutoFDxt

Pin  2 - I/O Data0         Pin 15 - I  -ERROR

Pin  3 - I/O Data1         Pin 16 - O  -INIT

Pin  4 - I/O Data2         Pin 17 - O  -SLCTIN

Pin  5 - I/O Data3         Pin 18 -    Ground

Pin  6 - I/O Data4         Pin 19 -    Ground

Pin  7 - I/O Data5         Pin 20 -    Ground

Pin  8 - I/O Data6         Pin 21 -    Ground

Pin  9 - I/O Data7         Pin 22 -    Ground

Pin 10 - I  -Ack           Pin 23 -    Ground

Pin 11 - I  Busy           Pin 24 -    Ground

Pin 12 - I  PE             Pin 25 -    Ground

Pin 13 - I  SLCT
```

There is one problem with using the parallel port, and that is how the application is timed. In the original IBM PC (and even the PC/AT), the port read and write times were predictable (i.e., no write could take less than 125 nsecs). This is no longer true in new PCs, which run considerably faster than the original PCs and register read/write times can be less than 20 nsec (less than one fifth than what a "standard" PC was capable of). To confuse things even more, modern PCs are capable of executing in a manner similar to the original PCs, if the parallel port is plugged into the "ISA" bus as opposed to being part of an ASIC connected directly to the processor.

By using the "BIOS" parallel port functions, the timing will adhere to the original standard values. But using the BIOS functions will require that the handshaking lines are used. (Nothing is free.)

The bottom line is, before using the parallel port in a PC, make sure you understand how your application is timed and make allowances for different types of PC parallel ports. Personally, I avoid interfacing to the parallel port if at all possible (the printer port violates philosophy statement number one above).

Transferring data and instructions through a PC's keyboard/mouse port is best saved for very specific applications (such as providing an external keypad or special pointing device), and the output from the microcontroller should be valid keyboard scan codes. In this discussion, I am only going to present the keyboard interface that was designed for the PC/AT (the original PC uses a different interface), which is a device capable of sending and receiving data. (Figure 4.24.)

Keyboard scan data is clocked synchronously between devices using a data format similar to asynchronous data. (Figure 4.25.)

Data can travel in either direction from the PC or from the keyboard (although, for obvious reasons, data is sent from the keyboard much more often).

If you were to design a microcontroller interface between the keyboard and PC, it would have to monitor the clock and data signals of both devices, and if data was being sent, if it was meant for the "downstream" device, the microcontroller would have to pass it along. If data was being sent from the microcontroller to the PC and the keyboard was transmitting, then the keyboard data would also have to be buffered (saved) and then transmitted to the PC.

I hinted above at the idea of "scan codes" from the keyboard. In the PC, data is sent as "scan codes," which are actually key positions in the keyboard.

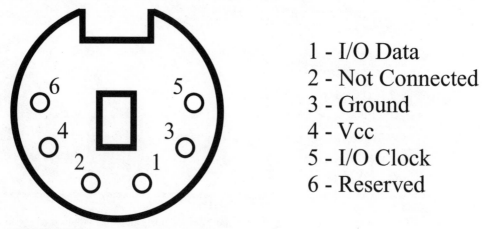

Figure 4.24 PC/AT keyboard connector pinout.

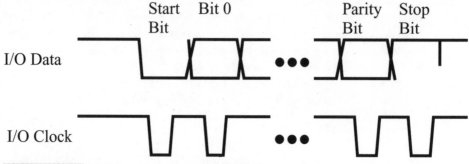

Figure 4.25 PC/AT keyboard data waveform.

The Scan Codes (in Hex) for the PC/AT are:

F1 – 0x005	F3 – 0x004	F5 – 0x003	F7 – 0x083	F9 – 0x001
F2 – 0x006	F4 – 0x00C	F6 – 0x00B	F8 – 0x00A	F10 – 0x009
"`" – 0x00E	Tab – 0x00D	Ctl – 0x014	LSH – 0x012	Alt – 0x011
"1" – 0x016	"Q" – 0x015	"A" – 0x01C	"Z" – 0x01A	" " – 0x029
"2" – 0x01E	"W" – 0x01D	"S" – 0x01B	"X" – 0x022	CPL – 0x058
"3" – 0x026	"E" – 0x024	"D" – 0x023	"C" – 0x021	Ins – 0x070
"4" – 0x025	"R" – 0x02D	"F" – 0x028	"V" – 0x02A	Del – 0x071
"5" – 0x02E	"T" – 0x02C	"G" – 0x034	"B" – 0x032	
"6" – 0x036	"Y" – 0x035	"H" – 0x033	"N" – 0x031	
"7" – 0x03D	"U" – 0x03C	"J" – 0x038	"M" – 0x03A	
"8" – 0x03E	"I" – 0x043	"K" – 0x042	";" – 0x041	
"9" – 0x046	"O" – 0x044	"L" – 0x04B	"." – 0x049	
"0" – 0x045	"P" – 0x04D	";" – 0x04C	"/" – 0x04A	
"–" – 0x04E	"[" – 0x054	"'" – 0x052	RSH – 0x059	
"=" – 0x055	"]" – 0x05B	Ent – 0x05A	End – 0x069	
BS – 0x05D	Hme – 0x06C	Lft – 0x06B	Dwn – 0x072	
ESC – 0x066	Up – 0x075	5 – 0x073	PgD – 0x07A	
NL – 0x076	PgU – 0x07D	Rht – 0x074	+ – 0x079	
SL – 0x077	PS – 0x07C	– – 0x07B		
SR – 0x084				

BS – "BackSpace"	Hme – "Home"	Lft – Left Arrow
NL – "Num Lock"	PgU – "Page Up"	5 – "5" in Keypad
SL – "Scroll Lock"	PS – "Print Screen"	Rht – Right Arrow
SR – "System Request"	Ent – "Enter	– – "–" in Keypad
CPL – "Caps Lock"	RSH – Right "Shift"	LSH – Left "Shift"
Dwn – Down Arrow	PgD – "Page Down"	Ctl – "Ctrl"

Note that when receiving data from the keyboard, you'll have to watch for the Shift, Alt, Ctrl, CapsLock, NumLock, and ScrollLock keys. This might affect how the scan codes being sent from your device are interpreted by the PC. This is also true for commands sent from the PC to the keyboard.

When the key is lifted, a final scan code is sent to the PC with 0x0F0 sent before it. This allows the PC to know when the key is no longer pressed, and it doesn't have to keep executing the repeat function (if it is being carried out in software running in the PC).

The PC can send a number of commands to the keyboard:

0x0FF	- Restart the microcontroller in the Keyboard.
0x0FE	- The Keyboard is requested to resend last character sent
0x0F7-0x0FD	- NOP. Ignore these commands
0x0F6	- Set Default (Power Up) condition
0x0F5	- Set Default, but stop Scanning the Keyboard
0x0F4	- Enable Scanning of the Keyboard
0x0F3	- Set Typematic. Parameter Following Specifies Scan Rate
0x0EF-0x0F2	- NOP. Ignore these commands
0x0EE	- Echo. The keyboard returns 0x0EE
0x0ED	- Set Indicator LEDs. Next Character specifies LED States

After each of these commands, the keyboard responds with an "Ack" (0x0FA).

The mouse/pointing device port uses a similar interface, but typically the PC does not send data to it. For this reason, often in PCs the hardware is not available in the port to transmit the data from the PC. To be on the safe side, when using this port, pointing data (i.e., mouse and cursor positions) should only be sent.

The last interface to be presented to you is the "Industry Standard Architecture" ("ISA") bus. This is a microprocessor bus that makes various signals from the processor available. There are probably other busses available in your PC (i.e., "PCI" and "EISA"), but the ISA is the most traditional device interface (and the one that is easiest to do).

In the following chart, I have provided the 8-bit interface signals. I have not included the 16–bit signals because I presume the extra data bits will not be used with an 8–bit microcontroller. This chart is looking down at the "slot," with the back of the PC at the top:

BACK OF CARD	COMPONENT SIDE
B1: Ground	A1: –CHKCHK
B2: RESDRV	A2: SD7
B3: +5V	A3: SD6
B4: IRQ2	A4: SD5
B5: –5V	A5: SD4
B6: DRQ2	A6: SD3
B7: –12V	A7: SD2
B8: –NOWS	A8: SD1
B9: +12V	A9: SD0
B10: Ground	A10: CHRDY

BACK OF CARD	COMPONENT SIDE
B11: –MEMW	A11: AEN
B12: –MEMR	A12: SA19
B13: –OW	A13: SA18
B14: –IOR	A14: SA17
B15: –DAC3	A15: SA16
B16: DRQ3	A16: SA15
B17: –DAC1	A17: SA14
B18: DRQ1	A18: SA13
B19: –REFRESH	A19: SA12
B20: BLCK	A20: SA11
B21: IRQ7	A21: SA10
B22: IRQ6	A22: SA9
B23: IRQ5	A23: SA8
B24: IRQ4	A24: SA7
B25: IRQ3	A25: SA6
B26: –DAC2	A26: SA5
B27: TC	A27: SA4
B28: ALE	A28: SA3
B29: +5V	A29: SA2
B30: OSC	A30: SA1
B31: Ground	A31: SA0

In this subsection, I am only going to introduce the concept of reading and writing to a device on the ISA bus. If you are interested in implementing an ISA/microcontroller interface—especially if you want to use interrupts or DMA ("direct memory access"—you should consult the references listed at the end of the book.

The pins are defined as:

–CHKCHK	– Channel Check. When Asserted, causes NMI at PC's Processor
SD7–SD0	– System Data Bus
CHRDY	– Channel Ready. When Asserted, inserts wait states in Bus I/O
AEN	– DMA Active Indicator. When Asserted DMA Controller is active
SA19–SA0	– System Address Bus

–RESDRV	– System Reset. Driving line low will reset the PC
IRQx	– Interrupt Request Lines. Drive high to request an interrupt
DRQx	– DMA Request Lines. Drive Low to Request DMA operation
DACx	– DMA Acknowled Lines. When Low, DMA is Active
–MEMR	– Memory Read Command Line
–MEMW	– Memory Write Command Line
–IOR	– I/O Space Read Command Line
–IOW	– I/O Space Write Command Line
–REFRESH	– Active when system board Dynamic RAM Refresh is active
–NOWS	– No Wait State. I/O operations without Processor Wait States
TC	– DMA Terminal Count. When asserted DMA Operation complete
ALE	– Bus Address Latch Enable. Asserted when SA0–SA19 is Valid

The basic address and data lines can be used to generate reads and writes as shown in Figures 4.26 and 4.27.

As noted, the "AEN" line is asserted when a direct memory access controller has taken over the bus. This line should always be checked to be low when wiring a microcontroller to the bus to ensure that invalid reads and writes don't affect its operation. (Figure 4.28.)

When debugging a microcontroller (or any other device) on the ISA bus, if a logic analyzer or oscilloscope is used to probe the bus, "ALE" or the output of the address decoder should be used as a trigger.

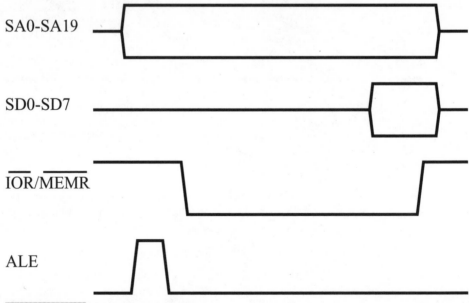

Figure 4.26 ISA bus read waveform.

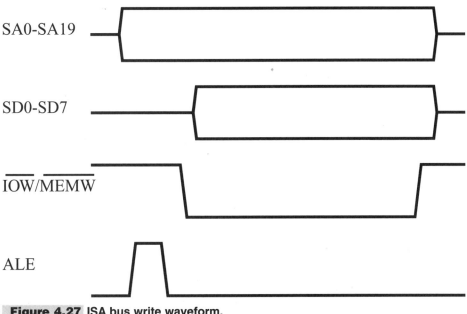

Figure 4.27 ISA bus write waveform.

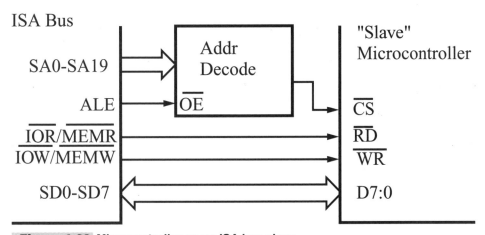

Figure 4.28 Microcontroller as an ISA bus slave.

A very big consideration when using a microcontroller as an ISA bus adapter is "where" the microcontroller will be located in the PC's I/O space or memory. The Intel x86 architecture contains a separate I/O space from the memory area (doesn't use "memory mapped I/O"). In the 8-bit ISA bus, there is nominally one megabyte of memory that can be accessed, or 1024 I/O addresses.

The I/O space in the x86 is capable of selecting up to 64K of I/O addresses, but in the original PC specification, this 16-bit address bus was reduced to 2 bits or only 4096 unique addresses. (When the PC was designed, 1024 different addresses was deemed to be more than enough, so the upper 4 bits were ignored in the I/O device decoders).

Normally, ISA adapters are designed to interface with the I/O space, but as you probably suspect, most of the 4096 addresses have been defined for various adapters and in terms of memory space, very few systems have any memory addresses available in the first 16 megabytes of the address space (let alone the first megabyte). All this means that you will have a difficult time specifying addresses for the microcontroller that is not already used for other devices. This is the primary reason why I do not recommend developing microcontroller applications that access the ISA bus directly.

Now you're probably wondering how you are going to interface with the PC's bus. While I haven't addressed it in this book, the first microcontrollers to have "universal serial bus" ("USB") interfaces built in have just come on the market. The popularity of these devices will correspond to the rise in the prevalence of the USB hardware available in PCs and software support available in operating systems. USB operates in a manner similar to CAN (like CAN, it is designed for very local networks, although it is designed for transmitting large amounts of data).

You may have noticed that in this subchapter, I have been quite vague on which PC register addresses to use and actual timing. This was done deliberately to ensure that any PC interfacing that you do is done with an appropriate PC hardware reference. Taking time to correctly choose the interface and addresses will ensure that your application will work successfully on a wide variety of PCs.

APPLICATION/SYSTEM DEVELOPMENT

CONTENTS AT A GLANCE

Device Selection

Now that I've gone through all the different aspects of embedded microcontrollers, you probably feel like a starving person who has been given a menu. To try to relieve some of this anxiety, I want to go through the different aspects of choosing the correct device for your planned application.

Before listing all the different aspects of choosing a device, I just wanted to point out that choosing a device may be a chore within microcontroller families and not just trying to choose between the different device families. If you have already been working with members of a microcontroller family, you are probably aware that there is a great range of devices within most families, with a wide range of features and options.

Before you begin to decide which device to use, I strongly recommend creating a questionnaire with decision points similar to the ones in the questionnaire below:

APPLICATION NAME:

Number of Input Pins:
Number of Output Pins:
Number of I/O Pins:

Reset Type:
Clocking Type/Accuracy:
WDT Required:
Control Store Code Protect:
Power Type Available:

Asynchronous Serial I/O Required:
Synchronous Serial I/O Required:
Size of Tables Required:
PWM I/O:

Type of Analog I/O Required:

Final Application OTP:

Desired Package Type:

Programming Language to Be Used:

Desired Part Cost:

With this chart, you can go through different devices looking for the best fit. In seeing different devices, you may want to change your application specifications to better match the features available in a specific microcontroller.

Features and Architectures

When comparing available features of a device to the list of desired features, always be thinking about different ways of doing things. Asynchronous serial I/O may be required but may be implemented by writing directly to pins and receiving data via a pin change interrupt. Not using a microcontroller with a built-in UART may result in a cheaper application/product.

Gauging the amount of control store space can be difficult (especially when the application is going to use a high-level language for development). Always aim high, and if a device with a smaller control store can be used, then change your specification to include this part.

Recognize that some architectures will make some software techniques very difficult or even impossible. But when discussing features and architectures, you should probably be looking at microcontrollers that you are already familiar with, rather than trying to "boil" the ocean and look at everything that's out there. Once you have found every possible device along with all the required information to make an informed decision, the "window" for the application/product will have passed.

Development Systems and Software

There's not a lot to discuss here other than to make sure that there are languages you want to work with and there are tools available that you are familiar with. What I found to work for me is to choose a development system, language, and environment and stick with it. Over time you will learn it and its features intimately, which will make you more efficient.

This also includes host systems. You will probably find that some development systems do not work on the PC/workstation that you are most familiar with. But, many systems today have emulators that will allow software to be written for other platforms and operating systems.

If you are using a system that emulates a PC, you will have to make sure that the programmer and emulator you are planning on using will work in the application. Even if everything works fine, I would still recommend buying a cheap 386/486 PC that can run Windows 3.11, 95, or NT and running the programmer/emulator from there for your application development. Most development tools are written for the "Wintel" platform, which will ease your search for finding systems/tools that work together.

You may have very strong reasons for not using a PC, but these reasons become insignificant very quickly if you can't find software or a tool that will run on your system.

Availability and Resources

These are probably the most important two aspects in selecting which microcontroller to use for an application. Don't be surprised if you find the "perfect" device for an application, only to discover that you can't find anybody who stocks it or who can tell you how to program it. This has happened to me many times, and it can be quite frustrating.

Some manufacturers create devices for specific applications (and are only built during one manufacturing run). These devices go into data sheets and catalogs but never seem to make it to the distributor's shelves. With the Internet and many distributors having Web pages, you can quickly and easily query them to find out if they stock a particular device without going through the frustration of designing the application for the part and not being able to get it.

When I say "resources," I mean books, Web sites, courses, and seminars with application information, hints, example code, etc. One of the more recent innovations on the Internet is the listserver, which is a mail distribution program devoted to a specific topic (like a family of microcontrollers). This allows information and questions to be distributed to a wide variety of people very quickly. These resources can make a huge difference in the development of an application (especially when it doesn't work and you've spent hours staring at a screen trying to figure out what the problem is).

Device Self-Testing

If you are working on a commercial product or an application where proper operation is critical, it's always a good idea to include code that will test the primary components (microcontroller) along with their interfaces to other devices. This will give the application a chance to notify the user and stop the application from attempting to execute.

Testing the interfaces between the microcontroller and external devices wired to it is generally pretty easy. These tests generally consist of sending bit patterns (i.e., 0x055 and 0x0AA) on the data bus to the external device and reading it back. Often bus devices will have a mode/register that will allow this. This can also be known as a "presence" test because along with testing the bus and interfaces, this detects the presence of the external device.

If you are working with a parallel bus (which also includes a parallel "microprocessor" type of bus), you may want to write the test value at the test address and then another invalid value at a different address before reading back the test value. In some systems, you may find that a value will "float" on the data bus (primarily due to capacitance coupled with a quick read operation after the write) for some period of time. Writing an invalid value to another address will ensure that the read is executed properly. I've been caught by this problem a couple of times over the years— a "presence/bus" test that returns a good value even though the device I've tried to write to/read back from is not even on the bus. The "presence/bus" pattern should be specified in such a way that none of the devices on the bus will execute (other than storing and reading back the value) and will indicate whether or not the external device is wired correctly.

The same test can also be performed inside the microcontroller on its internal hardware. Of particular interest is to check the built in memory (RAM and ROM). RAM can be tested before the application begins to initialize the hardware (both inside and outside the microcontroller) using standard patterns. ROM (what I call "control store"), on the other hand, if it can be read, is read through and a checksum is produced and compared against an expected value.

When referring to reading control store, this operation may not be possible in "true" Harvard-architected devices because the control store cannot be read by the processor. (Even if it could, the instruction word size is probably greater than the data word size which would cause problems figuring out how to handle the data.)

After all the interfaces and memory have been checked, then the actual function of the various devices can be checked. For this operation, "feedback" capabilities should be built into all devices. For example, if you had an analog output, this could be feedback to an analog input to ensure that the output voltage is correct. (Figure 5.1.)

In a processor, you may want to execute every instruction before starting the application. This used to be widely done. For example, if you have an old IBM-PC *Technical Reference*, you will see that in the "POST" ("power-on self-test") listing provided in the book, one of the first self-tests executed is a series of instructions designed to test every instruction's execution with the different addressing modes. Now it is not as important because the increased reliability of microelectronics has made possible processor failure extremely rare, and the increased complexity of modern chips has made such tests impractical.

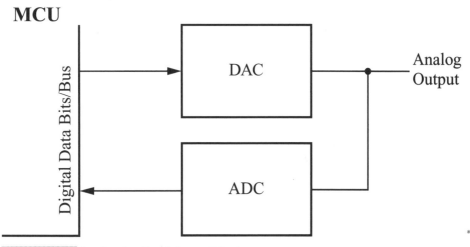

Figure 5.1 Analog feedback for self-test.

Now, after reading this subchapter, you're probably thinking that I've lost it. The extra work, control store, and hardware involved to put in all of these tests just aren't reasonable in terms of effort or cost.

For many applications I would agree with you; if I were designing a "R2D2" key chain that used a microcontroller to flash some LEDs and make some beeping sounds, I wouldn't even think about putting in a self-test.

But if I were about to undergo open heart surgery, I don't think I'd feel very comfortable thinking that the engineers that designed all the heart-lung machines, health monitors, resuscitation equipment, etc. didn't put in very exhaustive self-tests (or ongoing self-monitors).

Programmers

When developing an application, you will typically use parts with E(E)PROM control store. This will allow you to "burn in" the current level of code into a device to test and debug the application. This means that you must have a suitable programmer for the device and application (if in-system Programming is to be used on prototypes). There are a few things you should be aware of in regard to programming. Through the course of the book, I will introduce you to a number of different programmers that provide more functions that just programming the microcontroller.

Most microcontroller manufacturers sell programmers (which also may contain built in emulators) for introducing users to their products. These are known as "developer's kits" and are often the best deal you can get in electronics. Usually these kits include, along with the programmer/emulator: sample parts, an assembler/simulator/IDE, data books, and often a CD-ROM with device datasheets in Adobe ".PDF" format. They're designed to provide you with everything you need to begin developing applications for the devices. They typically cost around $100, and the package is worth much more, especially if all the parts are priced separately. If a developer's kit is available for the device you want to use, I highly recommend buying one, even if you are a hobbyist on a limited budget.

Manufacturers of commercial E(E)PROM programmers also provide adapters and software to program devices on their equipment. While they are usable for application development work, I prefer using a developer's programmer kit (which usually has an integrated development environment) and using the commercial programmer for production.

As noted earlier in this book, many devices are available as "in-system programmable" which means that they can be programmed in the target circuit. For devices with EEPROM/flash control store, this means that the application code can be updated without pulling the part (a significant advantage for SMT parts that are not easily removed or easily socketed).

ISP microcontrollers require a relatively long period to program (usually measured in tens of seconds or minutes) when compared to devices that are programmed using a parallel protocol. Each address write can take anywhere from 10 msec to 250 msecs. This is important to know and understand when planning your manufacturing process. While it is often possible to program most devices on an ICT tester, doing so here may be tying up a very expensive piece of test equipment for a task that can be done elsewhere. It may be best to design a custom programmer that can interface with the product and program the microcontroller's "offline."

ISP devices typically devote a number of pins to transferring data to and from the programmer. If the microcontroller is to be programmed in system, then the rest of the circuit in the system must be designed so that the programming operation doesn't affect any other circuits and the other circuits don't affect the programming operation. One way to ensure that the microcontroller doesn't interact with the other devices in the circuit is to provide a central driver disable on the programming header, which will disable all devices connected to the microcontroller.

Application Debug

Over the years I have developed a strategy for debugging microcontroller applications that I find is very effective and results in a high-quality finished product.

I like to think of it as not debugging applications at all.

After reading the previous sentence, you probably feel that I am being facetious or very arrogant. Actually, I'm neither; what I am trying to say is that I only develop applications using I/O functions that have been thoroughly debugged before I integrate them into an application. In 8-bit embedded microcontroller applications, the I/O functions generally consist of eighty percent or more of the software. When developing an application's constituent I/O functions, I develop them singly and only go on to the next one when the current one has been completed, tested, and debugged.

Another way to describe my style of software development is to note that I use a "bottoms-up" approach.

Now, in something like PC applications, this is not really applicable because the range of I/O opportunities is quite limited and generally provided by the operating system (or is part of the language). But in a microcontroller, the I/O Functions usually are a major part of the applications development effort. In the "Software" chapter, I made the comment that general I/O functions provided with high-level languages are usually too large or too nonspecific to be usable in most applications; this means you should develop standard routines that work with your style of programming.

When developing an application, I generally follow this order of developing and integrating the functions of an application:

1. **User** output functions.
2. **User** input functions.
3. **Bus** I/O functions.
4. **Miscellaneous** I/O functions.

This order will give me the needed software and hardware interfaces to create simple debug routines and programs to test out the current I/O function. So if I have to do an application that has a 4x4 keypad, an LCD, interface to an I2C serial EEPROM, and analog inputs that are to be recorded into the EEPROM, I would first get the LCD routines running, followed by the keypad, so the I2C bus and analog inputs can be interfaced by routines written for user I/O. If the application doesn't have a user interface, I may first add a serial I/O interface so that I have a debug console.

Now if you have an emulator, you may think that the application development method outlined above isn't required. I would argue that it is because it forces you to keep the number of "variables" that you are debugging at any one time to a minimum.

Going back to my original statement, you're probably thinking that I actually do debug the application and I would concede that I do. The important point I want to make is that I do the detailed debug before the final application has been completed. This is important because as I add I/O functions to the application, I have a good feeling that all the pieces that I am using work correctly and I avoid the momentous task of debugging the final application when I've burned the software into the microcontroller and it's just sitting there doing nothing.

Once the I/O function has been created, I simulate it as much as possible to ensure that it will operate the way I expect it to. Debugging an I/O function using the simulator can be made easier by developing a "stimulus file," which will contain input that can be repeated to debug the function. The UMPS IDE can allow "virtual" I/O devices to be used in the debug process, eliminating the need to develop special stimulus files.

After the simulation, if the function doesn't work, I have a pretty good idea that the problem is "external" to the software, which is to say that it could be a bad wiring connection or incorrect assumption about what the input will be. These problems can generally be pretty easy to find with a voltmeter, logic probe, or oscilloscope.

SIMULATORS

The primary application debug tool that I use when developing a microcontroller application is the hardware simulator. A simulator is a software program that runs an application against a "model" to allow the user to observe how the code runs. Often it is part of an integrated development environment that allows debug of the actual source in an environment where the code can be changed and re-assembled/compiled very easily.

Despite being a part of the development process, simulators are not very easy tools to learn to use. If you are unfamiliar with them, it may take you several weeks to understand all the features that you will need to use to debug an application. Part of the problem is going through the plethora of options that you are given (different breakpoints, output options, stimulus and asynchronous input, register and data display, and modification windows, etc.).

The best way to get familiar with simulators that I've found is to use a program that you've developed. (I avoid "example" code because this means that not only am I learning the simulator, but I have to learn the program as well.) I find I become productive faster by writing and debugging a program that just turns on an LED, rather than going through a program that someone else has written.

A very important advantage of simulators is their repeatability. If you want to understand why a block of code isn't working properly, you can repeat it over and over again until you understand what the problem is (and then "tweak" the code to see how changes affect the execution at the problem part).

This repeatability can be enhanced by the use of "stimulus files." These files are used to provide complex input data streams and waveforms to the simulator. The big problem with stimulus files is that they are a lot of work to develop. This is not necessarily bad or unproductive work, just a lot of work you'll have to think about. This thinking will involve designing the test case to be used, as well as how the code should execute the stimulus file.

Stimulus files are generally in a text format that is pretty predictable when the operation of the file is understood. Stimulus files consist of input states that are specified to change at different instruction clock values.

For example, let's say that we have to create a stimulus file that will be used by a simulator to test a serial read function, and I want to send the asynchronous character 0x00D (ASCII carriage return).

The stimulus file would look something like:

```
Step    Bit
   1     1      ;  Line Idle (Nothing being Sent)
                ;   - Wait for the Application to Initialize
1000     0      ;  Start Bit
1104     1      ;  Bit 0
1208     0
1312     1
1416     1
1520     0      ;  Bit 4
1624     0
1728     0
1832     0
1936     1      ;  Stop Bit
2040     1      ;  Line Idle
```

This stimulus file assumes that the instruction cycles ("step") are 1 usec long and the data is sent at 9600 bps (which has a bit period very close to 104 usecs). If the application clock cycle were ever to change, then all the stimulus files would have to be changed as well.

For arbitrary waveforms, I'll observe them on a storage oscilloscope (and maybe print them out). This will be used as the basis of the stimulus data to be used. When I was learning how to read an I/R TV remote signal, this is the method that I used. Through "cut and paste," a good editor will allow you to develop complex applications fairly efficiently, but it will still be work.

For this reason, in my list of "to dos" I have an item that is to write a stimulus data generator that is capable of taking macros and reference events relative to other ones. Although, with tools like "UMPS," this is becoming less and less important.

I said previously that a simulator is a good tool for debugging repeatable events. What they aren't good at is debugging "Glitches" or unexpected, asynchronous or nonrepeatable events. For this reason, you may have to use an emulator which can "trace" the instruction execution (and I/O signals) to find out exactly what the problem is.

Simulators also only take events at instruction cycle boundaries. This means that some asynchronous events, which will cause an interrupt, can cause an immediate or delayed reaction, depending on when in the instruction cycle input data is sampled. While this is not a "glitch," it may be something that requires more than a simulator to find.

EMULATORS

The most sophisticated (and expensive) tool that you can use to debug a microcontroller's application code and electrical interface is an "emulator." An emulator is a device that replaces the microcontroller in a circuit and can execute a program under your control. For the most part, emulators are excellent tools, although I have some concerns about how they are used in the development process.

A full "AC speed" emulator generally consists of a "bondout" chip that is connected to a host PC or workstation. A "bondout" chip is often a normal production microcontroller chip, but instead of being packaged in a standard interface, additional wires are attached to pads connecting to the control store bus and the processor control signals. These extra connections allow the chip to interface with an external RAM control store (instead of the built-in EPROM or ROM control store) which is interfaced to the host PC/workstation. This interface allows test programs to be easily downloaded to the bondout chip. (Figure 5.2.)

The bondout chip's I/O pins are interfaced to a connector that can be plugged into the application circuit, replacing the actual microcontroller.

Emulators usually have very similar interfaces to a simulator. The difference is they can't run a stimulus file (their input is from the "real" world) and are really designed for debugging an application as it runs on hardware.

Along with the emulators described here, there are "emulators" that are a mix between true emulators and simulators. Rather than using a bondout chip, these emulators consist of a microcontroller that is connected to a host system and is plugged into the application's circuit to run the object program one instruction at a time in a manner similar to how an interpreter executes source code. Generally, this executing is a hundred times or more slow than the actual speed of a microcontroller in the application circuit. This type of emulator is a lot cheaper than a "true" emulator (a "true" emulator can cost $1,000 or more, while this type

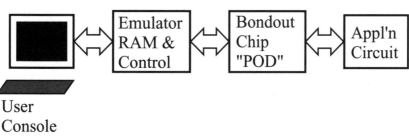

Figure 5.2 Emulator block diagram.

of emulator usually costs upwards of $100). Despite this limitation, this type of emulator can give quite an accurate representation of how the microcontroller will execute in the application and really is an excellent tool for learning how to interface to a microcontroller.

My major complaint about how emulators are used is that I find they are often treated as application development tools. I find that a lot of application developers, when they have emulators, tend to use them to "try something out" and eventually turn these experiments into a product.

This manner of application development is very inefficient and could result in a "buggy" final product because the up-front work of specifying the interfaces is not being carried out in a methodical fashion and all the implications of the design are not properly thought out.

EXAMPLE APPLICATIONS

In each section detailing a different embedded microcontroller, I have gone through a number of applications to show you how to create an application and review any problems or tricks that I may have encountered along the way. As part of creating these applications, I have tried to first introduce you to the different devices and how they should be set up for executing and then extending to a fairly complex application. By no stretch of the imagination are the contents of this book sufficient to provide you with enough information to develop a wide range of applications. Instead, what I'm trying to do is give you enough information to get started and create your own application with a minimum of help.

Device Programming

When I developed the applications for the different microcontrollers, I used programmers available in "development kits" from the manufacturers. This was done primarily to ensure that you had a reliable and fairly inexpensive method of programming the parts. As I will often say, a manufacturer's development kit is usually the best way to start using a part because it is generally very easy to connect to a PC using standard interfaces and software (i.e., "Windows") and will not require special debugging to get it working properly on your PC.

Another good reason for buying manufacturer's development kits is that, along with the programmer, they usually contain all the bits and pieces (i.e., cabling) to interface the programmer to a PC or workstation and the necessary software and tools for developing applications, simulating them, and burning them into a microcontroller. They often also contain sample parts, meaning that you can start running as soon as you get the kit. If you were to sum up all the parts and cost them out, you would find that the individual parts, would cost more than the kit.

In terms of software, for all the applications I have chosen to use assemblers and simulators primarily available from the manufacturer. Even though in some cases (notably the 68HC05, 8051, and PIC) there are many different third party tools (including many that are available free of charge), I have not used them. I have included these tools on the CD-ROM included with this book so you can sample this software and work through the example applications with me.

First MCU Application

The purpose of the "First MCU application" is to introduce you to the specific device. As part of this introduction, after completing the application you will be able to:

■ Develop assembler code (or BASIC for the Stamp).
■ Simulate/debug the application.
■ Program a target device with the code.
■ Executing the microcontroller in circuit.
■ Program interrupt handlers.

The application uses the circuit shown in Figure 6.1.

This circuit will flash one LED at a frequency of one to four Hertz (so it can be seen easily) while turning on the second LED when the button is pressed down. In most of the applications, the flashing LED will be handled by a timer, and the LED on/off code will be controlled by a timer that interrupts the mainline of the code.

In all the microcontroller examples, there is actually a program that is provided before this one, and that's something that just flashes a single LED. As will be seen, I usually develop an application feature by feature (testing each feature as it is completed) until the entire application is up and running. As well as being the first program on the road to getting the application completed, this is also a good example application for getting a device programmed and running for the first time.

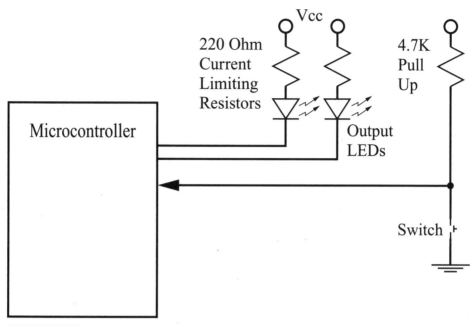

Figure 6.1 First application: flash some LEDs.

Clock/Thermometer Application

Probably the most substantive demonstration of what an embedded microcontroller can do is this application. The purpose is to provide a real time clock (which is settable by the user) that shows the current time as well as the current temperature. The clock and temperature output will be displayed on a LCD display. (Figure 6.2.)

The thermometer used is the Dallas Semiconductor DS1820, which is a "1-wire" digital thermometer. It is available in a variety of packages; the one that I used is a three-pin package that looks like a plastic transistor package. Dallas Semiconductor has come up with the "1-Wire" ™ interface that allows bidirectional data transfers between a host system and an external peripheral (like the DS1820).

The DS1820 has many features that would be useful in a variety of different applications (such as the ability to share the single-wire bus with other devices (a unique serial number is burned into the device that allows it to be written to individually) and the ability to powered by the host device). However, I use it as a basic device, and in the examples provided in this book, I power it from the Vcc available to the microcontroller and only have one device on the bus at a given time. I refrained from discussing the "1-Wire" bus interface in the networking discussion earlier in the book because it is specific to Dallas Semiconductor products (and you'll get a good introduction of it here).

Data transfers over the "1-Wire" bus are initiated by the host system (in the application cases, this is the microcontroller) and are carried out 8 bits at a time (with the LSB bit transmitted first). Each bit transfer takes at least 60 usec. The "1-Wire" bus is pulled up externally (as shown in Figure 6.2) and is pulled down by either the host or the peripheral

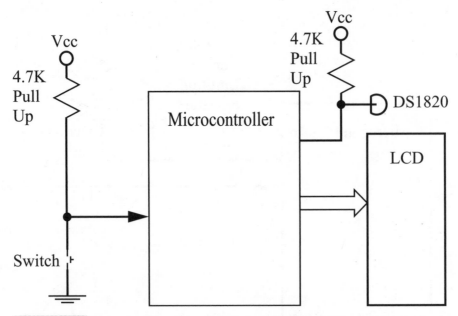

Figure 6.2 Second application: digital clock/thermometer.

device (in this case, the DS1820 digital thermometer) to transfer the data. If the bus is pulled down for a very short interval, a "1" is being transmitted. If the bus is pulled down for more than 15 usecs, then a "0" is being transmitted. (Figure 6.3.)

All data transfers are initiated by the host system. If it is transmitting data, then it holds down the line for the specified period. If it is receiving data from the DS1820, then the host pulls down the line, releases it, and then polls the line to see how long it takes for it to go back up. During data transfers, I have made sure that interrupts cannot take place (because this would affect how the data is sent or read if the interrupt takes place during the data transfer).

Before each command is set to the DS1820, a "reset" and "presence" pulse is transferred. A "reset" pulse consists of the host pulling down the line for 480 usecs to 960 usecs. The DS1820 replies by pulling down the line for roughly 100 usecs (60 to 240 usecs is the specified value). To simplify the software, I typically did not check for the presence pulse (because I knew in the application that I had the thermometer connected to the bus). In another application (where the thermometer can be disconnected), putting a check in for the "presence" pulse may be required.

To carry out a temperature "read" of the DS1820, I carried out the following instruction sequence:

1. **Send** a "reset" pulse and delay while the "presence" pulse is returned.
2. **Send** 0x0CC, which is the "skip ROM" command, which tells the DS1820 to assume that the next command is directed towards it.
3. **Send** 0x044, which is the temperature conversion initiate instruction. The current temperature will be sampled and stored for later read back.
4. **Wait** 500+ usecs for the temperature conversion to complete.
5. **Send** a "reset" pulse and delay while the "presence" pulse is returned.

6. **Send** 0x0CC, "skip ROM" command again.
7. **Send** 0x0BE to read the "scratchpad" RAM that contains the current temperature (in degrees Celsius times two).
8. **Read** the nine bytes of "scratchpad" RAM.
9. **Display** the temperature by dividing the first byte by 2 and sending the converted value to the LCD. (If bit 0 of the second byte is returned from the "scratchpad" RAM, the first byte is negated and a "-" is put on the LCD display.)

The total procedure for doing a temperature measurement takes about 5 msecs. A good (and simple) test of whether or not the thermometer is working is to pinch it between your fingers and watch the display value go upward.

In this application, I used a standard clock frequency to demonstrate how the timer can be used to provide a consist interval, even though the clock isn't a power of two (which would make application a lot simpler). This involves putting in dead instructions in the timer interrupt handler to make sure as close to the exact number of instructions is actually executed. Also, logic has been added for converting the timer value to a standard clock value and taking into account the user-entered current time setting.

I have tried to vary how the LCD is interfaced in each of the different devices. This is to give you an idea of how the three different methods presented can be wired and programmed in an actual application.

You're probably thinking that this application is a bit forced and not very representative of what a real application would be. Actually, it isn't at all forced and is very representative; the real power of a microcontroller is in its ability to interface with different external devices (in this case, the button, the LCD, and the DS1820) and run multiple tasks (in this case, the real-time clock, and the thermometer), even though an explicit multitasker or RTOS is used in only the 68HC0ST.

Also, you'll probably see better, more efficient ways of doing the application. The code and circuitry presented here is more designed to be used as a learning tool than as an actual application or product. As such, I think they do a pretty good job and give you an idea of how the device works in an actual, fairly complex application.

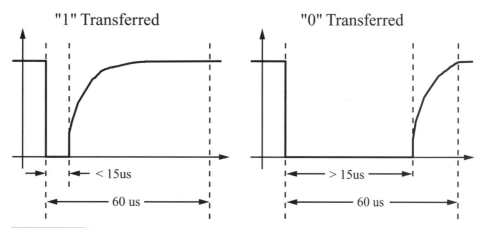

Figure 6.3 Dallas Semiconductor 1-wire data bit waveforms.

Device-Specific Application

Along with the two previous applications, I have created an application for each micro-controller that is designed to illustrate some other aspects of the device or points that I have written elsewhere in the book. While I'm calling these applications, "device" specific, for the most part they are pretty general and the principles demonstrated there can be expanded to other devices.

8051

THE 8051 MICROCONTROLLER

When you first think of Intel, you tend to think of it as a company totally devoted to PC computer systems. Along with developing the first microprocessor (the 4004) in the 1970s, the company was involved right from the beginning with developing microcontrollers. The microcontroller development effort resulted in the 8051 architecture, which was first introduced in 1980 and has gone on to be arguably the most popular microcontroller architecture available. (Figure 7.1.)

A second-generation microcontroller product, the 8051, is a very complete microcontroller with a large of amount of built-in control store (ROM and EPROM) and RAM (respectably large even for today), enhanced I/O ports, and the ability to access external memory. The original 8051 was also quite fast, with a 20-MHz maximum clock speed.

Whereas most of the other microcontrollers measure their success in terms of total units sold, the 8051 can claim an unusual honor. The 8051 is, far and away, the device that is manufactured by the most companies. This is actually quite an advantage for the part

Figure 7.1 Dallas Semiconductor 8051 HSM microcontrollers.

because each manufacturer has enhanced the 8051 in terms of features or speed and has made the architecture very accessible to a wide range of applications.

As I go through this section, I will primarily focus on what I will call the "original," "classic," "stock," "true," 8051 and 87C51. The 87C51 is a version of the 8051, with the "7" indicating that it has EPROM control store and the "C" indicates that it is a CMOS part.

The standard features of the 8051 are:

- 24-MHz clock speed.
- 12-clock cycle per instruction cycle.
- 4 Kbytes of control store.
- 128 bytes of RAM.
- 32 I/O lines.
- Two 8/16-bit timers.
- Multiple internal and external interrupt sources.
- Programmable serial port.
- Interface for up to 128 Kbytes of external memory.

Many of the different manufacturers' devices have improvements and extensions to these features, and while I'll point out some of them, for the most part I will use the Intel 87C51 as the "standard" (although I'll tend to use the generic term "8051").

8051 Suppliers

Right now, there are more than 10 vendors building their own versions of the 8051. These versions range from being pin, code, timing, and feature compatible with the 87C51 to having significant enhancements to the original design in terms of speeding up program execution or adding different features to the part. For one manufacturer, the enhancements actually consist of providing fewer features to the 8051 reference standard. The original 8051 may seem rather featureless when compared to the varied part numbers of the PIC and 68HC05, but when the range of features from all manufacturers is tallied, the 8051 has at least as diverse a feature set as any microcontroller.

Even though Intel is the originator of the 8051 architecture, the company has not made a lot of changes to the original device. The most significant changes made to the 8051 are the "MCS-151" and "MCS-251" microcontrollers. These pin- and code-compatible devices offer significant performance improvements over the original 8051 and 87C51 devices.

Atmel, which is a newcomer to the microcontroller field, offers "shrunk" 8051 compatibles (along with its line of AVR microcontrollers), which are available in a 20-pin package. This smaller version of the 8051 has made the architecture more accessible to smaller/cheaper applications. The Atmel versions of the 8051 ("AT89S1051" and "AT89S2051") also use EEPROM technology for control store and nonvolatile data storage, which makes the 8051 useful for education and for hobbyists to experiment with.

In this section, I will focus on the Dallas Semiconductor "high-speed microcontrollers" ("HSM") devices for the example applications. With the "HSM," Dallas Semiconductor has lead the way more than any other 8051 vendor to improve speed in the operation of the architecture. The "HSM" 8051's compatible microcontrollers execute code two to three times faster than the "stock" parts.

One of the most interesting microcontrollers available is the Dallas Semiconductor encrypted (or soft program) microcontroller. This device will allow the download of an application and store it in an encrypted format in an external SRAM. This chip is very useful in remote sensor applications, where the microcontroller or data may not be physically secure.

Philips Semiconductor has the most feature-rich collection of 8051-based microcontrollers of any vendor. When developing an application that will require external peripherals, I highly recommend that you check out Philips' catalog of parts because there is a good chance that there will be a Philip's part number that will do exactly what you are looking for without any external devices. Along with the wide variety of "standard" 8051 parts, Philips also has the "XA" architecture, which is an enhancement to the original 8051 architecture to allow 16-bit data processing.

One of the interesting developments of the early 1980s was the creation of "piggybacked" microcontrollers and microprocessors. With these devices, a standard EPROM or ROM was literally plugged into the back of the processor chip. The advantage of this method was that the processor chip would not have to be removed from a product when the code was updated. The combination would be cheaper because they wouldn't be built with hybrid technologies (logic and EPROM/ROM require different manufacturing processes). Another advantage of this method is fewer pins and board space used for external memory. These advantages are reflected in some of Oki's 8051 products, which are built without control store but will take an EPROM/ROM chip plugged into the top of the chip.

8

8051 PROCESSOR ARCHITECTURE

8051

The 8051 processor architecture is "Harvard" based with external memory read/write capabilities built in as part of the architecture. The 8051's architecture is really a "typical" MCU architecture; if you compare the architecture to the AVR or the PIC, you shouldn't have any problems with understanding how the 8051 works relative to these parts. But if you are expecting the 8051 to work like the 8080 or 8086 (i.e., Intel microprocessors) you are in for quite a shock.

The CPU

The basic 8051 architecture, from a high level, isn't all that different from the other Harvard architectures presented in this book. With the architecture shown in Figure 8.1, the basic 8051 should look like the "Harvard" architecture I presented earlier in the book. For the most part, the 8051 isn't a difficult device to program. There are a few quirks, but once you understand them you should feel pretty comfortable with the design. The two areas that I will expand upon are the memory organization in general (including the "control store" and "register" boxes in Figure 8.1) and how "registers" are implemented specifically.

To explain how the registers work, I'm going to apply a magnifying glass to the "register" box. (See Figure 8.2.) I have broken up the first 256 addresses by how the registers are accessed by "direct" addressing (which is when the register address is specifically given in the instruction) and "indirect" addressing (when the register address is located within an index register).

You might note that I have marked the direct addresses 020h to 02Fh differently in Figure 8.2. These 16 bytes can be accessed as 128 bits as well as bytes. Some of the bits in the special-purpose registers (in address 080h and above) can be accessed directly, although others could be loaded into the bit-addressable (addresses 020h to 02Fh) area, modified, and then stored back into the special-purpose ("I/O") register area if individual bits were to be modified. The 128 bits can also be accessed as 16 regular RAM bytes.

If you directly address 080h to 0FFh, you will be accessing the "special purpose ("I/O") register area" of the 8051. This register area is reserved for processor and I/O peripheral registers. (Figure 8.3.)

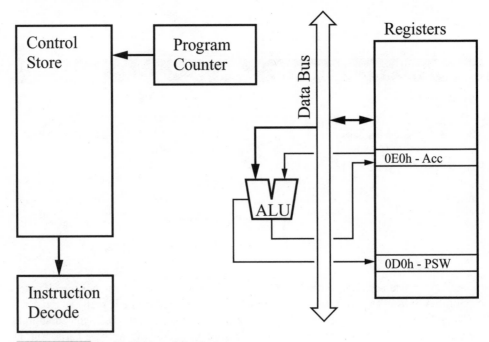

Figure 8.1 Basic 8051 architecture.

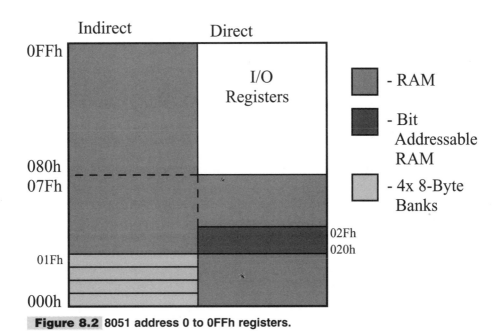

Figure 8.2 8051 address 0 to 0FFh registers.

Common 8051 Registers

0FFh	
	0F0h - "B" Register
	0E0h - Accumulator
	0D0h - PSW
	0B0h - Port3
	0A0h - Port2
	090h - Port1
	083h - DPH
	082h - DPL
	081h - Stack Pointer
080h	080h - Port0

Figure 8.3 Standard 8051 special purpose register addresses.

The shaded areas are addresses that may or may not have hardware registers for controlling peripheral functions. The areas that aren't shaded are the "standard registers," which are available in all 8051s. I have refrained from extending the "standard" register definitions to anything more than an absolute minimum because with all the different 8051 manufacturers, there are a number of "standard" peripherals and their associated registers are not available in every device.

The special function registers I have identified are the stack pointer, index pointer "DPL" and "DPH", I/O port addresses, the status register "program status word" or "PSW," and accumulators. I will present more information on these registers elsewhere in the book.

All "direct addressing" can only access the first 256 addresses in the memory space (which is marked as "Registers" in Figure 8.1). To access RAM bytes at addresses above this 256-address space, you'll have to use an index register (such as "DPTR," which is made up of the "DPL" and "DPH" registers).

"Indirect" (or "indexed") addressing uses either the stack pointer (the "SP" register identified above) or an index register ("DPTR" for example). The special function registers (at address 080h to 0FFh) cannot be accessed by indirect addressing. Many manufacturers have put in 128 bytes of RAM that can only be accessed here by the stack pointer or an index pointer.

With RAM put into the "indirect space" at the same addresses as the "special function registers" something funny starts to happen; you can access 384 different RAM bytes and I/O registers in the first 256 addresses of the 8051. This is 256 addresses of RAM (which can only be fully accessed by using indirect addressing instructions) and 128 addresses of special function registers (which can only be accessed using direct addressing instruc-

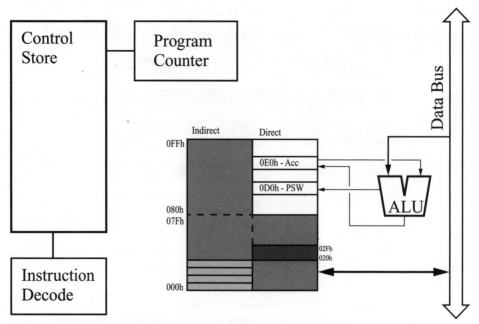

Figure 8.4 8051 architecture with register direct addressing.

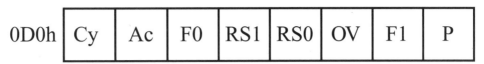

0D0h	Cy	Ac	F0	RS1	RS0	OV	F1	P

Figure 8.5 8051 program status word (PSW).

tions). When I first read this in the Dallas Semiconductor's HSM documentation, I really ended up shaking my head.

With this information on the register area, I can now expand the basic architecture to the block diagram shown in Figure 8.4. In describing the special-purpose registers, I think I left a few open questions. The first is what are all the special-purpose registers that I identified? I will go through the processor specific registers here but leave the I/O-specific registers for later in this section.

The accumulator registers ("A" and "B") are used to store temporary values and the results of arithmetic operations. If you flip through the arithmetic and bitwise instructions quickly, you'll see that "B" is just about never used. In fact, it is only used for multiplication and division. The accumulators can be accessed either as part of an instruction or as addresses 0E0h or 0F0h for "ACC" (which is the special function register identification for the accumulator) and "B," respectively.

The "program status word" (most commonly known as "PSW") is the status register for the 8051. It is defined as shown in Figure 8.5, the "CY" and "AC" bits being the full-carry and half-carry flags. "CY" is set when an addition or subtraction causes a carry to or a borrow from the next highest byte of the number (which allows easy manipulation of 16 bit or larger values). The "AC" or half-carry flag is set when an addition or subtraction makes the lower nybble change the value (by one) of the upper nybble. These two status flags are in all the microcontrollers presented in this book.

Looking at the PSW definition, there is one flag you would expect to see but don't. That is the "zero" flag (which is set when the result of an arithmetic, bitwise, or shift/rotate is equal to zero). Checking for zero is handled differently in the 8051. The "jz" instruction tests the contents of the accumulator ("A") and carries out the jump if the contents of the register are equal to zero. I will expand on this operation in the "8051 Instructions" chapter later in this section.

The "RS0" and "RS1" bits are used to select which of the four 8-byte "banks" is currently being used. These 8-byte banks are used for providing single byte arithmetic instructions. By providing a very small area to operate out of smaller and faster instructions can be used in your application. One aspect of the 8-byte banks that you should be aware of is that the two least significant registers of the Bank (identified as "R0" and "R1") can be used for index addressing in the 256-address RAM area.

Another item I have not addressed so far is the operation of the stack pointer and how it can only access the first 256 addresses of the RAM register area. Upon power up, it is set to 007h, but personally, I like to change it to the top of RAM, or at least address 028h.

This may seem a bit strange, and there are a few things I really haven't explained here. The stack's "push" and "pop" instructions increment the stack pointer (rather than decrement the stack pointer as is done in many other devices). This means that setting up the stack pointer to give it maximum space in a stack area, you have to give it the lowest address of the stack area, rather than the highest addresses as you would with most other devices.

In the HSMs, I set the stack pointer address to 080h because the RAM is only accessible by the index registers (which the stack pointer is one). Giving the stack pointer the bottom of the accessible area, I can put arrays at the top of the first 256 addresses and not really have to worry about whether or not the arrays or the stack will write over each other's data area.

The "DPTR" is a 16-bit index register that can access up to 64K different addresses starting at the 256-address register space. It is primarily designed for transferring data to/from the external memory area, and I'll discuss it in more detail in the next sub-chapter.

With the special registers, the current block diagram is as shown in Figure 8.6. You can see how the stack pointer ("SP"), "DPTR," "A," and "PSW" registers are all accessible from the direct register area and how they interact with the 8051's register data and address buses.

With this, the block diagram of the 8051 is just about complete. The only change I would make is adding a multiplexer selection between reading an immediate value in the instruction or using a value in the register space. This is shown in Figure 8.7.

With this graphic, I consider my block diagram of the operation of the 8051 to be complete. Compare it to the block diagram contained in the Dallas Semiconductor's 80C320 data sheet (Figure 8.8).

You'll see just about no relation between the two diagrams. Going further with this, if you look at my block diagrams for different devices compared to the block diagrams provided by the manufacturers, you'll probably notice great discrepancies (or, in the case of the 8051, no relationship at all) in the two diagrams.

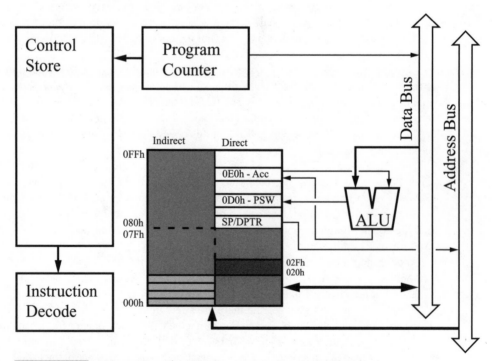

Figure 8.6 8051 architecture with register indirect addressing.

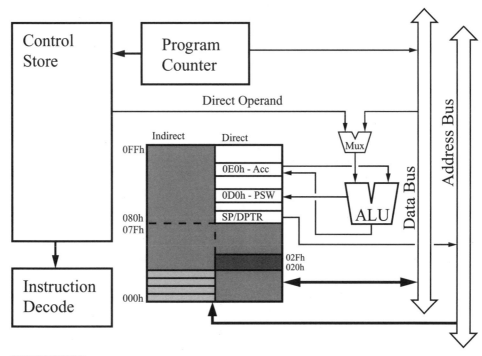

Figure 8.7 8051 architecture with immediate addressing.

These discrepancies really come from how I try to understand how the devices work. I tend to focus on instruction execution and try to understand what has to happen inside the processor for the instruction to execute properly. My block diagrams tend to simplify how the peripheral hardware interfaces to the processor (although I will expand on the interfaces later in each section).

Is this the right way to learn how the different microcontrollers and their processors work? I don't know, but I do know that it is a very effective way for me to learn how they work and visualize how data moves inside the devices.

8051 Addressing Modes

The 8051's addressing modes are designed from the perspective that data access priority should reflect how the data is to be accessed. In most applications, very few variables are accessed a lot, some quite a bit, and most quite infrequently. In designing the 8051, Intel used this philosophy to specify the single-byte/12-clock-cycle-instruction cycle for determining how data would be accessed. Accessing the current register banks only takes 1 byte and 12 cycles. This is followed by the 2-byte/24-clock instructions into the first 256 register addresses and the 3-byte, multiple instruction cycle access to the memory above the first 256 addresses.

This can be shown graphically as Figure 8.9. It is a good one to remember when developing complex applications in assembler. As you are writing the code, you should be asking

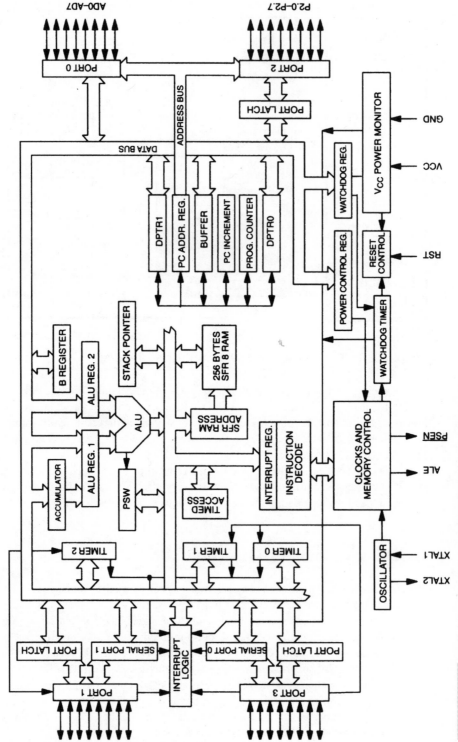

Figure 8.8 Dallas Semiconductor DS80C320 block diagram.

yourself what is the distribution of the instructions accessing the variables, and is it optimized to execute in the fewest number of cycles and require the fewest number of control store bytes?

The first addressing mode really isn't an addressing mode at all. "Immediate" addressing passes the value to be executed as part of the instruction. The immediate value is specified by placing a "#" character in front of the immediate value:

```
add   A, #77  ;  Add "77" to the Accumulator
```

This instruction will add decimal 77 to the contents of the accumulator and store the result back into the accumulator.

"Bank" addressing allows you to access a byte in the current register bank. This is the most efficient (both in terms of clock cycles and control store) method of accessing data. Most register instructions execute in one register cycle and only require 1 byte to execute the instruction. The 8 bytes are known as "R0" though "R7."

"Direct" memory addressing differs from register addressing in that any byte within the first 256 register addresses can be accessed by specifying an 8-bit address. When using this mode, there are a few things to watch out for. The first is RAM addresses 080h to 0FFh (if the device you're using has RAM at these locations) and cannot be accessed by direct addressing (instead you'll have to use an indirect mode). If you specify an instruction like:

```
mov   A, 088h
```

You'll load the accumulator with the contents of the "TCON" register (at 088h) rather than the contents of a RAM byte. The second thing to note is something that always bites me when I'm developing an 8051 (and 68HC05) application. I always forget to put in the "#" character for immediate addressing, and I inadvertently wind up with an instruction that uses direct addressing. This seems to be my number one syntax problem when developing 8051 code, and it means I have to be especially careful when I'm simulating an application to make sure the correct addressing mode is being used.

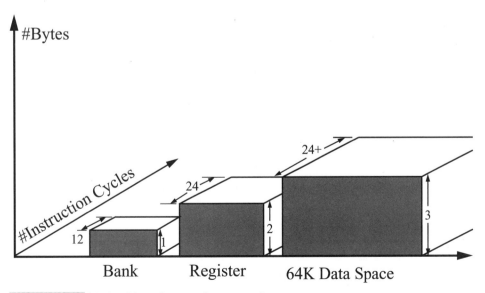

Figure 8.9 8051 addressing mode comparison.

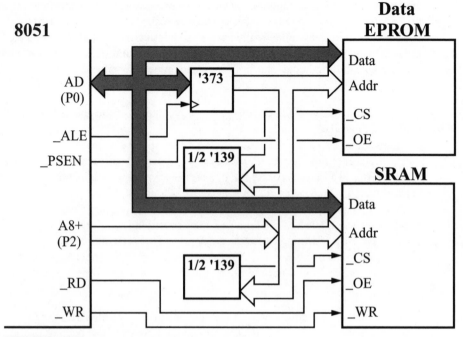

Figure 8.10 8051 external memory access.

"Register indirect" addressing uses "R0" or "R1" as an 8-bit index register to access a byte in the first 256 addresses of the data space.

```
orl   A,@R0
```

The register indirect is identified by the "@" character before either "R0" or "R1." Using any other bank registers will result in an error.

The "DPTR" register can also be used as a 16-bit index register. This addressing mode can also be enhanced with an offset for accessing data structures in data space memory. This mode is known as "register indirect with displacement."

When you want to read a table out of control store (i.e., read a string of ASCII characters), the "movc A, @A+PC" instruction can access an offset from the current address. This offset has to be arithmetically generated before the instruction can be used.

The remaining addressing modes are used for changing the current program counter. You will see similar modes in the other microcontrollers. These modes are expanded on in the "8051 Instructions" chapter. Actually, the different data-addressing modes are also explained in more detail in the "8051 Instructions" chapter as well.

External Addressing

At the start of this section, I introduced the 8051 as a device that could access up to 64K bytes of program memory and 64K byte of variable SRAM. Looking through what I've shown above in this chapter and looking at the data sheets, you're probably wondering how this is accomplished. The 8051 is designed with a built-in external memory interface that uses the "P0" and "P2" I/O port bits for accesses. (Figure 8.10.)

Anytime an address (either control store or data space) is greater than what's in the 8051, the external I/O is activated and the 8051 tries to access external memory. If you're familiar with other microcontrollers, you might wonder how this is possible with a "typical" microcontroller's I/O pin design. You might want to skip ahead and look in "8051 Hardware Features" to see what I'm talking about and see how different bit states are output.

When accessing external memory, first the least significant 8 bits of the address are output, followed by either reading or writing data.

The external control store byte read waveform looks like Figure 8.11, which is actually how the 8085/8088 microprocessors access external 8-bit memory. For RAM, the "_RD" ("Read") and "_WR" ("Write") pins are used instead of "_PSEN" (which is used to access external control store). In the Dallas Semiconductor HSM 8051s, the length of time used for reading/writing data can be extended or the cycles "stretched." This is analogous in the "PC universe" as adding wait states. "Stretching" the accesses may be required when going from a "true" 8051 to a HSM part because of the latter's faster instruction cycles, or allow "slower" devices to be accessed without violating their timing specifications.

Now, if you want to provide external memory (or devices) on the 8051's external buses but don't want to use the entire 64K address space, you could put these devices at high memory, which means that the I/O pins are always high and can be used for functions other than providing memory addresses.

For example, an application could be designed where 2K SRAM is required, along with some additional pins, and two pins are still required for bit I/O purposes. The 8051 and SRAM could be wired as in Figure 8.12.

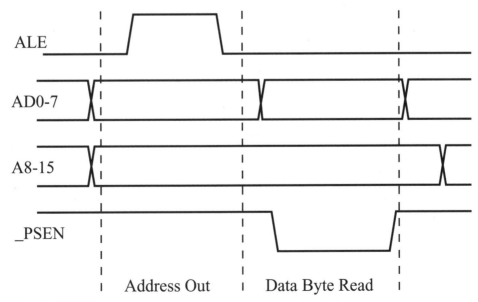

Figure 8.11 8051 external ROM read cycle.

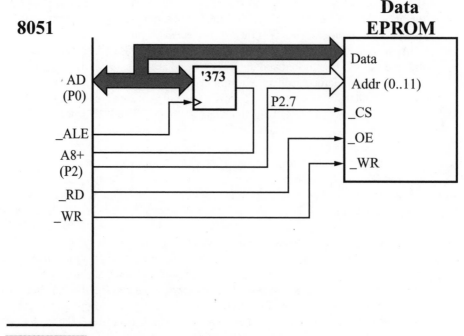

Figure 8.12 8051 2K external SRAM wiring.

In this scheme, the P2.5 and P2.6 pins are available for bit I/O because they will not change state during SRAM access. If the bit in the address is set, then its external I/O state will not change. This means that the SRAM pins should always be set high (or left at their initial value of all high) to prevent problems that could prevent certain addresses from being accessible.

Previously, I mentioned that I/O devices could be interfaced with the 8051, and this can be done very simply by using one of the P2 bits for the _CS or clock pin on the device. One example 8051 application shows a memory-mapped I/O solution using address line decoding.

In Figure 8.13, writes to "Device 1" could be carried out by writing to address 0FE00h, Device 2 can be read at 0FD00h, and the ROM (Device 0) could be read starting at 0FC00h. This scheme allows each device to be accessed without affecting any of the others or requiring extensive "glue" logic to determine whether or not reads of writes should be carried out. The lower 8 address bits are used for selecting registers or addresses within the peripheral devices.

One really interesting thing that can be done with the 8051 is to use one memory for both control store and RAM. This is done by ANDing PSEN and RD together. (See Figure 8.14.)

By doing this, I've now created an 8051 application that can write to its control store (an immediate use would be for creating an 8051 experimental debug tool for downloading code into the SRAM).

It also poses an interesting philosophical question—by creating this circuit, have I created a "Von Neumann"-architected processor or a Harvard architecture?

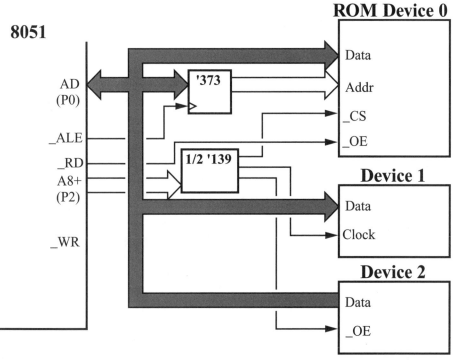

8.13 8051 external memory-mapped I/O.

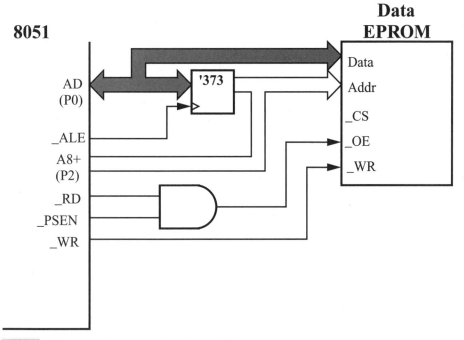

8.14 8051 shared control store/data RAM.

Interrupts

The 8051's control store memory map can be shown as Figure 8.15. Address 0 is the reset (and watchdog timer overflow) execution vector address. When the 8051 is reset, execution jumps to this address. When an interrupt request is acknowledged, execution jumps to the appropriate address (i.e., interrupt 0 goes to address 03h, interrupt 1 goes to address 0Bh and so on). At first blush, this isn't very exciting; all the other microcontrollers presented here operate in a similar manner.

The exciting thing is, while the other microcontrollers operate in a similar fashion, they don't provide memory space to allow an application to handle each individual interrupt directly in line. The 8 bytes of control store available for each interrupt handler can either be used to house the entire interrupt handler or jump to a more substantial handler.

I always look for features built into devices; that makes my life easier. By "easier" I'm trying to say that I have to do less thinking. Having 8 bytes available for instructions makes simple interrupt handlers (i.e., reset timer interrupt and increment a real-time clock value) very easy to implement.

If you're thinking that the 8 bytes are probably not sufficient to save the context registers before handling the interrupt, you're probably correct. But, since there is no zero flag in the 8051's PSW register, this should not be an issue unless you are going to use add and subtract (which could change the carry/half byte carry PSW bits). Simple bit sets and register increments and decrements can be accomplished without changing the PSW contents.

8051 Instruction Execution

The 8051 processor core is designed differently than most other microcontrollers (including all the others presented in this book). The 8051 contains a microcoded processor; this is in contrast to the other microcontrollers which use a hardwired one. (Figure 8.16.)

What is a microcoded processor? This is really a processor within a processor, or a state machine that executes each different instruction as the address to a subroutine of instructions. When an instruction is loaded into the "instruction holding register," certain bits of the instruction are used to point to the start of the instruction routine (or microcode) and the "uCode Instruction Decode and Processor" logic executes the microcode instructions until an "instruction end" is encountered.

As a quick aside, I should point out that having the "instruction holding register" wider than the "control store memory" is not necessarily a mistake. The control store in the 8051 is only 8 bits wide and quite a few of the instructions are more than 8 bits. This could mean that before an instruction can be executed, the entire instruction may have to be loaded into the holding register (which can take additional time).

A "hardwired" processor uses the bit pattern of the instruction to access specific logic gates (possibly unique to the instruction), which are executed as a combinatorial circuit to carry out the instruction. (Figure 8.17.)

Each of the two methods offers advantages over the other. A microcoded process is usually simpler than a hardwired one to design and the actual design can be implemented faster and with less chance of having problems at specific conditions.

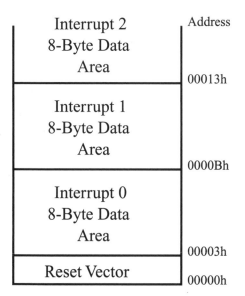

Control Store

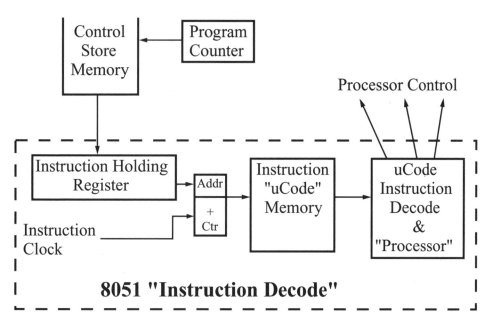

Figure 8.15 8051 interrupt addressing.

8051 "Instruction Decode"

Figure 8.16 The 8051's microcoded processor.

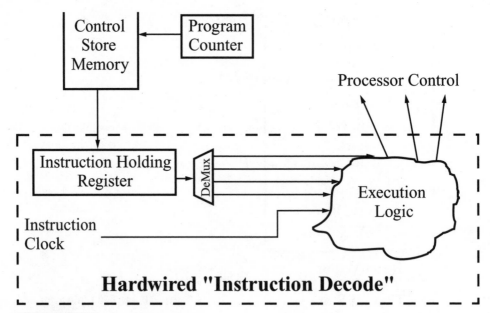

Figure 8.17 Hardwired processor.

A great example of the quick and easy changes that a microcoded processors allows was a number of years ago when IBM wanted to have a microprocessor that could run 370 assembly language instructions. Before IBM began to design its own microprocessor, the company looked around at existing designs and noticed that the Motorola 68000 had the same hardware organization as the 370 (although the instructions were completely different). IBM ended up paying Motorola to rewrite the microcode for the 68000 and came up with a new microprocessor that was able to run 370 instructions, but at a small fraction of the cost of developing a new device.

A hardwired processor is usually a lot more complex because the same functions have to be repeated over and over again in hardware. (How many times do you think that a register read or write function has to be repeated for each type of instruction?) This means that the processor design will probably be harder to debug and be less flexible than a microcoded design, but it will probably run a lot faster.

The "true" (original) 8051 used a microcoded processor, which requires 12 to 24 clock cycles for each instruction to execute. (Compare this to any of the other microcontrollers presented in this book; every other one runs at a fraction of this.)

In this subchapter, I will present three 8051-compatible devices that have been aimed at improving the execution speed of the 8051's instruction set.

INTEL MCS 151/251

Intel's MCS-151 and MCS-251 microcontrollers are an enhancement to the original 8051 with a number of changes and improvements. These improvements include enhancing the instruction set for 16/32-bit data transfers, up to 16 Mbytes of SRAM addressability (and, going with this a stack capable of being 64K bytes, rather than the original 256 bytes) and, most importantly (to this discussion, anyway), the instructions execute in as few as two or four clock cycles.

The MCS-151 and MCS-251 are available versions that are pin and software ("binary code") compatible with the 8051. One of the interesting (for me) aspects of Intel's descriptions of the parts states that the MCS-151 and MCS-251 can be run at slower speeds to carry out the same amount of processing as the 8051 they replace. In doing this, the microcontroller requires less power and produces less EMI (electrical noise) on the board.

This is interesting to me because I usually associate a change like this with being able to get more speed out of the device, not use it as a method to stay at the same speed. I guess I've been brainwashed by the continual improvements in PC and workstation technology into thinking that technology improvements only mean faster computers.

The MCS-151 is basically a replacement for the 8051 with the same instruction set and features. The MCS-251 is an enhancement to the 8051/MCS-151, both in terms of instruction speed (the MCS-251 can run up to 15 times faster and the MCS-151 can run up to five times faster than a "stock" 8051). Both the MCS-151 and MCS-251 use a hardwired processor capable of "pipelining" (reading ahead) instructions, which is a primary reason for the faster program execution.

DALLAS SEMICONDUCTOR "HIGH-SPEED" MICROCON-TROLLERS

For the 8051 applications presented in this book, I will be using the Dallas Semiconductor "high-speed microcontrollers" ("HSM") devices. Dallas Semiconductor was the first to come up with the idea of changing the 8051's microcoded processor core with a hardwired one. This change has resulted in instructions taking 4, 8, 12, or 16 clock cycles per instruction for an improvement of one-and-a-half to three times over a "true" 8051 running at the same clock speed.

This change to the instruction timing means that the Dallas Semicondutor HSM parts cannot just be dropped into an application and expected to run with just a slower clock (which is what you should be able to expect with the MCS-151). The nonlinear improvement in instruction execution (Dallas Semiconductor's research has shown that a 2.5 times improvement can be expected going to the HSM microcontrollers from the "stock" 8051s) may cause some problems when porting a working application. But, if you work exclusively with the timers providing critical delays, you shouldn't have any problems with moving the code between a "true" 8051 and a Dallas Semiconductor HSM.

In the diagrams showing how the 8051's instructions execute, I have included both the original 8051s as well as the HSM's instruction clock cycle counts.

8

8051

8501 HARDWARE FEATURES

One of the biggest problems I had writing this section of the book was determining what a "generic" 8051 actually is. With the many manufacturers there are a lot of features that are specific to different manufacturers and their devices. As I go through the different hardware features available to the 8051, I will identify manufacturer-specific features and comment on different devices.

Packaging

The 8051's packaging is very straightforward, with the primary packaging being a 0.600"
DIP. In Figure 9.1, I have shown the standard 8051 along with an ATMEL 20 Pin version
of the 8051.

The 8051 is also available in a variety of different SMT packages. The SMT packaging
pinout does not correlate directly to the PTH pinout, which means that before specifying
an SMT part when you go from a prototype (which used a PTH part) to production, you
should understand the differences between the two pinouts and make allowances for them.

The Intel pinout standard has been followed, for the most part, in the other manufacturers' versions of the 40-pin DIP. I included the Atmel part in Figure 9.1 because it has
many of the same features of the "true" 8051, but has a much-reduced pinout.

Parallel Input/Output

Despite having the simplest parallel I/O pins available in any of the microcontrollers presented in this book, the 8051s are the most radically different in operation and capabilities.
(Figure 9.2.)

The pullup (and associated transistor) are not available on all ports (the "true" 8051 has
port 0 without pullups on the pins, while ports 1, 2, and 3 all have the integral pullups).
The best way to describe the 8051's parallel I/O ports is as being open-collector (actually
"open-drain") with optional pullups.

AT89C2051

_Reset	Vcc
P3.0 (RXd)	P1.7
P3.1 (TXd)	P1.6
XTAL2	P1.5
XTAL1	P1.4
P3.2 (_INT0)	P1.3
P3.3 (_INT1)	P1.2
P3.4 (T0) P1.1 (AIN1)	
P3.5 (T1) P1.0 (AIN0)	
Gnd	P3.7

8051

P1.0	Vcc
P1.1	P0.0 (AD0)
P1.2	P0.1 (AD1)
P1.3	P0.2 (AD2)
P1.4	P0.3 (AD3)
P1.5	P0.4 (AD4)
P1.6	P0.5 (AD5)
P1.7	P0.6 (AD6)
_Reset	P0.7 (AD7)
P3.0 (RXD)	_EA/Vpp
P3.1 (TXD)	ALE/_PROG
P3.0 (INT0)	_PSEN
P3.3 (INT1)	P2.7 (A15)
P3.4 (T0)	P2.6 (A14)
P3.5 (T1)	P2.5 (A13)
P3.6 (_WR)	P2.4 (A12)
P3.7 (_RD)	P2.3 (A11)
XTAL2	P2.2 (A10)
XTAL1	P2.1 (A9)
Gnd	P2.0 (A8)

Figure 9.1 Atmel AT89C2051 and Intel 8051 DIP packages.

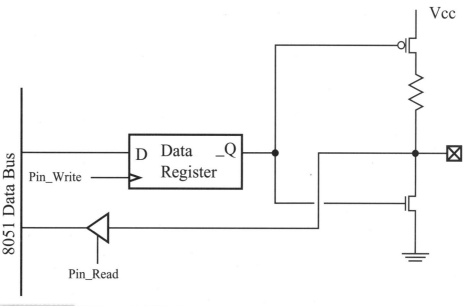

Figure 9.2 8051 parallel I/O pins.

Looking at Figure 9.2, you're probably wondering how the 8051s I/O pins actually work as bidirectional logic pins. The other microcontrollers presented in this book all have I/O pins with explicit output drivers.

When you first look at Figure 9.2, you can see the "totem pole" output of the pin quite clearly. When the bit is loaded with a "1," the top transistor is turned on, and current can flow through the pullup. A "0" will turn on the lower transistor, which will pull the line to ground. A "0" will also turn off the top transistor at the same time.

This means that the pin is always being driven; how is a logic value read from the pin?

When a "1" is loaded into the output flip-flop, the (weak) pullup is easily overpowered by most other logic drivers. In many ways, this I/O pin design will make wiring some circuits easier (i.e., applications that require an integral pull-up) and some harder (i.e., ones that the pin has to source current). If the 8051 has to source anything more than tens of microamps, the output will have to be redriven.

With just the weak pullups, the pin may take a relatively long time (on the order of microseconds) to transition from a low- to a high-voltage output. Dallas Semiconductor provides high-current drivers on the I/O pins that drive the pin high (without the pullup) for two clock cycles to avoid this problem. Also, when using peripheral I/O devices (such as a serial port), you may find that the pins are actually being driven high, rather than just pulled up. This is a function of the peripheral, and the I/O pin cannot take advantage of this.

Timers

The 8051's internal timers are probably the most flexible of the general-purpose timers in the microcontrollers presented in this book. Four operating modes are available, which gives you a great deal of control over your application with a minimum of software overhead. Timer 0 and timer 1, which are 8/16-bit timers, are generally available together in the various 8051s. The four different operating modes reconfigure the timer hardware to carry out different tasks. (Figure 9.3.)

"TLn" and "THn" are the 8-bit timer low and high bits for each of the timers, with "n" determining which timer the register is referencing (i.e., "TL0" is the low 8-bit register for timer 0).

The "clock source" can be either the instruction clock (which can have it's speed reduced by a prescaler) or an external I/O pin and is selected by the "timer mode" ("TMOD") register using the "C/_T" bit. The timer mode selection bits of TMOD select which mode the timer runs in.

"Mode 0" configures one of the timers as a 13-bit timer by setting the overflow path through bit 4 of the "TLn" counter, rather than bit 7 (which is how "mode 1" operates, with the resulting counter being 16 bits in length).

"Mode 2" is commonly used for providing a baud (bit/data) rate generator for the built-in serial port. Only "TLn" is used for counting. When it counts past 0FFh it is reloaded with the value in THn (via the "tri-state buffer") and restarts counting. The device's serial port can use the output overflow and use it as part of the "baud rate generator."

Timer mode 3 uses timer 0 with both TL0 and TH0 as two independent timers. This mode can only be executed on timer 0 because this mode requires both an internal and external clock source and the configuration will not allow timer 1 to operate with the external clock pin. TH0 is driven by an external pin, and TL0 is driven by the instruction clock. The most obvious application that would use mode 3 is as a tachometer, counting the number of external events happening in a given amount of time (as monitored by TL0).

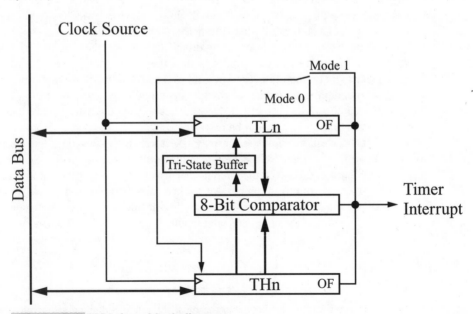

Figure 9.3 8051 timer block diagram.

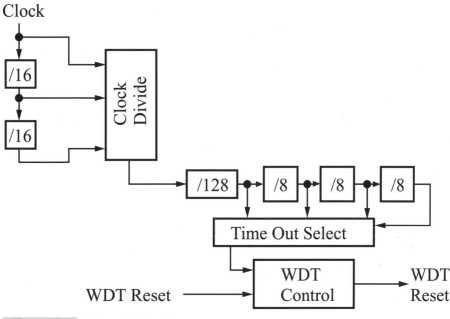

Figure 9.4 8051 watchdog timer.

In the enhanced "8052" version, there is a "timer 2," which operates strictly as a 16-bit timer. Timer 2 can be used for capturing and measuring pulses coming in from an external source. It can also be used as a baud rate generator for the second serial port in the microcontroller.

Note that the cycle interval loaded from THn in mode 2 is the overflow value (256 for timer 0 and timer 1 and 65,536 for timer 2) less the number of cycles you want to wait. A calculation showing how this works to get a useful delay is shown later in this chapter when I discuss the serial ports.

WATCHDOG TIMER

The watchdog timer available on some 8051s is used to either wake up the microcontroller from sleep, reset a program that is running amok, or interrupt the microcontroller's operation. Like the other microcontrollers presented in this book, the 8051's watchdog timer can be reset only in software. (Figure 9.4.)

Using the "clock divide" control and the "time out select," the 8051's watchdog timer will take anywhere from 128K to 17 billion clock cycles to time out. In more practical terms, if the 8051 were being run by a 12-MHz clock, the timeout interval would be between 10 msec and 24 minutes.

To reset the WDT, a "timed access" write has to be carried out:

```
mov    0C7h, #0AAh   ;  Send Control Pattern
mov    0C7h, $055h
mov    WDCON, $002h  ;  Reset the WDT
```

This sequence of instructions is used to prevent inadvertent resetting of the watchdog timer if the program is out of control. This "timed access" approach is also used on other

8051 peripheral functions to prevent accidental setting or resetting of external hardware interfaces.

After the 0AAh/055h has been written to the timed access register, the reset operation has to execute within four instruction cycles. To ensure that this always happens, interrupts should be masked before the first write and enabled after the reset instruction.

Serial Input/Output

The 8051 serial port is a very complex peripheral, able to send data synchronously and asynchronously in a variety of different transmission modes. (Figure 9.5.)

The block diagram in Figure 9.5 will probably appear to be different than the other serial ports shown for the other microcontrollers. A big reason for this is the ability of this serial port to run in both synchronous and asynchronous modes.

For synchronous mode (mode 0), the instruction clock is used. Data is transmitted and received by the RX pin, and the clock is provided by the TX pin. In synchronous mode, the 8051 can only master (i.e., provide the clock to move data in or out). (See Figure 9.6.)

The synchronous data transfer is initiated by writing to the serial data port address. Note that the "TX" pin is used for the clock output while the "RX" pin is for data transfer (both in and out). Data is transferred or, more accurately, is valid on the rising edge of the clock pulse.

When a character is received, a hardware interrupt can be requested or the status of the data transfer can be monitored by polling the "RI_n" bit in the serial control register

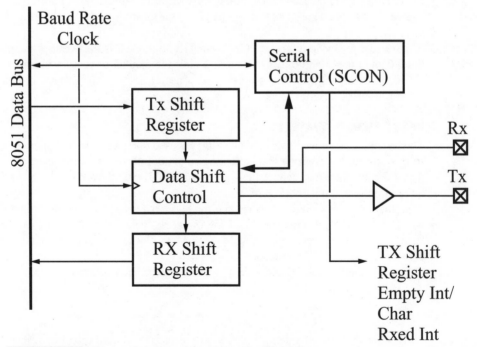

Figure 9.5 8051 serial receiver/transmitter block diagram.

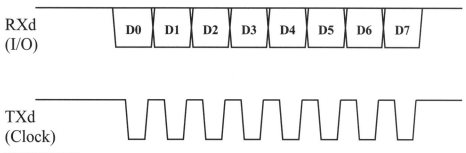

Figure 9.6 8051 synchronous serial waveforms.

("SCON"). For synchronous transmission, the data rate is the oscillator frequency divided by 4 or 12.

For asynchronous data transmission in the "stock" 8051, the data rate is the instruction clock divided by 32 or 64. This means that data transmission speed is dependent on the actual speed of the microcontroller. To get a 9600-bps asynchronous serial I/O, the maximum speed the 8051 can run at is 7.372800 MHz (which is $9600 \times 12 \times 64$). This mode of asynchronous transmission is "mode 1" in the 8051.

Sending data is initiated by writing a byte into the "TX shift register." The 8051 does not have the "TX holding register" that many other devices have in their asynchronous serial communications hardware. This means that loading the holding register while a byte is being shifted out is not possible. To get the maximum string transmit rate, you will have to poll the "TI" bit of the SCON register and load the TX shift register after the previous byte has been shifted out.

In other microcontrollers, the "TX holding register" is simply kept loaded with the next character, and when the data shift out has completed, this value is loaded into a shift register and sent out. The software can poll on the "holding register" empty bit or wait for a "holding register" empty interrupt. This method can allow faster transmission of data without having to continually monitor the state of the data shift out.

When a byte (which can be 8 or 9 bits long) has been received, the "RI" bit of SCON is set.

Hardware interrupt requests can be made when the TX shift register is empty or the RX shift register is full. The interrupt enable bits are located in the "interrupt enable" ("IE") register. When in the interrupt handler, this bit must be specifically reset (it is not reset automatically when the interrupt handler begins to execute, as the timer interrupt hardware does).

The asynchronous clocking scheme used in the "true" 8051 is a problem when an application is to use different asynchronous data rates. To help alleviate this, on Dallas Semiconductor HSM parts, the serial port has been modified to allow four different operating modes instead of the 8051's two. The two additional modes are designed to help the application designer run the 8051 at "standard" frequencies (i.e., multiples of 1 MHz) and use "standard" data rates.

Rather than using the instruction clock as the source for the serial data rate, these two additional modes use the overflow of Timer1 or Timer2 (if Timer2 is available).

For Timer1, the data rate is defined as:

```
DataRate = ( 1 + SMOD ) * Timer1OverflowRate / 32
```

or for Timer2:

```
DataRate = Timer2OverflowRate / 16
```

The second option is only available to serial port zero.

Now you're probably looking at this formula and wondering how you are going to get the timer overflow value.

By rearranging the formula:

```
Timer1OverflowRate = 32*DataRate / ( 1 + SMOD )
```

which is in the units of cycles/second (hertz). Inverting the formula to get the actual overflow interval, we get:

```
Timer1OverflowPeriod = ( 1 + SMOD ) / ( 32*DataRate )
```

Which is in seconds. But we want to get a time value in terms of clock cycles (which can be used to determine the value to load in the timer to get the overflow value):

```
Timer1OverflowCycles = ( 1 + SMOD )*ClockFrequency / ( 32*DataRate )
```

So, if we wanted 9600 bps in a 80C320 running at 12 MHz (and assuming SMOD is zero):

```
Timer1OverflowCycles = 12 MHz / ( 32 * 9600 bps )
                     = 39.063
```

A value of "39" will be used in Timer1 to determine the reload interval. To get the actual value, this value has to be taken away from 256 (the value in the Timer during an overflow). This means that 217 will be loaded into Timer1 to get 9600 bps in the 80C320.

With a cycle count of 39 being used rather than 39.063, there will be an error rate of 0.16%. This error rate is quite minuscule and over a 10-bit packet (assuming "8-N-1" data transmission) will have a total error of 1.6% from the computed center of the first bit.

Dallas Semiconductor Encrypted 8051

If you are data logging applications where access to the recorder may not be secure or if you are going to be shipping a product and there is the possibility of the code being pirated, you might want to consider using the Dallas Semiconductor line of secure 8051s ("DS5000"). These parts provide a method of scrambling both the data and program memory. If an attempt to read the encrypted data through the microcontroller is made, the data is automatically erased.

The encrypted parts use external SRAM chips for both control store and RAM above address 0FFh but still have the 8051's full 32 I/O pins (with peripheral features) available for the application. (See Figure 9.7.)

In Figure 9.7, there are a few things that you should be aware of. The first is that the device controls the power to the external SRAM. With an additional lithium battery, the external SRAM becomes an "NV-RAM" ("nonvolatile static" RAM), and its contents are not lost on power down. The encryption "keys" are kept inside microcontroller registers (if power is lost, so are the keys).

The program is downloaded into the DS5000 using a serial protocol. When the device first powers up, an initial boot program executes and looks for a programmer attached to

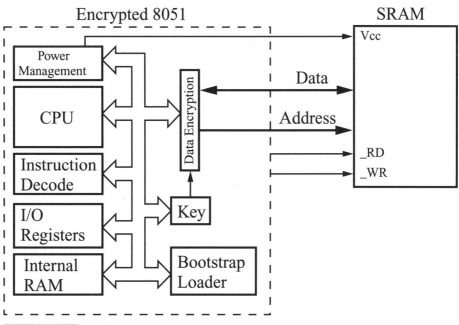

Figure 9.7 DS5000 block diagram with external encrypted memory.

the serial I/O pins. If there isn't any programmer attached to the device, execution is passed to the contents of the SRAM.

Dallas Semiconductor has made the encrypted 8051 chip available with an optional real-time clock as well as assembled chips, SRAMs, and lithium cells on a "SIMM"-like form factor. These assembled units are guaranteed to retain the information in the SRAMs for 19 years.

One of the interesting uses for the encrypted parts is to create a cheap emulator out of one of these parts. The emulator's memory would be used to store both the control software as well as the application being debugged. The design of the DS5000 parts would allow the full 32 I/O lines to be used in the application, even though external memory is with the microcontroller.

Programming

When I first looked at writing this subchapter, I was going to discuss programming the "true" 8051 and not any of the other manufacturer's versions of the 8051 that are available. As I researched to understand how different manufacturer's 8051s (actually 87C51 for the EPROM programmability), I discovered that there are a lot of different methods of programming, and that almost an entire book would have to be devoted to the subject.

The information provided here can be used to program an Intel 8751 and Dallas Semiconductor EPROM-based HSMs. For other devices with other algorithms, you should consult their data sheets before attempting to burn a program into them. You should also purchase a programmer capable of programming the device you want to use.

9

8051

When programming the 8051, a circuit has to be created for programming the device. With the 8751 and Dallas Semiconductor HSM parts, the circuit looks like Figure 9.8.

Each byte is set up with an address before it is written into the control store EPROM. (See Figure 9.9.)

The "ALE/Prog" pin is cycled five times for the EPROM write to take place. The crystal (which is in the range of 4.0 to 6.0 MHz) is used to make sure the bus is operating during the programming cycle to pass data through the microcontroller's busses. A 48-clock cycle wait is the specified time between programming bytes in the control store EPROM. At 4 MHz, this is 12 usecs.

To enter programming mode, reset must be high, _PSEN is low, and ALE is driven high, waiting for the command to toggle the data in.

MODE	ALE/PROG	_EA/VPP	P2.6	P2.7	P3.3	P3.6	P3.7
Pgm Code	Toggle 5x	+12.5V	0	1	1	1	1
Verify	+5V	+5V	0	0	0	1	1
Wrt Encrypt	Toggle 5x	+12.5V	0	1	1	0	1
Pgm Lock	Toggle	+12.5V					
Bit1		1	1	1	1	1	
Bit2		1	1	1	0	0	
Bit3		1	0	1	1	0	
Read Sig	+5V	+5V	0	0	0	0	0

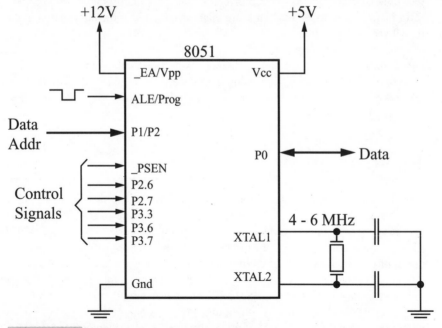

Figure 9.8 8051 programming connections.

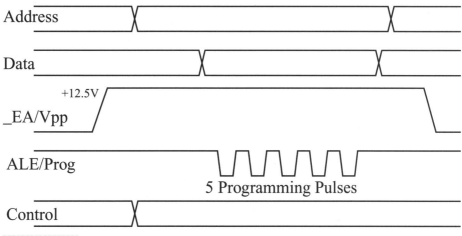

Figure 9.9 8051 programming waveform.

From the table on page 184, you can see that there are a number of things I haven't discussed yet about the 8051.

The first is the "encryption array." These 64 bytes of EPROM are used to change the memory values upon verify so that the program data cannot be read back easily.

The algorithm used to read back a byte is:

```
Output = Control( Address ) ^ !Encrypt( Address & 3Fh )
```

Where "control" is the EPROM control store array of instructions and "encrypt" is the 64-byte array (which only uses the lower 6 bits of the address).

There is one thing to notice with this scheme, and that's if areas of the EPROM are left unprogrammed (all ones), then the contents of the encryption EPROM can be read out directly. To avoid this, a pattern other than 0FFh should be stored in the remaining EPROM. Ideally, this code should not be repeating. I have done things like append source code, e-mail notes, or whatever to the end of the program source to provide random data. You could also repeat the program to the end of memory or put in an algorithmic value (which can be surprisingly easy, as is shown in "Appendix—Common Assembler Commands").

The "lock bits" are three EPROM bits used to specify how external memory is to operate and whether or not the control store Contents can be read back. By executing each of these commands, a single lock bit is programmed.

The lock bit operation is defined as:

LEVEL	LB1	LB2	LB3	MODE
1	U	U	U	All Bits Unprogrammed - No features Enabled
2	P	U	U	Prevents "movc" from Storing Internal Data to External Memory
3	P	P	U	Level 2 plus no verify readback and "movx" can't read internal SRAM
4	P	P	P	Level 3 plus no external program execution

The three signature bytes have addresses of 30h, 31h, and 60h and are used to read the type of device the microcontroller is during programming. Address 30h is used for the device's manufacturer (89h is Intel, 0DA is used for Dallas Semiconductor, and 1Eh is used for Atmel). Address 31h returns the "model number" for the device, and address 60h provides an extension to the "model number." For specific 8051-compatible microcontrollers, the device's data sheet must be consulted to get the signature information.

Ordering Information

Ordering any part is obviously specific to the manufacturer. In Figures 9.10 through 9.12, I have shown the 8051 part number specifications for Atmel parts.

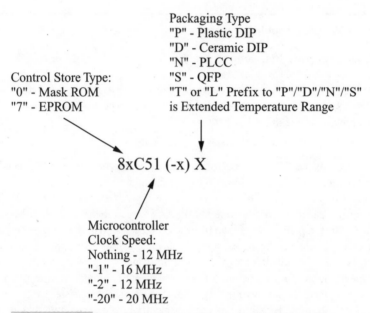

Packaging Type
"P" - Plastic DIP
"D" - Ceramic DIP
"N" - PLCC
"S" - QFP
"T" or "L" Prefix to "P"/"D"/"N"/"S"
is Extended Temperature Range

Control Store Type:
"0" - Mask ROM
"7" - EPROM

8xC51 (-x) X

Microcontroller
Clock Speed:
Nothing - 12 MHz
"-1" - 16 MHz
"-2" - 12 MHz
"-20" - 20 MHz

Figure 9.10 Intel 8051 part number ordering information.

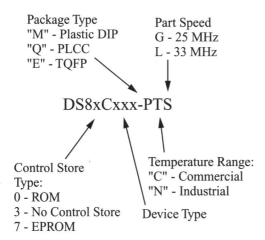

Package Type
"M" - Plastic DIP
"Q" - PLCC
"E" - TQFP

Part Speed
G - 25 MHz
L - 33 MHz

DS8xCxxx-PTS

Control Store
Type:
0 - ROM
3 - No Control Store
7 - EPROM

Temperature Range:
"C" - Commercial
"N" - Industrial

Device Type

Figure 9.11 Dallas Semiconductor high-speed microcontroller part number ordering information.

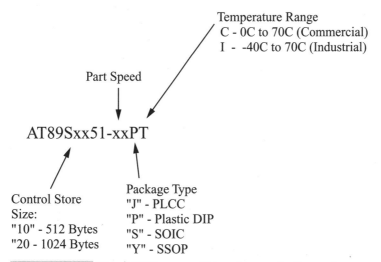

Temperature Range
C - 0C to 70C (Commercial)
I - -40C to 70C (Industrial)

Part Speed

AT89Sxx51-xxPT

Control Store
Size:
"10" - 512 Bytes
"20 - 1024 Bytes

Package Type
"J" - PLCC
"P" - Plastic DIP
"S" - SOIC
"Y" - SSOP

Figure 9.12 Atmel 8051 compatible microcontroller part number ordering information.

9

8051

8051 APPLICATION DESIGN

CONTENTS AT A GLANCE

Power Input

System Oscillators/Clocks

Reset

Interrupts

Instruction Storage

8051 RTOS and Monitor Program
Design

Developing 8051 applications is different from the other devices. This is not to say it is harder, just different. In many respects, the other microcontrollers are quite homogeneous, whereas the 8051 does things a bit differently. Personally, I like this because studying a device that works differently from others can give me ideas in solving problems with the other microcontrollers.

Power Input

With the wide number of different 8051s available from different manufacturers, you should be able to find an 8051 that works under just about any conditions or environment. In terms of extremes, you should be able to find an 8051 that will run in the hot/cold and "noisy" environment of a car engine or be powered by a single alkaline "AAA" battery for a child's toy.

A typical use of an 8051 (or any microcontroller) is to provide +5 volts to "Vcc" or "Vdd" and 0 volts to "Gnd" or "Vss." (Figure 10.1.)

A 0.1-uF capacitor should be placed physically very close to the Vcc pin with very short wires leading to the anode (positive pin) of the capacitor. The cathode of the capacitor is connected to the ground pin. This capacitor is known as a "decoupling capacitor" and is used to filter the power supply going into the chip during output transients and other instances of high current need.

That's it for hooking up power on most 8051s and just about any other microcontroller. If low voltage battery power is to be used in an application, then the same circuit will be used with the lower supply voltage.

What if you are planning to use a device that requires a more complex power arrangement? The only reply I can make to this is, find another microcontroller. There are too many devices available that don't require fancy power supplies; in fact, most microcontrollers will run quite happily with very "dirty" and "noisy" power supplies.

I realize that there may be specific applications in which one device may work better than others, but in this case you should be looking at specifying the device to the power, not the other way around. Power sourcing can be very crucial in an application; for this reason, you should be making it as robust and simple for all the active devices in the application.

System Oscillators/Clocks

Connecting an external crystal to an 8051 is quite simple with very few options. For a "parallel-cut" crystal (or a ceramic resonator without internal capacitors) the circuits shown in Figure 10.2 are used, or an external oscillator can be used (Figure 10.3).

What made the 8051 stand out initially was the very fast speeds it could run at (up to 20 MHz for the "stock" 8051). Now there are 8051 devices that are capable of running at 33 MHz and more. This fast clock speed was tempered somewhat by the number of clock cycles to run each instruction (this is discussed in the "8051 Architecture" chapter).

One interesting feature of the Dallas Semiconductor 8051 "high-speed microcontrollers" ("HSM") is the internal "ring oscillator," which runs between 2 and 4 MHz. This built-in oscillator is designed to reduce the power required by the microcontroller in sections of the application where the timing is noncritical.

There is something you should be aware of with the built-in ring oscillator, and that's the microcontroller's inability to power up using it. If you are going to use the ring oscillator exclusively, a crystal oscillator or external clock has to be provided to get the microcontroller running initially and be available for critically timed sections of the application.

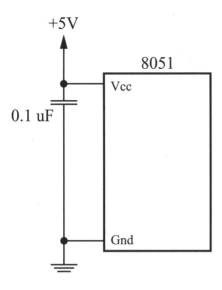

Figure 10.1 8051 power connections.

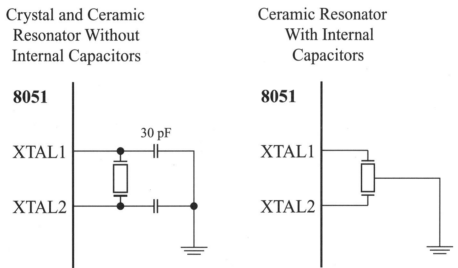

Figure 10.2 8051 crystal and ceramic resonator system oscillators.

Reset

Reset in the 8051 works differently than in any of the other microcontrollers presented in this book. Reset in the 8051 is positive active, which means that the processor runs when the reset pin is held low. This is in contrast to the other devices, which all have a negatively active reset (i.e., the microcontroller runs when the line is high).

Many of the 8051s available have an internal pull down and RC delay circuit built in to delay the processor's start up until the built-in oscillator's operation has stabilized. This means that for the most part, you'll be able to avoid having to put anything on the reset pin

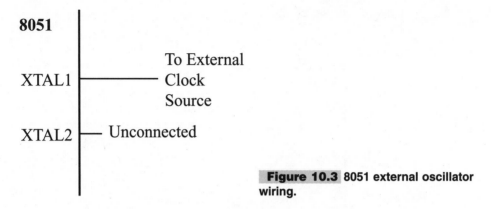

Figure 10.3 8051 external oscillator wiring.

(other than a switch connected to Vcc to allow you to reset the 8051 during debug). In the "true" (Intel) 8051s, you may have to connect a 0.1-uF capacitor to Vcc and reset to ensure that the microcontroller's execution will be held back long enough for the oscillator to stabilize. (Figure 10.4.)

Interrupts

I really thought long and hard about what I wanted to say about interrupts in the 8051 application design section, and I decided that I could summarize it in three words:

"Keep it short."

This is probably the best advice I can give you for any application and microcontroller. There are many reasons for this. In the 8051, if the interrupt handler can reside within the 8 bytes of the vector, you will have a pretty good program storage management and avoid the problems of having to do nested interrupts or relocating them.

The 8051's instruction set is rich enough that resetting an interrupt and setting a flag to indicate it happened can be kept well within 8 bytes (in the LCD clock/thermometer application, I was able to keep the interrupt handlers to 3 bytes each). For many interrupts, once the handler has begun to execute, the requesting hardware is reset, eliminating the need for you to reset the interrupt source yourself.

The 8051's architecture makes writing interrupt handlers the easiest of the devices presented here. By keeping any interrupt handler small to both execute in the fewest cycles and reside within the 8-byte interrupt location, you don't have to worry about whether or not nested handlers are required, resulting in a simplified application.

Instruction Storage

In the other Harvard-architected microcontrollers presented in this book (the PIC and AVR), the instruction length is constant (this is not quite true in the AVR, but most instructions are 16 bits long). This is not true at all for the 8051; the instructions can be 1, 2, or 3 bytes long.

While this may not seem like a significant issue, it can have serious ramifications on how much space is needed for the application software and how much time is taken by the program. This can ultimately make the application more difficult to implement. The 8051's control store space is only 8 bits wide, so putting the register operand of the instruction:

```
add A, Reg
```

in the current 8-byte bank, you can halve the number of bytes to store the instruction and cycles needed for executing it. To get the contents of "Reg" from elsewhere in the data space, the amount of memory and cycles saved is even more dramatic. For example, when accessing indexed data, using one of the bank's index registers can take five times or more instructions and cycles to execute the same operation, adding the contents of a register to the accumulator and storing the result back into the accumulator.

This means that carefully planning out how the program storage is implemented significantly improves the performance. I highly recommend that when planning out your 8051 mathematical operations, you must plan to use the data available in the current bank whenever possible.

8051 RTOS and Monitor Program Design

Real-time operating systems and monitor (also known as "debugger") program capability is not something most people investigate when first learning to use a microcontroller. This is unfortunate because I feel that understanding if and how these types of programs could work in a processor means that you understand the device well enough to write tools (which is what an RTOS and monitor program basically are) for others and have a superior understanding of the devices, which will allow you to take on just about any application given to you.

The 8051 is unusual and has the only processor architecture presented in this book that I would attempt implementing both an RTOS and debugger/monitor on. This is due to the 8051's available registers, very flexible stack, and ability to access external memory (as both control store and data). In this subchapter, I will show how these application tools can be implemented on the 8051 architecture.

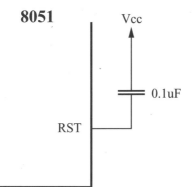

Figure 10.4 8051 reset with an external capacitor.

The most important concern about implementing an RTOS is understanding how to access the stack data. In some devices (i.e., the PIC) there is no way to access the data in the program counter stack (either reading or writing). In the 68HC05, the stack's contents can be accessed, but the actual stack value cannot be read from or written to. (Despite this, later in the book, I will show an RTOS that I have been able to implement on the 68HC05.)

The reason why you want to access a device's stack is to change tasks in an RTOS. The stack information (i.e., subroutine return address and context register information) is crucial to being able to restart the task at the point where it was stopped. The stack can be used as a repository for all of a task's information, which is usually easier to implement than with loading and unloading via an index register.

The 8051 consists of four 8-byte "banks" that can be used for very fast data accessing and processing. For an example RTOS, I would suggest that bank 0 be used for task-specific information and the PSW, accumulator, "B" register, DPTR, and SP registers be identified as task-specific context registers. All these registers would have to be saved in the task's specific information ("task information block").

Following this scheme, the 8051's data space would look like Figure 10.5.

In this scheme, 16 bytes would be used for a task information block. This would be made up of eight bank registers, the six SFR registers specified above, and two bytes for the return address. The 8-byte bank registers would contain RTOS request information, and the DPTR would point to a messaging block. With this scheme, four tasks could be saved in addresses 040h to 07Fh.

There is one problem with this proposed implementation: no tasks can call subroutines. This is because if the task is calling a subroutine and a hardware interrupt request is serviced, then more space will be required on the stack than available. To avoid this problem,

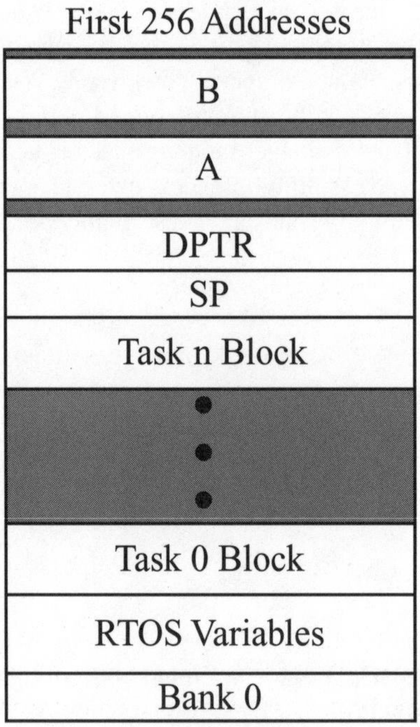

First 256 Addresses

Figure 10.5 Example 8051 RTOS memory organization.

in an actual implementation, you would increase the size of the task information block to allow subroutine return addresses and parameters to be saved on the stack.

This task block scheme recognizes that our "basic" 8051 only has 128 bytes of RAM available, and the low 64 bytes will be used for RTOS-specific data, messages, and task-specific information. When you read through "mykeRTOS" later in the book (in the 68HC05 section), you'll see that this actually leaves you with more resources than in the 68HC05J1A's "mykeRTOS" implementation.

Messaging would be carried out by "DPTR" and R0 of the Task 0 Bank. The DPTR message could either use the contents of DPL and DPH to store the message or what they point to as the message. "R0" would be a command byte telling the RTOS and receiving task what to do with the message.

If 128-RAM bytes are insufficient for your application, a device with up to 256 internal bytes of RAM could be used or external RAM could be added to the 8051. Note that if external memory is used, a stack area will have to be set up in the first 256 addresses and the data stored on it will have to be saved in the Task Information Block. The operation of copying data to and from a task information block will increase the number of cycles overhead that the RTOS will require for task switching.

To make a task request, the request and parameters would be loaded into the various registers, and then a label would be called as a subroutine.

The last part of the previous sentence may seem like a strange way of describing a subroutine. The reason why it's strange is that in this case, you are not calling a subroutine. You are actually jumping to the RTOS and saving the return address. The RTOS may appear to the tasks as subroutines, but in actuality the label will store the task information and switch to another task before "returning."

At the task request label, all the context information (the bank registers and special function registers identified above) would be "pushed" onto the task's stack, and then the stack pointer itself would be pushed onto the stack or saved in a specific location of the task information block. Following this, the stack pointer would be used as an offset to the task information to allow the RTOS to access different registers (which contain RTOS request and parameter information).

Switching to another task would be accomplished by retrieving the new task's stack pointer and "popping" the various registers before returning from the "subroutine."

I consider a monitor program to be a follow-on to an RTOS. This is to say that before you attempt to write a monitor program, you should understand how to write an RTOS. This might sound strange to you because a monitor works so much differently from an RTOS, but there are actually many concepts that are common to both types of applications (namely, executing a program from another one and monitoring its operation from a central piece of software).

One of the biggest issues for the monitor is its ability to update its own control store. The 8051 is actually well suited to this either by using the DS5000 encrypted (or "soft") microcontroller and updating the SRAM shared between the control store and data space. A "regular" 8051 could be used by connecting an external SRAM and ANDing the _PSEN and _RD lines to the SRAM's _OE pin.

Being able to update the program memory is important for two reasons. The first, and most obvious, is the need to be able to load new programs into the device without having to burn a device each time a change is to be tried out. The second (and less obvious) is the need to be able to put in "breakpoints" by writing a "call" instruction at the appropriate address while saving the original contents of the address. Like using a "call" instruction for the RTOS instructions, "call" should be used for breakpoints so the address of execution is made available on the stack.

It's really beyond the scope of what I want to do in this book to explain how a monitor program would be implemented. This is largely because of the different options available (i.e., running with an IDE on a PC or using a customer interface communicating with a "dumb" terminal). But understanding the concepts and knowing what's involved with the program's implementation will give you better insights on how to implement shared control store and data space memory as well as safely changing program execution.

8051 DEVELOPMENT TOOLS

CONTENTS AT A GLANCE

Assemblers

High-Level Languages

"S-Record" Object Files

Dallas Semiconductor DS87000
Programmer

The flip side of the coin of having many manufacturers for a device is that no one company is going to take a very strong interest in providing development tools for the device. The reasons for this should be pretty obvious; any tool you develop can be used on your competitor's product, and if you change your part to achieve some exclusivity, you are no longer compatible with the "standard" or "stock" part.

This means that for the 8051, there are not very good code development, simulator, and programming tools available for the 8051 (at least not to the level of Microchip's "MPLAB" or Atmel's "AVR Suite") that can be downloaded free of charge off the Internet when you want to investigate and evaluate a part.

These comments do not reflect on the many commercially available tools for the 8051. There are some really excellent tools available, and in this section I present one of them, the "UMPS" ("Universal MicroProcessor Simulator"). My comments are really directed toward the hobbyist or engineer who wants to "test drive" an application without having to pay for a program that may not be used again.

Assemblers

To program, the 8051 is much more similar to a 68HC05 than an Intel 8080 or 8086. In a "typical" Intel microprocessor, you would have an instruction that looked like:

```
add    A, B
```

which would operate like:

```
A = A + B
```

This is not as pervasive in the 8051 as in the microprocessors because of the extra space needed for storing the instruction and the addresses of the operands. Instead the data is processed through the accumulator (but the same format is still used as described in the "8051 Instructions" chapter).

In the "8051 Instructions" chapter, when I discuss the operation of the different jumping addressing modes, I just want to point out that when you use an assembler, you should have an understanding of how jump addressing ("small," "page," or "long") is implemented.

When writing 8051 assembler code, there are a number of things to watch and plan for. While I've covered most of these items elsewhere in this section, I thought it would be a good idea to review them.

1. **Reset** is at address 000h, and the 8-byte interrupt address/handler blocks immediately follow. Chances are, your first instruction will be a jump to the mainline code.
2. **Design** your code so that it works out of a single 8-byte register bank as much as possible. This will reduce program space and cycle overhead.
3. **Variables** that are often accessed should be located in the first 256 addresses (again, to speed up program execution and reduce the number of bytes needed to store the program).
4. **If** at all possible, design your interrupt handlers to execute within 8 bytes and simply place these 8 bytes in the appropriate interrupt handler block.
5. **When** executing "timed access" code, make sure interrupts are disabled. An interrupt during the 055h/0AAh write will cause problems.
6. **If** using "immediate addressing" on an instruction, make sure a "#" character is in front of the constant, else the constant value will be interpreted as an address in the first 256 addresses.

The above list is really a set of rules to follow when developing your application in order to minimize the problems you will have debugging later.

As for additional information on writing 8051 assembler code, it is really assembler specific. The code formats used for different assemblers are actually pretty generic, but specific commands may have to be entered for proper operation of the assembler. For example, when developing the 8051 example applications for this book, I assembled the code using the "UMPS" assembler and a freeware assembler from the Internet. The code was not directly usable or common between the two assemblers; commands had to be changed for the source file to assemble cleanly between the two programs.

High-Level Languages

The 8051 architecture is interesting because of the extremes it works with. The 8051 is probably the most difficult architecture presented in this book to create a high-level language compiler that produces the simplest, smallest, and fastest assembler code for arithmetic operations and it's the easiest for writing a compiler that will allow efficiently manipulating large blocks of data. These two aspects are not necessarily mutually exclusive, but they will affect how the compiler operates.

Ideally, an 8051 application should run all its arithmetic operations out of the current 8-byte bank and the accumulator. Keeping all variables within a single bank will result in the smallest and fastest code. If code has to be moved in and out of the active register banks the code will become very clumsy very quickly.

For example:

```
VarA = VarB + C   ;  "VarA" and "VarB" variables are NOT
                  ;    the Accumulator and "B" register.
```

If all three variables were in the current bank, the code could be:

```
mov     A, VarB   ;  1 Byte/12 Cycles
add     A, C      ;  1 Byte/12 Cycles
mov     VarA, A   ;  1 Byte/12 Cycles
```

Now, if "VarA," "VarB," and "C" were all in the first 256 addresses (but not in the same bank), the code would change to using "direct" addressing on each of the three instructions. This new code would take twice as many cycles and take up twice as many bytes of control store.

If "VarA," "VarB," and "C" were located anywhere within the 64K data area, the best code that could be written would be:

```
mov     DPTR, VarC   ;  3 Bytes/24 Cycles
movxA, @DPTR         ;  1 Byte/24 Cycles  - Load "C"
mov     Temp, A      ;  1 Byte/12 Cycles  - Save "C"
mov     DPTR, VarB   ;  3 Bytes/24 Cycles
movxA, @DPTR         ;  1 Byte/24 Cycles  - Load "B"
add     A, Temp      ;  1 Byte/12 Cycles  - Acc = B + C
mov     DPTR, VarA   ;  3 Bytes/24 Cycles
movx@DPTR, A         ;  1 Byte/24 Cycles  - Save B + C in "VarA"
```

The general case shown above requires more than three times the memory and over four times the cycles to execute over the "best" case of using three variables in the currently active bank.

With this wide variance in performance, it is definitely worth the compiler writer's time to develop a strategy of how data is to be manipulated. By reducing data movement to and from the current bank, the first 256 addresses and the 64K data area, the final program can be made much more efficient.

Some strategies for carrying this out include keeping arithmetic variables grouped in banks and then switching between banks to operate on the data directly. Another strategy could be grouping all the arithmetic variables in the same block of memory, the start of which is pointed to by the DPTR or one of the two index registers in the current bank. In the latter case, data could be accessed using the index registers much faster and using less space than if it were moved into temporary registers in the current bank.

The ability of the DPTR to access memory across the entire 64K data space and the availability of instructions to update the register quickly means that the large amounts of data can be accessed quickly. While data structures are really beyond the scope of this book, looking back over the instructions should give you some ideas of how to store data in blocks that are pointed to by the DPTR and can be accessed with offsets from the DPTR address.

This capability makes the 8051 ideally suited for implementing data loggers and collection devices, simple terminal data switches, and other applications where large amounts of data must be manipulated within the device quickly.

"INHX8M" Object Files

The Intel "INHX8M" is the most common object file format; in fact, pretty well all embedded microcontrollers use this object file format (which is also referred to as a ".hex" file). In this book, along with the 8051, the PIC and the AVR use this object file format.

If you were to look at a ".hex" file that was produced by an assembler or compiler, you would see something like the file below, which was created for a PIC application:

```
:10000000A601A701AB018E288C00030883128D0086
:100010000B11AB0A0D0883008C0E0C0E0900A80111
:10002000A201A3011E081F04031908001F082106CE

    :

:0A04F000A40B782AA50B782A080057
:02400E00F13F80
:00000001FF
```

All the information needed to load the microcontroller's control store is located in this file. You should note that no symbolic information is located in this file (that is usually produced by the compiler or assembler specifically for a specific debugger or emulator).

Each line is broken up into a number of fields, which are used to specify to the programmer or wherever the file is going to be used. The fields are defined by columns and are defined as:

COLUMNS	IDENTIFIER	COMMENTS
1	Line Start	Always ":"
2-3	2* Bytes in Line	Two Times Number of Bytes to be loaded
4-7	Data Start Addr	The Address where the Data will be stored
8-9	Data Type	"00" - Data, "01" - File End
10-11	2nd Byte in Data	Each Byte is represented as hex value, in LSByte 1st
12-13	1st Byte in Data	
14...	Program Data	Additional Bytes of Program Data
End-2	Check Sum	Line Total & 0x0FF = 0

Typically, up to eight 16-bit words can be stored on each line. If we were to take the third last line in the example above, we can break up the data and show what is actually in it.

Columns 2–3 are "0A," which is two times the number of 16-bit words in the line. In this case, there are five words.

Columns 4-7 are "04F0," which is the address the data is to be written at. Note that this 16-bit number does not use Intel byte ordering; instead, the high byte appears before the low byte.

The next two columns are both "0," which indicates that data is being sent in the line.

Starting at column 10 are five 16-bit words of program data:

```
0BA4
2A78
0BA5
2A78
0008
```

The last two columns are the checksum. You've probably noticed that each data byte is broken up into two hex characters. These values are added up, subtracted from 0x0100, and the result is used for the checksum.

For the example above, the data bytes are summed as:

```
  0A
  04
  F0
  00
  A4
  0B
  78
  2A
  A5
  0B
  78
  2A
  08
+00
——-
 3A9
```

This sum is then ANDed with 0x0FF and subtracted from 0x0100 to get the checksum:

```
 100
 -A9    (= 0x03A9 & 0x0FF)
——-
  57
```

If you look above, you'll see that "57" is the last two columns of this line.

The last line looks pretty boring (just the data type set to 1 and a checksum of FF), but this is all that's required to indicate that the object file is ended.

Dallas Semiconductor DS87000 Programmer

To program the Dallas Semiconductor 87C520s used in the applications, I used the Dallas Semiconductor DS87000 programmer (Figure 11.1). This device connects to a PC via a serial port and uses the PC to download object code from ".hex" files and control the operation of the programmer. This programmer can be used for all "true" 8051s using the programming algorithm described elsewhere in this section.

When I got the programmer working, it really worked very well, although I had two main difficulties with the package. The program software for the PC was located on a 5.25" diskette. I don't know what your PC is like, but I consider 5.25" diskettes to be a relic of the early days of personal computing (not to mention something that is very dangerous to play Frisbee with, but that's another story), and I really just focus on electronically transferring data. In the rare cases where the target PC isn't attached to a network, I rely on using 3.5" or recordable CD-ROMs for transferring data between PCs.

With this type of attitude, you can imagine that I had problems finding a PC with both a 5.25" drive and a 3.5" drive. Actually, I was never able to do it. But I did find an old IBM PC/AT with a 5.25" drive that I could connect up to a laptop using a null modem cable. To save you the same problem if you decide to go with the DS87000, I have included the "DS87000.EXE" PC Control program on the CD-ROM.

The second problem was a result of the 25-pin D-shell RS-232 connector provided for attaching to a PC. This connector is attached to a RJ-11-terminated phone cable for connecting the PC to the programmer. Like the 5.25" diskette, my PC uses 9-pin D-shell connectors. And, like the 5.25" diskette, none of the PCs I have access to just have 25-pin D-shell serial connectors. My original plan was to use 9 to 25 D-shell converters and gender changers, but this didn't work out for me and became very complex.

Instead, I got a female D-shell connector with an integrated RJ-11 connector and wired it to match the 25 pin D-shell as is shown in Figure 11.2.

Figure 11.1 Dallas Semiconductor DS87000 HSM programmer.

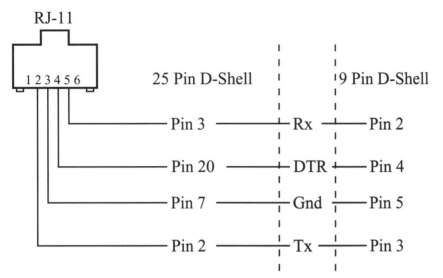

Figure 11.2 Dallas Semiconductor DS87000 HSM programmer 9-pin D-shell cabling.

With this wiring done, the programmer worked like a charm. The PC's screen allows you to select the port to be used with the programmer as well as downloading the data with a variety of options (including serializing each part programmed) and a script facility for repetitive programming. The programming software also allows you to select how many bytes of the 87C520's EPROM are to be programmed, read, or verified. If, for no other reason, the amount of EPROM burned should be the same size as the program to keep the programming time to a minimum (although the devices are programmed very quickly).

11

8051

8051 INSTRUCTION SET

CONTENTS AT A GLANCE

All three of the Harvard-architected microcontrollers presented in this book execute instructions differently. In each microcontroller (the 8051, PIC, and AVR), a different way of thinking will have to be applied in how programs are structured to efficiently move and manipulate data.

You may be surprised to discover that the 8051 instructions execute very similarly to the 68HC05; data has to be first stored in an accumulator before operating on it. I would strongly urge you to look at the "8051 Architecture" chapter before reading through the instruction set to understand such concepts as data banks and addressing before you will be able to really understand how the different instructions operate.

One thing that you will notice in the "Arithmetic," "Bit Operators," and "Data Movement Instructions" subchapters is that I have lumped instructions together even if they use different addressing modes (which, in some cases causes an extra instruction cycle). In doing this, I am able to pare down the 101 op codes of the 8051 to 62.

For the 8051's instructions for "Indirect" addressing, I have indicated the index register (either R0 or R1 of the current bank) with an "i" (i = 0 for R0 and i = 1 for R1). For "register" addressing, "rrr" is used to specify which register is being accessed within the bank.

Data Movement Instructions

Before you can begin to process data, you have to understand how to move it within the microcontroller (and in the 8051's case especially, how to access external memory). The 8051 has a number of instructions for transferring data within (and without) the device.

One of the most important aspects of the 8051 that you will have to understand is the instruction format and conventions. The typical data movement (and arithmetic) instructions are in the format:

```
ins    Parm1, Parm2
```

"Parm1" is the destination of the operation's result and the optional first parameter of the operation. "Parm2" is generally a value brought into the instruction.

This means:

```
mov    A, R0
```

executes as:

```
A = R0
```

and

```
add    A, R0
```

executes as:

```
A = A + R0
```

The AVR uses this instruction format, whereas the 68HC05 never has two parameters in an instruction, and the PIC operates somewhat differently, with the result of an operation optionally stored in the PIC's accumulator (or "w" register). For the AVR, the same "right to left" data movement convention is used.

When you see "A" in the 8051's instruction set, this means the accumulator ("ACC" at address 0E0h). The "A" register is actually part of the instruction and cannot be replaced with another register. If there is only one direct address parameter in an instruction, "ACC" will have to be explicitly specified rather than just "A" (in fact, just putting in "A" for a parameter will result in a syntax error when the code is assembled).

With this background, you should have a good idea how the "mov A, operand" instruction works (Instruction 12.1). For each of the four addressing modes (immediate, register, indirect, and direct), the operand is copied into the accumulator.

The same goes for the "mov operand, A" instructions (Instruction 12.2). The contents of the accumulator are copied into the operand (addressed as a register as an 8-bit direct address or an 8-bit indirect address).

"Mov Operand1, Operand2" (Instructions 12.3 and 12.4) are used to pass data without using the accumulator as an intermediate step (i.e., using the two instructions "mov A, Operand2"/"mov Operand1, A").

The "mov C, bit" and "mov bit, C" instructions (Instructions 12.5 and 12.6) are useful for getting and storing individual bits without affecting other bits in a register.

If you look at the bit pattern, you'll notice that 8 bits are available for addressing. But when I described the 8051's architecture, I pointed out that there were 128 general-purpose bits located at address 020h to 02Fh (which only requires 7 bits for addressing). When bit 7 of the bit address is set (in these and the bit instructions), bits in the special function register space are accessed. These bits are in the ACC, PSW, B, P0, P1, P2, and P3 registers primarily.

So, to retrieve the least-significant bit from P1, the instruction:

```
mov C, P1.0
```

is used where the digit after the period (".") after "P1" is the bit number.

How useful are these instructions? If you compare the 8051's "Ap1" code to any other microcontrollers, you'll see how simple it is to transfer the logic level at the button to the LED.

Indexed addressing into the 64K data space can use either a bank index register ("R0" or "R1" in the current 8-byte register bank) or the DPTR register using the "mov" and "movx" instructions (Instructions 12.7, 12.8, and 12.9). If a "true" 8051 is used, the external address starts at 00080h and as discussed elsewhere, some 8051s have 256 internal RAM bytes that are accessed internally using index registers. When the "Ri" register is used, only the first 256 addresses can be accessed. When "DPTR" is used for the index, then the entire 64K data space can be accessed.

Loading the two 8-bit index registers in the current bank is as simple as "Mov Rn, #Const," and loading the 16-bit DPTR register can be done in a similar manner with the "mov DPTR, #Const" instruction (Instruction 12.10).

There are two other forms of the indexed address instruction. The first is the stack operations "push" and "pop" (Instructions 12.11 and 12.12). These two instructions work as you would probably expect except that the instructions:

```
push A
```

and

```
pop A
```

are invalid and will return an assembly error. These are the single parameter instructions I was referencing above.

These instructions operate on a direct address (rather than an implied one such as the accumulator), so the correct format for pushing and popping the accumulator is:

```
push ACC
```

and

```
pop ACC
```

Tables can be implemented easily using the "movc A, @A+Index" instructions (Instruction 12.13). If the program counter is used as the index register, the accumulator will be loaded from control store. When "DPTR" is specified as the index register, the data is loaded from the 64K data space.

12

8051

To implement a table read from control store (i.e., reading a message), the following code could be used:

```
ReadTable:                 ;   Return the Offset in ACC in "Table"

    add        A, #(Table-GetTable)
    movc       A,
GetTable:                  ;   Get the Offset at "A" plus
    ret                    ;   Return to the caller

Table:                     ;   The Table Elements are located here
    db         'H'
    db         'e'
    db         'l'
    db         'l'
    db         'o'
    db         0           ;   ASCIIZ String End
```

The last two data movement instructions are the exchange instructions ("xch" and "xchd," Instructions 12.14 and 12.15). The "xch A, Operand" instruction exhanges the contents of the accumulator with the specified register. Its operation can be modelled as:

```
Temp = ACC
ACC = Operand
Operand = Temp
```

"Xchd A, @Ri" executes in a similar manner to "xch" except that only a bank index register can be used to specify the operand register's address and only the lower four bits of the two registers are exchanged.

Instruction: "mov A, Operand"

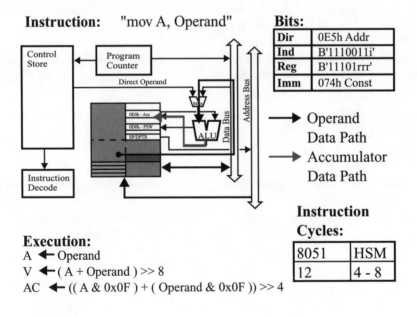

Bits:

Dir	0E5h Addr
Ind	B'1110011i'
Reg	B'11101rrr'
Imm	074h Const

→ Operand Data Path

→ Accumulator Data Path

Instruction Cycles:

8051	HSM
12	4 - 8

Execution:

A ← Operand

V ← (A + Operand) >> 8

AC ← ((A & 0x0F) + (Operand & 0x0F)) >> 4

Example:

mov A, #123

MCU: 8051

; Put 123 into the Acc

Instruction 12.1 8051 mov A, operand instruction.

Instruction: "mov Operand, A"

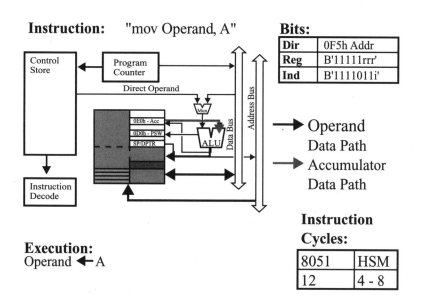

Bits:

Dir	0F5h Addr
Reg	B'11111rrr'
Ind	B'1111011i'

➡ Operand
  Data Path
➡ Accumulator
  Data Path

Execution:
Operand ← A

Instruction Cycles:

8051	HSM
12	4 - 8

Example: **MCU:** 8051

mov A, #123   ;   Put 123 into "R2"
mov R2, A

Instruction 12.2 8051 mov operand, A instruction.

Instruction: "mov Direct, Oprnd"

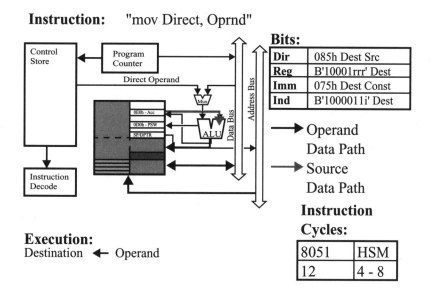

Bits:

Dir	085h Dest Src
Reg	B'10001rrr' Dest
Imm	075h Dest Const
Ind	B'1000011i' Dest

➡ Operand
  Data Path
➡ Source
  Data Path

Execution:
Destination ← Operand

Instruction Cycles:

8051	HSM
12	4 - 8

Example: **MCU:** 8051

mov B, #123   ;   Put 123 into "B"

Instruction 12.3 8051 mov direct instruction.

Instruction: "mov Rn, Oprnd"

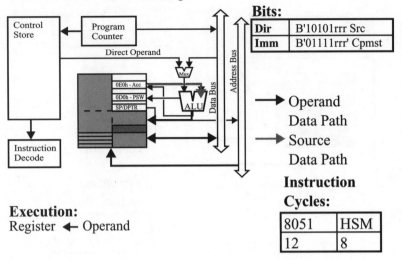

Bits:

Dir	B'10101rrr Src
Imm	B'01111rrr' Cpmst

→ Operand
  Data Path

→ Source
  Data Path

Instruction Cycles:

8051	HSM
12	8

Execution:
Register ← Operand

Example:

mov R2, #123

MCU: 8051

;   Put 123 into R2

Instruction 12.4 8051 mov Rn, operand instruction.

Instruction: "mov C, Bit"

Bits: 0A2h Bit

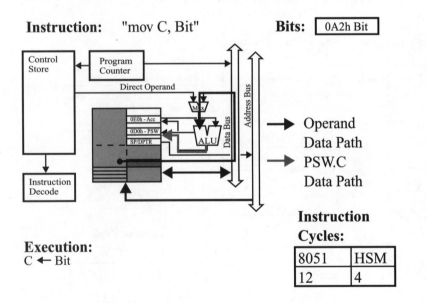

→ Operand
  Data Path

→ PSW.C
  Data Path

Instruction Cycles:

8051	HSM
12	4

Execution:
C ← Bit

Example:

mov C, P0.7
mov P2.6, C

MCU: 8051

;   Move P0.7 to P2.6

Instruction 12.5 8051 mov C, bit instruction.

Instruction: "mov Bit, C" **Bits:** | 092h Bit |

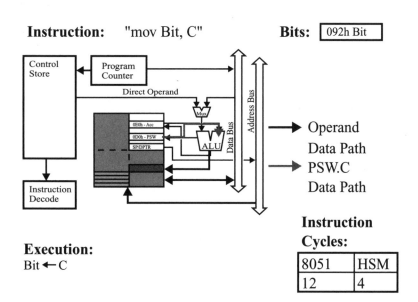

Operand
Data Path
PSW.C
Data Path

Instruction Cycles:

Execution:
Bit ← C

8051	HSM
12	4

Example: **MCU:** 8051

mov C, P0.7   ;   Move P0.7 to P2.6
mov P2.6, C

Instruction 12.6 8051 mov bit, C instruction.

Instruction: "mov @Ri, Operand"

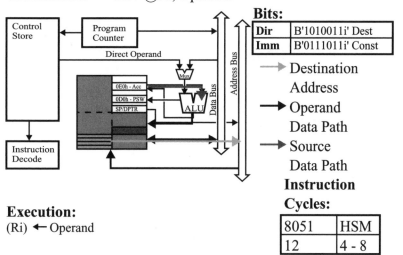

Bits:
Dir	B'1010011i' Dest
Imm	B'0111011i' Const

Destination
Address
Operand
Data Path
Source
Data Path

Instruction Cycles:

Execution:
(Ri) ← Operand

8051	HSM
12	4 - 8

Example: **MCU:** 8051

mov @R0, #123   ;   Put 123 into Byte Pointed
                     ;   to by R0

Instruction 12.7 8051 mov @Ri, operand instruction.

Instruction: "movx A, @Index"

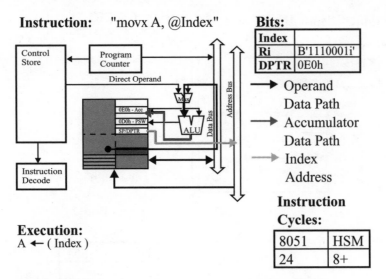

Bits:

Index	
Ri	B'1110001i'
DPTR	0E0h

➤ Operand
  Data Path

➤ Accumulator
  Data Path

➤ Index
  Address

Instruction Cycles:

8051	HSM
24	8+

Execution:
A ← (Index)

MCU: 8051

Example:

mov DPTR, Buffer   ;   Read from the Start
mov A, @DPTR   ;   of the Buffer

Note: When "DPTR" is used as the Index, the
          Data Read may be altered by "Wait" States.

Instruction 12.8 8051 movx A, @index instruction.

Instruction: "movx @Index, A"

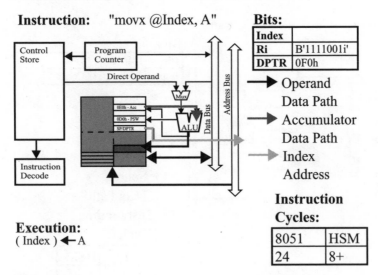

Bits:

Index	
Ri	B'1111001i'
DPTR	0F0h

➤ Operand
  Data Path

➤ Accumulator
  Data Path

➤ Index
  Address

Instruction Cycles:

8051	HSM
24	8+

Execution:
(Index) ← A

MCU: 8051

Example:

mov DPTR, Buffer   ;   Write to the Start
mov @DPTR, A   ;   of the Buffer

Note: When "DPTR" is used as the Index, the
          Data Read may be altered by "Wait" States.

Instruction 12.9 8051 movx @index, A instruction.

Instruction: "mov DPTR, Const

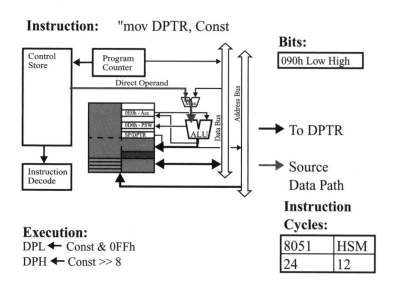

Bits:

| 090h Low High |

To DPTR

Source
Data Path

Instruction
Cycles:

8051	HSM
24	12

Execution:
DPL ← Const & 0FFh
DPH ← Const >> 8

Example: **MCU:** 8051

mov DPTR, ButStart   ;   Set DPTR to Start of
                                       ;   the Buffer

Instruction 12.10 8051 mov DPTR, const instruction.

Instruction: "push direct"   **Bits:** | 0C0h Addr |

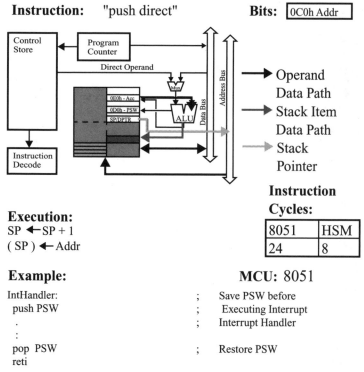

Operand
Data Path
Stack Item
Data Path
Stack
Pointer

Instruction
Cycles:

8051	HSM
24	8

Execution:
SP ← SP + 1
(SP) ← Addr

Example: **MCU:** 8051

IntHandler: ;   Save PSW before
  push PSW   ;   Executing Interrupt
  .   ;   Interrupt Handler
  :
  pop PSW   ;   Restore PSW
  reti

Instruction 12.11 8051 push direct instruction.

12

8051

Instruction: "pop direct"   **Bits:** ODOh Addr

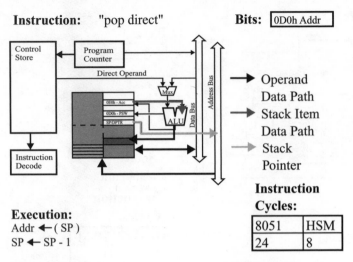

Execution:
Addr ← (SP)
SP ← SP - 1

Instruction Cycles:

8051	HSM
24	8

Example: **MCU:** 8051

IntHandler:	;	Save PSW before
push PSW	;	Executing Interrupt
.	;	Interrupt Handler
:		
pop PSW	;	Restore PSW
reti		

Instruction 12.12 8051 pop direct instruction.

Instruction: "movc A, @A+Index"

Index	Bits
DPTR	093h
PC	083h

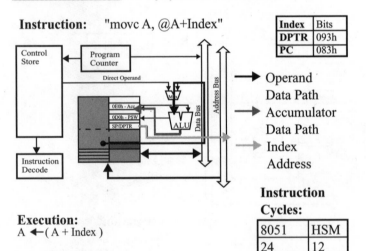

Execution:
A ← (A + Index)

Instruction Cycles:

8051	HSM
24	12

Example: **MCU:** 8051

mov DPTR, Buffer	;	Read from the Third
mov A, #2	;	Byte in the Buffer
movc A, @A+DPTR	;	Located in 64K
	;	Memory Space

Note: When "DPTR" is used as the Index, Data
Memory is Read. When "PC" is used, then
Control Store is Read.

Instruction 12.13 8051 movc A, @A+index instruction.

Instruction: "xch A, Operand"

Bits:

Dir	0C5h Addr
Ind	B'1100011i'
Reg	B'11001rrr'

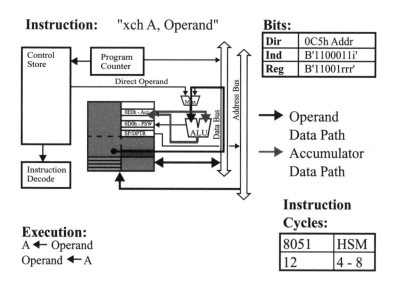

Operand
Data Path

Accumulator
Data Path

Execution:
A ← Operand
Operand ← A

Instruction Cycles:

8051	HSM
12	4 - 8

Example: **MCU:** 8051

xch A, P1   ; Swap Contents of A and
                             ; Port1

Instruction 12.14 8051 xch A, operand instruction.

Instruction: "xchd A, Operand"

Bits:

Ind	B'1101011i'

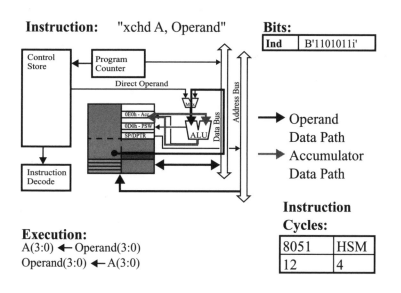

Operand
Data Path

Accumulator
Data Path

Execution:
A(3:0) ← Operand(3:0)
Operand(3:0) ← A(3:0)

Instruction Cycles:

8051	HSM
12	4

Example: **MCU:** 8051

xchd A, TL0   ; Swap Low 4 Bits of A and
                             ; Timer0 Low Byte

Instruction 12.15 8051 xchd A, operand instruction.

Arithmetic Instructions

The 8051 really has a very complete set of arithmetic instructions even when compared to the other microcontrollers. This may be surprising to you because the 8051 has fewer arithmetic instructions than in some of the others, but a very complete set of functions can be implemented in the 8051.

Addition (Instruction 12.16) is very straightforward in the 8051 with the operand added to the contents of the accumulator. As I have pointed out elsewhere in this section, there is no zero flag available in the 8051's status register (the "PSW"). So, if a "jz" or "jnz" instruction is going to execute based on the result of an operation, that result has to be in the accumulator before the conditional jumps are executed.

The "addc" instruction (Instruction 12.17) is an addition instruction in which the carry flag is added to the result. This instruction is used to allow addition of 16-bit and larger numbers. For example, adding two 16-bit values in the current bank (or even the first 256 addresses) would be:

```
mov   A, VarB     ;   VarB = VarB + C
add   A, C        ;   Add the Low 8 Bits First
mov   VarB, A     ;   Store the Low 8 Bit Result
mov   A, VarB+1   ;   Add the Higher 8 Bits
addc  A, C+1
mov   VarB+1, A
```

The subtraction instruction, "Subb" (Instruction 12.18), is really a subtract with carry (which is used as a borrow flag). This means that you must be aware of the carry flag at all times the "subb" instruction is used. This shows how subtracting two 16-bit values is implemented:

```
mov   A, VarB     ;   VarB = VarB - C
clr   C           ;   Clear Carry before Subtraction
subb  A,C         ;   Subtract the Low 8 Bits
mov   VarB, A
mov   A+1         ;   Subtract the High 8 Bits
subb  A, C+1
mov   VarB+1, A
```

Incrementing and decrementing (Instructions 12.19 and 12.20) in the 8051 is very straightforward, with no PSW bits being changed by the result. As well as the register, direct, and indirect addressing modes, the accumulator can be operated upon directly.

As you go through later sections on other microcontrollers, you'll see that the zero flag of the status register is integral for performing basic operations like a 16-bit increment. In the 8051, this can be carried out in a similar manner, but it's important to remember that it is the result for testing zero on (when the lower 8 bits of a number are equal to zero after an increment, the upper 8 bits have to be incremented as if the carry flag were set from the lower 8-bit increment).

```
inc   Var          ;   Increment the Lower 8 Bits
xch   A,Var
cjne  A,#0,incSkip ;   The Lower 8 Bits are Not equal to zero
  inc Var+1         ;    Increment the High 8 Bits
```

```
incSkip:
   xch   Var,A              ;  Save the result of the Lower 8 Bit increment
```

A 16-bit decrement requires using the "subb" instruction instead of the "decrement" to set the carry/borrow "flag" when the lower 8 bits have gone from 0 to 0FFh (which requires a decrement of the upper 8 bits):

```
   mov   A, Var    ;  Decrement the Lower 8 Bits
   clr   C
   subb  A, #1
   mov   Var, A
   jnc   decSkip   ;  If Carry Set, then Decrement the Upper 8 Bits
    dec  Var+1
decSkip:
```

I've separated "inc DPTR" (Instruction 12.21) from the increment/decrement instructions because it operates on the 16-bit "DPTR" register (which is made up of the "DPL" and "DPH" special function registers). Unfortunately, there isn't a "dec DPTR" instruction that goes along with this one.

But the "dec DPTR" can be simulated with the following code:

```
   dec   DPL             ;  Decrement the Low 8 Bits
   xch   A,DPL           ;  Put the Value in "Acc" to Test it
   cjne  A,#0FFh,Skip    ;  Do we Have 0FFh after Decrement?
    dec  DPH             ;  Yes, Decrement the High 8 Bits
Skip:
   xch   A,DPL           ;  Replace DPL
```

"DA A" (Instruction 12.22) is executed after an add or subtract of two BCD (binary coded decimal) values. A "BCD" number is defined as "0" to "9" in each of the two nybbles of a byte. After executing "DA A," the contents of the accumulator are valid BCD and the carry flag is set appropriately for the next BCD operation (i.e., if two 16-bit (4-digit) numbers are added together).

A few notes on "DA A." The first is, "DA A" does not work correctly after subtraction. For BCD in the 8051, there is no way to indicate negative values (so there is no easy way to subtract BCD values). Finally, "DA A" is not used to convert a hex byte to a BCD value.

The "mul AB" instruction (Instruction 12.23) will multiply two 8-bit numbers together (which were stored in the accumulator and "B" register). The result is 16 bits long and is stored back into the accumulator (low byte) and "B" (high byte). This hardware multiplication is quite fast and can be used for implementing audio frequency signal DSP functions on the 8051.

If you were to use the "mul AB" instruction to multiply two 16-bit numbers, note that to get the correct result, the following formula is used:

```
Result = ( VarB * VarC ) + (( VarB+1 * VarC ) * 0100h ) +
         (( VarB * VarC+1 ) * 0100h ) + (( VarB+1 * VarC+1 ) * 010000h )
```

where "VarB" and "VarC" are two 16-bit variables that are to be multiplied together. This formula will ensure that the correct 32-bit result will be produced.

Hopefully, the formula won't look too imposing; it is actually quite easy to implement as assembler code. Multiplying values by 0100h or 010000h is really just shifting the results

12

8051

up by 8 or 16 bits (which means putting them in specific byte positions of the 32-bit (4-byte) result).

The "div AB" instruction (Instruction 12.24) divides the contents of the accumulator by the contents of the "B" register. The quotient is put into "A," and the remainder is put into "B."

This instruction is probably most useful for data conversion. For example, converting a byte into a 3-digit decimal number could be accomplished by:

```
mov    A, Number      ;  Store the Number
mov    B, #100        ;  want to Get the Hundreds and Remainders
div    AB
mov    Hundreds, A    ;  Store the Hundreds of the Number
mov    A, B           ;  Repeat for tens and ones
mov    B, #10
div    AB
mov    Tens, A        ;  Store the Tens of the Number
mov    Ones, B        ;  Store the Ones of the Number
```

This can be compared to the code used by the other microcontrollers to do time/ temperature conversions in the second of the example applications. This code runs much faster, is simpler, and takes up less space.

In Intel's 8051 documentation, it is suggested that "div AB" be used as a fast multiple shift-right instruction. Personally, I wouldn't use it for that purpose because it cannot be used easily for 16-bit numbers (which is what I find I'm often shifting), but it could be very effective carrying out a virtual shift on single bytes.

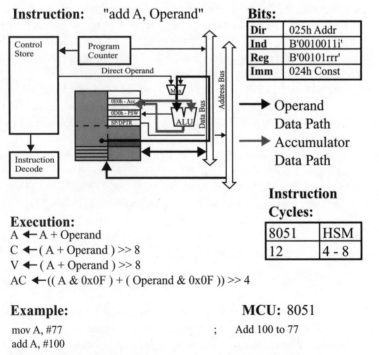

Instruction: "add A, Operand"

Bits:

Dir	025h Addr
Ind	B'00100011i'
Reg	B'00101rrr'
Imm	024h Const

Operand
Data Path
Accumulator
Data Path

Instruction Cycles:

8051	HSM
12	4 - 8

Execution:

$A \leftarrow A + \text{Operand}$
$C \leftarrow (A + \text{Operand}) \gg 8$
$V \leftarrow (A + \text{Operand}) \gg 8$
$AC \leftarrow ((A \ \& \ 0x0F) + (\text{Operand} \ \& \ 0x0F)) \gg 4$

Example: **MCU:** 8051

mov A, #77   ;   Add 100 to 77
add A, #100

Instruction 12.16 8051 add A, operand instruction.

Instruction: "addc A, Operand"

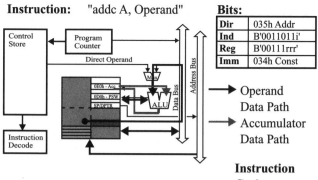

Bits:

Dir	035h Addr
Ind	B'0011011i'
Reg	B'00111rrr'
Imm	034h Const

→ Operand
Data Path
→ Accumulator
Data Path

Instruction Cycles:

8051	HSM
12	4 - 8

Execution:

$A \leftarrow A + Operand + C$

$C \leftarrow (A + Operand + C) \gg 8$

$V \leftarrow (A + Operand + C) \gg 8$

$AC \leftarrow ((A \& 0x0F) + (Operand \& 0x0F) + C) \gg 4$

Example: **MCU:** 8051

```
mov A, #77          ;    Add 100 to 77 as a
add A, #100         ;      16 Bit Addition
mov Temp, A
clr A
adc A, #0
mov Temp+1, A       ;    Store Result's High
                    ;        8 Bits
```

Instruction 12.17 8051 addc A, operand instruction.

Instruction: "subb A, Operand"

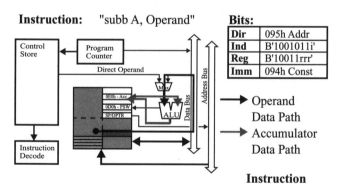

Bits:

Dir	095h Addr
Ind	B'1001011i'
Reg	B'10011rrr'
Imm	094h Const

→ Operand
Data Path
→ Accumulator
Data Path

Instruction Cycles:

8051	HSM
12	4 - 8

Execution:

$A \leftarrow A - (Operand + C)$

$C \leftarrow (A - (Operand + C)) \gg 8$

$V \leftarrow (A - (Operand + C)) \gg 8$

$AC \leftarrow ((A \& 0x0F) - ((Operand \& 0x0F) + C)) \gg 4$

Example: **MCU:** 8051

```
mov A, #100         ;    Subtract 77 from 100
add A, #77
```

Note: "Subb" is a subtract with borrow operation.
Before subtracting, make sure "Carry" is
in the correct state.

Instruction 12.18 8051 subb A, operand instruction.

Instruction: "inc Operand"

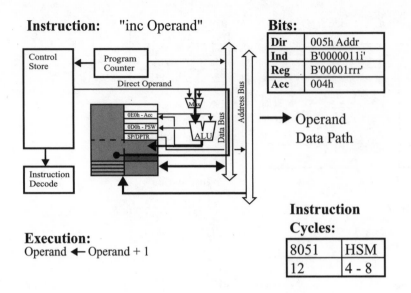

Bits:

Dir	005h Addr
Ind	B'0000011i'
Reg	B'00001rrr'
Acc	004h

→ Operand
Data Path

Execution:
Operand ← Operand + 1

Instruction Cycles:

8051	HSM
12	4 - 8

Example: MCU: 8051

inc R0   ;   Increment R0 of the
                        ;   Current Bank

Instruction 12.19 8051 inc operand instruction.

Instruction: "dec Operand"

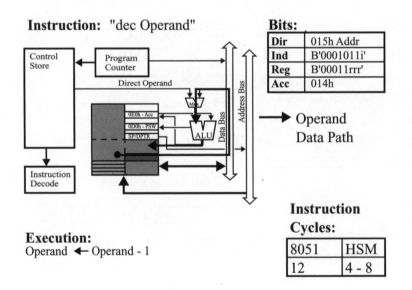

Bits:

Dir	015h Addr
Ind	B'0001011i'
Reg	B'00011rrr'
Acc	014h

→ Operand
Data Path

Execution:
Operand ← Operand - 1

Instruction Cycles:

8051	HSM
12	4 - 8

Example: MCU: 8051

dec @R0   ;   Decrement the Byte
                        ;   Pointed to by R0

Instruction 12.20 8051 dec operand instruction.

Instruction: "inc DPTR" **Bits:** 0A3h

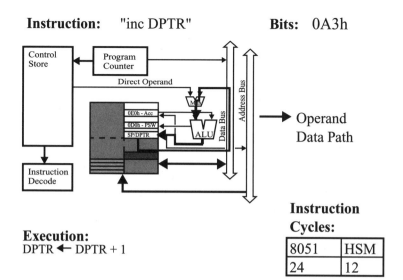

→ Operand
Data Path

Execution:
DPTR ← DPTR + 1

**Instruction
Cycles:**

8051	HSM
24	12

Example: **MCU:** 8051

inc DPTR ; Increment the Pointer to
 ; External Memory

Instruction 12.21 8051 inc DPTR instruction.

Instruction: "DA A" **Bits:** 0D4h

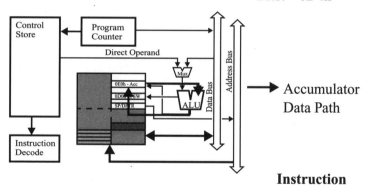

→ Accumulator
Data Path

**Instruction
Cycles:**

8051	HSM
24	12

Execution:
if (AC == 1) || ((A & 0x0F) > 9))
  A & 0x0F ← (A & 0x0F) + 6
if (C == 1) || ((A & 0x0F0) > 0x090))
  A & 0x0F0 ← (A & 0x0F0) + 0x060

Example: **MCU:** 8051

mov A, #077h ; Add two BCD Numbers
add A, #042h ; Note that the high
da A ; Four Bits will be "1"

Instruction 12.22 8051 DA A instruction.

Instruction: "Mul AB"   **Bits:** 0A4h

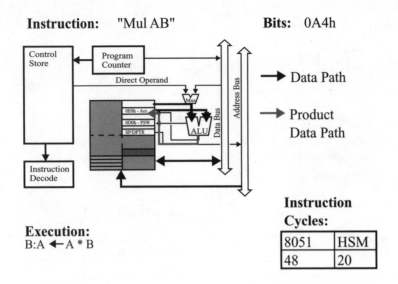

Data Path

Product
Data Path

Execution:
B:A ← A * B

Instruction Cycles:

8051	HSM
48	20

Example: **MCU:** 8051

mov A, #077h   ;   Find the Product of
mov B, #042h   ;   two Numbers
mul AB

Instruction 12.23 8051 mul AB instruction.

Instruction: "Div AB"   **Bits:** 084h

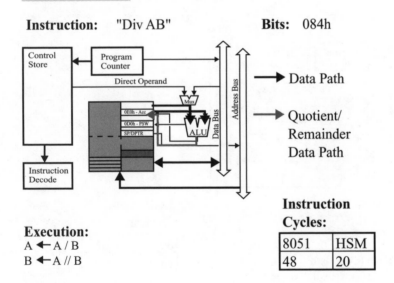

Data Path

Quotient/
Remainder
Data Path

Execution:
A ← A / B
B ← A // B

Instruction Cycles:

8051	HSM
48	20

Example: **MCU:** 8051

mov A, #077h   ; Get the Tens and ones of
mov B, #010h   ;   a Number
div AB

Instruction 12.24 8051 div AB instruction.

Bit Operators

Manipulating bits is important in any computer processor, but in a microcontroller these functions take on a very great level of importance. This is due to the requirement of many applications to handle bit-sized I/O. The 8051's bit instructions (which are known as "logical instructions" and "Boolean variable instructions) are well defined and will make your applications easier to develop.

The "standard" bitwise operations are available in the 8051. These include ANDing an 8-bit value with another value (Instructions 12.25, 12.26, and 12.27), ORing the bits of value with another (Instructions 12.28, 12.29, and 12.30), and XORing a value with another value (Instructions 12.31, 12.32, and 12.33). These three types of instructions do not affect any of the PSW bits (although a conditional jump on zero can be checked with the "jnz" and "jz" instructions).

One of the nice features of the 8051 is that individual bits can be manipulated as if they were full bytes. The "anl C, Bit" and "orl C, Bit" (Instructions 12.34, 12.35, 12.36, and 12.37) instructions perform logical operations on the carry flag and another bit, with the result being stored in the carry flag. The results of these operations can be stored or used in "jc" and "jnc" (jump on carry flag state) instructions. The value being brought in can be inverted as well.

This feature is useful if you wanted to implement a bit XOR. Remembering that XOR is defined as:

```
A ^ B = ( A & !B)  | ( !A & B )
```

We could code a bit XOR operation as the following macro:

```
MACRO xorlbit Parm1, Parm2    ;  XOR Parm1 and Parm2 and store result in
   mov  C, Parm1              ;   "Carry"
   anl  C, !Parm2             ;  Do "A & !B"
   mov  ACC.5, C              ;  Store the Result
   mov  C, Parm2              ;  Do "!A & B"
   anl  C, !Parm1
   orl  C, ACC.5              ;  Combine the Results
ENDMACRO
```

Note that I store the temporary result (the value of "Parm1 & !Parm2") in one of the temporary flags in the PSW. This operation may be halted halfway through by an interrupt. If this is to be used as an autonomous instruction, you may want to mask interrupts before changing this bit during execution of the XOR function.

Along with logical operations on bits and bytes, full bytes and bits can be cleared (Instructions 12.38, 12.39, 12.40), bits can be set (Instructions 12.41 and 12.42), and bits and bytes can be complemented (Instructions 12.43, 12.44, and 12.45). The complement instructions invert the state of the bits (either as a single bit or XORing the byte with 0FFh). Note that for each operation, when a bit is specified, it can either be the carry flag or a specific bit in the register space.

The rotate instructions are useful for moving data bits into specific places for testing (i.e., from the carry flag) or shifting in and out (Instructions 12.46, 12.47, 12.48, and 12.49). Personally, I only use the "rlc" and "rrc" instructions. Simply rotating a value within itself is not that useful and is potentially disastrous when used as a power of two multiply or divide.

The last bit instruction doesn't modify bits at all. The "swap" instruction (Instruction 12.50) exchanges one nybble for another. This instruction is useful when you wish to display the two digits in a byte (either as two nybbles or as a byte).

12

8051

Instruction: "anl A, Operand"

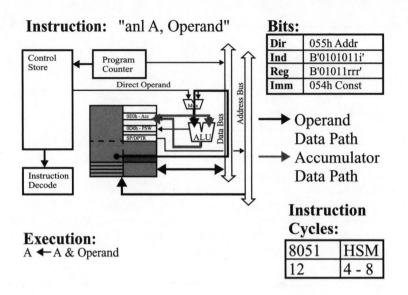

Bits:

Dir	055h Addr
Ind	B'0101011i'
Reg	B'01011rrr'
Imm	054h Const

→ Operand Data Path

→ Accumulator Data Path

Instruction Cycles:

8051	HSM
12	4 - 8

Execution:
A ← A & Operand

Example: **MCU:** 8051

mov A, #77   ; And 100 to 77
anl A, #100   ; To get 68 Decimal

Instruction 12.25 8051 anl A, operand instruction.

Instruction: "anl Register, A"

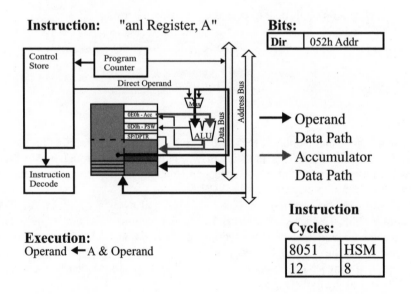

Bits:

Dir	052h Addr

→ Operand Data Path

→ Accumulator Data Path

Instruction Cycles:

8051	HSM
12	8

Execution:
Operand ← A & Operand

Example: **MCU:** 8051

mov A, #77   ; And the Register with
anl Register, A   ; 77

Instruction 12.26 8051 anl direct, A instruction.

Instruction: "anl Register, Const"

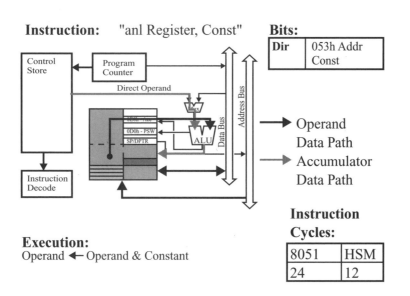

Bits:

Dir	053h Addr
	Const

→ Operand
Data Path
→ Accumulator
Data Path

Execution:
Operand ← Operand & Constant

**Instruction
Cycles:**

8051	HSM
24	12

Example: **MCU:** 8051

anl P0, #1   ; Clear Everything But
                           ;   P0.0

Instruction 12.27 8051 anl direct, const instruction.

Instruction: "orl A, Operand"

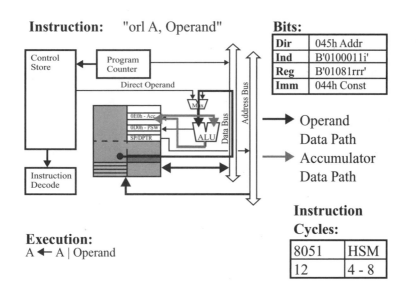

Bits:

Dir	045h Addr
Ind	B'0100011i'
Reg	B'01081rrr'
Imm	044h Const

→ Operand
Data Path
→ Accumulator
Data Path

Execution:
A ← A | Operand

**Instruction
Cycles:**

8051	HSM
12	4 - 8

Example: **MCU:** 8051

mov A, #77   ; OR 100 to 77
orl A, #100   ;   To get 109 Decimal

Instruction 12.28 8051 orl A, operand instruction.

12

8051

Instruction: "anl Register, A"

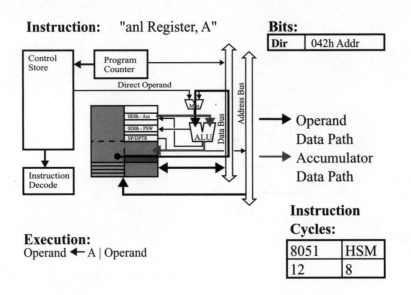

Operand
Data Path
Accumulator
Data Path

Instruction Cycles:

8051	HSM
12	8

Execution:
Operand ← A | Operand

Example: **MCU:** 8051

mov A, #77   ; OR the Register with
orl Register, A   ;   77

Instruction 12.29 8051 orl direct, A instruction.

Instruction: "orl Register, Const"

Bits:

Dir	043h Addr
	Const

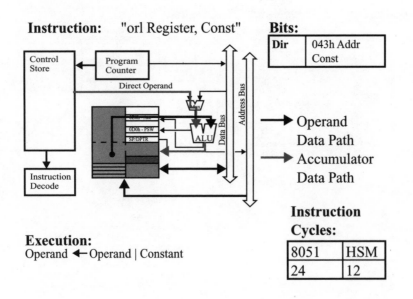

Operand
Data Path
Accumulator
Data Path

Instruction Cycles:

8051	HSM
24	12

Execution:
Operand ← Operand | Constant

Example: **MCU:** 8051

orl P0, #1   ; Set P0.0

Instruction 12.30 8051 orl direct, const instruction.

Instruction: "xrl A, Operand"

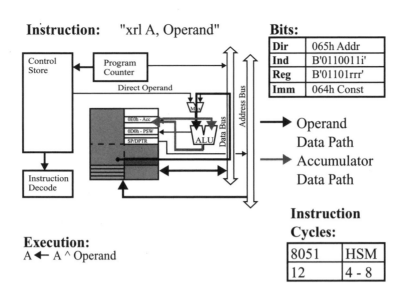

Bits:

Dir	065h Addr
Ind	B'0110011i'
Reg	B'01101rrr'
Imm	064h Const

Operand
Data Path
Accumulator
Data Path

Instruction Cycles:

8051	HSM
12	4 - 8

Execution:
A ← A ^ Operand

Example: **MCU:** 8051

mov A, #77   ; XOR 100 to 77
xrl A, #100   ; To get 41 Decimal

Instruction 12.31 8051 xrl A, operand instruction.

Instruction: "xrl Register, A"

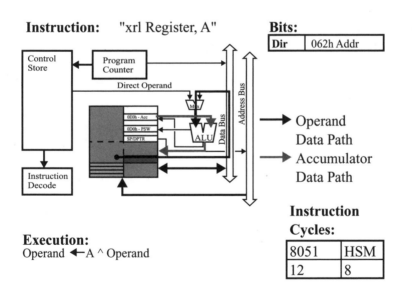

Bits:

Dir	062h Addr

Operand
Data Path
Accumulator
Data Path

Instruction Cycles:

8051	HSM
12	8

Execution:
Operand ← A ^ Operand

Example: **MCU:** 8051

mov A, #77   ; XOR the Register with
xrl Register, A   ; 77

Instruction 12.32 8051 xrl direct, A instruction.

12

8051

Instruction: "xrl Register, Const"

Bits:

Dir	063h Addr
	Const

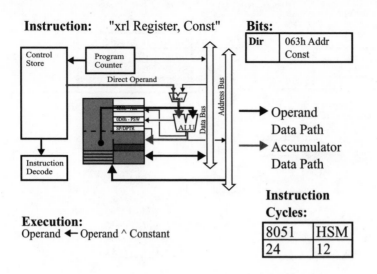

Operand
Data Path
Accumulator
Data Path

Instruction Cycles:

8051	HSM
24	12

Execution:
Operand ← Operand ^ Constant

Example: **MCU:** 8051

xrl P0, #1   ; Toggle P0.0

Instruction 12.33 8051 xrl direct, const instruction.

Instruction: "anl C, Bit"

Bits:

Dir	082h Bit

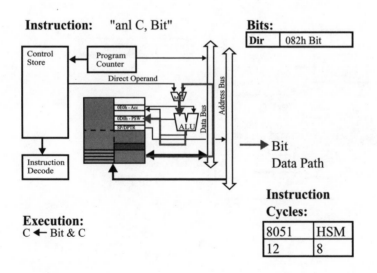

Bit
Data Path

Instruction Cycles:

8051	HSM
12	8

Execution:
C ← Bit & C

Example: **MCU:** 8051

anl C,P1.4   ; And the Bit with Carry

Note: Bits greater than 0x07F Are in the
            Special Function Register Block

Instruction 12.34 8051 anl C, bit instruction.

Instruction: "anl C,!Bit"

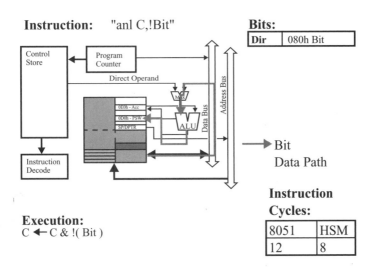

Bit
Data Path

Execution:
C ← C & !(Bit)

Instruction Cycles:

8051	HSM
12	8

Example: **MCU:** 8051

anl C,!(P1.4)   ; And the Inverted Bit with
                                 ; Carry

Note: Bits greater than 0x07F Are in the
            Special Function Register Block

Instruction 12.35 8051 anl C, !bit instruction.

Instruction: "orl C,Bit"

Bits:

Dir	072h Bit

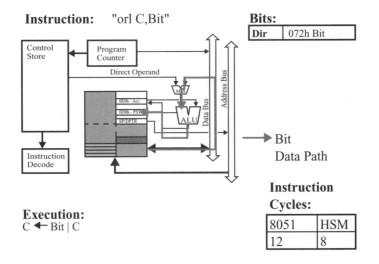

Bit
Data Path

Execution:
C ← Bit | C

Instruction Cycles:

8051	HSM
12	8

Example: **MCU:** 8051

orl C,P1.4   ; OR the Bit with Carry

Note: Bits greater than 0x07F Are in the
            Special Function Register Block

Instruction 12.36 8051 orl C, bit instruction.

12

8051

Instruction: "orl C,!Bit"

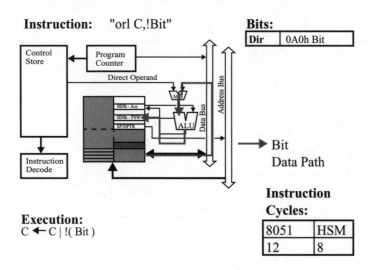

Bit
Data Path

Execution:
C ← C | !(Bit)

Instruction Cycles:

8051	HSM
12	8

Example: **MCU:** 8051

orl C,!(P1.4)   ; OR the Inverted Bit with
                                 ; Carry

Note: Bits greater than 0x07F Are in the
            Special Function Register Block

Instruction 12.37 8051 orl C, !bit instruction.

Instruction: "clr A"

Bits:

Dir	0E4h

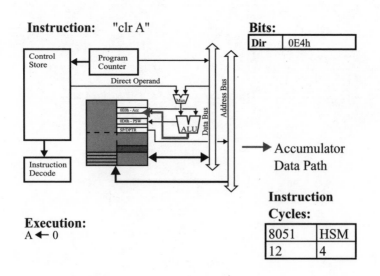

Accumulator
Data Path

Instruction Cycles:

8051	HSM
12	4

Execution:
A ← 0

Example: **MCU:** 8051

clr A   ; Clear the Accumulator

Instruction 12.38 8051 clr A instruction.

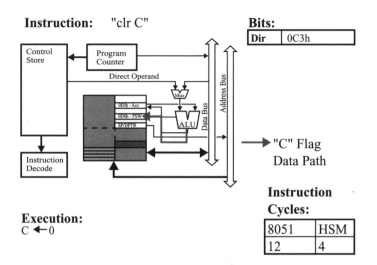

Instruction: "clr C"

Bits:

Dir	0C3h

→ "C" Flag
Data Path

**Instruction
Cycles:**

8051	HSM
12	4

Execution:
C ← 0

Example: **MCU:** 8051

clr C   ; Clear the Carry Flag

Instruction 12.39 8051 clr C instruction.

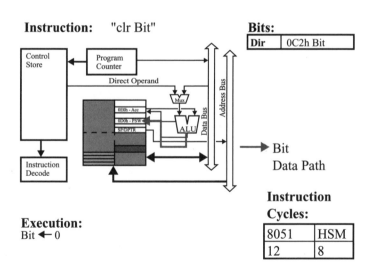

Instruction: "clr Bit"

Bits:

Dir	0C2h Bit

→ Bit
Data Path

**Instruction
Cycles:**

8051	HSM
12	8

Execution:
Bit ← 0

Example: **MCU:** 8051

clr P2.3   ; Clear the I/O Bit

Note: Bits greater than 0x07F Are in the
        Special Function Register Block

Instruction 12.40 8051 clr bit instruction.

12

8051

Instruction: "setb C"

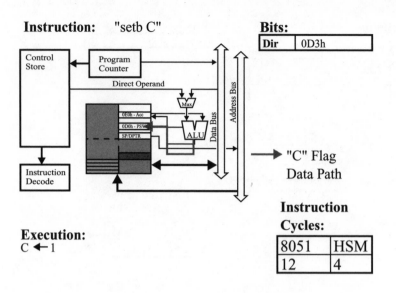

Bits:

Dir	0D3h

→ "C" Flag
Data Path

Execution:
C ← 1

Instruction Cycles:

8051	HSM
12	4

Example: **MCU:** 8051

setb C   ; Set the Carry Flag

Instruction 12.41 8051 setb C instruction.

Instruction: "setb C"

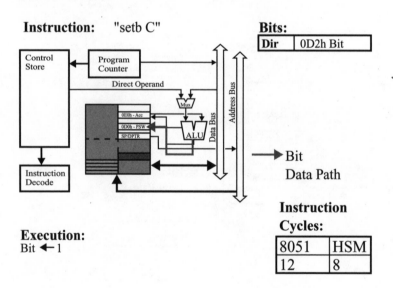

Bits:

Dir	0D2h Bit

→ Bit
Data Path

Instruction Cycles:

8051	HSM
12	8

Execution:
Bit ← 1

Example: **MCU:** 8051

setb PSW.RS0   ; Change the Current
                                          ; Register Bank

Note: Bits greater than 0x07F Are in the
            Special Function Register Block

Instruction 12.42 8051 setb bit instruction.

Instruction: "cpl A"

Bits:

Dir	0F4h

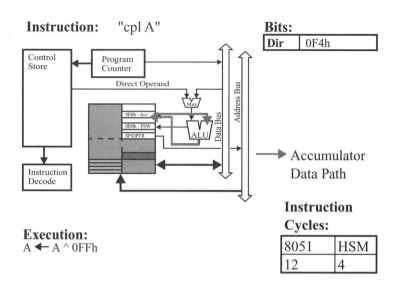

→ Accumulator
Data Path

Execution:
A ← A ^ 0FFh

Instruction Cycles:

8051	HSM
12	4

Example: **MCU:** 8051

cpl A   ; Negate the Value in the
inc A   ; Accumulator

Instruction 12.43 8051 cpl A instruction.

Instruction: "Cpl C"

Bits:

Dir	0B3h

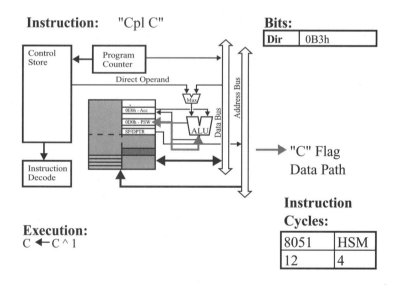

→ "C" Flag
Data Path

Execution:
C ← C ^ 1

Instruction Cycles:

8051	HSM
12	4

Example: **MCU:** 8051

cpl C   ; Complement the Carry Flag

Instruction 12.44 8051 cpl C instruction.

12

8051

Instruction: "cpl C"

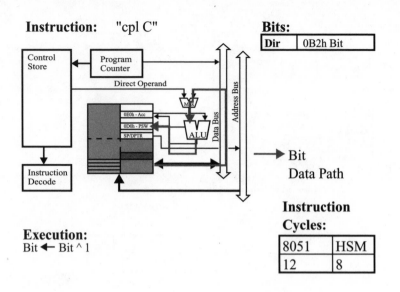

Bits:

Dir	0B2h Bit

→ Bit
Data Path

Execution:
Bit ← Bit ^ 1

Instruction Cycles:

8051	HSM
12	8

Example: **MCU:** 8051

cpl P1.4   ; Complement the I/O Bit

Note: Bits greater than 0x07F Are in the
Special Function Register Block

Instruction 12.45 8051 cpl bit instruction.

Instruction: "rr A"

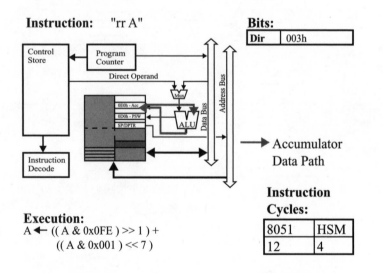

Bits:

Dir	003h

→ Accumulator
Data Path

Execution:
A ← ((A & 0x0FE) >> 1) +
        ((A & 0x001) << 7)

Instruction Cycles:

8051	HSM
12	4

Example: **MCU:** 8051

rr A   ; Rotate Accumulator by one
                                         ; Bit

Instruction 12.46 8051 rr A instruction.

Instruction: "rl A"

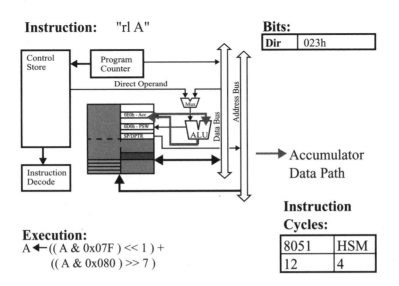

Bits:

Dir	023h

→ Accumulator Data Path

Execution:
$$A \leftarrow ((A \, \& \, 0x07F) << 1) + ((A \, \& \, 0x080) >> 7)$$

Instruction Cycles:

8051	HSM
12	4

Example: **MCU:** 8051

rl A   ; Rotate Accumulator by one
                             ; Bit

Instruction 12.47 8051 rl A instruction.

Instruction: "rrc A"

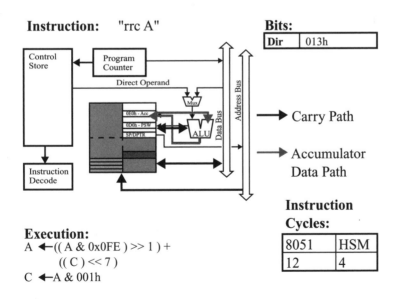

Bits:

Dir	013h

→ Carry Path

→ Accumulator Data Path

Execution:
$$A \leftarrow ((A \, \& \, 0x0FE) >> 1) + ((C) << 7)$$
$$C \leftarrow A \, \& \, 001h$$

Instruction Cycles:

8051	HSM
12	4

Example: **MCU:** 8051

rrc A   ; Rotate Accumulator by one
                             ; Bit through the Carry Flag

Instruction 12.48 8051 rrc A instruction.

12

8051

Instruction: "rlc A"

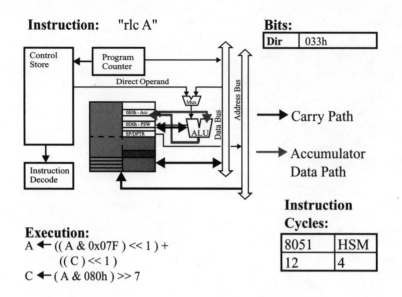

Bits:

Dir	033h

→ Carry Path

→ Accumulator
Data Path

Execution:

$A \leftarrow ((A \; \& \; 0x07F) \ll 1) +$
$\qquad ((C) \ll 1)$
$C \leftarrow (A \; \& \; 080h) \gg 7$

Instruction Cycles:

8051	HSM
12	4

Example: **MCU:** 8051

rlc A   ; Rotate Accumulator by one
                           ; Bit through the Carry Flag

Instruction 12.49 8051 rlc A instruction.

Instruction: "swap A"

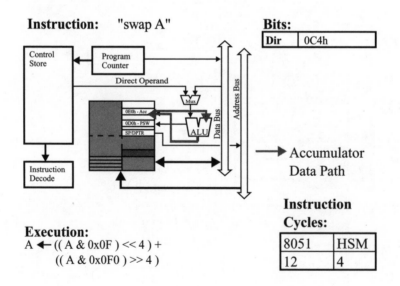

Bits:

Dir	0C4h

→ Accumulator
Data Path

Execution:

$A \leftarrow ((A \; \& \; 0x0F) \ll 4) +$
$\qquad ((A \; \& \; 0x0F0) \gg 4)$

Instruction Cycles:

8051	HSM
12	4

Example: **MCU:** 8051

swap A   ; Swap the Nybbles in the
                           ; Accumulator

Instruction 12.50 8051 swap A instruction.

Execution Change Operators

Jumping around in the 8051 is very straightforward with the only real wrinkle being a result of how the PSW register works (without a zero flag the "jz" and "jnz" instructions work differently than you might expect and definitely differently than how the other microcontrollers execute this instruction).

For jumping to new addresses, there are three different modes of operation. The "small" jump ("sjmp") is a relative jump from −128 to +128 byte addresses from the start of the next instruction. Despite its limitations, the small jump is probably the instruction that will be used the most in your 8051 applications.

The "page" jump ("ajmp" and "acall") instruction jumps to an offset within the current 11 bit (2K) address "page." This means that care must be taken not to jump outside the curent page.

In Figure 12.1, you can see how you can get into trouble with the "ajmp" instruction. The second time it is used, the jump actually goes to the "LabelB" offset within the current page, but "LabelB" is not in the same page. This means the jump will stay in the current page and go to the wrong absolute address.

The last type of jump is the "long" jump ("ljmp"), which will allow jumps anywhere in the 64K control store address space. This jump would probably be preferable to be used in all cases, but it requires an extra byte of storage as well as an extra instruction cycle in some 8051s (namely the HSMs).

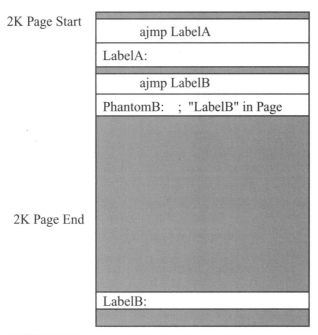

Figure 12.1 Jumps within the current 2K page.

The different types of jumps are shown in the "jmp" instruction explanation (Instruction 12.51).

Subroutines in the 8051 work largely as expected, with the "call" instruction (Instruction 12.52) return address "pushed" onto the stack, and at the end of the subroutine a "ret" instruction (Instruction 12.53) is executed to "pop" the return address from the stack. The "call" instruction can use either page or long addressing.

In some 8051 assemblers, simply specifying "jmp" or "call" as the instruction will cause the assembler to select the "best" jump addressing mode. This type of operation is preferable because it cuts down on the amount of thinking the programmer has to do and automatically compensates when the program grows in size.

If you are familiar with the operation of other processors, you might be surprised to discover that the stack pointer increments as part of the "push" operation. This is opposite to many other devices where a "push" causes the stack pointer to be decremented. The issue with this is in setting up stack the stack pointer will have to be initialized to the start of the stack area (rather than at the "end" of the stack area, as is done in most other processors).

"Reti" (Instruction 12.53) works just like the "ret" instruction except if it is executed within an interrupt handler, the 8051s interrupt hardware will be reset to allow execution of the handler for the next interrupt.

The operation of the "reti" instruction really precludes the use of nested interrupts (which is possible in some of the other devices). This is another reason why the interrupt handlers should be as short (in terms of instructions and cycles) as possible.

Table jumps are accomplished using the "jmp @A + DPTR" instruction (Instruction 12.54). In this case, DPTR is set up with the start of a table and the accumulator is set up with the offset within the table.

```
mov     DPTR, #Table    ;   DPTR = Start of Table
mov     A, Index        ;   Get the Index Address
clr     C               ;   Multiply by 2 for the actual Address
rlc     A
jmp

Table:
ajmp    Element0        ;   Jump to the Different Elements
ajmp    Element1
  :
```

In this example, the index address is multiplied by two (shifted left by one) to get the correct table offset (each "element" is two bytes long).

The basic conditional jumps use bit states (Instructions 12.55, 12.56, and 12.57). These relative jumps are taken if the carry flag or the specified bit are either set or reset.

The "jbc Bit, Label" is an interesting instruction because the bit tested for the jump is cleared if it is set. This instruction is useful as a "semaphone" instruction in an RTOS.

As use for a semaphore "test and set" instruction, the jump would be taken if the semaphone flag is available. The code the operation jumps to would notify the task that it now has control of the bit.

The jump on zero/not zero instructions (Instruction 12.58) test the contents of the accumulator for zero as the condition for the jump. This means that if these instructions are to be used, then after an operation affecting a value, the accumulator cannot be changed.

The last conditional jump instruction is the compare and jump if the result is not equal to zero (Instructions 12.59 and 12.60). These instructions can be used with the test register (the accumulator or another register) not set to zero or set to a value that is used for the jump instruction. Instead of just checking for zero, the compare value can be any arbitrary byte as well.

The decrement and jump if not zero instruction (Instruction 12.61) is used for counting loops.

```
    mov    R2, #7
Loop:                        ;  Loop 7x
    :
    djnz          R2, Loop   ;  Decrement Counter and Jump if Not Zero
```

The example code above will loop seven times before continuing The last instruction (and in many ways the least) is the "nop" (Instruction 12.62). The nop will simply take up a byte and one instruction cycle to operate. The primary purpose of the nop is to help ensure that timing is correct. Although as it is equal to 00h, it can be used to "take out" erroneous instructions when debugging an application, rather than erasing and reprogramming the device.

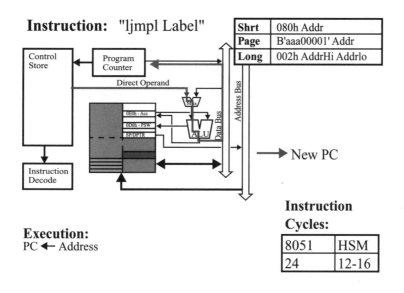

Instruction: "ljmpl Label"

Shrt	080h Addr
Page	B'aaa00001' Addr
Long	002h AddrHi Addrlo

New PC

Execution:
PC ← Address

Instruction Cycles:

8051	HSM
24	12-16

Example: **MCU:** 8051

sjmp Label   ; Jump to "Label"
:
Label:

Instruction 12.51 8051 sjmp label instruction.

Instruction: "acall Label"

| Page | B'aaa10001' Addr |
| Long | 012h AddrHi Addrlo |

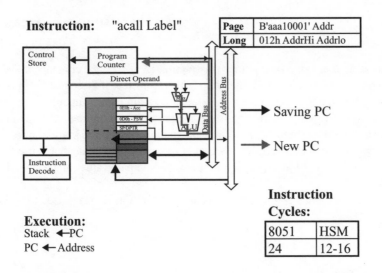

Saving PC

New PC

Execution:
Stack ◄─PC
PC ◄─ Address

Instruction Cycles:

8051	HSM
24	12-16

Example: **MCU:** 8051

lcall Label   ; Jump to Subroutine "Label"
:
Label:

Instruction 12.52 8051 acall label instruction.

Instruction: "ret"

Bits

| Ret | 022h |
| Reti | 032h |

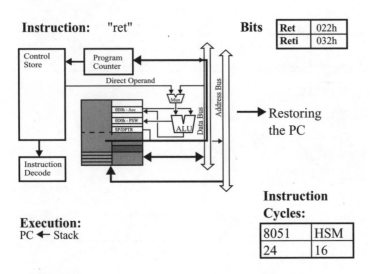

Restoring the PC

Execution:
PC ◄─ Stack

Instruction Cycles:

8051	HSM
24	16

Example: **MCU:** 8051

lcall Label   ; Jump to Subroutine "Label"
:
Label:
:
ret   ; Return from Subroutine

Note: "Reti" Works similarly to "Ret" but resets
the 8051's Internal Interrupt Hardware.

Instruction 12.53 8051 ret and reti instructions.

Instruction: "jmp @A+DPTR"   **Bits:** 073h

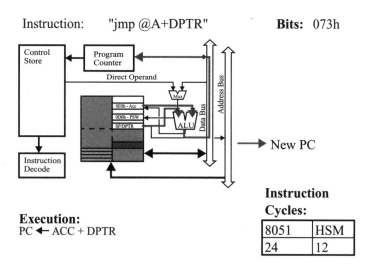

Execution:
PC ← ACC + DPTR

Instruction Cycles:

8051	HSM
24	12

Example: **MCU:** 8051

```
mov DPTR, #Table_Start
mov A, #Table_Element
jmp @A+DPTR        ; Jump to Element in Table
```

Instruction 12.54 8051 jmp @A+DPTR instruction.

Instruction: "jnb Bit, Label" **Bits:**

Jb	020hBit Addr
Jnb	030h Bit Addr

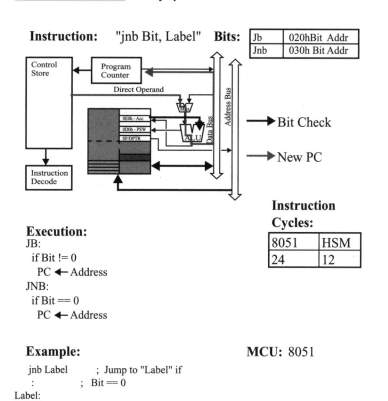

→ Bit Check

→ New PC

Instruction Cycles:

8051	HSM
24	12

Execution:
JB:
 if Bit != 0
   PC ← Address
JNB:
 if Bit == 0
   PC ← Address

Example: **MCU:** 8051

```
jnb Label      ; Jump to "Label" if
   :           ;  Bit == 0
Label:
```

Instruction 12.55 8051 jb bit, label and jnb bit, label instructions.

12

8051

Instruction: "jc Label"   **Bits:**

Jc	040h Addr
Jnc	050h Addr

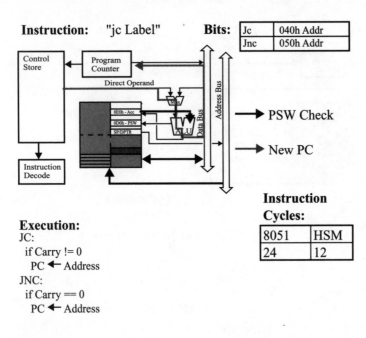

→ PSW Check

→ New PC

Execution:
JC:
  if Carry != 0
    PC ← Address
JNC:
  if Carry == 0
    PC ← Address

Instruction Cycles:

8051	HSM
24	12

Example: **MCU:** 8051

jc Label   ; Jump to "Label" if Carry
  :   ; Set Previously
Label:

Instruction 12.56 8051 jc label and jnc label instructions.

Instruction: "jbc bit, Label"   **Bits:**

Jbc	020h Bit Addr

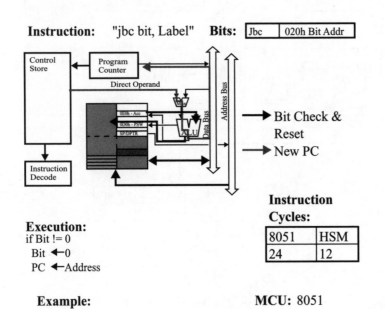

→ Bit Check & Reset

→ New PC

Execution:
if Bit != 0
  Bit ← 0
  PC ← Address

Instruction Cycles:

8051	HSM
24	12

Example: **MCU:** 8051

jbc Semaphore, Label   ; Jump to "Label" if
  :   ; RTOS Semaphone Set
Label:

Instruction 12.57 8051 jbc bit, label instruction.

Instruction: "jnz Label"

Bits:

Jz	060h Addr
Jnz	070h Addr

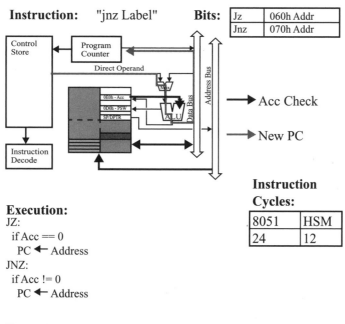

➤ Acc Check

➤ New PC

Execution:

JZ:
  if Acc == 0
    PC ← Address
JNZ:
  if Acc != 0
    PC ← Address

Instruction Cycles:

8051	HSM
24	12

Example: **MCU:** 8051

jz Label   ; Jump to "Label" if Acc == 0
  :
Label:

Instruction 12.58 8051 jz label and jnz label instructions.

Instruction: "cjne A, #37, Label"

Bits:

Dir	0B5 Direct Addr
Imm	0B4 Immediate Addr

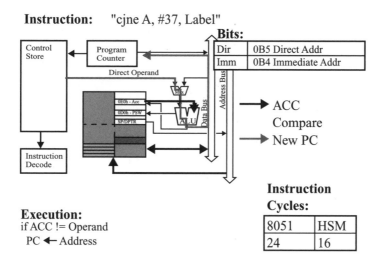

➤ ACC Compare

➤ New PC

Execution:

if ACC != Operand
  PC ← Address

Instruction Cycles:

8051	HSM
24	16

Example: **MCU:** 8051

cjne A, #37, Label   ; Jump to "Label" if
  :   ; ACC != 37
Label:

Instruction 12.59 8051 cjne A, #const, label instruction.

Instruction: "cjne Reg,Operand, Label"

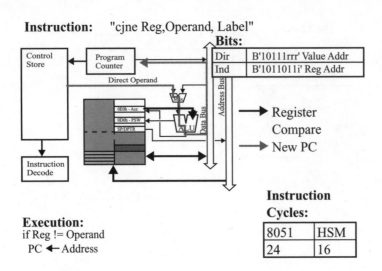

Bits:

Dir	B'10111rrr' Value Addr
Ind	B'1011011i' Reg Addr

→ Register
  Compare
→ New PC

Instruction Cycles:

8051	HSM
24	16

Execution:
if Reg != Operand
  PC ← Address

Example: **MCU:** 8051

cjne R2, #37, Label   ; Jump to "Label" if
  :   ; R2 != 37
Label:

Instruction 12.60 8051 cjne reg, operand, label instruction.

Instruction: "djnz Rn, Label"

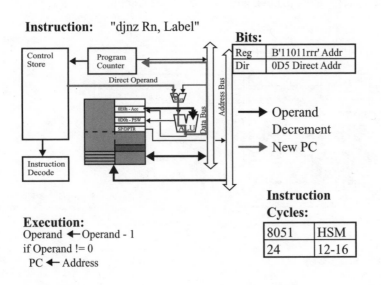

Bits:

Reg	B'11011rrr' Addr
Dir	0D5 Direct Addr

→ Operand
  Decrement
→ New PC

Instruction Cycles:

8051	HSM
24	12-16

Execution:
Operand ← Operand - 1
if Operand != 0
  PC ← Address

Example: **MCU:** 8051

mov R0, 8   ; Loop 8x
Loop:
  :
djnz R0, Loop   ; Skip "Label" Jump
                               ; if --R0 == 0

Instruction 12.61 8051 djnz Rn, label instruction.

Instruction: "nop"   **Bits:**   000h

Execution: **Instruction Cycles:**

8051	HSM
12	4

Example: **MCU:** 8051

nop   ; Delay one instruction Cycle

Instruction 12.62 8051 nop instruction.

8051 EXAMPLE APPLICATIONS

For this chapter, I guess I should discuss a couple of things first. For this book, I didn't use a "true" 8051 for the example applications. Instead, the Dallas Semiconductor HSM 80C520 was used. The reason for using this part was largely due to my interest in working with the HSM architecture; I wanted to work with as fast a processor as possible (I guess I felt the need for speed). If you were to implement these applications on a "standard" 8051 (which uses 12 clock cycles for each instruction cycle), then you may have to retime the applications (or increase the clock speed).

One of the aspects of the 8051 that disappoints me is the unavailability of "true" assembler and simulators from a device manufacturer. In all the other devices presented here, I have been able to present the manufacturer's tools on the CD-ROM. Unfortunately, my search of the Web did not turn up any tools that I wanted to put on the CD-ROM. Actually, this isn't true; if you are looking for an assembler, look for the "MetaLink" product; I did get a chance to play around with it and I was happy with what I found. Unfortunately, I couldn't say the same for a simulator; the best that I could find was documented and written in German.

This problem actually turned out to be a blessing because in this search, I discovered Virtual Micro Design's "UMPS" which is an acronym for "Universal Microprocessor Program Simulator" and is the most impressive code development tool that I have seen. UMPS is an "IDE" (integrated development environment) with two very interesting characteristics, the first being that it will assemble and execute code designed for a wide range of devices (all the microcontrollers presented in this book and more), which means that with UMPS you only require one code development tool for working with a variety of different devices.

The second advantage of UMPS is its unique method of simulating applications. Rather than requiring a "stimulus" file, UMPS allows you to create a virtual circuit that your application interacts with, which means that testing your code under a variety of stimuli or input conditions can be implemented simply by the click of a mouse.

In this chapter, I will demonstrate how UMPS can be used to help with the development of an application. Later in the book, in the "Appendix—UMPS," I provide more information on the tool, along with ordering information.

First Application

As you go through this book, I expect that you'll end up being pretty sick of turning on a couple of LEDs (one by a timer and the other by pressing a button), but it really is a good first application for the microcontroller and other, more advanced applications can be built from it. (Figure 13.1.) As I go through this application's development, I will also go through a simple UMPS tutorial to give you an idea of how UMPS can be used to debug an application.

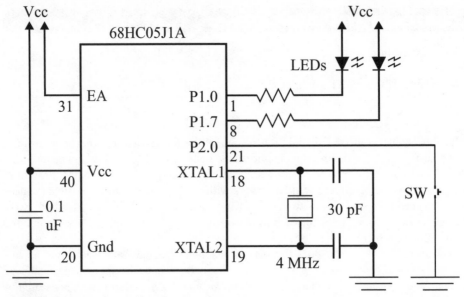

Figure 13.1 Flashing LEDs with an 87C520.

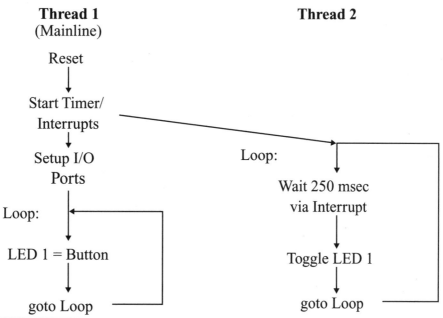

Figure 13.2 First application execution flow.

The basic operation of this application is to have two "threads" running concurrently. The first thread (which I'll call the "mainline") initiates the second thread and then loops passing the state of a button to the second LED. The second thread stays dormant until a timer overflows and interrupts the execution of the first task and toggles the state of the first LED.

As a flowchart, this looks like Figure 13.2.

This flow is repeated for all the microcontrollers presented in this book. In the application, the microcontroller's oscillator, I/O pins, and interrupt handlers are demonstrated.

The code for this application is very simple—probably the simplest of all the devices:

```
;   AP1 - Flash an LED and Button LED

;   This Application Flashes an LED and polls a switch and returns the
;    switch value on a second LED.

;   Myke Predko
;   97.11.19

;   Hardware Notes:
;   80C520 Running at 1 MHz
;   P1.7 is the Flashing LED
;   P1.0 is the Button LED
;   P2.0 is the Button

 org 0
  ajmp    Mainline

 org 0Bh                         ;   Timer0 Interrupt
  cpl     P1.7                   ;   Flip Bit 7
  reti
```

```
    org  020h                      ;   Program Mainline
Mainline:

    clr  CKCON                     ;   Use Internal /12 Clock for Timer0
    mov  TMOD,#%00000001           ;   Timer0 - Uses Internal Clock
                                   ;            - Run in Mode 1
    mov  TCON,#%00010000           ;   Start Timer0 running

    mov  IE,#%10000010             ;   Enable the Timer 0 Interrupt

    mov  P1,#081h                  ;   Make LED Bits High
    mov  P2,#1                     ;   Make All P2 Bits Low except for Button

Loop:

    mov  C,P2.0                    ;   Get the Button Value
    mov  P1.0,C                    ;   Save it as the LED

    ajmp Loop
```

The code executes exactly as Figure 13.2 shows the execution flow. With the code written, we can now test it out in a simulator before building the circuit and burning the code into a device.

As I indicated at the start of the chapter, I used "UMPS" for debugging this application. A demo version of UMPS can be found on the CD-ROM and is explained in greater detail in "Appendix—UMPS."

After UMPS has been installed, it can be started from Windows. When UMPS has loaded itself, you have to select the microcontroller to be used. By clicking on "Configure" and then "Load CPU..." you can select the "DS80C320" (which is a down-level version of the 87C520, which is the 8051 device that I actually used for the 8051 example applications).

Loading the application will be accomplished by clicking on "File," "Load," and then selecting the file to load (for this case it's "AP1.ASM"). (Figure 13.3.)

This is the UMPS editor. It works very similarly to a "typical" Windows editor except that same operations use different key sequences. As you enter your code, comments are italicized and marked in blue. Assembly directives are marked in red, and instructions are shown in boldface print. Your screen probably won't look exactly like this one; I like to stretch out the source code window to show the full line.

Now you can assemble the code either by selecting "Program" and then "Compile" or by clicking on the yellow "Lightning bolt" on the tool bar. You will be prompted for the source file name and if it needs to be saved before assembly.

When the assembly step executes, a window will pop up showing you the current status of the assembly operation. The UMPS assembler will stop on the first failure encountered, and when you clear the window from the editor, the failing line will be highlighted.

One hint on entering code in UMPS. Do not put spaces in the instruction parameters (even after a comma). UMPS is unable to parse this and you will end up with an error that doesn't make any sense ("ERROR PASS 2: Rn or Pn Expected"). All parameters have to be lumped together.

Now that you have the application code correctly assembled, you can start to play. As I said earlier in this chapter, the UMPS simulator does not use a stimulus file; instead, virtual hardware is "wired" to the device. You can add the two LEDs and a switch by clicking on "Configure" and then "Resources."

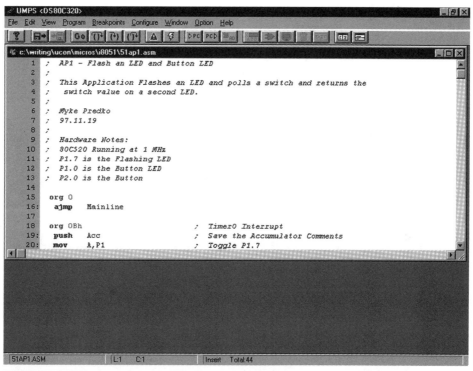

Figure 13.3 UMPS with application code loaded.

Once this is done, a large window will come up. On the tool bar, you can now select "ADD" and place two "LED (Red, Green, Yellow)" on the window, followed by a "Push Button." Your screen will look something like Figure 13.4.

Next, I like to resize the resources window to be as small as possible, and I put it in the lower left-hand corner of the screen. To "wire" up the devices, select on one of the LEDs (which will be known as the "Flashing LED" or "LED 1") and click on the plug symbol or "Connect." (Figure 13.5.)

To wire the Flashing LED (connected to P1.7) click on "Anode" and 'Always "1"' followed by "Connect." This will "Connect" the LED's anode to Vcc. Next, repeat this for the Cathode (negative connection) and connect it to P1 bit 7. When you're finished, the screen will look like Figure 13.6.

With this complete, click on "OK" to save the connections and repeat this for the second LED being connected to P1 bit 0.

The switch is a bit trickier to wire in UMPS. After selecting the switch, click on "Configuration" or the little monitor icon on the tool-box line. (Figure 13.7.)

In the "Switch Configuration" window, click on "Push Button" and deselect it, which will bring up different button selections. Make sure "1" when open is selected and "OK" out of the window. With the correct switch selected, you can now wire it. Using the "Connect" icon (the plug), select "Out" to P2 bit 0 and "In" to 'Always "0"'. This will give you a switch that will pull the pin down to ground.

To leave the "Resources" mode, click on "Exit" in the yellow box on the tool bar.

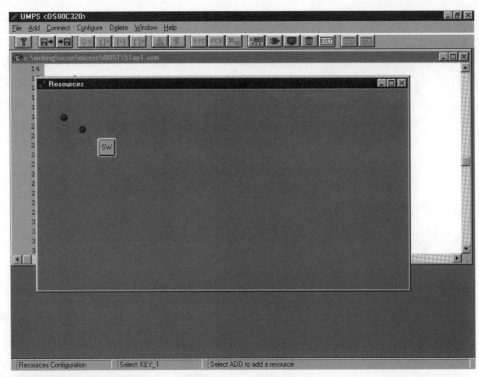

Figure 13.4 UMPS with 2 LEDs and switch resource.

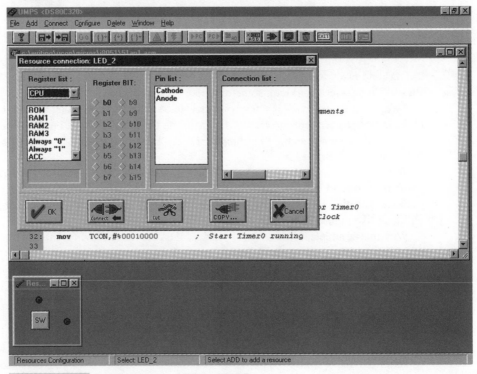

Figure 13.5 Connecting an LED in UMPS.

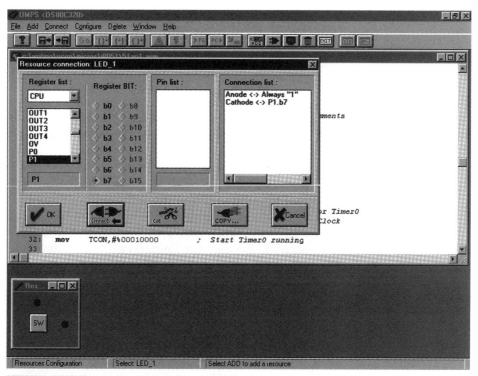

Figure 13.6 Final LED wiring in UMPS.

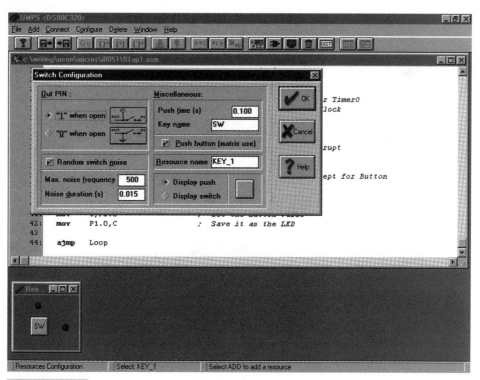

Figure 13.7 Specifying switch configuration in UMPS.

With the "wiring" completed, you can now display the registers used to monitor the execution of the application. Click on "Configure" and then "CPU Registers" to select which registers to monitor. To put the accumulator in this window, click on "ADD" and select "ACC." This will be repeated for each of the registers.

In this example, I monitor the "Acc," "PSW," "SP," "PC," "TL0," "TH0," "P1" and "P2" registers. After adding these registers, I then click on the monitor icon or "display" option and select different colours for the different registers and, more importantly, I can select the radix of the registered value to be displayed.

Once the registers were defined, I resized the window and put it underneath the source code beside the "Resources" window. (See Figure 13.8.)

Finally, we are ready to start simulating the program. You may want to reassemble to make sure the correct object code is going to be used.

From this point, UMPS works like any other simulator, with "go" starting execution, and you can watch how the program executes (clicking on the switch will turn on the second LED and the first LED will turn on and off). Now you might find that UMPS stops when the timer overflows. By clicking on "Options" and then "Run Mode..." you will be able to disable this feature as well as set a specific microcontroller clock speed (among other options). For this application, the microcontroller will use a 4-MHz clock. (Figure 13.9.)

After doing all this, you're probably asking if it's worthwhile to actually build the circuit just to watch the LEDs turn on and off.

Well, in this case, it really is important to go through and burn the 87C520s and build the circuit. In the order of writing this book, I ended up doing the 8051 last. This was

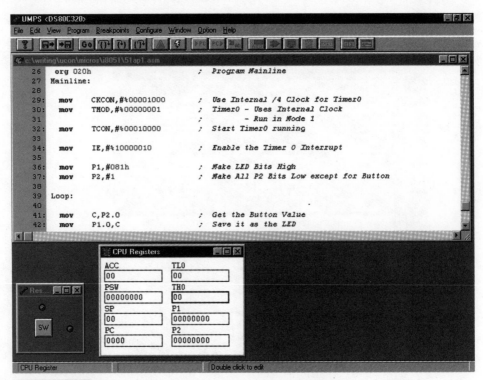

Figure 13.8 Specifying CPU register to monitor in UMPS.

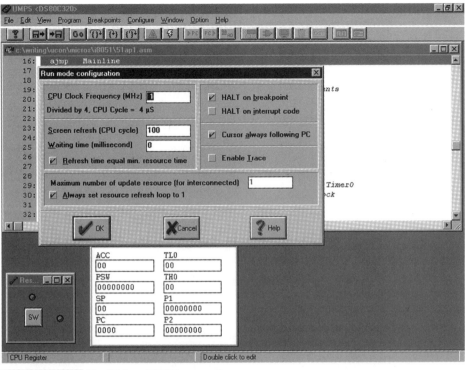

Figure 13.9 Modifying UMPS operation.

because of the difficulty I had in finding good tools to work with. While UMPS had told me that my software was good, there really were a few things I had to learn about burning the parts and building the circuit.

The first problem I had was in getting the programmer to talk to my PC. How I got the programmer running is detailed in the "8051 Development Tools" chapter elsewhere in this section.

Once I had created my own RS-232 interface for the programmer, I had to get the 87C520 to run. I had been used to the other microcontrollers, which were very easy to get running. This wasn't quite the case with the 87C520. With my basic circuit, I had two problems, which meant that the application would not start up.

The first problem was that I had left the "EA" bit floating. To run from the EPROM, this bit has to be held high (as shown in Figure 13.1). If it is pulled low or left floating (or unconnected), then the 8051 tries to execute out of an external EPROM.

The second problem was that I took the circuit I had used for all the other microcontrollers for the device's oscillator (it was a 1-MHz "strip-cut" crystal with two 30-pF capacitors), and this wouldn't work with the 87C520. To fix this problem, I replaced the crystal with a "parallel cut" 4-MHz crystal and the circuit worked without any problems. To be perfectly honest, the circuit did work without any problems, but the "flashing" LED was turning on and off too quickly. The instruction clock divisor was changed from divide by four to divide by twelve to reduce the speed of the flashing to approximately twice per second (from eight times).

I do want to comment on the code above. If you compare the final compiled data size, you'll see that it is much smaller than all the other microcontroller's code (less than half in most of the other cases). This is largely due to the 8051's very complete instruction set and specifically the bit-specific instructions. If you compare the mainline loop of the program above to any of the others, you'll see what I mean.

When you compare this code with the other microcontroller's applications, you'll see that in the interrupt handler and mainline loop, the 8051's application is much simpler and will probably run much faster than any other microcontrollers, even though the "true" 8051 requires much more than the average number of clock cycles per instruction cycle. As I go through the book, I talk about the idea of not determining the speed of a processor simply by the number of cycles per instruction. In specific cases, such as this, some microcontrollers will show a marked advantage over other devices. For this application, the 8051 "CISC" Harvard-architected processor is the most efficient and easiest to program (as well as requiring the fewest instruction bytes to run).

Real-Time Clock and Thermometer

The circuit itself is actually quite simple with the LCD wiring primarily dictated by the simplest layout that I could come up with for wiring the display to the 87C520 on a bread board. (Figure 13.10.)

If you skip along to the other three "true" micrcontrollers, you'll see that each of the schematics are very similar for each of the different devices. The major differences are in what I call the "core." The "core" is the microcontroller and the connections required for it to run properly. This is really just the circuit required to get the microcontroller to run in the first application.

As I said above, I wired the LCD to the microcontroller in such a way that it would very easy to connect the LCD to the microcontroller on a breadboard. This was done by wiring the LCD to the pins on one side of the 87C520. I was then able to concentrate on the remaining parts (the "Setting" button and DS1820), both of which are very easy to wire up together.

With the circuit designed, I now want to go through the process that I use for developing the software. You will see this approach in pretty well all the applications (although in the first application, I typically didn't follow this approach because the application code was very simple and was designed more to understand how the microcontroller actually works in a circuit).

The first program is always used to make sure the miccontroller is capable of running in the application. This could really be simply toggling an unused bit periodically to make sure the MCU will run without any problems. My "AP2.ASM" code actually does more than this; I write the message "Hello" on the LCD and begin the development of a routine to write a string to the LCD.

Developing this program was greatly simplified by using UMPS. Actually, there was no real debug to do on the application once I had "Hello" on the UMPS' LCD display.

The next program ("AP2V2.ASM") was instrumental in developing the clock display; the timer is enabled, and each second the current minute is updated once per second. The actual display code doesn't require too much explanation, but I should point out how the one second time is calculated because it's probably not terribly intuitive and may be a bit confusing if you try working through it yourself.

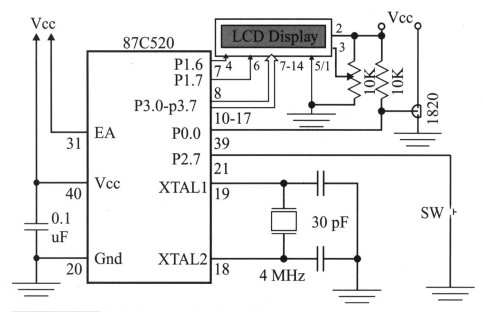

Figure 13.10 87C520-based digital clock/thermometer.

The 87C520, running at 4-MHz clock cycles (1-MHz instruction cycles) and a divide-by-four counter with Timer 0 running in "Mode 1" will be interrupted once every 65,536 msecs. This means that approximately 16 interrupts will happen each second.

When I first set up this application in the PIC, each time the PIC was interrupted, I reloaded the timer with a value that would cause an interrupt at exactly the second value. This was a fair amount of work to figure out how to do and wasn't absolutely precise.

So I came up with a better solution.

In the 87C520, I use a 24 bit second fraction counter, the high byte of which is incremented each time Timer 0 overflows. The mainline code monitors the high byte of the second fraction counter and notes the passage of a second each time the high byte of the counter is equal to 16.

Now, rather than resetting the second fraction counter, I subtract 1,000,000 from it (the actual value it will have is 1,048,576). This means that the remainder is left over for the next second. After a number of seconds (actually only two seconds), this remainder will become large enough so that only 15 interrupts are required for the counter to be greater than 1,048,576 and then reset back to a value close to an actual second. So, while each "second" in the code is not exactly one second, over time it will average out so that the time is correct.

With the timer being incremented, the next piece of code to write is to get the clock running. This is done in "AP2V3.ASM." In this program, every second when the second fraction timer reaches or exceeds 1,048,576, the "setting button" is checked and if it is pressed, then the time is updated.

Actually, regarding setting the time, I've come up with an algorithm that I'm quite pleased with and made my application debug quite a bit easier. In this algorithm, after the minute has been updated using an "Increment" variable, this variable is shifted once to the left (with new bit zero filled in with a "1") to a maximum of 03Fh (63 decimal).

With this algorithm, the longer you hold down the button, the larger the time increment is and when it reaches the maximum, the hours are incremented at a rate of one per second (with the minutes of each hour being set to zero). With this scheme, the clock can be updated a full 24 hours in less than 30 seconds with a remarkable amount of control.

Anyway, that's enough back patting.

The final aspect of the application's development is getting the DS1820 digital thermometer working (the final code is in "AP2V4.ASM"). For some reason, this caused me a lot of grief for the 87C520 and took about two days to properly time (in comparison, I was able to get the PIC's second application DS1820 interface working in less than half a day and the 68HC05's working in about a day (including changing the system clock crystal to a faster speed)).

Looking back over it, the biggest problem I had was matching the 87C520's instructions in such a way that the DS1820 would get the proper timings. A bit of it was due to fatigue and being quite honestly sick of redoing the application "yet again," but most of it was due to the fact that the single wire interface can be difficult to time up to. If I were to go through this application again for each of the five microcontrollers, I would probably choose an I2C digital thermometer or some other thermometer that has a synchronous serial interface.

Marya's Talking Keyboard

In developing the applications for this book, I tried to choose projects that would show off the capabilities of microcontrollers. For this one, I wanted to show how external devices could be interfaced to the 8051's buses and show how a microcontroller can interface to a keyboard. The resulting project polls a "qwerty" keyboard and when a key is pressed, displays the key on a 16-segment LED and "speaks" the letter. The genesis for the project really came from my two-and-a-half-year-old daughter, who likes to play with an old keyboard I bought at an electronics surplus store a few years ago; I thought it would be fun to wire it up to some electronics to give her some feedback and help her learn letters and numbers. (Figure 13.11.)

Just as a word of caution, this was a real junkbox project with the keyboard, LED display and speech synthesizer being parts that are probably not available in catalogs. In this application's write up, I do want to go through determining how the devices were actually wired and how I interfaced them to the microcontroller.

Despite this project taking from my junkbox the three major I/O peripherals used, this project never really deviated from my original design.

This circuit has three devices connected to the "P0/P2 bus" as memory mapped I/O: two 74LS374s which are used for the 16 segment LED display and a General Instruments SP0256. These devices are written to and are selected by a 74LS138, which demultiplexes addresses A8 to A10 and is enabled by "_WR." The output is used as clocks for all the devices on the P0/P2 bus.

One of the big things that you should notice in Figure 13.12 (and on the P0/P2 bus) is the lack of a 74LS373 connected to Port0 to latch in the low 8 bits of the address while a data byte is being transferred. I don't have to worry about the low 8 bits of address for the devices because I specified their addresses on 256 address boundaries, which eliminated the need to

Figure 13.11 Marya's talking keyboard.

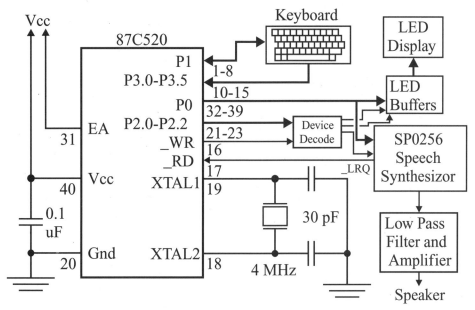

Figure 13.12 87C520-based talking keyboard schematic.

latch the lower 8 bits. Eliminating the '373 from the circuit simplifies the wiring somewhat (and you can see from Figure 13.12, I needed all the help I could get here).

Power for the circuit is supplied by a 9-volt radio battery. The "typical" power supply circuit that I use is Figure 13.13.

This circuit will take voltage from a "wall wart" or a 9-volt battery equally well. If you want to use a 6-volt (i.e., four "AA" batteries) supply, a 78C05 should be used. I always put a "power on" LED in all my applications. This is a nice visual indicator that power is available and there aren't any problems (like the power being shorted).

When I built the circuit, the first peripheral I built and tested was the LED display. The LED display that I used is a 16-segment LED display that can display a number of different "alphanumeric" characters. The display itself is a "common anode" type, which means that a positive voltage is supplied to the device and to light the LEDs in a specific pattern, different LED connections are pulled to ground. The outputs of the '374s are always enabled (which means that Pin 1 of the '374s is pulled to ground) and the outputs have a series 220-ohm current-limiting resistor to make sure the current capabilities of the LEDs and '374 are not exceeded.

74LS374s are latched parts, which means that once I wrote a byte to them, it would be stored until the next one. This was important because it meant that I wouldn't have to scan through the displays. They were "set and forget."

The circuit itself was built on a prototyping card which meant I ended up with a real mess of wiring to do. In the interests of trying to keep my sanity, I tried to keep the wiring as short as possible, which means that there isn't a real order to how the LED was wired. Once the device was wired, I used "AP3V3.ASM" to figure out which segments were wired to which bits of the two '374s (which were located at addresses 00000h and 00400h of the 87C520's external data space memory map).

After running this program, I determined that the LED display was wired as:

```
- 8 - - 8 -          With:  "#" Being the '374 Bit at Address 000h
|\   |   / |                 "_#" Being the '374 Bit at Address 0400h
7 6  4 _2  _6
|  \ | /   |
-_1 - -_7 -
|  / | \   |
5 2  3  1  _5
|/   |   \ |
-_3 - -_4 -
```

With this information, I was then able to represent the different alphanumeric characters ("0" through "9" and "A" through "Z"). Blank was specified as setting all the bits high. "AP3V4.ASM" is a test program that runs through all the different characters.

With this done, it was now time to wire up the SP0256. This device was first made available about 15 years ago from General Instruments (which, interestingly enough became "Microchip" sometime afterward) and when written with a byte, will convert that byte to a "phoneme" (which is a basic English sound) and output it as a PWM signal.

In Figure 13.14, I have shown how the device is wired and not included any pins that are left unconnected.

The "_LRQ" pin is reset when the operation has completed (phoneme has been output and the device is ready to accept the next one). After a phoneme is output, the _LRQ bit (connected to "_RD" on the 87C520) is polled until it goes low, at which time the next phoneme can be sent.

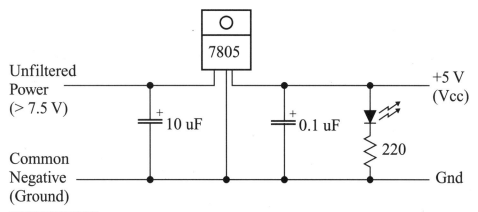

Figure 13.13 Basic +5-volt power supply for microcontroller applications.

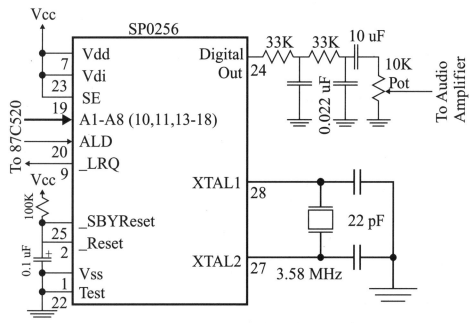

Figure 13.14 General Instruments SP0256 speech synthesizor wiring.

Now, if you're like me and like to test the circuit every step of the way, you will find that the SP0256 is not a very satisfying device. As I said above, the speech output is a PWM signal that does not give you a lot of useful information by looking at it (it just looks like a square wave with some jitter). It does look like a much more reasonable audio signal once it has run through the low-pass filter (the mess of resistors and capacitors connected to "audio out"). The "audio amplifier" is an LM386 wired as a standard audio amplified connected to an 8-ohm speaker for the speech output.

If you get a copy of the "actual" SP0256 data sheets, you'll notice that the specified clock is 3.12 MHz. I replaced this with a color-burst frequency (3.579545 MHz) crystal without any problems. If you are want to go with a 3.12-MHz crystal, you may have to have one custom made (which isn't impossible, but will take several weeks).

The SP0256 controls (which are described as "address bits") use the following phonemes (the sounds of which are capitalized):

ADDRESS	PHONEME	ADDRESS	PHONEME
0	10 msec pause	32	abOUt
1	30 msec pause	33	dOg
2	50 msec pause	34	pIG
3	100 msec pause	35	Vest
4	200 msec pause	36	GUest
5	bOY	37	SHiver
6	mY	38	aZure
7	End	39	bRave
8	Come	40	Favour
9	Power	41	Kite
10	Gym	42	Camera
11	Never	43	Zoo
12	pIn	44	boNG
13	To	45	Light
14	Ran	46	Window
15	sUccess	47	repAIR
16	Micro	48	WHen
17	Test	49	Yummy
18	THe	50	CHart
19	mE	51	URn
20	rAY	52	greatER
21	Dog	53	tOW
22	dO	54	THe
23	cAUght	55	Sissy
24	tOp	56	Now
25	YEti	57	How
26	cAt	58	stoRage
27	Hat	59	chARm
28	Bat	60	jAR
29	THIn	61	Gone
30	lOOk	62	Lazy
31	fOOd	63	draB

As you look through this list, you'll probably feel like a number of the sounds are repeated. This is not quite true. Some of the sounds that seem to be the same are subtly different. When chosing the phonemes for a given word, you might want to try all the options before finalizing on the pattern of the word.

The quality of the speech that comes out from this chip ranges from very good to virtually unintelligible. In this application, when I output a letter or a number, I first have the application "say" "letter" or "number." These words come through very clearly, but some of the numbers and letters do not and in some cases the last sound is continually output (although this might be a function of my not spending enough time with the application trying to come up with the "best" sound combination).

When specifying the phonemes for a word, it helps to break up the word into each of its constituent sounds.

For example, the letter "X" can be characterized as:

1. Short "e"
2. "K"
3. "s"

which uses addresses 7, 41, and 55 and sounds pretty good.

With the I/O functions defined, I finally turned my attention to developing the keyboard input interface. As I said above, the keyboard that I used was a surplus unit that I had bought a number of years ago (and actually used in an application in *Programming and Customizing the PIC*). There was no documentation that came with the keyboard, so I had to figure out how it was wired.

The first thing that I did was set up a matrix, and using a DMM, I "beeped" out every key with the two different connector pins. With this information, I created the matrix below:

PIN	1	2	3	4	5	6	7	8	9	10	11	12	13	14	15
1					"V"	"R"			"4"		"M"	"J"	"F"	"7"	"U"
2					"C"	"E"			"3"		","	"k"	"D"	"8"	"I"
3					"X"	"W"			"2"		"."	"L"	"S"	"9"	"O"
4						Ctrl			Fctn		"="	" "	Shift		Ent
5							"E"	"Z"							
6							"T"	"Q"							
7									"5"		"N"	"H"	"G"	"6"	"Y"
8									"1"		"/"	";"	"A"	"0"	"P"
9										Caps					
10															
11															
12															
13															
14															
15															

Once this was done, I manipulated the table until I could get a good understanding how the keyboard was wired and what would be the best way to wire it to the 87C520. The design point I decided upon was setting up eight rows (or register bits) for each column. I defined the "row" as where I put the pull up and the "column" as the pin I pull to ground.

The data was transformed into the following table, where the rows and columns are the pin numbers on the connector:

COLUMN ROW ->	5	6	9	11	12	13	14	15
1	"V"	"R"	"4"	"M"	"J"	"F"	"7"	"U"
2	"C"	"E"	"3"	","	"K"	"D"	"8"	"I"
3	"X"	"W"	"2"	"."	"L"	"S"	"9"	"O"
4		Ctrl	Func	"="	" "	Shift		Enter
7	"B"	"T"	"5"	"N"	"H"	"G"	"6"	"Y"
8		"Q"	"1"	"/"	";"	"A"	"0"	"P"
10			Caps					

With this information, I was ready to specify the wiring. Looking at my design, I noticed that P1 had all 8 bits not specified and P3 had bits 6 and 7 used for the bus interface. My reaction to this was to "drop" row 10 (which only has the capital letter lock) from my design, which meant I only required 14 bits in total (with 8 of them being common).

To read the pins, I wrote 0FFh to P1 and used it as the bit receiver. P3.0 to P3.5 was used as a set of rows to be pulled down individually to see if any of the keys were pressed. Normally, the P3 bits were left "high," except to scan a row. If the row read back in P1 is not equal to 0FFh, then one of the keys is pressed. Knowing the bit pattern in P1 and the bit pulled low in P3, we can determine which key is pressed by figuring out the first low bit in P1 (which is accomplished by rotating the bits into the carry flag until the carry flag is low).

When you look at the final code for this application ("AP3V7.ASM") you might feel like I cheated on the actual application. I didn't debounce the keyboard inputs. Actually, with the way that I wrote the application, this wasn't necessary. After a key is determined to be pressed, I output the character on the LED, "say" the character, and then wait one second before polling for the bit to be released. Once the bit is released, I wait a quarter of a second before resuming the polling of the key, which should be enough time for the released key to stop bouncing.

Is this a "proper" way of doing the application? It works very well, so if that's your measurement then the answer is "yes." I think the answer to the question is really in the question; in this case, because speaking the character can take a large fraction of a second, high speed operation (i.e., touch typing) is not possible and this simple method of debouncing is appropriate for this application. If I were designing an application where high-speed data entry via the keyboard was required, then I would not use this scheme for debouncing the keys.

Sample SP0256 parts as well as wiring data sheets are available from:

B.G. Micro
P.O. Box 280298
Dallas, Texas 75228
1(800)276-2206 or (972)271-5546
Fax: (972)271-2462

email: bgmicro

@bgmicro.com

//www.bgmicro.com

8051 SUMMARY

CONTENTS AT A GLANCE

8051 Resources	Listservers
Web Sites	Companies

I feel like I have not given as complete a description of the 8051 as I do for the other devices, but when I measure what I've written here to the 8051's datasheets, I think I have done a reasonably complete job. The original 8051 "reference standard" really hasn't been updated by Intel in a long time and its peripheral features have been "frozen" at their 1980 level.

Despite this, a lot of other manufacturers have greatly improved upon the original 8051 design and feature set. If you were to look at the Philip's Web site, you would get a pretty good idea of a number of different peripheral features that are built into their line of 8051s.

The 8051 interface hardware is radically different from the other microcontrollers presented in this book. This is not a bad thing, but something you have to be aware of. I was able to get the example applications running with very few interfacing problems, despite the differences between the 8051 and other devices I am more familiar with. If you look back at the timer interrupt handlers, you can really see that the 8051 hardware has been designed for the programmer to quickly and easily update the operation of the devices.

I really like the 8051's architecture and instruction set. Both are very powerful and efficient in terms of instruction cycles and memory usage. Once you have grasped the bank register versus first 256 RAM address versus 64K data space issues, you shouldn't have any problems programming the device. Actually, this three-tierd method of providing memory with separate special function registers is, in my mind, the best register/RAM layout provided by any microcontroller presented in this book.

There are, however, two concerns that I have with the device and architecture. The first is the lack of good free tools available for the architecture. While the 8051 is very popular right now, I can see it losing ground to other microcontrollers simply because of the high-quality factory-supported development tools available for them. It would be nice to see more low-cost comprehensive support, either from third parties or device manufacturers.

My other concern with the 8051 architecture is the number of clock cycles required to execute each instruction. This is a performance limitation that is addressed in a number of different devices (i.e., the MCS-151, the "HSM" and "XA" devices), but it's unfortunate that a standard hasn't emerged for all 8051 manufacturers to embrace.

As I look over the Dallas Semiconductor's "HSM" part datasheets, I really feel that these devices are a good balance of modernizing the 8051 architecture and peripheral set while maintaining a high degree of compatibility with the original part.

8051 Resources

Developing this section of this book was actually the most difficult of any device. As noted at the start of the section, the 8051 is built by a number of different manufacturers, and each has focused on hardware but left developing tools up to third parties. The resources presented in this chapter only reflect a fraction of the companies and tools available, but they should give you a good set of pointers in discovering what is available.

Web Sites

One of the first things that I should present on the 8051 is Russ Hersch's excellent 8051 FAQ (Frequently Asked Questions) which is available at:

   ftp://rtfm.mit.edu/pub/usenet/comp.answers/microcontroller-faq/8051

This 50-plus-page document is an excellent source for all kinds of information about the 8051, including device and tool vendors.

For general information Web sites, here are my top eight:

   http://www.labyrinth.net.au/~steve/8051.html
   Good basic resource page. Has PaulMon on it, along with the AT89C2051 programmer.

   http://www.labyrinth.net.au/~steve/8051.html
   Good resource page. Was somebody asking about "dec DPTR?"

   http://www.ece.orst.edu/~paul/8051-goodies/goodies-index.html
   Home of PaulMon and other 8051 resources.

http://www.eg3.com/embe/gatox805.htm
Data book references and page references.

http://www.iotasys.com/
Software library for assemblers/disassemblers/compilers.

http://www.keil.com/c51/index.html
Software development house with a free evaluation kit.

http://www.tu-bs.de/studenten/akafunk/pr8051/
8051 tools/software for packet radio.

http://www.ece.orst.edu/serv/8051/
Another site with PaulM on tools, along with other hobbyist tools.

Listservers

Philips has provided a moderated listserver for discussions on 8051s in general and the Philips versions in particular. Subscribing to the list is accomplished by filling out the form at:

http://www.philipsmcu.com/join.html

Intel also has a newsgroup set up for the MCS-51 at:

http://www.intel.com/newsgroups/mcontrol.htm

Companies

The following six companies currently supply 8051s. I have included the company name along with its Web page and how to contact them using more traditional means:

Intel
http://developer.intel.com

Intel Corporation, Santa Clara
2200 Mission College Blvd.
Santa Clara, California 95052-8119
USA
Tel: (408) 765-8080
Fax: (408) 765-9904

Atmel
http://www.atmel.com

Atmel Corporate Headquarters
2325 Orchard Parkway
San Jose, Ca 95131
(408) 441-0311
Bulletin Board Service (408) 436-4309

Dallas Semiconductor
http://www.dalsemi.com

14

8051

Dallas Semiconductor
4100 Spring Valley Road
Suite 302
Dallas, TX 75244
Tel: (972) 788-2197
Fax: (972) 980-4290

ISSI

http://www.issiusa.com/month.html

Integrated Silicon Solution, Inc.
2231 Lawson Lane
Santa Clara, Ca 95054
(408)588-0800
Fax: (408) 588-0805

Philips

http://www.philipsmcu.com

Philips Semiconductors
811 East Arques Avenue
P.O. Box 3409
Sunnyvale, CA 94088-3409
Tel. 1(800) 234-7381
Fax. 1(800) 943-0087

Siemens

http://www.siemens.de/Semiconductor/products/ICs/34/mc_home.html

Siemens Microelectronics
10950 North Tantau Avenue
Cupertino, CA 95014

MOTOROLA 68HC05

MOTOROLA 68HC05

MICROCONTROLLERS

If you're an old guy like I am, you probably first learned assembly language programming on the Motorola 6800. The 6800 was one of the first 8-bit microprocessors available, and even though the architecture is over 25 years old, it is still viable and used as a microcontroller processor architecture. A great testament to the longevity and viability of the design is the announcement by Motorola of April of 1997 that over two billion 68HC05s had been delivered to customers. (Figure 15.1.) The 68HCxx series is best known as "HC05," "HC08," and "HC11." These abbreviations will be used throughout this section.

Motorola has created a very complete line of microcontrollers, the 68HC05 (and the 68HC08, which is based on the 68HC05). The high end of the line includes the 68HC11, which has a slightly different architecture and more features (such as a built-in multiply instruction). All 68HCxx series microcontrollers use the "Von Neumann" or "Princeton" architecture and "CISC" (complex instruction set computer) methodologies exclusively. This makes the 68HCxx somewhat unique in the world of micrcontrollers, but if the wide

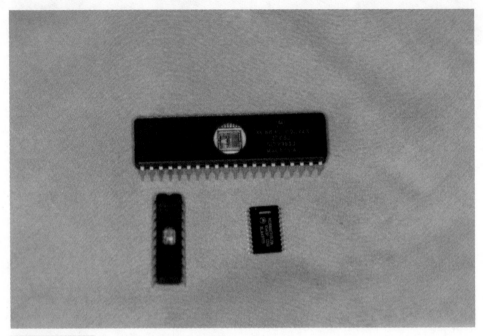

Figure 15.1. Example 68HC05 parts.

range of applications is any indication (from pagers to automotive controllers), the architecture is very capable.

Using the Princeton architecture means that the 68HCxx can implement some applications easier than the other microcontrollers. In the applications chapter, later in this section, I will demonstrate this with a 68HCxx RTOS.

I am going to focus in on the 68HC05 primarily. From this, you should be able to pick up information and concepts needed for the 68HC08 (which is really very similar and part of the same family as the 'HC05) and 68HC11. The HC11 (as it is best known) is quite a bit different (although offers quite a bit better performance), but using the techniques I outline in this book, you should still be able to work with it very easily.

At the time of writing this chapter, there are over 180 different HC05 part numbers (not including different packaging types), each with a different function and features. The range of features available in the 68HCxx parts is truly staggering.

To make it easier to understand what each family does, the HC05 parts are broken up by "letter" codes as listed in the following table:

LETTER CODE	DESIGNATED PURPOSE	FEATURES/COMMENTS
"B"	Automotive/ Industrial	ADC, PWM DAC, SCI, EEPROM - Designed for Wide Temperature Range Applications
"BD"	Television/ Monitors	Hor/Vert Synch Processors, PWM DAC - Designed for Computer Monitors

LETTER CODE	DESIGNATED PURPOSE	FEATURES/COMMENTS
"C" & "D"	General Purpose	High Pin Count, SCI, SPI, I2C, 16 Bit Timer
"C0"	64K External Memory	No built-in ROM/RAM - Designed for Interfacing to External Memory
"CC"	Video Applications	CCTV Decoders, OSD, I2C, ADC, PWM DAC, PLL - Designed for TV/VCR Applications
"E"	General Purpose	PLL, EEPROM, ADC - Telecommunications and General Purpose Applications
"F"	Telecom	DTMF, DTMG, SPI - Telecommunications
"G"	General Purpose	Very High Pin Count, ADC, SPI, PWM DAC, PLL
"J" & "K"	General Purpose	16 and 20 Pin Devices, 15 Bit Timer
"JB"	USB Intface	Designed for USB Applications
"L" & "LN"	LCD Drivers	LCD Drivers, SCI, SIOP, ADC, EBI, DTMF, PLL - LCD Driving Applications/Telephones
"M"	VFD Drivers	Vacuum Fluorescent Driver
"MC"	Motor Control	ADC, Multiple PWMs
"MP"	Motor Control	Multiple ADCs, Six Channel PWM
"P"	General Purpose	28 Pin Device, ADC, SIOP, EEPROM
"RC"	Remote Controls	IR LED Modulation Circuit
"SC"	Security Applications	Restricted ROM Access, Die Serialization, Available in Dies or Packages
"T"	Television/VCR	OSD, ADC, PWM DAC, I2C
"V"	Automotive	J1850, VReg, ADC, PWM DAC, SPI, EEPROM
"X"	Automotive	CAN, VReg, ADC, PWM DAC, SCI, EEPROM

15

The letter code system is also used for the HC08 and HC11 (although different letters correspond to different functions in the different devices).

Many of these devices were designed for specific applications and not for general availability. This means that you may find a device that meets your requirements perfectly but is not available. For learning about the device and simple applications I find the best method of selecting a Motorola 68HCxx devices is to choose from a distributor's catalog, finding the one that best meets your requirements, rather than going through Motorola datasheets exclusively.

THE MOTOROLA 68HC05
PROCESSOR ARCHITECTURE

The CPU

The Motorola 68HC05 (and 68HC08) processor is based on the 6800 microcoprocessor and is a true "Von Neumann" or "Princeton" architected CPU. This means that the instruction memory, RAM registers, and I/O registers are all placed in the same memory space. (Figure 16.1.)

As I've noted earlier in the book, this architecture offers a number of advantages in terms of software flexibility. Along with being able to allow RTOS and debuggers/monitors, programs can be downloaded into RAM and tested and debugged without going through the EPROM programming/erasing steps.

The Accumulator

The architecture shown in Figure 16.1 can be implemented (and has been in a number of processors), but it may not be considered optimal in terms of instruction length or in total cycles per instruction.

For example, adding two numbers and storing the result in a third register would have the form:

```
add Reg1, Reg2, Result   ;  Result = Reg1 + Reg2
```

This would require 4 to 7 bytes to store the instruction (1 or 2 bytes for the address of each of the three registers and 1 byte for the instruction itself) and a minimum of 10 instruction cycles to execute.

This may be hard to understand, so I wanted to list out all the operations for the instruction:

1. Load instruction into "decoder" hardware—Seven cycles.
2. Load "Reg1" into ALU input #1—One cycle.
3. Load "Reg2" into ALU input #2 and perform "ADD"—One cycle.
4. Store result of "ADD" in "result"—One cycle.

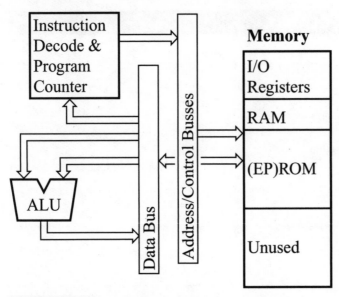

Figure 16.1 Basic 68HC05 processor architecture.

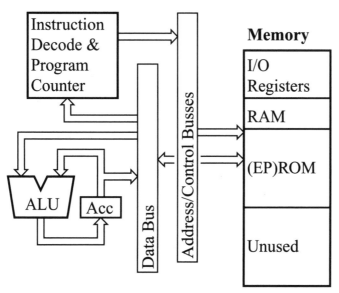

Figure 16.2 68HC05 architecture with accumulator.

This is not the best solution because it means that latches have to be put in the inputs of the ALU, and if the result is an intermediate value, a register to store this value will have to be used in RAM (which there isn't a lot of). Also, the instruction decoder will have to have enough space for all the information of the instruction to decode it (and issue appropriate commands to the ALU) as well as drive the address/control buses. This can be very complex if immediate or indexed parameter addressing is required as well.

To eliminate this complexity, a temporary register has been added to store the result of an operation as well as provide the second input to the ALU. (Figure 16.2.)

With this, arithmetic operations now store their result in the accumulator ("Acc") for use in subsequent operations or store directly into RAM.

The "LDA" ("load accumulator") instruction is used to load the accumulator with a temporary value that can be arithmetically combined with another value. (Figure 16.3.)

An example of one of these arithmetic operations is the "ADD" instruction, which adds a value from memory to the accumulator and stores the result back in the Accumulator. (Figure 16.4.)

Finally, when all this is done, the result (in the accumulator) can be stored back in memory. (Figure 16.5.)

Now, looking over this, you're probably thinking that this would take a lot more cycles and instruction memory than the example instruction above. Actually, the total difference is reasonably small (9 actual bytes for the 3 instructions, as opposed to 4 to 7 for the full instruction and 10 instruction cycles, which is the same as the full instruction) when implemented as 3 instructions in the 68HC05. But, as noted above, carrying out the operation above as three instructions makes the design of the device much simpler and allows a great deal of flexibility that will be discussed in the "register and data addressing" subchapter below.

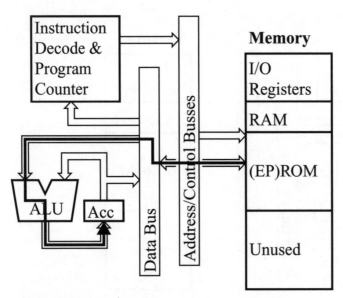

Figure 16.3 68HC05 LDA instruction data path.

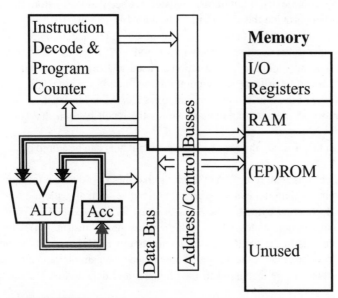

Figure 16.4 68HC05 ADD instruction data path.

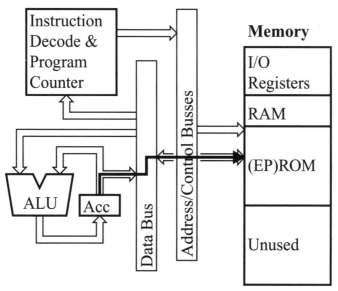

Figure 16.5 68HC05 STA instruction data path.

The Condition Code Register

The Motorola 6800 architecture uses memory-mapped I/O for peripheral feature registers, but the primary context registers cannot be accessed directly. Instead, they are updated during different operations (arithmetic instructions, interrupts, etc.) and accessed by others.

The first processor register in this catagory is the "condition code register" (known as the "STATUS" register in many other processors). This register is updated either by specific instruction (i.e., "SEC" sets the carry flag) or execution uses one of the register's bits as an input parameter (i.e., "BEQ" jumps to the specified offset if the zero flag is set). But, for the most part, the register is updated after an arithmetic instruction (i.e., "ADD" can update the carry, zero, half-carry, and negative flags of the CCR register). (Figure 16.6.)

The CCR register is defined with the following flags:

BIT	FLAG NAME	DESCRIPTION
0	Carry/Borrow	Set when Addition/Subtraction Outside Bounds
1	Zero	Set when the Result of an Operation = 0
2	Negative	Set when the Result of an Operation & 0x080 != 0
3	Interrupt Mask	When Set, Interrupts Enabled/Allowed
4	Half-Carry Flag	Set when Addition/Subtraction on First Nybble > 15
5	Not Used	= 1
6	Not Used	= 1
7	Not Used	= 1

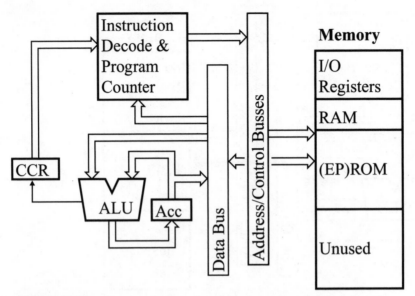

Figure 16.6 68HC05 architecture with CCR (status) register.

The carry flag is set when the result of an addition is greater than 0x0FF or the result of a subtraction is less than zero. This is used to indicate in 16-bit (and larger) numbers that the next hex digit (8 bits long) is either incremented (for addition) or decremented (for subtraction) when the result is outside the bounds of an 8-bit number.

For example, adding two 16-bit numbers and storing the result in another 16-bit number can be done simply with the code:

```
lda  Reg1 + 1    ;  Get the Low Byte of the first Number
add  Reg2 + 1    ;  Add the Second to the First
sta  Result + 1  ;  Store the Low Byte of the Result
lda  Reg1        ;  Get the High Byte of the First Number
adc  Reg2        ;  Add 2nd to 1st (with Carry from low 8 Bits)
sta  Result      ;  Store the High Byte of the Result
```

There are a few things to note in this code. The first is the order of the data in a 16-bit number. In Motorola processors, the high byte always comes first (is at the lower address). This will be discussed elsewhere in this section. If the "ADC" instruction did not exist, then the carry flag would have to be used to set a value in "Result" for later (i.e., if it's set, then "result" would be loaded with 1, else it would be cleared).

This can be shown as:

```
clr  Result      ;  Clear the High Byte of the Result
lda  Reg1 + 1    ;  Add Low Bytes together and Save in "Result"
add  Reg2 + 1
sta  Result + 1
bcc  CarrySkip   ;  If Carry Set, Increment High Byte of Result
inc  Result
CarrySkip:
lda  Reg1        ;  Now, Add the High Bytes to "Result" and Store
add  Reg2
add  Result      ;  Add Sum to Result (Incremented due to Carry)
sta  Result
```

The carry flag is also set if the result of a subtraction operation is less than zero. The "SBC" (subtract with carry flag) works similarly to the "ADC" instruction; the result has one subtracted from the result. Note the difference in how the carry/borrow flag operates in the 68HCxx and the PIC (which does not use the carry flag as a borrow flag with subtraction operations).

The zero flag is set upon completion of an operation if the result is equal to zero. This means that either:

```
or     0      ;   "OR" the Accumulator with Zero
```

or

```
and    $FF    ;   "AND" the Accumulator with all bits set
```

can be used to test the contents of the accumulator and set the zero flag if it contains zero without changing the contents of the register (although, chances are, after the previous operation, the zero flag will be set or reset appropriately upon its completion). The "LDA" instruction will set the zero flag based on the value loaded into the accumulator (which should help eliminate the need for these instructions to test the value in the accumulator)— but not affect the state of the carry flag.

The negative flag is set when the result of an operation has set the top bit (bit 7) of the accumulator. Like other processors, the 68HCxx only handles negative numbers implicitly, as two's complement numbers, not explicitly identifying the value as positive or negative and handling it differently, depending on the case.

The interrupt mask is not truly an execution flag (like the other flags in the CCR) and cannot be affected by an arithmetic instruction. "Interrupt Mask" is read by the Instruction Decode hardware when an interrupt request is encountered. If it is reset (equal to zero), then the interrupt is latched and is executed when the bit becomes set. The interrupt process will be described in greater detail later in this chapter.

The last bit to be concerned about in the 68HCxx CCR is the "half-carry" flag. This bit is set when the low nybble of the addition or subtraction requires a carry/borrow from the high nybble of the value. This flag is usually required in algorithms that use single bytes to store each digit of a value.

In this case, the following subroutine would be used to increment the digits in a 2-digit hex number (in which each digit is stored in a byte):

```
IncNumber:                 ;   Increment Number, Carry Value between Digits

   lda   1                 ;   Add "1" to the Lowest Digit
   add   Digit + 1
   sta   Digit + 1
   bhcc  IncNumEnd         ;   It has not rolled over 15

   clr   Digit + 1         ;   It has, Clear the Value
   lda   1                 ;   Add "1" to the Highest Digit
   add   Digit
   sta   Digit
   bhcc  IncNumEnd

   clr   Digit             ;   Have to Clear the High Digit

IncNumEnd:                 ;   Finished, Return to Caller

   rts
```

The three most significant bits of the CCR register are always "1." You're probably asking yourself, what does this matter? But for applications like RTOS', where the CCR has to be loaded with an initial value, knowing the values of the CCR bits to load is important.

Register and Data Addressing

I think this is a good time for a quick aside to explain a significant difference between the 68HC05 (and other Motorola processors) and other devices. Motorola 8-bit processors (like the 68HC05) reverse the sequence of bytes in 16-bit numbers as compared to other processors.

In most processors, 16-bit numbers are stored low byte and then high byte. For example, in an 8051, you may look at a 16-bit value and see:

```
0x03412
```

This value is actually "$1234." As you work with processors that do this, you will be able to make the translation mentally and it will seem very natural to you (after all, the low byte is being put in the low address). If you've ever done any PC programming, you'll know that this is how the PC's processor stores 16-bit values.

In the 68HC05, you would see the same value represented as:

```
$1234
```

You're probably thinking this is great, completely intuitive, and there's no problem. You're probably wondering why I'm making a big deal of this. The reason why I'm making a big deal about this is because this is completely different from all the microcontroller processors presented in this book (and most other processors available on the market). In many ways, it's not a big deal, but something you have to be aware of and understand when to mentally flip the bytes and when not to.

The addressing modes of the 68HC05 are:

- "Inherent." A processor register is specified as part of the instruction (i.e., "INCA," the accumulator is incremented).
- "Immediate." The operand is included in the instruction (i.e., "ADD #2," add two to the accumulator).
- "Direct." The address of the register in the first 256 memory locations is included in the instruction (i.e., "lda $37", loads the contents of address $37 into the accumulator).
- "Extended." A 16-bit register address is included in the instruction (i.e., "goto $1234" changes the program counter to $1234).
- "Indexed, no offset." The 8-bit address is taken from the index register.
- "Indexed, 8-bit offset." An 8-bit offset is added to the value in the Index Register to calculate the data address.
- "Indexed, 16-bit offset." A 16-bit offset is added to the value in the index register to calculate the data address.

In this subchapter, I will discuss the first four addressing modes, and in the next subchapter, I will introduce the index register and how data is accessed using it. One of the most important points I should mention at this time is each basic instruction takes up one byte; when a parameter is passed to the instruction (i.e., data address or value) more bytes are added to the instruction. To execute each instruction, at least two (and up to eleven) instruction cycles are required.

Inherent addressing is the most basic method of accessing data. As I indicated above, the register (and often the bits of the register) are indicated as part of the instruction. Some examples of this instruction are "INCX," which increments the index register (and is not to be confused with "INC,X" which increments the data location pointed to by the index register) or "BCS," which branches if the carry flag of the CCR is set. All instructions with inherent addressing and no branch address are 1 byte long and take 2 or 3 instruction cycles to execute.

Immediate addressing is placing the value to be operated upon in the instruction and is denoted by placing a "#" character before the value. For example "ADC #12" will add "12" to the contents of the accumulator and increment the result if the carry was set before the addition took place. Instructions with immediate values take up 2 bytes and at least 3 instruction cycles.

Direct addressing is used to access memory in the first 256 addresses of the memory map. After the instruction byte, the 8-bit (1 byte) address of the register is specified (bit 8 and all the more significant bits are reset when the address is generated). An example would be clearing a specific byte in the RAM area; the instruction "CLR byte" would be used, which would have the machine code "$3F byte." Like immediate addressing, direct addressing requires 2 bytes per instruction and requires at least 3 instruction cycles.

Extended addressing would probably be better defined as "extended direct addressing." As the latter name implies, a direct address capable of accessing the entire 68HC05 memory space is passed with the instruction in "extended" addressing. This means that the instruction has been extended to 3 bytes (and at least 4 instruction cycles). As a rule of thumb, if an instruction is capable of direct addressing, then it is also capable of extended addressing.

THE INDEX REGISTER

The 68HC05 architecture has a single 8-bit index register that can access memory anywhere inside the microcontroller's memory map. When an index addressed instruction is executed, the value in the index register is input into the instruction decode circuitry and an address is output on the databus for the indexed instruction. (Figure 16.7.)

You're probably wondering how the index register can access memory anywhere in the 68HC05's memory space if it is only 8 bits wide (which can only access up to 256 memory locations). It is done by adding an offset to the index register. Using the index register, there are three different addressing modes associated with it.

The first mode is "indexed, no offset" in which the index register is used with no offset. Each instruction is 8 bits long and takes at least as many instruction cycles as a "direct addressing" instruction. Because the index register is only 8 bits long, only the first 256 addresses in memory can be accessed.

When you first look at how "indexed, 8-bit offset" addressing works, you might be confused as to its purpose. In this addressing mode, an 8-bit offset is added to the index register, allowing any byte from 0 to 510 ($1FE) to be accessed. This will probably seem like a minor improvement in the basic "indexed, no offset" addressing mode.

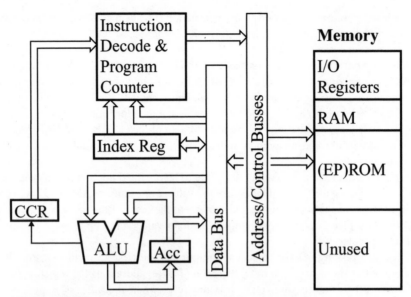

Figure 16.7 68HC05 architecture with index register.

Actually, it's a great improvement in terms of developing software for the 68HC05 and simplifies compiler development. The reason is that most RAM for the different 68HC05 devices is located in the first 512 addresses of the memory map. This means that arrays and other data structures can be accessed according to their start location (or offset). This eliminates the work required in other microcontrollers where the correct address (including offset) must be combined and placed in the index register before accessing memory.

With "indexed, 8-bit offset" addressing, the offset can be up to $FF (or 255). When this is combined with the values in the index register (up to $FF), the highest address that can be accessed is $1FE or 510 (which is 255 plus 255). The addresses are not wrapped around the $100 address boundary.

As you might have guessed, "indexed, 16-bit offset" addressing could also be referred to as "extended indexed addressing with offset." A 16-bit value is added as an offset to the value of the index register to create a 16-bit address.

While "indexed, 16-bit offset" addressing will give you access to the full 68HC05 memory space, it will not allow you access to larger than 256-byte arrays in memory. This gave considerable problems in the early days of microprocessors (back in the mid-to-late 1970s when we used to beat the skins we used for clothing on rocks by the river to clean them, following which we'd go kill a brontosaurus for dinner). Specifically, the problem was most prevalent in the 6502 used in the Apple II computer.

The solution to the problem was to create a 16-bit index register in software using self-modifying code. Actually, there are two solutions to the problem. The first (and probably more "correct") method of solving this problem is to use the 8-bit index register with a 16-bit offset to the start of each 256 byte (8-bit) address "block." In the 68HC05, a read could be accomplished by the following code:

```
Index16:            ;  Read the Index at X16
  ldx   X16+1       ;  Setup the Index Register
```

```
    lda    X16            ;  Now, Load the Accumulator with High 8 Bits
    bne    Index16_1      ;  Not in the First 256 Bytes, Go to Next one

    lda    X              ;  Read the byte in the First 256 Bytes
    rts                   ;  Return to Caller

Index16_1:                ;  Is the address in the second 256 Bytes?
    deca                  ;  Decrement the Counter
    bne    Index16_2      ;   If not == 0, then try next 256 Byte "block"

    lda    ($100), X      ;  Read the byte in the Second 256 Bytes
    rts

Index16_2:                ;  Is the address in the third 256 Bytes?
    .
    :
                          ;  And so on for the next 254 256 Byte blocks
```

Needless to say, this is a pretty tedious way to program. Also, this program will take 1,025 instructions (for 1,791 bytes of program storage) and anywhere from 21 to 3,582 instruction cycles. This space usage and instruction variability is unacceptable (especially considering that the 16-bit index write takes up even more memory and instruction cycles).

Now this could be improved in some microcontrollers that have a jump-to table (and from there, the index read could be made). This would have the advantage of making the subroutine execute in the same number of instructions each time (but would still require a lot of program storage). Unfortunately, the 68HC05 processor doesn't have a jump-to table instruction.

The second solution is the self-modifying code example I was talking about above. To carry out the 16-bit indexed read, the following code would be used:

```
Index16:                     ;  Read the Index at X16
    lda    X16               ;  Setup the Read Address
    sta    Index16_Read+1    ;  Change the Read Address
    lda    X16+1
    sta    Index16_Read+2
Index16_Read:                ;  Read Instruction
    lda    $1234             ;  Start with Dummy 16 Bit Address
    rts                      ;  Return to Caller
```

This solution takes considerably fewer memory bytes (only 12) and the same number of instruction cycles each time it's executed (24). The "write" version of this code is slightly more complex (and requires a holding register) but is still very simple. The code must be located in RAM and modifies itself (at the second and third bytes after "Index16_Read"), which is probably something you've been taught is the worst thing that you can ever do when programming.

Well, from a purist's point of view, yes it is the programming equivalent of mass murder. But if you have to implement a long table (longer than 256 bytes) anywhere in memory and only have an 8-bit index register, this is the best way of implementing a 16-bit index register.

The Program Counter

If you've worked with other Princeton-architected processors, the 68HC05's program counter will be very similar to what you would expect. The Program Counter registers cannot be written to explicitly.

If you've worked with 8-bit microprocessors, then there is one difference in the 68HC05's that you should be aware of; the 68HC05's program counter can only access the maximum memory available in the device and not a full 64K (using a full 16-bit addressing). So if you are using a 68HC0C8, there is 7.8K of EPROM and PROM control memory and 0.2K of RAM, then the program counter will be thirteen bits long (and able to access the 8K of memory and nothing more). Once the program counter has reached $1FFF (8191) it will "roll over" to 0 and not increment to $2000, which is what you'd expect if you'd worked with 8-bit microprocessors that have 16-bit program counters. (Figure 16.8.)

In Figure 16.8, you'll see that I've changed the name of the "Instruction Decode & Program Counter" box in the previous architecture diagrams. The reason for this will be shown as we go through the next few features available in the 68HC05.

The program counter is updated by the branch, jump, call, and return instructions and cannot be accessed directly. But as I've discussed elsewhere in the book, to implement monitors and RTOS,' access to the program counter is necessary.

Accessing the program counter can be done indirectly by using the stack. After a call or interrupt request, the data in the stack is in a known state. Typically in an RTOS or monitor program, the "kernel" software is initiated with an interrupt. To return to the executing program, a new program counter value will be put back onto the stack.

For example, if you were in a subroutine which was called when the Stack pointer was at the top of the stack, you could return to an arbitrary point in the 68HC05 by using the following code for the "return":

```
SubEnd:                 ;  Jump to New Location
    lda  NewAddr        ;  Load the Stack with the New Return Address
    sta  StackTop - 1   ;  StackTop == $FF for 68HC05C8
    lda  NewAddr + 1    ;  Now, Load the Low Byte of the Return Address
    sta  StackTop - 2
    rts                 ;  Return from Subroutine
```

Now you may be thinking that this is a complex way of implementing a "jump" or "goto," but this will allow jumping to an arbitrary location anywhere in the memory space (which cannot be accomplished by any single instruction). With this code, you are going to have to make sure you understand exactly where the stack is pointing to before writing to the stack area.

THE STACK

The 68HC05's processor, like the processors in other microcontrollers, stores subroutine program counter and interrupt context registers on a stack to allow easy and fast retrieval upon return from subroutines and interrupt handlers. The 68HC05's Von Neumann architecture means that the stack is accessible by the processor (because there is one memory space). Although there are some restrictions compared to other Von Neumann processors you may be familiar with, the accessible stack pointer is a very flexible architecture feature that will help you to implement very complex applications, impossible in many of the other microcontrollers presented in this book.

The stack pointer is a 6-bit index register with an offset at $0C0. It could also be thought of as an 8-bit index register with the top 2 bits always set. This means that the register can access RAM from address $0C0 to $0FF.

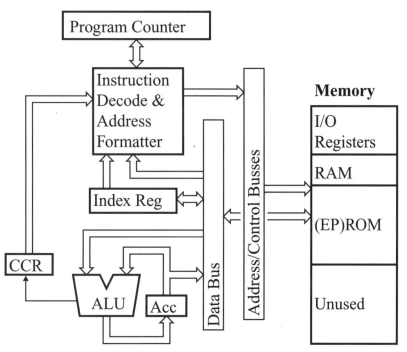

Figure 16.8 68HC05 architecture with program counter.

To better illustrate how the stack works in the 68HC05, Figure 16.9 shows the areas which it can access.

The "reset stack pointer" ("RSP") instruction sets the stack pointer to $0FF. When a subroutine is called, the instruction pointer to the next instruction is saved on the stack (least-significant address byte first). For an interrupt, not only is the program counter saved on the stack, but the CCR, accumulator, and index registers are also saved. Five bytes are saved for an interrupt request, where two bytes are saved for a subroutine call.

When specifying the stack for an application, you have to specify from $0FF down and set aside the amount of space required for the worst-case situation. For example, if in your mainline you have one nested subroutine (each subroutine requiring 2 bytes of stack space for the return addresses) and an interrupt handler that calls no subroutines (requiring 5 bytes for the return address and context register information), 9 bytes from $0F7 to $0FF has to be reserved for the stack.

The 68HC05's stack cannot be used for storing data (as can be normally done in most Von Neumann architectures). The context registers are saved during interrupts, but critical registers that are changed in the subroutine will have to be saved explicitly in variables at the start of the subroutine and restored before returning from the subroutine.

Above I demonstrated how the stack would be modified to change the program counter indirectly. For most applications, this type of action is not required. Instead, upon starting program execution, the stack pointer is reset to $0FF (the top of the stack area), and during execution the stack pointer can be ignored.

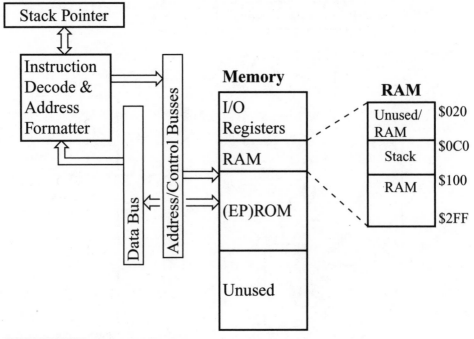

Figure 16.9 68HC05 stack pointer.

Reset

Reset for the 68HC05 is pretty typical for a microcontroller. Once power and reset are active, the built-in oscillator starts up and before the processor begins to execute by getting the reset vector, a 4064 cycle delay is put in to make sure the clock is valid.

Once the delay has completed, then the reset vector (the first address to be executed) is loaded from the "user vectors" at the end of the EPROM memory. In Figure 16.10, the boot sequence for a 68HC05J1A (with 1232 bytes of EPROM) is shown.

This is a pretty typical for a microcontroller and would allow for the _Reset line to be connected directly to Vcc. If an external oscillator is going to be used, in the "MOR" ("mask option register"), the 4064 cycle delay can be reduced to 16 cycles to speed up the initialization sequence.

In the previous diagram, you should note that for every two clock cycles, one instruction cycle is executed in the 68HC05. This means that if you have an instruction that requires two instruction cycles, four clock cycle periods will be requried to execute the instruction.

Also, if you're working with an application that you are planning on resetting often (i.e., if a test program is going to be downloaded into RAM), you should probably use the following circuit for _Reset, which is controlled by switch "SW" (when it's pushed down, the 68HC05 is reset). (Figure 16.11.)

BOOT ROM

In many 68HC05 devices, there are a few routines in mask ROM that are designed to make programming the device easier. This ROM is known as the "boot ROM," and when the

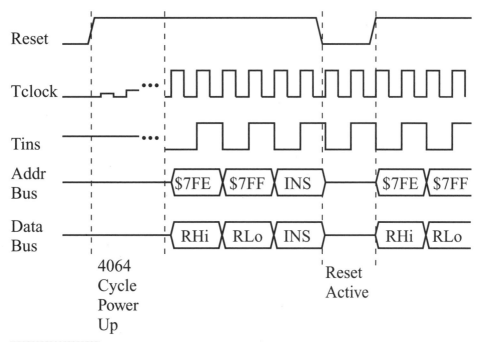

Figure 16.10 68HC05 power up and reset timing.

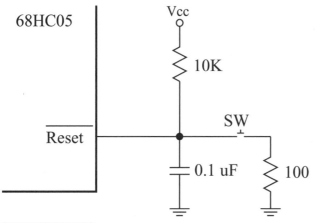

Figure 16.11 Example 68HC05 reset circuitry.

input pins are set to a specific state, this ROM is enabled (rather than the program burned into the 68HC05), allowing a program to be downloaded (either serially or in parallel) into the 68HC05, and then it is programmed directly into the EPROM. Using the boot ROM allows in-system programming of the 68HC05 or allows a very simple programmer to be developed for burning the devices. The 68HC05C8 is a device that is well equipped for using such a simple external programmer.

Interrupts

Interrupts are really an extension of the reset circuitry. When an interrupt request is encountered and the "mask" bit is enabled, the program counter is set to a specific value to respond to a specific interrupt. The 68HC05 is a bit different from other devices described in this book as the operation of multiple interrupt handlers (each one specific to an interrupt source) can be nested with very few concerns about how multiple interrupts co-exist.

Like reset, the location the interrupt handler begins to execute at is specified by address vectors programmed in the top of the user EPROM area. For the 68HC05C8, the following vectors have been defined:

VECTOR Source	INTERRUPT	CPU Request	VECTOR ADDRESS
Reset	N/A	Reset	$1FFE-$1FFF
SWI	Software Interrupt	Interrupt	$1FFC-$1FFD
IRQ	External Interrupt	Interrupt	$1FFA-$1FFB
Timer	Timer Interrupt	Interrupt	$1FF8-$1FF9
Asynch	SCI Interrupt	Interrupt	$1FF6-$1FF7

The address loaded at each of these locations is specified in the source file and burned into the EPROM at programming time. For "reset," the CPU is forced into a specific state (with specific power-on values for the various registers) before the reset vector is retrieved and loaded into the program counter.

If an interrupt request is executed, before the appropriate vector is loaded, the context registers are stored on the stack in the following order:

1. High byte of the program counter.
2. Low byte of the program counter.
3. Index register.
4. Accumulator.
5. Condition code register.

This requires up to ten instruction cycles to execute (with loading the interrupt vector).

Because all the "context" registers are saved at the start of the interrupt and the "RTI" ("return from interrupt") instruction restores these registers, implementing an interrupt handler is really quite simple. It is actually further simplified by the use of multiple vectors for each of the different interrupt request sources.

Implementing nested interrupts (both from multiple sources and from the same source) is quite simple, as long as the stack space isn't violated. To allow nested interrupts, once in an interrupt handler, the interrupt mask bit (bit 3 of the CCR) must be reset (using the "CLI" instruction) as soon as the interrupt source has been reset.

Peripheral Register Access

As I've shown in the architectural diagrams above, the peripheral registers are in the first 20 hex (32 decimal) bytes of the memory space. In all 68HC05s, the I/O control or peripheral registers are accessed by directly writing and reading to these addresses.

Except for the port control and I/O register addresses, there isn't any convention used for the addresses of the different devices. Actually, there is also quite a bit of difference between the functions in different addresses, so this is not totally a bad thing. If the same ports were used for different devices, then operation of the peripheral would become a hit-or-miss affair, with some commands working as expected and others not working at all. Putting the registers at different addresses for different devices will ensure that the applications being "ported" between devices will have to be properly reassembled/recompiled.

For the port addresses, the first four registers are the I/O bits for the "A" through "D" ports. If a port isn't available on the device, the register is unused. So, for a 68HC05J1A, which only uses two I/O ports, addresses $002 and $003 are left unused. The output-pin-enable registers are located at the next four addresses (i.e., PORTA "data direction register") are located starting at address $004.

68HC05 RAM Operations

An important philosophical point of the 68HC05 (and all Motorola 8-bit embedded microcontrollers) is that the RAM is not only available for variables and stack data but that code can also be loaded into it. This feature is used often to debug applications without having to erase and reburn the device's EPROM. Instead, the application (or parts of it) are downloaded into the 68HC05 using ROM code developed to take data from a host computer and put it into RAM.

In most 68HC05s, there is relatively little RAM available. Because of this, applications can be developed using an incremental approach with debugged code burned into EPROM and experimental code for debug downloaded into RAM for testing. This method can make the need for an emulator redundant and allow program development using a monitor program (i.e., Motorola's "BUFALO" monitor) and the actual chip to be put in the product with a host interface (i.e., RS-232).

MOTOROLA 68HC05 HARDWARE FEATURES

CONTENTS AT A GLANCE

When I first introduced you to the 68HC05, I indicated that at the time of writing, there are about 180 different electronic designs for the device available. This is really a mind-boggling number of different devices (when you include different packaging options, this means that there are literally about a thousand different 68HC05 part numbers that are possible). What may be confusing is the lack of availability of various devices that exactly meet your requirements.

Motorola works on a unique business model for providing 68HC05 devices. Like most complex devices, the 68HC05 is built from "macros" of different functions (i.e., put a processor with some RAM, EPROM, and I/O pins, and you have a microcontroller). But rather than provide set devices as part of a marketing plan, Motorola allows its customers to specify products that best suit the needs of the application and then work with Motorola to provide a part that exactly meets the customer's needs.

A great illustration of this is the following diagram from Motorola showing the functions laid out on a CMOS die (in this case a 68HC05C8). (Figure 17.1.)

Looking at Figure 17.1, you should be able to imagine that if your application required another serial I/O port, a new block could be put down on the die. This is almost exactly how Motorola works with a customer to come up with a new 68HC05 part number.

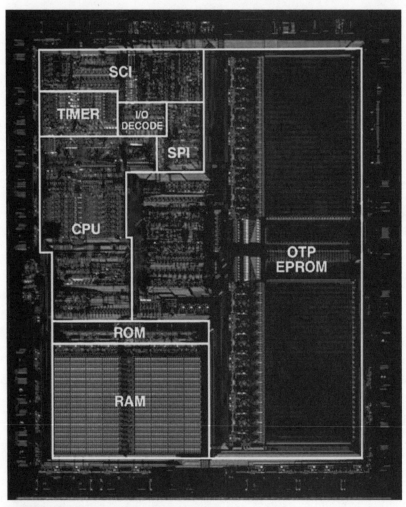

Figure 17.1 68HC05C8 chip layout.

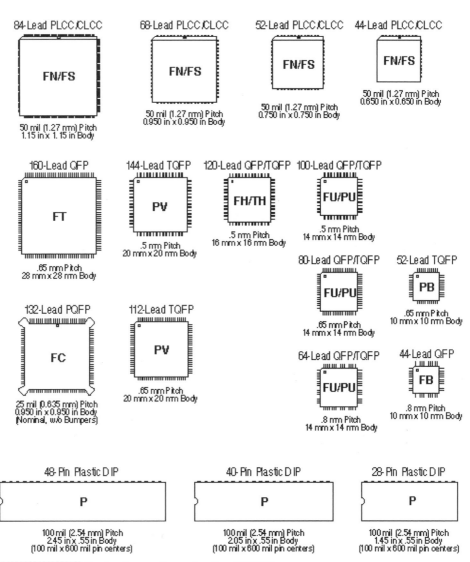

Figure 17.2 Packaging options for the 68HC05.

All 68HC05s (and all devices identified as "68HCxx") are built using CMOS logic technology.

Packaging

Like all the microcontrollers presented in this book, the different versions of the 68HC05 are available in many different packages. Figure 17.2 will give you an idea of some of the different packages available.

The letters in each of the packages indicate how the device to be ordered (i.e., a 68HC05C8 in a 40-pin plastic DIP package would be ordered as a "68HC05C8ACP" with the "AC" being device specifications).

What is not shown in Figure 17.2 is a number of different packages available for different devices. Motorola makes many EPROM devices available in ceramic-windowed packages, plastic ball grid array (PBGA) packages, as well as single dies. When looking at 68HC05 parts, it's important to know exactly what all the packaging options are for the parts.

System Clock

Like most microcontrollers, the 68HC05 is capable of connecting to a crystal with very little support hardware. One aspect of the 68HC05 that is somewhat unusual with regards to other devices is the relatively slow maximum speed the device is capable of. In many ways, this is offset by the "CISC" architecture and the wide variety of internal options. The 68HC05 family is also restricted by the relatively few available clocking options.

The usual method of clocking is by using an external crystal or ceramic resonator, as shown in Figure 17.3.

The crystal is used as a feedback device for a NAND gate. Actually, this is basically how crystal oscillators are implemented in all microcontrollers and clocking circuits. When "_STOP" is disabled (at a high-voltage level), the NAND gate behaves as an inverter, with the output taking a specific amount of time to pass through the crystal to the input of the inverter. "Rs" has a value on the order of 10 megohms and the external capacitors are between 20 and 30 pF.

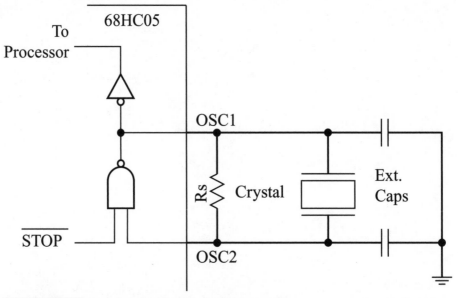

Figure 17.3 Crystal-based 68HC05 system clock.

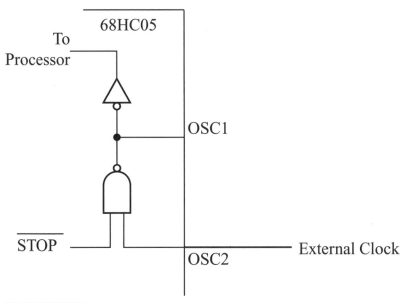

Figure 17.4 External 68HC05 system clock.

One interesting aspect of this circuit is that the "STOP" instruction drives an input gate that can turn off the oscillator. This is a very obvious and tangible difference between the "STOP" and "WAIT" instructions; STOP does stop everything in the processor and only restarts the oscillator when the reset is asserted or an interrupt on the "IRQ" pin is requested.

The 68HC05 can also be driven by an external clock (Figure 17.4).

With this circuit, the 68HC05 can be driven externally throughout the full frequency range, which is DC to 4 MHz. This maximum frequency may seem to be rather low, especially compared to other devices presented in this book, but it is adequate for most applications. This low clocking speed is offset by the use of only two clock cycles per instruction cycle, very complete instruction set and the wide variety of peripheral hardware options designed for the 68HC05.

In some later devices, there is the option for an external RC oscillator network, but other than this, the 68HC05 does not have any more clocking options.

Logic Technology

Not surprisingly, all the different 68HC05 family devices use CMOS technology for primary logic functions. The 68HC05 requires a few milliamperes of current to run at 1 to 4 MHz. This is very standard for all the devices presented in this book.

For devices designed for application development, EPROM is used with a windowed part. OTP EPROM parts are available, but as will be discussed later in this chapter, the 68HC05 does not have many of the same capabilities as other microcontrollers for ISP during the manufacturing process.

Interrupts

Like the other microcontrollers, interrupts are very easy to implement in the 68HC05. Actually, interrupts are easier to implement in the 68HC05 than in the other microcontrollers because the processor execution context registers are automatically saved at the start of the interrupt handler and restored during the interrupt handler return.

Typical interrupt flow can be seen in (admittedly confusing) Figure 17.5. This diagram is intended to represent what happens in the 68HC05 when an IRQ hardware interrupt request is received by the processor. I have numbered each of the actions taken in handling an interrupt. These are the same actions taken in the other devices to ensure reliable operation.

In "1," the processor is running normally with the interrupt bit of the CCR reset, and the "IRQE" (IRQ interrupt enable) bit of the ISCR register is set. This will cause an interrupt request upon a falling edge on the "_IRQ" pin. During the instruction at "Addr," the interrupt request is received.

Because the "IRQE" bit is set and the "I" bit of the CCR is reset, the interrupt will be executed. The context registers (accumulator, index register, CCR, and program counter) are pushed onto the stack. Note that the program counter is actually pointing to the instruction at "Addr+1." If the stack pointer is at the end of the stack (has a value less than $C4), the stack will wrap around to $FF. This obviously will mean that the stack is trashed. In this case, the top of the stack is trashed (either overwriting return information or data).

Once the context registers are saved, the appropriate interrupt vector is pulled out of the user EPROM vector area and loaded into the program counter and the "I" bit of the CCR is set. This is "3" in the diagram.

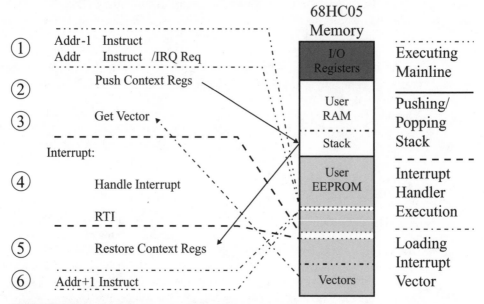

Figure 17.5 68HC05 IRQ pin interrupt processing.

"4" shows the interrupt handler executing. In the interrupt handler, the only hardware-specific action to be taken is that the "IRQR" (interrupt reset) bit of the ISCR register has to be reset. At the end of the interrupt ("5"), the "RTI" instruction will restore the context registers (i.e., pop the accumulator, index register, CCR, and program counter off the stack) and reset the "I" bit of the CCR which will allow another interrupt to execute.

At "6," the 68HC05 has resumed executing the mainline at the intstruction after the interrupted one.

The "port A I/O pin interrupts" will cause a (different) interrupt when one of the four state pins (Bits 0 through 3) goes high. This interrupt actually works in the same way as the "_IRQ" pin does, but requests an interrupt when one of the pins goes high.

Many other peripheral devices in the 68HC05 can cause interrupts, and separate interrupts are available in the user EEPROM's "vector area." This means that a separate handler can be implemented for each different interrupt source, or a single handler can be used for all interrupt sources and the interrupt identification registers can be used to determine the pending interrupts.

Unlike Harvard-architected machines, nested interrupts can be very effectively implemented. This is because of the stack and execution structure (i.e., all the context registers are placed on the stack when the interupt request is acknowledged). To implement nested interrupts in the 68HC05, the "I" bit of the CCR has to be reset and sufficient stack space has to be allocated for any contingency.

The software interrupt instruction works in exactly the same manner as the other interrupts (including setting the "I" bit of the CCR), except that if the "I" bit of the CCR is set when the instruction handler is encountered, the interrupt handler will still execute. As I discussed in the "68HC05-instructions" chapter, the software interrupt can be used as a PC "BIOS"-like function in the 68HC05. If you are familiar with the "BIOS" (and "DOS") interrupts in the IBM PC, you'll know that the carry flag and accumulator can be used for passing data back and forth.

This could be accomplished in the 68HC05, but there are a few things to watch for. The first is, the "BIOS" SWI interrupt should be from the mainline (and not in a subroutine). This will allow you to easily find the various registers to modify the contents for return (i.e., change the carry flag in the saved CCR before executing the "RTI" instruction). Secondly, make sure that the "SWI" uses a different interrupt handler than the hardware interrupts. This will allow you to easily determine that the BIOS interrupt is executing.

In the RTOS presented in the "68HC05 Example Applications" chapter, I will show how "SWI" can be implemented as an interface to the RTOS for requesting system operations and changing data states.

Parallel Input/Output

The 68HC05's I/O pins are actually quite a bit different from the other devices. The largest difference is really based on the philosophy of how the voltage at the I/O pin is sensed. In the 68HC05, if a pin is in input mode, the state at the I/O pin is returned, but if the pin is in output mode, the current output value is returned, which may or may not be the actual value at the I/O pin. (Figure 17.6.)

17

MOTOROLA 68HC05

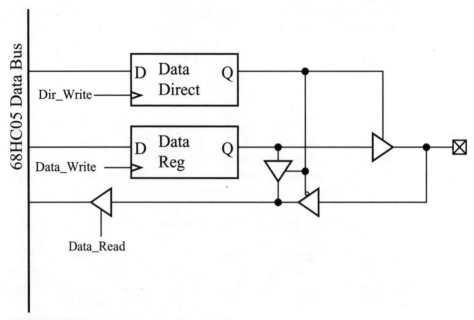

Figure 17.6 68HC05 parallel I/O pins.

If you look at Figure 17.6, you'll see that if the I/O pin is in the input state (output of "data direct" is reset), the state of the pin will be returned. But if the I/O pin is in the output state ("data direct" output is set), then reading back from the port will read the programmed-in value for the pin output.

The 68HC05 is also unusual in that some pins on some devices can have enabled pull downs (normally in microcontrollers a pull up is put on the pin). These pull downs are enabled by resetting the "PDI" bit in the MOR and then setting a pin as input and resetting the appropriate bit in the "pull down register." While this sounds very complex, it's really quite simple. (Figure 17.7.)

Because the pull down only works when the pin is in input mode, adding a button for control to the 68HC05 is very simple. (See Figure 17.8.)

In output mode, the I/O pins can sink and source enough current to drive LEDs and most other outputs that are required. High current devices will have to be driven through a power amplifier system.

Programmable Timers

The timers available to the 68HC05s work differently than in other devices. This is because a different philosophy was used in their design. Rather than allowing the user to specify a time interval, the 68HC05's timers run continuously with the application code monitoring the current state (or waiting for a specific delay). In this subchapter, I'm going to show how this philosophy works in a very simple implementation (the timer in the 68HC05J1A) and a more complex configuration in the 68HC05C8.

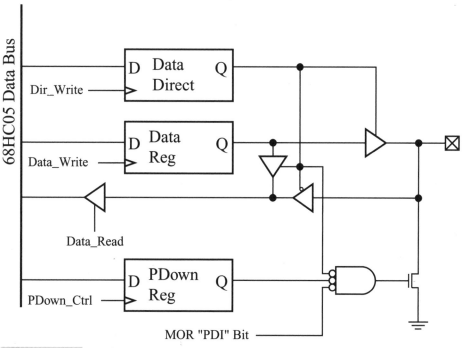

Figure 17.7 68HC05 parallel I/O pins with integral pull down.

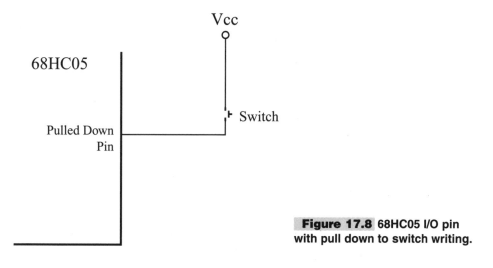

Figure 17.8 68HC05 I/O pin with pull down to switch writing.

The J1A's clock continually runs from the microcontroller's instruction clock (the external clock divided by two). When the timer overflows an interrupt request can be made. (Figure 17.9.)

There are a number of things to note in this circuit. The first and the one that will have the most impact to your application development is that the 8-bit timer cannot be written to by the program and is "free running" (which is to say that it is continually counting the number of execution cycles, whether you want it to or not). In other microcontrollers, the clock can be used to provide a specific delay, which will interrupt the processor. This means that specific delays cannot be built in using the 68HC05J1A's timer except if timer polling loops are put into the code.

For example, if you wanted to delay 50 instruction cycles before outputting data, you would use the code:

```
lda  TCR    ; Get the Value of TCR in 50 Instruction Cycles
add  #10
Loop        ; Wait for the timer to be updated
  cmp  TCR    ; Each Loop takes 5 Instruction Cycles
  bne  Loop   ; Timer has not counted down
```

The next point to be aware of is that the timer's overflow is used to clock a "postscaler," and this postscaler output (or the overflow itself) can be used to trigger an interrupt request. This postscaler can be used to provide a variable delay (which is a rough power of two of the instruction clock—256, 4K, 8K, 16K, 32K or 256K cycles between interrupts based on how the "timer control/status register" is set).

The last thing I want to point out is that the output of the timer is used to drive the "COP" ("computer operating properly") watchdog timer. This means that the COP timeout is dependent on the number of instructions executed, not on the amount of time that has

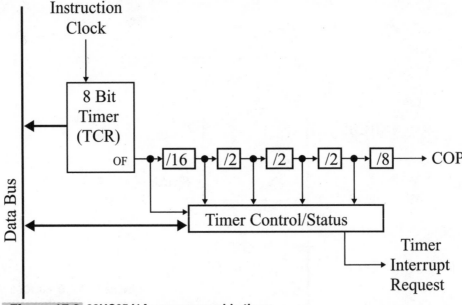

Figure 17.9 68HC05J1As programmable timer.

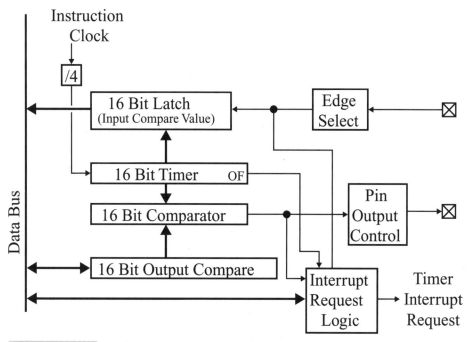

Figure 17.10 68HC05C8s programmable timer.

passed. This is different from the other microcontroller's watchdog timers and could cause problems in some applications if the clock speed is changed.

The 68HC05J1A's timer may seem very simple and restricted to the other microcontroller's timers, but it can be used to pretty good advantage, as is shown in the example applications.

The 68HC05C8's timer is quite a bit more complex than the 'J1A's but still follows the same basic operating philosophy. (Figure 17.10.)

A major difference between this timer and the 'J1A's is the lack of the overflow dividers. This means that if this timer is to be used as a real-time clock timer, the delay is always 256K instruction cycles. But, the "16-bit output compare" register can be used to provide much more precise timing with an interrupt request when a specified timing delay has passed.

To enable this feature, the following pseudo-code could be used:

```
A = Timer             ;  Get the current timer value

Compare = A + Delay   ;  Calculate value at the end of the Delay

Enable Interrupts

Wait for Delay        ;  Loop Until Flag Set by Timer Interrupt
```

When the comparator outputs that the timer matches an expected value, an output pin can be affected. This operation is known "output compare mode" of the timer.

"Input capture mode" is used to capture the timer value at a specific event (observed at an I/O Pin). For example, if you were measuring how "wide" a pulse is, the following steps could be used:

1. Enable capture on rising edge of the "TCAP" pin (which is used to latch in the timer value).
2. Wait for the rising edge.
3. Save the "input compare value."
4. Enable capture on the falling edge of the pulse.
5. Wait for the falling edge.
6. Save the input compare value.
7. The pulse width = 6. – 2.

The only issue to watch for with measuring pulses as described above is that the 16-bit timer can overflow before the falling edge is received. To make sure information is not lost, you should enable the overflow interrupt and use it to keep track of how many overflows take place between the rising and falling edges of the pulse.

"COP"

"COP" is the acronym for the "computer operating properly" timer. This is the 68HC05's "watchdog timer," and it is enabled in the "MOR" or "COP control register" at programming time. Like watchdog timers used in other devices, if this timer is not periodically reset by the application software, the processor will be reset. When the "COPEN" (COP enable) bit is set, the COP will run without any way in software to disable it.

The COP is driven by the processor clock (in other devices, the watchdog timer may be driven by a separate oscillator). This means that if a "STOP" instruction is executed, the COP will stop running. For this reason, the "WAIT" command should be used in applications that use the COP, and when "WAIT" is executed, the time to an interrupt should not be any longer than the time out interval.

Resetting the COP is different for the different members of the 68HC05 family. In some devices, simply writing a "0" to a COP control register bit is all that's required. In other devices, writing $55 and then $AA as part of a timed instruction sequence is required. Personally, I like the more complex method of resetting the COP register; this means that to correctly reset the COP, the two write operations can be placed in very disparate areas of the application, if the software has begun to run amok (which is the purpose of a watchdog timer to determine and reset the processor), then there is a much lower opportunity for the COP to be reset as a matter of course.

In some 68HC05 devices, if the clock is missing for a certain length of time (between 5 and 100 usecs), the processor will be reset as a clock failure has been detected. When this feature (known as "clock monitor reset") is enabled, the input clock cannot be less than 200 kHz or there is the possibility of an inadvertent and incorrect clock monitor reset being asserted.

Analog Input/Output

The 68HC05's optional ADC is an enhancement to a standard digital I/O pin. Compared to other microcontroller families' built-in ADC, the 68HC05's is very fast. (Figure 17.11.)

The "ADC control" is a successive approximation converter, which means that it starts with the most significant bit of the voltage ratio and works its way down to figure out the correct voltage ratio to 8 bits.

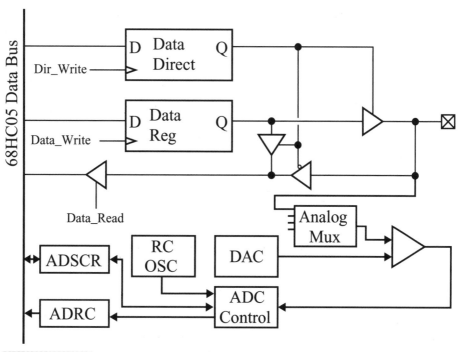

Figure 17.11 68HC05 parallel I/O pin with ADC.

The algorithm used is something like:

```
DACOutput = 0                    ;  "DACOutput" contains Voltage Output AND
                                 ;    Result
BitChange = $80                  ;  Start Checking at the Halfway Point
while BitChange != 0             ;  Go down through Each Bit
   DACOutput += BitChange        ;  Turn on the Current Voltage
   if Vin < DACOutput            ;  If the Output is > Input, then don't
      DACOutput -= BitChange     ;    set this bit
   endif
   BitChange = BitChange >> 1    ;  Check the Next Bit Down
endwhile                         ;  Conversion is Complete
```

Typically in "integrating ADCS," an incrementing voltage is compared against the input voltage until the incrementing voltage is greater than the input voltage. When the incrementing voltage is greater than the input voltage, then the ADC operation stops and the value of the incrementing voltage is returned. If the ADC is working to 8-bit precision, up to 256 comparisons will be made—but not necessarily. The time required to carry out this type of conversion is also variable (which can be a big problem in some applications).

The 68HC05's ADC will carry out the same number of comparisons irregardless of the value of the input voltage, and the number of comparisons (8) is much less than the average number of comparisons that an integrating ADC requires (approximately 128).

Setting up and using the ADC hardware is quite simple, with the first priority being specifying the voltage input "Vrh." This input is used by the DAC to determine the "ratiometric" voltage for comparison. The "ratiometric voltage" is a 10-dollar way of saying that the DAC output is some ratio (determined by the DAC's input) of Vrh to Vss (ground).

Using a separate input for this voltage will allow you to measure input values to a reasonable degree of accuracy.

The analog multiplexer is used to select between different pins for input and internal measurements based on Vrh. The internal measurement can be Vrh (in which a value of $FE is expected), Vrh/2 (which should return $7F or $80), or Vss (which will return a value of $00). The internal measurements can be used to check the operation of the ADC.

Once the circuit has been wired and put into operation, the "ADON" bit of the "ADSCR" (ADC status and control register) is enabled and a 100-usec delay is put in for the ADC to power up and stabilize. If the 68HC05's clock is less than 1 MHz, then the ADC's internal RC Clock should be enabled and another 100 usec delay should be put in to allow it to stabilize.

Now you are ready to do analog measurements. After selecting the analog input pin (which should have its digital input and output drivers disabled to make sure there is no opportunity of unwanted voltage/current sources and loads), the ADC continuously measures the input line. When reading the current input voltage, the ADC data register ("ADRC") should be read, which clears the ADC completion ("CCF") flag of "ADSCR" input status, and then poll "CCF" until the current conversion completes. Each conversion takes about 32 usecs to execute, which means the maximum continous sampling speed would be approximately 30 kHz.

Serial Input/Output

There are five modules available within the 68HC05 for serial communications. In this subchapter, I will focus on the two most popular modules, the "SCI" (serial communications interface is used for asynchronous serial data transfer) and the "SPI" (serial peripheral interface, which is designed for interfacing with synchronous serial devices).

The "SCI+" is an enhancement to the "SCI," which can output the transmitter clock with the data for outputting serial data to a clocked device (such as a serial-to-parallel converter). The "simple serial I/O port" ("SIOP") is a synchronous serial port that can be used in a single master (the 68HC05) system. Finally, the "I2C" port is designed to access I2C devices (with multimastering) directly.

SCI MODULE

The universal asynchronous receive/transmit ("UART") serial port is a full-duplex serial port that is very easy to interface with and provides some interesting features that make it easier to develop application code for than the UARTs available in other microcontrollers. Like most other microcontroller UARTs, the SCI sends data in typical non-return to zero (RS-232) format and can send or receive strings via maskable interrupts.

The core of the SCI transmitter consists of two registers. The first register is a holding register (which is known as "SCDAT") that is used to load the shift output register. This is done when the shift output register is empty. (Figure 17.12.)

When the SCDAT register is empty or the transmision is complete, an interrupt can be generated by enabling the appropriate bit in the "SCSR" register. A character can be queued in the SCDAT register while another character is being transmitted by the shift register. By keeping the SCDAT register filled with data (which can be indicated by an inter-

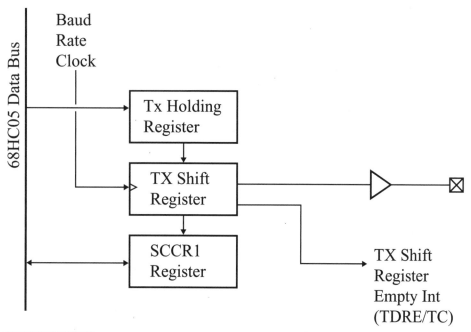

Figure 17.12 68HC05 SCI transmitter block diagram.

rupt or polling the TDRE bit of the SCSR register), data can be sent continuously without any pausing between a character's stop bit and the next's start bit.

The start, stop, parity bits are inserted into the "TX shift register" when the data is transferred from the SCDAT register. The number of bits to be sent in each character (eight or nine) is specified by the "M" bit of the "SCCR1" register. The last data bit can be a parity bit, the value of which is calculated by software.

The 8 or 9 data bits may seem like a restriction for certain applications (such as those that only use 7 or fewer data bits per word), but fewer bits can be accommodated by simply setting the high bits of the data to "1," which will be interpreted by the receiver as a Stop bit and idling line.

The receiver is somewhat more complex than the transmitter (which is to be expected). (Figure 17.13.)

The input line is sampled at 16 times the actual data speed. This allows the "data check" hardware to sample the incoming data and determine whether or not the start bit is valid and where the middle of the incoming data is to ensure reliable data input. Once the input bit has been determined to be valid, then data is shifted into the "Rx holding register" (also known as "SCDAT," but when accessing the transmitter, "SCDAT" is written to and when reading incoming data, the address is read from).

An interrupt can not only indicate a character received, but it can also indicate an error with the data coming in. This error is known as a "data overrun" and is asserted when a new character is received before the current character in the Rx holding register has been read (reading the register resets a check bit, which is set if a byte is received and the contents of the holding register haven't been read).

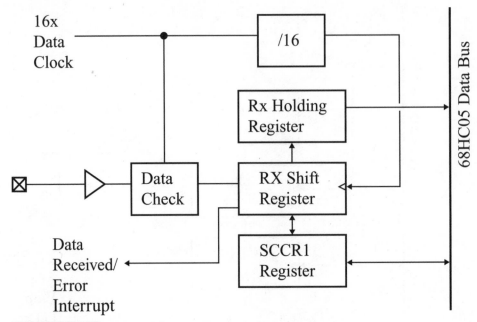

Figure 17.13 68HC05 SCI receiver block diagram.

The clock module used to generate the data clock for the SCI has a major difference from the clock circuitry used in other microcontroller families' UART ports. (Figure 17.14.)

As you look at Figure 17.14, you'll probably feel like the clock generator looks quite normal. The incoming signal is divided by the "prescaler" to create a "standard" reference frequency. This frequency is then divided down again to get the actual baud rate.

Where the big difference comes in between the 68HC05's SCI data rate clock and other device's UART clocks is in the ability of the prescaler to divide the clock by 13.

Actually, the clock can divide the incoming clock by a number of different amounts, as the following chart will show. But it's the ability of dividing the clock by 13 that makes it very useful.

SCP1	SCP0	DIVIDE	CRYSTAL FREQUENCIES	
			4 MHZ	**2 MHZ**
0	0	1	125.00 kHz	62.60 kHz
0	1	2	41.67 kHz	20.83 kHz
1	0	4	31.25 kHz	15.63 kHz
1	1	13	9.60 kHz	4.80 kHz

Dividing the system clock by 13 at 4 MHz results in a 9600-bps reference frequency that allows direct interfacing at standard RS-232 data rates without having to use a clock running at a special frequency. The chart below shows how the "SCR" bits can be used at

4 MHz to produce different RS-232 standard data rates from dividing down the "reference speed" of 9600 bps:

SCR2	SCR1	SCR0	DIVIDE	4 MHZ DATA RATES
0	0	0	1	9600bps
0	0	1	2	4800bps
0	1	0	4	2400bps
0	1	1	8	1200bps
1	0	0	16	600bps
1	0	1	32	300bps
1	1	0	64	150bps
1	1	1	128	75bps

The "SCR" and "SCP" bits are located in the "BAUD" Register.

SPI MODULE

The 68HC05's serial parallel interface ("SPI") module differs quite a bit from the synchronous serial subsystems available in other microcontrollers because it is primarily designed for interfacing to serial/parallel converters rather than to a synchronous serial

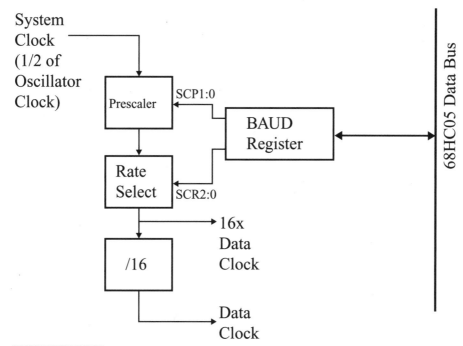

Figure 17.14 68HC05 SCI receiver/transmitter clock generator.

protocol. This difference makes it very easy to interface a 68HC05 to something like a '374 wired as a serial-to-parallel converter.

Figure 17.15 shows a very simplified drawing of how the 68HC05's SPI hardware works. Data transfer is initiated when a byte is written to the "SPI shift register." Data transfer starts at the next clock edge (the clock speed is taken from the instruction clock and divided) and its most significant bit is transferred first.

As you can see in Figure 17.15, when the data is being shifted out, it is also being shifted in and can be read out from the "RX buffer register" (which is at the same address as the write to the "SPI shift register"). Normally when shifting out, the "slave select" pin is pulled high (to allow data output, but when data is not to be driven out, the line can be pulled low. The "slave select" pin has nothing to do with the mode that the SPI runs in (the mode is actually selected by the "MSTR" bit of the "serial peripheral control register").

When in "master mode," the data clock is generated internally (if it is in "slave mode," an external clock is used) and the clock division is specified by the SPR0 and SPR1 bits in the "serial peripheral control register."

SPR1	SPR0	SPI CLOCK DIVISOR
0	0	2
0	1	4
1	0	16
1	1	32

The SPI can be used for synchronous serial protocols (i.e., "MicroWire"), but there are a number of rules that would have to be observed. The first is that multimastering on the buses using the SPI hardware is not possible (because there is no clock synchronizing hardware). For slave mode, an external pin would have to be polled to see if the 68HC05 is being selected.

I would not recommend using the SPI as an I2C interface for a number of reasons. The first is the lack of open collector drivers. While this can be easily overcome by the use of external open collector drivers, the other problems really make implementing I2C using SPI more trouble than it's worth. These problems include the SPI port's lack of a comparator register for incoming addresses and the ability to send and check an acknowledge bit at the end of the data. Before you despair at the idea of having to write an I2C interface for your application, I should point out that in many 68HC05s there is a I2C-specific port available with these features that will allow the microcontroller to use the protocol very simply.

Configuration ("Option") Register

In all 68HC05s, there is a register that is tasked with providing boot-up information. This register may have different names (for example, in the 68HC05C8 it is known as the "option register" and in the 68HC05J1A, it is known as the "MOR" ("mask option register")).

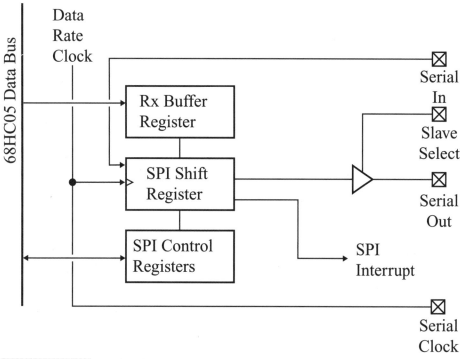

Figure 17.15 68HC05 SPI block diagram.

Regardless of what the name of the register is, it specifies many of the same functions and features for the different 68HC05 microcontrollers and these include:

1. Whether or not the EPROM contents can be read out.
2. Enable the watchdog timer ("COP").
3. Response of "Int" pin (level or edge triggered).
4. Memory configuration (RAM or EPROM).
5. Start up clock delay (16 or 4064 cycles).
6. Enable port pull downs.
7. Crystal oscillator operating mode.
8. Port pull down enable.

These options are very device specific, but I will comment on a few of them.

The "(EPM)SEC" bit, when enabled, will prevent a programmer from reading the contents of EPROM. After the program has been qualified and is being burned into production parts, enabling this bit will prevent others from being able to read back the software in the part.

In some 68HC05s, there are a number of user-selectable memory configurations that can be chosen, depending on the application. These configurations can swap EPROM for RAM or even PROM values.

The start-up clock delay shortening to 16 cycles is best used for applications where the 68HC05 is driven by an external clock. It really relies on the external clock being stable anytime the 68HC05 is to be active. The start-up clock delay can also be shortened to 16 cycles for devices that use an RC network for oscillators.

The location of the option register is part-number specific (it may be in the memory map or it may be not accessible by the processor). This affects how it is programmed and referenced in the source code.

Personally, I like to place all optional operating information in the source file and then have it available when the device is programmed. For some 68HC05s, this is not possible and the option register values must be specified at programming time (although many languages and assemblers do have directives for specifying the option register bit values).

Programming

One area in which I consider the Motorola embedded microcontrollers (the complete line, not just the 68HC05) to be deficient is in the area of programming. Motorola microcontrollers are generally very difficult to program, require specialized hardware, and cannot be programmed in after the part has been soldered into the application ("ISP").

Some 68HC05s have a "boot ROM" built in that contains a program that can be run at device boot to copy an EPROM that is wired to the 68HC05.

Some devices use the boot ROM to download a program directly from a host system (a PC).

Other 68HC05s (such as the 68HC05J family) require a separate programmer that will access and load the device's EPROM.

All three of these methods for loading the 68HC05s EPROM require quite a bit of hardware and a host system's intelligence. Because of this, the 68HC05s are not well suited to

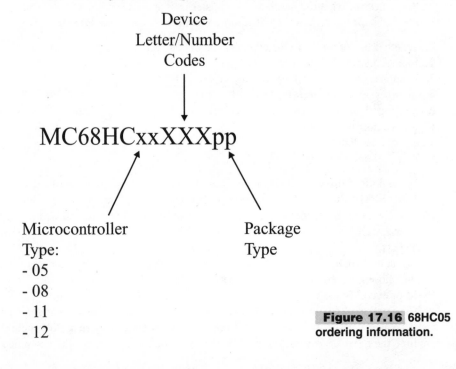

Figure 17.16 68HC05 ordering information.

be used in applications where the EPROM is loaded as part of the manufacturing process. Mask programmed ROM versions of the 68HC05 (and 68HC08, 68HC11, and 68HC12) are the choice for using the Motorola embedded microcontrollers in production.

Ordering Information

Ordering a specific Motorola microcontroller is based on the processor core ("68HC05," "68HC08," "68HC11, "etc.) and the feature code (i.e., "C8,""J1A" of the device). Packaging is specified at ordering time. (Figure 17.16.)

The 68HC05 package types are shown at the start of this chapter.

17

MOTOROLA 68HC05

68HC05 APPLICATION DESIGN

CONTENTS AT A GLANCE

Power Input

System Oscillators/Clocks

Reset

Interrupts

Real Time Operating Systems
"MYKERTOS"

Although designing 68HC05 applications really is quite simple, like most other simple embedded microcontrollers, there are a few peculiarities that you should be aware of that may cause problems in developing an application.

Power Input

Most 68HC05 part numbers are capable of running with a very wide range of power inputs. The practical range is from 3.0 to 7.0 volts (with 5.0 volts being the nominal design point). The current required is in the range of 1 to 5 milliamperes.

Like all the microcontrollers presented here, putting a 0.1-uF decoupling capacitor between Vdd and Vss is recommended.

System Oscillators/Clocks

The 68HC05 stacks up very well against the other devices present in this book. This is really quite amazing because the device and the architecture is 10 to 25 years older than the other microcontrollers that it is competing with. But there is one area in which the 68HC05 is less flexible, and that's in the area of the system oscillator and clocks.

For the most part, the 68HC05 is limited to using a crystal (or ceramic resonator) oscillator or external clock source and running between 1 and 4 MHz. This is in contrast to the other microcontrollers presented in this book, which can run between DC and 10s of kHz to 10s of MHz and with internal and external RC and LC oscillators.

The typical circuit for the 68HC05's clock is shown in Figure 18.1.

When setting up the oscillator, I found that in most cases, the feedback resistor (the "1–10 megohm" resistor in Figure 18.1) has to be put in to get the oscillator to run reliably. This is not a great hardship or expense, so I would just go with it in all applications.

Some newer devices (notably the 68HC05J series) are capable of running with an RC oscillator or an external clock source in a similar manner to other devices presented here. If an external clock is connected to the 68HC05, then the clock input should drive the "Osc1" pin.

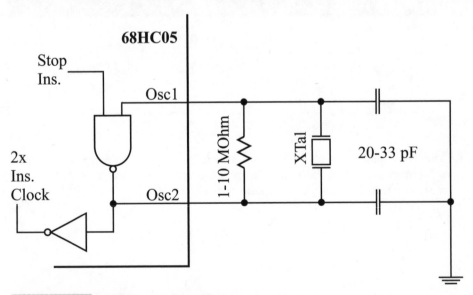

Figure 18.1 68HC05 crystal oscillator.

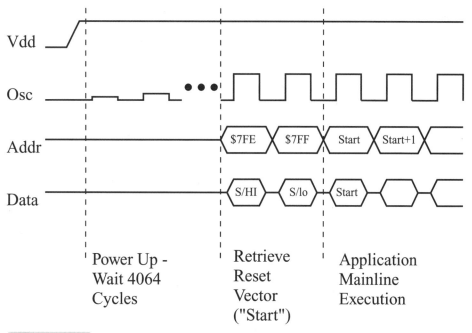

Figure 18.2 68HC05 power up sequence.

Reset

The "_Reset" pin used in the 68HC05 is primarily designed as a negative active pin that can be held up with a resistor (or wired to Vcc, although this is not recommended). Using a Resistor pull up on the _Reset pin will allow putting a momentary on switch connected to _Reset and ground for allowing simple resetting of the 68HC05 during application development.

When the 68HC05 powers up (or _Reset is pulled low and then released), the timing diagram looks like Figure 18.2.

When power is valid the Osc1/Osc2 pins start the internal oscillator (with external crystal circuitry) and then wait 4064 cycles for the clock to stabilize before beginning execution.

While the power-up sequence seems very standard, there is one aspect of the software power up that has to be explained, and that is how the initial execution location is determined. At the end of the 68HC05's EPROM space (note, this address is different for each different size of EPROM), there are a number of "vector" locations used for specifying the location of the mainline code, the code used to process the watchdog timer and interrupt handlers.

In application code, you will see something that looks like:

```
Mainline              ;  On Power-Up/Reset Execute from Here

    :                 ;  Miscellaneous Code

org EPROM_Size - 2    ;  Define the Power Up Vector
  db    Mainline
```

When the 68HC05 powers up, the two bytes at the end of the EPROM are retrieved and put into the program counter to be used as the first addresses for executing. This means that the initial code (along with the watchdog and interrupt vectors) can be located anywhere in the EPROM, allowing you quite a bit of flexibility in structuring how the program is stored in memory.

Interrupts

The 68HC05 is hands down the winner in ease of developing complex interrupt-handler routines. This is largely due to how the hardware responds to an interrupt request (and "swi" instruction) as well as the multiple interrupt vectors handling different sources. This built-in operation control also eliminates a lot of the thinking that goes into creating an interrupt handler. As I will show, a three-instruction interrupt handler is very possible and useful.

When an interrupt request is exected, all the context registers are pushed onto the stack in the following order:

1. Low byte of the program counter.
2. High byte of the program counter.
3. Index register.
4. Accumulator register.
5. CCR register.

When the interrupt has been handled, the "reti" instruction pops these registers off the stack and restores where the 68HC05 was executing when the interrupt happened. This means that as long as you've made space for the registers, you don't have any decisions to make about how the context registers are saved.

With the context registers taken care of, all you will have to worry about is resetting the interrupt hardware and indicating to the mainline that the interrupt happened.

For the timer, indicating via a flag that the timer has overflowed could be:

```
TmrInt                     ;  Timer Interrupt Handler Start

   bset    2,tscr          ;  Reset the Timer Interrupt Hardware

   bset    0,Flag_Var      ;  Set the Interrupt Flag

   reti                    ;  Return to the Mainline
```

Because the 68HC05 has a stack for saving all the register, it is possible to nest the interrupts. Some code for doing this could be:

```
TmrInt                     ;  Timer Interrupt with Nesting Allowed

   bset    2,tscr          ;  Reset the Timer Interrupt Hardware

   cli                     ;  Enable Interrupts inside this Handler

   :                       ;  Process the Timer Interrupt

   reti                    ;  Return to the Mainline
```

By enabling the interrupts (the "cli" instruction), an interrupt handler can be interrupted by a higher-priority interrupt. The reason why I call the other interrupt "higher" priority is because if the interrupt request is received during another interrupt handler's execution, that interrupt handler's execution is suspended until the interrupting handler has completed. Typically, the highest-priority interrupt does not unmask interrupts so that nothing else can interrupt it.

The last point to be made on the 68HC05's interrupt handlers is the multiple vectors available for different interrupts.

For example, in the 68HC05, I could implement a button press debounce using the timer and "int" pin interrupts. Blocking this out in psuedocode, it would look something like:

```
Setup Timer Delay 32 msecs     ;  The Button has to be down for 32 msec
Setup Timer Interrupt          ;    to be "debounced"

Setup Int0 on Falling Edge

Enable Global Interrupts

  :

ButtonFlag = 1                 ;  Now, Wait for the Button to be
while ButtonFlag == 1          ;    Debounced

  :                            ;  When Execution gets here, the
  :                            ;    Button is Debounced

ButInt                         ;  Button Interrupt Handler

  Reset Interrupt

  if ButtonFlag == 1
    Timer = 0                  ;  Have to Reset the Timer

  return from interrupt

TmrInt                         ;  Timer Interrupt - 32 msec has gone by

  Reset Interrupt

  ButtonFlag = 0               ;  Button has delayed 32 msec - Debounced

  return from interrupt
```

In the "ButInt" interrupt handler, the timer is reset to see if the timer can delay 32 msec before the next falling edge of the button pin (which means the button press is debounced). This is a good example of how simple a button press could be implemented because each line of psuedocode basically represents an assembly language line and shows how two interrupt handlers can coexist.

Real-Time Operating Systems

If you've never been exposed to real-time operating systems before this book, the way that I keep going on about them must leave you with the impression that they have significant advantages over straight, single-task programming. This is a statement that I feel is too strong; I would instead say that a RTOS can have significant advantages over single-task programming in certain applications.

These "certain applications" can be characterized as microcontroller applications that use different hardware subsystems for different tasks. A limited amount of multitasking can be done by using interrupts, but this can lead to problems because of the increased "intelligence" required in an interrupt handler, which leads to longer interrupt handling, which means that events may be missed or overwritten. Interrupts could be nested, but this increases the complexity of the resulting application code.

Instead, in an RTOS, the interrupt is handled as quickly as possible and the tasks that are waiting ("blocking") on the interrupt are enabled to execute. Because the interrupts are handled very quickly with just a few lines of code, all interrupts can be serviced in a reasonable amount of time after the initial request without having to resort to nesting the interrupts.

The 68HC05 lends itself very well to implementing an RTOS because of several features.

The first feature is the program-accessible stack. When an interrupt is requested, data is stored on the stack in the following order:

1. Low byte of the program counter.
2. High byte of the program counter.
3. Index register.
4. Accumulator.
5. Condition code register (CCR).

Knowing this, the current state of the currently executing mainline can be stored elsewhere and manipulated very easily.

Each "task" is really it's own "mainline" that can be used to handle a specific aspect of the application or hardware feature of the microcontroller. The five 8-bit registers saved above are all the execution (or "context") information required for a task.

The next feature that makes the 68HC05 well suited to RTOS applications is the software interrupt. Executing a "swi" instruction pushes all the context information for the task on the stack in the same manner as a hardware interrupt, which makes manipulating the data very consistant throughout the RTOS.

To a lesser extent, the "swi" instruction simplifies the operation of the RTOS because it is really a single-byte "jsr RTOS" instruction; the RTOS entry point can be located anywhere within the program, and object files can be linked in without worrying about where the RTOS entry point actually is. This eliminates the need to use "jump" instructions within the application source (which takes up 3 bytes compared to the 1 byte of the "swi" instruction).

Speed is an important consideration in a RTOS application, and the ease of manipulating the stack and the single-instruction operation of loading and saving the context registers (the "rti" and "swi" instructions, respectively) make the operations very quick. My benchmark, given to me by a professor at university years ago, was that the RTOS in the application should be able to execute a request and change the task in under a half millisecond (500 usecs). As you'll see in "MykeRTOS," this can almost be accomplished at 1 MHz.

Now the more cynical of you may think that this request execution and task switch speed is a function of how simple the hardware is, but I would argue that there is a lot more to it than that. The 68HC05 is well suited to running RTOS applications.

All this is not to say there aren't some deficiencies and concerns with the 68HC05 architecture in developing RTOS applications. The first is the inability of a 68HC05 program to read back the value of the stack pointer (although it can be reset). As you'll see in the "MykeRTOS," this means that calling subroutines from a task is not allowed because if the RTOS is "called" (using the "swi" instruction) from within a subroutine, the actual stack location is not known (to allow you to index to the context information saved on the stack). This inability to call subroutines from within tasks means that some functions may be repeated, which will increase the amount of memory required for an application.

The other concern is the lack of memory that's available in the lower-end devices. In "MykeRTOS," the device I originally designed the RTOS for (the 68HC70J1A) has 64 bytes of RAM. The task information blocks and RTOS overhead brings this value down to 17 bytes available for the application. This overhead primarily consists of the amount of memory required to save the context information of the various tasks. In a PC or workstation, this memory is a nit and basically insignificant, but in a small microcontroller it can be a very large percentage of the total RAM available.

"MykeRTOS"

When developing the 68HC05 RTOS for this book, I wanted to create as simple and small a full-featured RTOS as possible. My original goal was to try to keep the required code for the RTOS below 256 control store bytes and use less than 20 bytes of RAM. This would mean that not only would it offer a very small memory space overhead, but with so few instructions, it wouldn't take a lot of time to execute operating system functions.

The result that I am presenting here in this book takes up about twice as much memory resources as was my target above (47 bytes of RAM and 453 bytes of control store). Despite this, it is quite usable and it is in fact used to create the second example application for the 68HC05. The RTOS (called, immodestly, "mykeRTOS") is designed to execute four tasks simultaneously (although this could be expanded quite easily), loaded from a file called "RTOSAP.ASM." If the 68HC05J1A were the target microcontroller, there would be 17 RAM bytes and 779 control store bytes left for the application. None of the built-in hardware features (i.e., the timer or I/O pins) are required by the RTOS to operate. As you will see in the 68HC05 Example Applications chapter, this does leave you enough resources to create some pretty complex applications.

The first thing I took care of when developing this RTOS was determining how much space was required for each task and minimizing that. It has to be minimized to avoid squandering RAM resources, and handling passing data back and forth would be minimized (fewer control store instructions and few cycles to execute the operation of accessing the task information). I wanted to use the "SWI" instruction to be the RTOS request mechanism, which meant that the context registers (the accumulator, index, CCR, and program counter) would be saved automatically and available for reading and writing in RAM in the RTOS code. It also meant that in the RTOS, hardware interrupts would be masked, which means that the RTOS functions could execute without fear of being inadvertently interrupted, losing task information or having to save the RTOS context information somewhere. This method also gave me a consistent way of handling both RTOS requests as well as task interruptions (by using the "SWI" instruction, all the information is saved in the same format as when a hardware interrupt is handled).

18

MOTOROLA 68HC05

I wanted simple message passing, which meant I needed some space for the message or a pointer to the message. I decided that the message would be saved in the task information area, which would allow the message to be taken from variables or hardware registers but not affected while the sending task was waiting for the receiver to process the information. As I tried to figure out how big to make the message, I decided upon using 2 bytes that would be passed in the accumulator and index registers. With 5 bytes saved during an interrupt, 1 byte for the task status (this variable is known as "TSTATUS") and 2 bytes for the message, a total of 8 bytes is required for the "task information block."

Using two bytes for the message size is a nice comprimise; with too few bytes in the message, sending and receiving data would take many cycles. With too many, more RAM space is required than may be available (especially in a small device like the 68HC05H1A). Two bytes was really chosen as one byte for a command to another task and one byte as data. Using two bytes for the message was also nice with the "ICS05J1A" simulator that comes with the 68HC705JICS development kit, because each task could be displayed in a line of the debug window.

With the task information block defined, I decided upon allowing a maximum of four tasks and laid out the RAM memory usage (for the 68HC05J1A, which only has 64 bytes from $C0 to $FF) as Figure 18.3.

In this format, the task information blocks are located at the top of the RAM for easy monitoring in the simulator.

In Figure 18.3, you should notice that I have only left 5 bytes for the stack (and with it, the context registers). This is done because I wanted to minimize the amount of stack that needed to be saved for the individual tasks' context information. It was also done to make sure that the RTOS request was put in a place in memory I could continually find. This is an important point because the stack pointer in the 68HC05 cannot be accessed (although it can be reset to $FF) and I had to make sure that I knew where all the context registers were so they could be saved without trying to figure out where they were based on the current stack's status.

Only having a stack sufficient for a single interrupt means that each task cannot call a subroutine. This is not a terrible restriction, but it will affect your programming style.

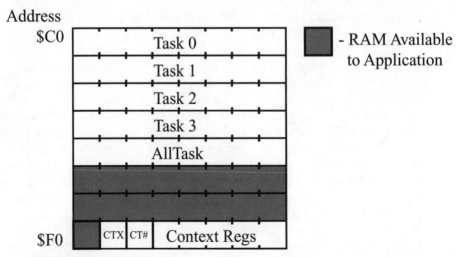

Figure 18.3 mykeRTOS memory usage map for 68HC05J1A.

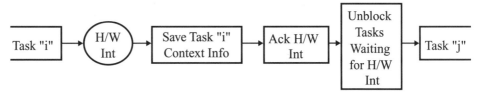

Figure 18.4 mykeRTOS interrupt response flow.

Actually, what it will do is lock down using tasks as subroutines, which is one of the most important functions of multitasking operating systems. Ideally, each task should control no more than one resource in the computer system or be in control of a process. Developing your applications with this style will ensure that multiple processes can access the same resources (what will be discussed later in this section is making sure that there aren't problems with multiple tasks communicating with a single task controlling a resource).

As I mentioned above, the "swi" instruction is used as the RTOS' interface because it stores all the registers in a standard format, allowing easy saving of the context information and retrieval of the RTOS request. The latter point is very important. If, in mykeRTOS, an interrupt is encountered during task execution, the flow will be Figure 18.4.

If a task is interrupted during execution, the context registers which were saved on the stack are stored in the task information block. The hardware interrupt is acknowledged (i.e., reset) and any tasks waiting (or "blocking") for the interrupt are marked as "executable." Once this is completed, the next available task begins execution.

When execution returns to the interrupted task (task "i" in Figure 18.4), it will resume execution at the point where the interrupt stopped it with the correct context register contents (because both the "swi" instruction and a hardware interrupt save the context registers in exactly the same format).

The task execution status byte ("TSTATUS") is used to indicate the current status of the task so that the RTOS can determine whether or not it can execute or if it's waiting for an event (an interrupt or a message). The values are defined as:

TSTATUS VALUE	DESCRIPTION/COMMENTS
$00	Task is Able to Execute
$Cn	Task is waiting for Task "n" to Acknowledge the Message Sent
$D0	Task is waiting for another Task to send a message to it
$3n	Task is waiting for the Interrupt "n" to execute. (For "mykeRTOS", the Timer Interrupt is defined as n = 0)
$FF	Task has ended, Task Information Block is available for a new Task

Having a task waiting ("blocking") on a message to be received or acknowledeged is the ability to pass messges back and forth in a sequential manner. This means that the actual program execution control can be specified.

As an example of how this is done is shown in Figure 18.5. In this example, if task 2 receives a $00 from task 1 after previously receiving a message from task 0, then the message is discarded, else it is sent on to task 3. In this example, task 2 is being used as a filter for task 3 (which normally processes everything coming through).

Looking back at Figure 18.5, there is one thing I should point out, and that's when working with an RTOS, it's always a good idea to draw out the tasks and how they interrelate. Sometimes the operation can be very hard to understand, but if you show how it's supposed to operate, it becomes much easier to see how the program is going to work. I usually try to plan out an RTOS application exactly as I've shown in Figure 18.5 and keep the actual diagram updated as part of the application documentation.

With everything I've written about here, you're probably noticing that I have left out one thing that's commonly available in other RTOS,' and that's giving different tasks different priority levels. In a typical operating system, certain tasks are given higher priorities and privileges (i.e., access to registers and data other tasks cannot access) than others. This is not implemented in "mykeRTOS" for two reasons; the first is the lack of resources. Typically in RTOS,' the tasks are put into queues according to their execution status. These queues require more RAM for saving them and more control store space for implementing them. The second reason is because with four tasks executing, I didn't see that having different priorities would be a major advantage.

Before going much further, I should point out that when you simulate the second example application (the LCD clock/thermometer), you'll notice that most of the time the application is waiting for a timer interrupt to initiate some action. With all the tasks blocked, either waiting on the timer interrupt, or waiting for a message from one of the tasks that is waiting on the timer interrupt, not a lot is happening. In fact, in this case the RTOS would be spinning forever, waiting for a task to become unblocked. This will be impossible because when in the RTOS, interrupts are masked.

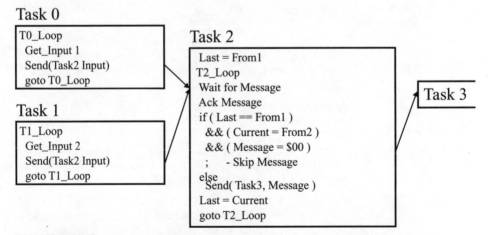

Task 0

```
T0_Loop
  Get_Input 1
  Send(Task2 Input)
  goto T0_Loop
```

Task 1

```
T1_Loop
  Get_Input 2
  Send(Task2 Input)
  goto T1_Loop
```

Task 2

```
  Last = From1
T2_Loop
  Wait for Message
  Ack Message
  if ( Last == From1 )
    && ( Current = From2 )
    && ( Message = $00 )
    ;    - Skip Message
  else
        Send( Task3, Message )
  Last = Current
  goto T2_Loop
```

Task 3

Figure 18.5 Using messaging to control program execution and operation.

So how do we solve this? It's actually pretty easy. I have created a small task called "AllTask" that serves two purposes. The first is to start the first task of the application. The second purpose of "AllTask" is to run in an endless loop (which simply requests the next task in the chain to execute) and allow interrupts to happen. When "AllTask" is interrupted, the RTOS takes over execution and frees all the blocked tasks.

To make an RTOS function request, the accumulator is set with a request number and the index register is loaded with any parameters required for the request. The requests that are available in "mykeRTOS" are:

REQUEST	INPUT		OUTPUT		COMMENTS
	A	X	A	X	
SetA	0	n	0	n	Set the "Acc Register" Byte of the Message Area
SetX	1	n	1	n	Set the "Index Register" Byte of the Message Area
ReadMsg	2	n	A	X	Read the Specified Message Number
			−1	−1	If the Message Number is not available
GetMsg	3	x	3	n	Returns the number of Messages Waiting for the Task
AckMsg	4	n	4	n	Acknowledge the Specified Message
			−1	−1	If the Message isn't available
StartTask	5	l	5	n	Start the Task with the High Byte of the Address already in the "Acc Register" Byte of the Message Area and the Low Byte in the Index Register for the call
			−1	−1	No Task Information Blocks Available
EndTask	6	x	N/A	N/A	The current task has outlived its usefulness - make the Task Information Block Available for another Task (the TSTATUS Byte is set to $FF)
NextTask	7	x	7	x	Jump to the Next Executable Task
SendMsg	8	n	8	n	Block until Task "n" Acknowledges the Message
WaitMsg	9	x	9	x	Block until a message has been sent to the task
WaitInt	10	n	10	n	Block until interrupt "n" has executed (n = 0 is for the Timer Interrupt)

18

The first five RTOS requests return to the requester immediately. The last six requests do not, and one of the first things that is done is to save the context information before servicing the request.

To start (or "initiate") a task, the current task's "A register" in its message area has to be set with the high byte of the address of the task. Next, a "StartTask" request is made with the lower byte of the address in the index register.

In "mykeRTOS," the code to start the "application" (from "AllTask") is:

```
ldx     #{Application>8}    ;  Setup the High Byte of "Application's"
clra                       ;   Start Address
swi                        ;  Acc = 0 = SetA
lda     #StartTask         ;  Now, Start the Task at "Application"
ldx     #Application&$FF
swi
```

The first RTOS request puts the address of "Application" (which is the start of the application code) into the messaging area for being picked up during the second request. Upon return from the "StartTask" request, you may want to save the task number returned because it may be different for different executions or it may be used by different tasks. It's also good practice to save it for other tasks to use it.

Sending a message is carried out in a similar manner. First the "Acc register" and "X register" are updated with the message to be sent to the specified receiver; next the "SendMsg" request is made with the sender's task number specified. When receiving a message, the accumulator and index ("X") registers are updated with the message sent from the specified receiver. When the receiver has read the message and there aren't any problems with the sender executing, it is acknowledged.

A typical message send/receive/ack could look like Figure 18.6. Going through this task execution path, we start out with both the sender and receiver tasks able to execute. The receiver blocks, waiting for a message to be sent to it, while the sender prepares the message to be put into it's "Acc Register" and "X Register" bytes. Once the message is sent, the sender blocks and the receiver becomes free. The receiver reads the message (after the "ReadMsg" request, the Accumuator and Index registers are loaded with the message), processes it and then acknowledges it. At the end of this process, the message has been sent and both tasks are able to execute.

The way "MYKERTOS.ASM" has been created, you just have to create a file called "RTOSAP.ASM" with the label "application" at the start of the application's code. When "MYKERTOS" is assembled, "RTOSAP" will be embedded into the file. The label "application" can be located anywhere in the file. Variables will begin at "ApVarStart" and up to 17 can be defined. While you could use unused "Acc register" and "X register" bytes of a task that doesn't send messages, I really don't recommend it because the task may be loaded into a different task information block (meaning that the "Acc register" and "X register" addresses, which are hard-coded addresses, will be wrong).

You should also note that in the RTOS, a number of variables and labels have been defined. Using them or redefining them to different values may cause some problems.

As presented in this book, "mykeRTOS" is defined for the 68HC05J1A, but it can be easily modified for other 68HC05s. If you were to do this, you could probably increase the number of tasks as well quite easily (although they all must be accessible by the index register).

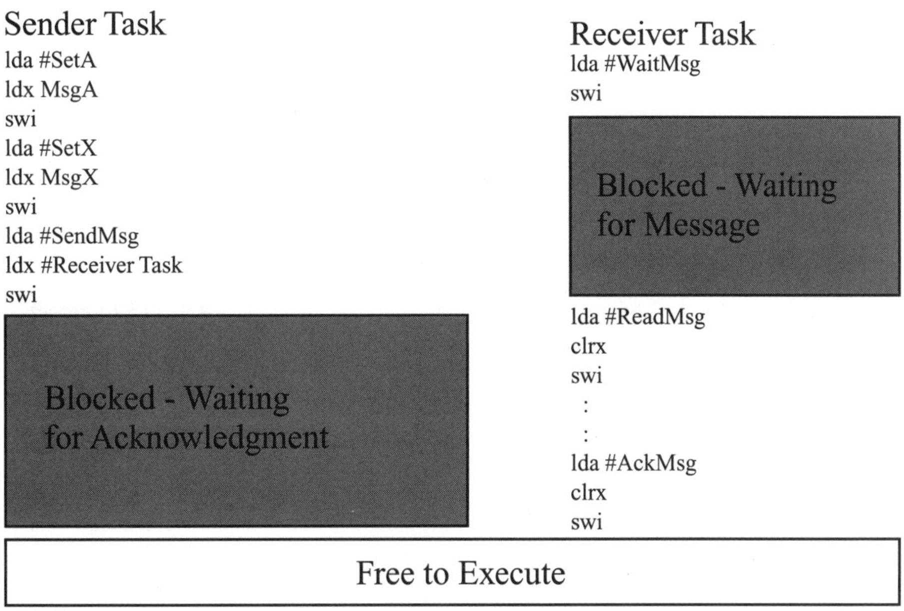

Sender Task
lda #SetA
ldx MsgA
swi
lda #SetX
ldx MsgX
swi
lda #SendMsg
ldx #Receiver Task
swi

Blocked - Waiting
for Acknowledgment

Receiver Task
lda #WaitMsg
swi

Blocked - Waiting
for Message

lda #ReadMsg
clrx
swi
:
:
lda #AckMsg
clrx
swi

Free to Execute

Figure 18.6 The mykeRTOS message send/receive/ack process.

There is one part of the "mykeRTOS" code that I would like to bring to your attention. This is how I implement a table of "jmp" instructions. Knowing that each "jmp" instruction requires three bytes, I have to multiply the index into the table by three and then do a short jump with this index to the start of the jump table.

Some generic code to do this would look like:

```
lda    Index            ;  Multiply the Index by 2
clc
asla
add    Index            ;  Add the Value Again to get 3x
tax                     ;  Put Index*3 into the Index Reg
jmp    Table_Start,X    ;  Do the Indexed Table Start

Table_Start

jmp    Table_Entry1     ;  Jump for Index = 0
jmp    Table_Entry2     ;  Jump for Index = 1
 :
```

Like all table jumps, this code has the advantage that it takes the same number of cycles no matter what table element is selected.

This is a pretty full-featured RTOS, and it runs pretty quickly (the worst-case task switch time for a 1-MHz clocked 68HC05J1A is 640 usecs). Now if you're familiar with real-time operating systems, you'll note that there are a number of things that could be added. Depending on the application, I might add a wait for semaphore (which is a flag that is used to serialize requests and is only accessed in the operating system to prevent other tasks from accessing it). There are probably other operating system functions that could be added as well.

18

MOTOROLA 68HC05

If you aren't familiar with RTOS, I hope all this hasn't been Greek to you and that you have been able to gleen something from this. I've tried to explain exactly how this (and other) RTOS' work. As I've noted, in the "68HC05 Example Applications" chapter, I use this RTOS to implement the LCD clock/thermometer, and you should get a few more insights into "mykeRTOS" and others.

Real-time operating systems can really make some programming applications simpler, but without really understanding what you are doing, they can be a nightmare. There are a number of excellent texts available for you to read on the subject. Don't be scared off because a workstation operating system using Windows/NT takes up several hundred megabytes of disk space; a useful multitasking operating system for microcontrollers can be written in a few hundred lines of code.

68HC05 DEVELOPMENT TOOLS

CONTENTS AT A GLANCE

Assemblers	Motorola "S19-Record" Object Files
High-Level Languages	Motorola 68HC705J1CS Development Kit

Being a descendent of the 6800, there are quite a few software development tools (assemblers, compilers, simulators, etc.) available for the 68HC05. Many of these tools are available free of charge on the Internet, and they range in quality from being terrific to quite poor. It also means that there are a number of tools available that work in different ways. Before settling on a specific tool, investigate several to find the one that's best for you.

Assemblers

If you're new to programming microcontrollers, you will probably find that, of the microcontrollers covered in this book, the 68HC05 is the easiest device to program (other than the Stamp) and understand the architecture. This is ironic because the 68HC05 is the only Von Neumann-architected device reviewed here, and Motorola is quite unique in its use of this architecture.

The reason why the 68HC05 is the easiest to learn to program is because the Von Neumann architecture is the most widely taught architecture when teaching basic assembly programming (and it is the basis of the Intel 80x6 microprocessor architecture used in the PC). (Figure 19.1.)

With this architecture, all arithmetic operations consist of three actions:

1. Load accumulator with first parameter.
2. Execute the operation with optionally the second parameter.
3. Store the result.

Normally, this is done using three different data addressing schemes: immediate (the parameter is part of the instruction), direct (the address of the parameter is specified as part of the instruction), and indirect (the address is located inside an index register). The 68HC05 works in exactly this manner. If you look at the code I've created for the two applications and "mykeRTOS," you'll see that this is handled in exactly this manner. It may seem cumbersome compared to how these three actions are handled as one or two instructions in the AVR and PIC.

Note that in Figure 19.1, I have not included a stack register. This is because there are no data "push" or "pop" instructions in the 68HC05. A data stack can be simulated by using the index register and the "incx"/"decx" instructions to change the index value (i.e., going up and down the stack). In this scheme, care must be taken to ensure that the index "data stack" and program counter stack areas never overwrite each other.

In the assembly langauge code I've written for the 68HC05 in this book, I have used the "org" statement to specify the start of the program at the start of the control store area. In the "CASM5J1A" program used with the 689HC705JICS, this is already defined in the compiler as "rom," and the end of the code area is noted in the compiler (much to my annoyance during the development of the second application with "mykeRTOS"). With the 68HC05, there is a good chance that the assembler that you are using is not programmed with the code limits as CASM5J1A has been, or has it identified at different locations (since many of the 68HC05s have different code sizes). You should keep this in mind when you're developing application code; the assembler may not have the appropriate limits in memory, and this will cause you to not use all the possible memory or use memory that doesn't actually exist in the part number you've specified.

One problem you might find when writing conditional branching is a message which states "Branch is to an address outside of range." This means that the branch is trying to conditionally branch to an address that is more than 127 addresses from the current program counter. This problem is easily solved by using branching around a "jmp" instruction.

For example, if you were writing assembler for the code:

```
if A == B then goto Label
```

You would originally code this as:

```
lda    A       ;  Compare A to B and if they are equal,
```

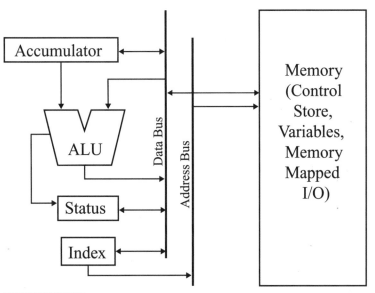

Figure 19.1 Classic Von Neumann architecture.

```
cmp    B         ;    Jump to "Label"
beq    Label
```

but the "beq Label" instruction is identified with the error stating "the jump is out of range." To avoid this, the complementary branch instruction is used to branch around a "jmp Label" instruction. In this case, the code will look like:

```
lda    A     ;   Compare A to B and if they are equal,
cmp    B     ;    Jump to "Label"
bne    $+5   ;   Branch Around Next Instruction
  jmp Label
```

The "$" (and "*") operators usually return the value of the program counter at the start of the instruction. This has to be understood when using the compiler because some use this character to indicate the address of the instruction after the current one. In the "bne $+5" instruction, if the value of A is different from B, program execution will jump to the address that is five bytes above the address of the start of the instruction. The "bne" instruction requires two bytes and the "jmp" instruction requires three bytes, which is why the address plus five bytes is used.

When branching around a "jmp" instruction like this, you should make sure what the "complementary" instruction actually is. If you are branching on something like a less than condition, this becomes quite a bit more complex.

High-Level Languages

After reading what I had to say about the 68HC05 and assembly langauge programming, you're probably thinking that the architecture is not well suited to high-level languages. I would tend to disagree with this assessment although with using a 68HC05 with a high-level language, there are some things to watch out for. As I read over this, I realize that these points are applicable to the other devices presented in this book as well.

If assembly language is going to be interspersed with the high-level langauage state-ments, do not modify the index ("X") register before changing it. Chances are the index register will be used for other aspects of the software (i.e., data stacks or pointers).

Because of the little RAM space available (and the fact that it is required for the pro-gram counter stack as well as variables), large arrays and data structures should not be used in a cavalier fashion because the microcontroller's processor does not have a lot of space devoted to it. Likewise, re-entrant subroutines should be avoided because the stack area may encroach on data areas. Division and floating-point operations should also be avoided if at all possible (because they tend to require large amounts of code and some temporary registers). I realize that some applications are impossible without these lan-guage features, but their use should be minimized as much as possible.

You should also look to use nonlinear programming techniques (such as an RTOS or state machine) to minimize the amount of actual code developed for an application. Also, these techniques are actually where an RTOS really shines, because they generally produce code that is very hard to follow, and if a symbolic debugger is available with the code, debugging them can be much easier than with assembly language source.

Writing a compiler is not a trivial task for the 68HC05, which might be surprising because of the length of time the architecture has been available and because its architec-ture is similar to that of computers such as the PC, where there are a plethora of different compilers available. The issue of writing a compiler for the 68HC05 is the limited RAM available and the difficulty in accessing it from compiled code.

Now you're probably asking yourself what "difficulty in accessing" the RAM from the compiler? There are five addressing modes, and they seem pretty simple and straightfor-ward. The issue for the compiler is accessing indexed or automatic variables. With only one index register that accesses RAM, there is going to be a lot of swapping its value in and out of memory. This becomes a problem when you realize that this swapping will require temporary variables to operate from and will require extra cycles to execute.

This leads me to the feeling that the best compiler for the 68HC05 is the simplest one possible, or if you are using a compiler with a low-end device such as the 68HC05J1A (with only 1200 bytes of program store), you should not use automatic variables, and keep complex operations (such as division) to an absolute minimum.

One thing to look for in a 68HC05 compiler is one that optimizes as much as possible. Looking back at the previous subchapter at the conditional branch, I showed how a branch instruction can be used to bypass a "jmp" instruction to an address that is more than 127 byte addresses away from the instruction after the branch instruction. In many compilers, this con-struct is always used, and you should look for a compiler that reduces this to a simple branch if the address is less than 127 byte addresses from the conditional jump instruction.

Motorola "S19-Record" Object Files

Motorola breaks the convention used by the other microcontroller companies by not using the Intel "INHX8M" hex file format. Instead, the "S19-record" object file type is used for all Motorola microcontrollers.

The "S19-record" is actually quite similar to the Intel format, but with a few differences you should be aware of. The "S19-record" got its name because every line of an object file begins with "S#," (either "S1" for data or "S9" for end of file).

An example ".s19" file is shown below:

```
S11303005FA680B700A6FEB7041A089ACC030C16A1
S110031008B600A880B70080120A1E008005
S10407F106FD
S10B07F8030F031803000300C2
S9030000FC
```

All the information needed to load the microcontroller's control store is located in this file. You should note that no symbolic information is located in this file (that is usually produced by the compiler or assembler specifically for a specific debugger or emulator).

Each line is broken up into a number of fields which are used to specify to the programmer or wherever the file is going to be used. The fields are defined by columns and work out as:

COLUMNS	IDENTIFIER	COMMENTS
1–2	Line Start	Always "S#" where "#" is either "1" or "9"
3–4	Bytes in Line	The number of bytes to the end of the Line
5–8	Data Start Addr	The Starting Address for Data in the Line
9–...	Data Pairs	Each Byte is represented as two hex 1characters.
End–2	Check Sum	Line Total & 0x0FF = 0x0FF

Typically, up to 16 bytes of data can be stored on each line.

If we were to take the first line in the example above, we can break up the data and show what is actually in it.

The first two bytes ("S1") indicate that the line is a data record.

The next two columns indicate how many bytes are in the line. Unlike the Intel file format, the number of bytes are not multiplied by two, and the number is for the total number of bytes following to the end of the line (including the data address and the checksum). In the first line, this value is "13," which is in hex, or "19" in decimal.

Bytes 5 through 8 are the address the data is to be put into. These bytes are "0300," which indicates that the code is to be put starting at address $0300.

Following the address is the instruction bytes in hex format. Like other numbers in Motorola micros, the numbers are in a very readable format, the first byte is the instruction and the next bytes are the instruction parameters in high-byte/low-byte format. This makes it very easy to compare the data in the ".s19" file to what is shown in the assembler listing.

The last two bytes are the checksum of the data after the first two bytes (i.e., the "1" or "9" are not included in the checksum). All the bytes on the line totalled and ANDed with $0FF will equal $0FF.

The last line is the "S9" record, which indicates the end of the file.

Motorola 68HC705J1CS
Development Kit

The Motorola 68HC705J1CS IDE and programmer package was what I used for developing the example 68HC06 applications (and RTOS) in this book. The 68HC705J1CS package consists of everything you'll require to develop 68HC705J1A applications and learn about the 68HC05. The "J1CS" package (usually pronounced "JICKS") consists of a programmer board (with everything required to start programming, including a serial cable and power supply), a sample windowed part, a diskette containing all the software required to develop assembly language programs, and a number of manuals explaining the 68HC705J1A and software operation. (Figure 19.2.)

The centerpiece of the package is the "RAPID" integrated development environment. This program is used to specify the software souce file to be assembled and burned into the microcontroller. RAPID does not work in terms of "projects" like several of the other IDEs presented in this book. Instead the currently active program is everything required for controlling the action of the assembler and there are no external options for the microcontroller, programmer, or simulator. Once RAPID is executing, a central editor is brought up and the assembler and simulator/programmer are invoked from this editor.

The editor itself works in a manner that's a combination of a MS-DOS line editor and a GUI editor. The control keys for the editor are somewhat awkward (although a better way of expressing it is to say the control keys and actions are not what I am familiar with).

Figure 19.2 Motorola 68HC705J1CS development kit.

When I developed the LED/button and RTOS/LCD clock/thermometer applications, I used another editor and used the RAPID editor for minor debug and updates.

The editor is capable of showing two files at once, (this was useful in editing "mykeRTOS" and the LCD clock/thermometer application), but there is one thing to beware of; if you initiate the assembler or simulator from the second screen, you'll end up deleting your primary source file. When I was working with RAPID I learned that after editing the include file for the RTOS ("RTOSAP.ASM"), I had to save it and quit the secondary window. I found this eliminated any chance of inadvertently deleting the primary file.

From the RAPID editor, the "CASM5J1A" cross-assembler program and the "ICS05J1A" simulator/JICS control software is started. The actual assembler/compiler and simulator/emulator/programmer and operating characteristics are selected by the "RINSTALL" program. For the most part, I ran "RAPID" with all the defaults except that I added the parameter to the assembly listing to show the contents of include files (which was critical for "mykeRTOS").

The CASM5J1A assembler program works very well for developing code for the 68HC705J1A and has some features that I really liked. As a rule, assemblers and compilers are not very interesting; they run and simply produce a listing and object code file (if there's no problems) or stop and indicate where the source syntax is invalid. CASM5J1A doesn't differ from this model, but it does integrate very well with RAPID. Syntax errors result in the editor being brought up to the invalid line in the source file.

Another nice feature of the CASM5J1A is the predefined microcontroller information available to the application source. All the registers and significant addresses are specified in the assembler without having to do it yourself or imbed an "include" file. This means that when you begin working with another 68HC05 model microcontroller, you'll have to use a different assembler.

ICS05J1A, RAPID's simulator/emulator/programmer, is quite a clever piece of code capable of communicating directly with the 68HC7-5J1CS development board. In discussing the ICS05J1A software, I'm going to discuss it in terms of each of the three major functions it provides with the development board. (Figure 19.3.)

The simulator software itself is quite slick and runs very quickly (on my Pentium 133, it runs at more than four thousand instruction cycles per second) in a MS-DOS full-screen session. Rather than use a windows-like GUI interface, small windows are built into a single screen and are continually updated as the simulator/emulator executes.

I have found the simulator screen to be very well laid out, although I would have liked the memory window to be a bit larger and able to display all the SRAM at the same time. This modification would have made debugging the RTOS application easier. Commands are entered through the keyboard into the "DEBUG F10" window (which is really a command line window). Specific functions or jumps to windows are preprogrammed as function keys. When looking over the code in the top righthand window, the up/down arrow keys will move the highlighted bar, and "F9" will execute the last instruction (which is useful for single-stepping through a program).

Breakpoints can be placed in the application during simulator/emulation by specifying either the address of the instruction or a label at that instruction. I'm only mentioning this because a bit of preparation is required for specifying breakpoints. Either a label has to be placed at the instruction you want to stop at, or you have to go back over the listing file and get the addresses where you want the breakpoints.

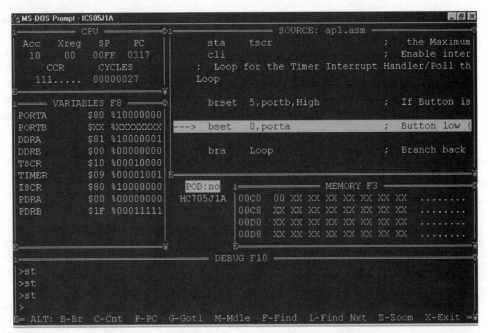

Figure 19.3 68HC705J1CS ICS05J1A user interface.

As ICS05J1A is loaded, the current program data (source and binary) is specified in the invocation and is loaded at the same time to be available to the simulator/programmer/emulator. The "J1CS" board connects to a PC via a 9-pin male D-shell connector to a serial port. This is a very standard interface. The interface typically runs at 115,200 bps for speed of emulation. Programming a part is carried out simply by entering the word "program" on the command line (in the "DEBUG F10" window) of IC05J1A. When you first go through the process, it may seem very manually intensive (you are prompted to turn switches on and off before putting the part into the programming socket), which may seem somewhat archiac compared to the other programmers discussed in this book, but it does work and program the part quickly. When I actually ran the programmer, I couldn't use the default serial port in my PC (COM1). I ended up running ICS05J1A from the MS-DOS command line using the format:

```
C:>ICS05J1A port pgm
```

Where "port" is the serial port and "pgm" is the program to simulate/emulate/burn into the 68HC705J1A.

Emulating the part consists of simply running an IDC 20-pin connected ribbon cable from the JICS board to the circuit. When ICS05J1A is running and the board (known as a "pod" in the software) is connected and powered up, a message "POD: YES" appears on the screen, and the I/O pin positions on the IDC connector are valid for the program. This method is very simular to the method I used to create the Stamp emulator. The only issue that you should be aware of is the relatively slow speed of the emulator's execution. I found that full instruction speed with the emulator running to be about 1000 instruction cycles per second. This speed makes the emulator useful for many applications, but for high-speed/critically timed applications (such as interfacing to the DS1820), the emulator cannot be used to help debug the application.

In terms of emulating hardware, there is one issue with the JICs that you should be aware of, and that's how the I/O pins are implemented. The JICs is run by a 68HC05C8, which emulates the I/O pins. This device does not have the pull-down capability on its I/O pins that the 68HC05J1A does. To compensate for this, two terminal blocks connected to the emulated pins and pull downs are available, and by simply shorting the pins to the pull down via the terminal block, the pull-down function can be added to the pin.

MOTOROLA 68HC05 INSTRUCTIONS

CONTENTS AT A GLANCE

The 68HC05 (and the other Motorola 6800-based processors and microcontrollers) have a very rich instruction set that allows a wide variety of applications. Part of the "standard" instruction set is the use of up to six possible primary data addressing modes. Like Motorola, I have kept the operators for different addressing modes together to help make referencing the instructions easier.

As I have noted elsewhere, the first byte of the instruction is the operand, with the following byte(s) being the parameters to the instruction. The number of cycles required to execute an operation is a function of the length of the parameters (0, 1, or 2 bytes for addressing). If you have a function that should be written to execute in a minimal amount of cycles, you should look at the different addressing modes to decide on the best data placement for carrying out the function. Typically, keeping all the data in the first 256 addresses (0 to $0FF) will keep the number of cycles required to a minimum.

In several situations, I have combined a number of instructions into a single type (this is most notably done with the "branch" instructions, in which I have reduced 18 instructions into two sheets). The reason for this is to put similar functions together and reduce the amount of searching that will have to be done to find the correct instruction.

Arithmetic Instructions

The basic operation in every processor is to move data from one place to another. In the 68HC05, this is accomplished by first loading a byte into a register and then storing it somewhere else. The primary instructions for carrying this out are the "LDA" and "STA" instructions, which load the accumulator and store its contents, respectively.

When you look at the sheets I've prepared for the two instructions (Instructions 20.1 and 20.2) you'll probably feel like the two instructions are not all that simple. There are six addressing modes for "LDA" and five for "STA." These modes were discussed in a previous chapter, but I want to go through them again for these instructions to show exactly how they work.

The first mode for loading is "immediate," in which a number is loaded into the accumulator. For example, if the accumulator is to be loaded with $12, it would go through the path shown in Figure 20.1.

The value to be loaded into the accumulator is in the next byte following the instruction ($A6 in this case). As with all other commands, the CCR bits are set according to the value loaded into the accumulator. When using an immediate instruction, always put a "#"

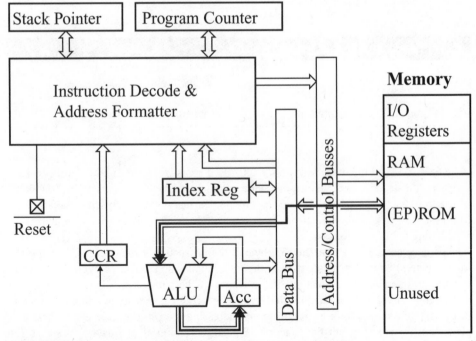

Figure 20.1 Immediate load into the 68HC05 accumulator.

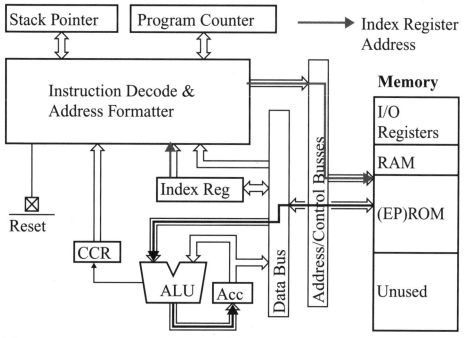

Figure 20.2 Index load into the 68HC05 accumulator.

(known as the "pound" sign or "octothorpe" for those who are very precise) in front of the value. To load the accumulator with 37, the instruction would look like:

```
lda #37
```

or

```
lda #$25    ;  For putting in a hex value
```

The "direct" and "extended" accumulator loads could be drawn in exactly the same way as I've done for the immediate instruction. But for "direct," the contents of the first 256 addresses and for "extended," the contents of any address in the whole memory space can be accessed. "Immediate" loads the accumulator with the contents of the byte after the instruction byte (the address is immaterial).

For indexed addressing, the contents of the index register (along with an optional off-set) are put on the address/control bus, and this address is used to select the register, the contents of which are read into the accumulator. (Figure 20.2.)

This address could have an 8- or 16-bit offset. Using this offset, a table could be implemented in the 68HC05 as:

```
HelloTable:
   DB    'H', 'e', 'l', 'l', 'o'
```

and to print the message out on an LCD, the following software could be used:

```
WriteHello:                 ;  Print the "Hello" Message on an LCD
  CLRX                      ;  Clear the Index Table
WriteHello_Loop:            ;  Loop Here until Done
  LDA HelloTable, X         ;  Load Table Value at Current Index into
                            ;    the Accumulator
```

```
JSR LCDOut              ;   Output the Character
INCX                    ;   Increment the Index Register
CPX #5                  ;   At the End of the Table?
BNE WriteHello_Loop     ;   Nope, Loop Around and do the Next Character
RTS                     ;   Return to the Calling Routine
```

With this code, "HelloTable" can be anywhere in memory. If it is located in the first 256 bytes of the 68HC05 (i.e., loaded into RAM), then the "LDA HelloTable, X" instruction will be one byte long (and take three instruction cycles), although the "CLRX" instruction would have to be replaced with "LDX #HelloTable" and the "CPX #5" instruction would have to be replaced with "CPX #HelloTable+5."

If it is located within the first 254 bytes of memory, then an index with an eight bit offset can be used for "HelloTable." And if the table or one of its elements are located above the first 254 addresses, then the instruction will take up 3 bytes and take 5 cycles to run.

Storing a value from the accumulator is carried out with exactly the same addressing options (except for "immediate," which does not mean anything in a "store" instruction). When storing the value in the accumulator, the addressing options used in fetching a byte from memory for "LDA" are used for storing the value in the accumulator in the "STA" instruction.

The index register can also be accessed directly using load and store instructions (Instructions 20.3 and 20.4). Using the "TAX" and "TXA" instructions (Instructions 20.5 and 20.6) the index register can also be used as a temporary storage register for the accumulator. As will be seen in the "MUL" instruction, the index register is used for more than just an index pointer into the program.

Arithmetic add and subtract instructions (Instructions 20.7, 20.8, 20.9, and 20.10) are very straightforward and very easy to use. "Add" adds a value to the accumulator and stores the result in the accumulator (and the condition code register). "Sub" subtracts a value from the accumulator and puts the result into the accumulator. As noted elsewhere, the "carry" flag becomes a "borrow" flag, set when the result of the subtraction is less than zero.

The add/subtract instructions with carry make complex operations much simpler. For example, implementing a 16-bit subtraction (A = B − C) can be done by:

```
LDA B+1     ;   Subtract the Lower 8 Bits First
SUB C+1
STA A+1
LDA B       ;   Subtract the Higher 8 Bits
SBC C       ;   Use the Subtract with Carry Flag
STA A
```

When you compare this to the PIC's (or any other processor that doesn't have an add with carry or subtract with carry instructions) 16-bit operations, you can see that having addition/subtract instructions with carry will greatly simplify program development.

In the 16-bit subtraction operation example above, the data is stored in the "Motorola" format—high byte followed by low byte.

The 68HC05 has a fast 8-bit multiply instruction (Instruction 20.11) that produces a 6-bit result. One of the most useful aspects of this instruction is its ability to produce a fraction of a value. For example, if you wanted to find one-tenth of a value, the following code could be used:

```
LDX # 256 / 10   ;   Get 1/10th of 256
LDA value        ;   Get the Value to divide by 10
MUL
STX Fraction     ;   Save the Value divided by 10
```

By multiplying by the fraction of 256 and only taking the high 8 bits, you are dividing by a constant fraction. This trick can also be used in the other processors discussed in this book, even if they don't have multiply instructions (and the operations are carried out in code).

All six addressing modes (immediate, direct, extended, indexed without offset, indexed with 8-bit offset and indexed with 16-bit offset) are available for the addition/subtraction instructions as well as the bit wise logic operations, AND, OR, and XOR (Instructions 20.12, 20.13, and 20.14). The bitwise operations work as expected, with the zero and negative flags being set based on the result and only the zero and negative flags changed.

Registers and data bytes can be cleared using the "CLR" instruction (Instruction 20.15). This instruction is the simplest way to load the integer zero into a register.

Loading an integer into a register or data byte can be done two different ways. If the byte to be set is in the EPROM (control store), then it can be explicitly programmed in the state by using the "db" command. For example, to load a message into EPROM (to be displayed later) the following code is used:

```
IntMsg
    db "Hello", 0   ;  Message to be looked up.
```

The second method is if the byte is in RAM. The "LDA #" and "STA" instructions are used as so:

```
    LDA #Integer    ;  Get the Value to load
    STA Register    ;  Into the Register
```

In a similar manner in which "CLR" will improve a load zero, "COM" (Instruction 20.16) will xor the value in the register with $0FF to get the complement. One aspect of this instruction to watch for (and may be unexpected) is that the carry flag is set. This means that the carry flag cannot be used as a flag passed to the instructions after the "COM" instruction.

To get the negative of a value, the "NEG" instruction is used (Instruction 20.17). This instruction converts the value in the register to an 8-bit "2's complement" number. If the "NEG" instruction wasn't available, the following instruction sequence would have to be carried out to negate a register:

```
    LDA #0                       ;  To get negative, Register = 0 - Register
    SUB Register
    STA Register
```

Which takes quite a few more instructions (which means more storage in terms of bytes and more instruction cycles).

Incrementing and decrementing instructions have been included in the 68HC05 as well (Instructions 20.18 and 20.19). They can be used for incrementing and decrementing 8-bit values very straightforwardly. In other microcontrollers, I show how a 16-bit increment can be implemented with a increment instruction that sets the zero flag, but even though the 68HC05 "DEC" instruction also sets the negative flag, a 16-bit decrement has to be implemented in the same way (with subtracting 1 from the lower 8 bits and then if the carry is set, decrementing the high 8 bits):

```
    LDA value+1     ;  Decrement the Low 8 Bits
    SUB #1
    STA value+1
    BCC dec16Skip   ;  Skip High 8 Bit DEC if Carry/Borrow Reset
    DEC value
dec16Skip:
```

You might be thinking that a 16-bit decrement could be implemented as:

```
DEC value+1      ;  Decrement the Low 8 bits
BPL dec16Skip    ;  If Result isn't Negative, Skip Next
DEC value        ;  Decrement the High 8 Bits
dec16Skip:
```

But, it is important to note that the negative flag in the CCR will be set if the result of "DEC value+1" is $80 to $FF, which will cause the high eight bits of the number to be decremented. The actual operation of this code is such that half the time the 16 bit number is decremented, the high byte will be decremented (rather than just 1/256th of the time as expected/wanted).

The 68HC05 has a number of data comparison instructions available for testing values. These instructions do a check on an operand and set the CCR status bits according to the value and the check.

The most basic comparison is testing a value to see if it is equal to zero (Instruction 20.20). The "TST" instruction sets the zero and negative flags for a value.

The "BIT" instruction (Instruction 20.21) will AND a value with the accumulator. The instruction name is a bit misleading; the purpose of this instruction is to AND the contents of the accumulator with another operand and set the zero and negative flags based on the result of the AND.

The "CMP" and "CMX" (Instructions 20.22 and 20.23) are traditional comparison operations. In "CMP," the operand is compared to the value in the accumulator. Along with the negative and zero flags, the carry and half carry flags are also affected.

The CMX instruction is used to compare the contents of the index register to a value. The primary purpose of this instruction is to see if the index register has exceeded any limits (this is very important in high-level languages that may check array limits). It can also be used in situations where the index register is used for temporary storage of a value.

There are three methods of shifting 8 bits of data in a register or memory location in the 68HC05. Arithmetic shifting can be thought of as multiplying and dividing. Logical shifting is best suited for shifting data out of a register in a bit-by-bit manner, and rotating takes a bit from and puts in a bit from the register into the carry register. Personally, I think having three types of shifting is overkill. In the PIC, I can do all three modes with the rotate through the carry flag.

As I pointed out above, "arithmetic" shifting is really multiplying and dividing a two's complement number by two and puts the end bit of the shift into the carry bit of the CCR (Instructions 20.24 and 20.25).

These instructions work as shown in Figure 20.3.

When a value is arithmetically shifted, either up or down (left or right, respectively), the sign of the value doesn't change.

"Logical" shifting is simply shifting the value up or down by one and putting the last bit to be moved into the carry bit of the CCR (Instructions 20.24 and 20.26).

The operations of the "logical shift" is as shown in Figure 20.4.

Note that the logical shift left is identical to the arithmetic shift left. For this reason, Motorola has made the "ASL" and "LSL" instructions identical (which is why I have put them together in my data sheets).

The final type of shifting instructions are the "rotate" operations (Instructions 20.27 and 20.28). In these instructions, the data is shifted once through the carry flag as is shown in Figure 20.5.

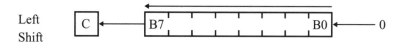

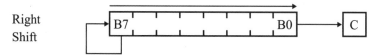

Figure 20.3 68HC05 arithmetic shift.

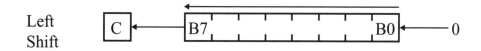

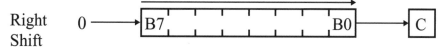

Figure 20.4 68HC05 logical shift.

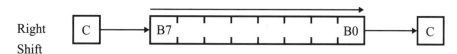

Figure 20.5 68HC05 rotate instructions.

This is the "shift" instruction typically available in most microcontrollers. With these instructions, the other two types of shift instructions can be emulated easily. For example, if you wanted to emulate an arithmetic shift right of a byte in RAM with the "ROR" instruction, the following code could be used:

```
  CLC                          ; Clear the Carry Flag
  BRCLR 7, Reg, NoCarrySet     ; If Bit 7 of Reg is Set, Set the Carry
  SEC                          ;  Flag before Shifting
NoCarrySet                     ; Now, Shift over Reg with Carry Set
  ROR Reg                      ;  Correctly
```

There are quite a number of different arithmetic operations available in the 68HC05. These instructions really follow the CISC philosophy that every possible operation should be available to the programmer. In the 68HC05's case, this is really a good thing because it helps make the application software much more efficient by minimizing the overhead of having to retrieve instructions (which cannot take place concurrently with the instruction execution as it does within a Harvard-architected microcontroller).

Instruction: "LDA Operand"   **Bits:** See Below

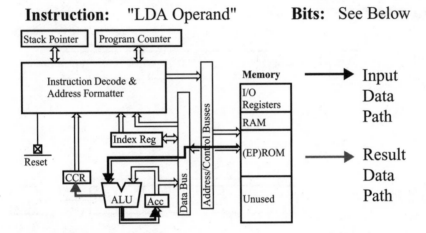

Execution:
Acc ← Operand
Z ← Operand == 0
N ← ((Operand & $080) >> 7) & 1

Instruction Cycles: 2-5

Example:
LDA Flags
EOR Bit
STA Flags

MCUs: 68HC05
; Flip Flag Bit

Addressing	Format	Bits	Cycles
Immediate	LDA #val	$A6 val	2
Direct	LDA reg	$B6 Adr	3
Extended	LDA reg	$C6 HAdr LAdr	4
Index No Off	LDA ,X	$F6	3
Index 8 Off	LDA Off,X	$E6 Off	4
Index 16 Off	LDA Off,X	$C6 HOff LOff	5

Instruction 20.1 68HC05 lda operand instruction.

Instruction: "STA Operand"   **Bits:** See Below

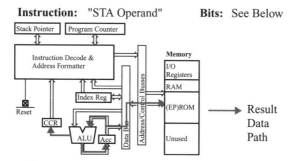

Execution:
Operand ← Acc
Z ← Acc == 0
N ← Acc >> 7

Instruction Cycles: 4-6

Example: **MCUs:** 68HC05
LDA First
STA First   ; Move a Byte

Addressing	Format	Bits	Cycles
Direct	STA reg	$B7 Adr	4
Extended	STA reg	$C7 HAdr LAdr	5
Index No Off	STA ,X	$F7	4
Index 8 Off	STA Off,X	$E7 Off	5
Index 16 Off	STA Off,X	$D7 HOff LOff	6

Instruction 20.2 68HC05 sta operand instruction.

Instruction: "LDX Operand"   **Bits:** See Below

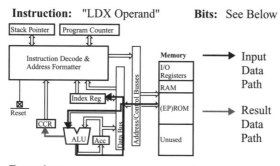

Execution:
X ← Operand
Z ← Operand == 0
N ← ((Operand & $080) >> 7) & 1

Instruction Cycles: 2-5

Example: **MCUs:** 68HC05
LDX Flags
LDA ,X   ; Flip Flag Bit
EOR Bit
STA ,X

Addressing	Format	Bits	Cycles
Immediate	LDX #val	$AE val	2
Direct	LDX reg	$BE Adr	3
Extended	LDX reg	$CE HAdr LAdr	4
Index No Off	LDX ,X	$FE	3
Index 8 Off	LDX Off,X	$EE Off	4
Index 16 Off	LDX Off,X	$CE HOff LOff	5

Instruction 20.3 68HC05 ldx operand instruction.

Instruction: "STX Operand"   **Bits:** See Below

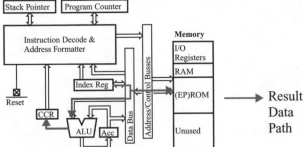

Execution:

Operand ← Index Reg
Z ← Index Reg == 0
N ← Index Reg >> 7

Instruction Cycles: 4-6

Example: **MCUs:** 68HC05
 STX Saved   ; Save the Current Index

Addressing	Format	Bits	Cycles
Direct	STX reg	$BF Adr	4
Extended	STX reg	$CF HAdr LAdr	5
Index No Off	STX ,X	$FF	4
Index 8 Off	STX Off,X	$EF Off	5
Index 16 Off	STX Off,X	$DF HOff LOff	6

Instruction 20.4 68HC05 stx operand instruction.

Instruction: "TAX"

Bits: $97

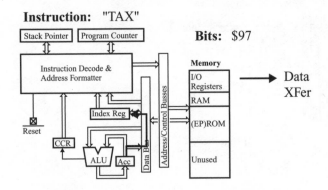

Execution:

Index ← Accumulator

Instruction Cycles: 2

Example: **MCUs:** 68HC05
 TAX   ; Temporary Storage of Acc
 LDA Reg
  :
 TXA   ; Restore Accumulator

Comments:

Instruction 20.5 68HC05 tax instruction.

Instruction: "TXA"

Bits: $97

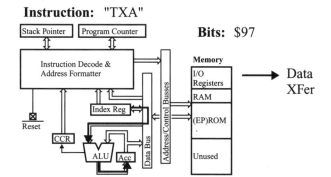

Execution:
Accumulator ← Index

Instruction Cycles: 2

Example:
TAX   ; Temporary Storage of Acc
LDA Reg
:
TXA   ; Restore Accumulator

MCUs: 68HC05

Comments:

Instruction 20.6 68HC05 txa instruction.

Instruction: "ADD Operand"   **Bits:**   See Below

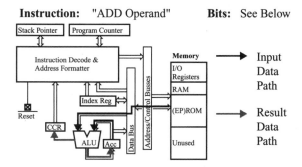

Execution:
Acc ← Acc + Operand
C ← (Acc + Operand) > $0FF
Z ← (Acc + Operand) == 0
H ← (((Acc & $0F) + (Operand & $0F)) >> 4) & 1

Instruction Cycles: 2-5

Example:
LDA First + 1   ; 16 Bit Addition
ADD Second + 1   ; First = First + Second
STA First + 1
LDA First
ADC Second
STA First

MCUs: 68HC05

Addressing	Format	Bits	Cycles
Immediate	ADD #val	$AB val	2
Direct	ADD reg	$BB Adr	3
Extended	ADD reg	$CB HAdr LAdr	4
Index No Off	ADD ,X	$FB	3
Index 8 Off	ADD Off,X	$EB Off	4
Index 16 Off	ADD Off,X	$CB HOff LOff	5

Instruction 20.7 68HC05 add operand instruction.

Instruction: "ADC Operand"   **Bits:** See Below

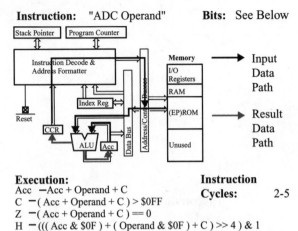

Execution:
Acc —Acc + Operand + C
C —(Acc + Operand + C) > $0FF
Z —(Acc + Operand + C) == 0
H —(((Acc & $0F) + (Operand & $0F) + C) >> 4) & 1

Instruction Cycles: 2-5

Example:
LDA First + 1   ; 16 Bit Addition
ADD Second + 1   ; First = First + Second
STA First + 1
LDA First
ADC Second
STA First

MCUs: 68HC05

Addressing	Format	Bits	Cycles
Immediate	ADC #val	$A9 val	2
Direct	ADC reg	$B9 Adr	3
Extended	ADC reg	$C9 HAdr LAdr	4
Index No Off	ADC ,X	$F9	3
Index 8 Off	ADC Off,X	$E9 Off	4
Index 16 Off	ADC Off,X	$C9 HOff LOff	5

Instruction 20.8 68HC05 adc operand instruction.

Instruction: "SUB Operand"   **Bits:** See Below

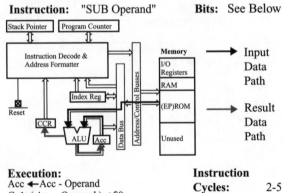

Execution:
Acc ←Acc - Operand
C ←(Acc - Operand) < $0
Z ←(Acc - Operand) == 0
N ←(Acc -Operand) >> 7

Instruction Cycles: 2-5

Example:
LDA First + 1
SBB Second + 1
STA First + 1
LDA First
SBC Second
STA First

MCUs: 68HC05

; 16 Bit Subtraction
; First = First - Second

Addressing	Format	Bits	Cycles
Immediate	SUB #val	$A0 val	2
Direct	SUB reg	$B0 Adr	3
Extended	SUB reg	$C0 HAdr LAdr	4
Index No Off	SUB ,X	$F0	3
Index 8 Off	SUB Off,X	$E0 Off	4
Index 16 Off	SUB Off,X	$C0 HOff LOff	5

Instruction 20.9 68HC05 sub operand instruction.

Instruction: "SUB Operand"   **Bits:** See Below

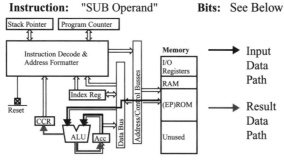

Execution:
Acc ← Acc - Operand
C ← (Acc - Operand) < $0
Z ← (Acc - Operand) == 0
N ← (Acc -Operand) >> 7

Instruction Cycles: 2-5

Example:
```
LDA First + 1      ; 16 Bit Subtraction
SBB Second + 1     ; First = First - Second
STA First + 1
LDA First
SBC Second
STA First
```

MCUs: 68HC05

Addressing	Format	Bits	Cycles
Immediate	SUB #val	$A0 val	2
Direct	SUB reg	$B0 Adr	3
Extended	SUB reg	$C0 HAdr LAdr	4
Index No Off	SUB ,X	$F0	3
Index 8 Off	SUB Off,X	$E0 Off	4
Index 16 Off	SUB Off,X	$C0 HOff LOff	5

Instruction 20.10 68HC05 sbc operand instruction.

Instruction: "MUL"   **Bits:** $42

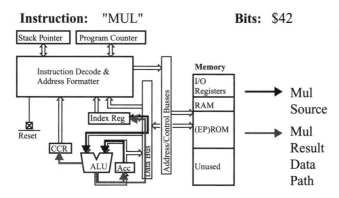

Execution:
X:A ← X * A
H ← 0
C ← 0

Instruction Cycles: 11

Example:
```
LDX #5          ;   5 x 7
LDA #7
MUL
```

MCUs: 68HC05

Instruction 20.11 68HC05 mul instruction.

Instruction: "AND Operand"   **Bits:** See Below

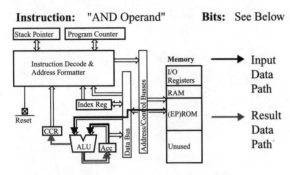

Execution:

Acc ← Acc & Operand

Z ← (Acc & Operand) == 0

N ← ((Acc & Operand) & $080) >> 7) & 1

Instruction Cycles: 2-5

Example: **MCUs:** 68HC05

LDA First   ;   Clear Masked Bits

AND Mask

STA First

Addressing	Format	Bits	Cycles
Immediate	AND #val	$A4 val	2
Direct	AND reg	$B4 Adr	3
Extended	AND reg	$C4 HAdr LAdr	4
Index No Off	AND ,X	$F4	3
Index 8 Off	AND Off,X	$E4 Off	4
Index 16 Off	AND Off,X	$C4 HOff LOff	5

Instruction 20.12 68HC05 and operand instruction.

Instruction: "ORA Operand"   **Bits:** See Below

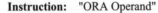

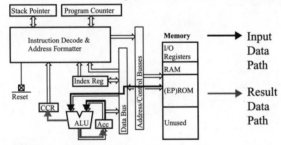

Execution:

Acc ← Acc | Operand

Z ← (Acc | Operand) == 0

N ← ((Acc | Operand) & $080) >> 7) & 1

Instruction Cycles: 2-5

Example: **MCUs:** 68HC05

LDA First   ;   Set Masked Bits

ORA #Mask

STA First

Addressing	Format	Bits	Cycles
Immediate	ORA #val	$AA val	2
Direct	ORA reg	$BA Adr	3
Extended	ORA reg	$CA HAdr LAdr	4
Index No Off	ORA ,X	$FA	3
Index 8 Off	ORA Off,X	$EA Off	4
Index 16 Off	ORA Off,X	$CA HOff LOff	5

Instruction 20.13 68HC05 ora operand instruction.

Instruction: "EOR Operand"   **Bits:** See Below

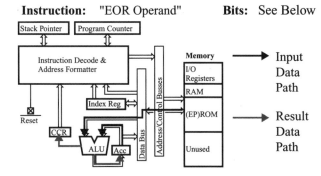

Execution:
Acc ← Acc ^ Operand
Z ← (Acc ^ Operand) == 0
N ← ((Acc ^ Operand) & $080) >> 7

Instruction
Cycles: 2-5

Example: **MCUs:** 68HC05
LDA Flags   ;   Flip Flag Bit
EOR Bit
STA Flags

Addressing	Format	Bits	Cycles
Immediate	EOR #val	$A8 val	2
Direct	EOR reg	$B8 Adr	3
Extended	EOR reg	$C8 HAdr LAdr	4
Index No Off	EOR ,X	$F8	3
Index 8 Off	EOR Off,X	$E8 Off	4
Index 16 Off	EOR Off,X	$C8 HOff LOff	5

Instruction 20.14 68HC05 eor operand instruction.

Instruction: "CLR Operand"   **Bits:** See Below

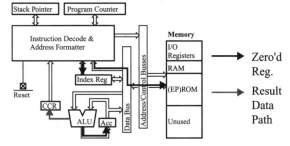

Execution:
Operand ← 0
Z ← 1
N ← 0

Instruction
Cycles: 3-6

Example: **MCUs:** 68HC05
CLR Variable   ;   Clear the Variable

Addressing	Format	Bits	Cycles
Inherent - A	CLrA	$4F	3
Inherent - X	CLRX	$5F	3
Direct	CLR Reg	$3F Adr	5
Index 0 Off	CLR ,X	$7F	5
Index 8 Off	CLR Off,X	$6F Off	6

Instruction 20.15 68HC05 clr operand instruction.

20

MOTOROLA 68HC05

Instruction: "COM Operand"   **Bits:**   See Below

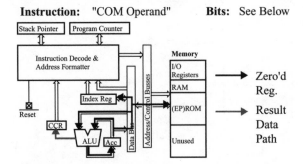

Execution:
Operand ← Operand ^ 0x0FF
Z ← (Operand ^ 0x0FF) == 0
N ← (Operand ^ 0x0FF) >> 7
C ← 1

Instruction Cycles: 3-6

Example: **MCUs:** 68HC05
   COM Variable   ;   Negate "Variable"
   INC Variable

Addressing	Format	Bits	Cycles
Inherent - A	COMA	$43	3
Inherent - X	COMX	$53	3
Direct	COM Reg	$33 Adr	5
Index 0 Off	COM ,X	$73	5
Index 8 Off	COM Off,X	$63 Off	6

Instruction 20.16 68HC05 com operand instruction.

Instruction: "NEG Operand"   **Bits:**   See Below

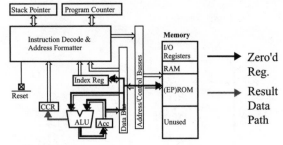

Execution:
Operand ← 0 - Operand
Z ← (0 - Operand) == 0
N ← (0 - Operand) >> 7
C ← (0 - Operand) < 0

Instruction Cycles: 3-6

Example: **MCUs:** 68HC05
   NEG Variable   ;   Negate "Variable"

Addressing	Format	Bits	Cycles
Inherent - A	NEGA	$40	3
Inherent - X	NEGX	$50	3.
Direct	NEG Reg	$30 Adr	5
Index 0 Off	NEG ,X	$70	5
Index 8 Off	NEG Off,X	$60 Off	6

Instruction 20.17 68HC05 neg operand instruction.

Instruction: "INC Operand"   **Bits:** See Below

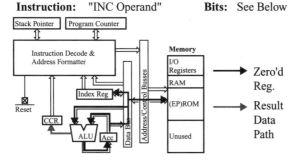

Execution:
Operand ← Operand + 1
Z ← (Operand + 1) == 0
N ← (Operand + 1) >> 7

Instruction Cycles: 3-6

Example: **MCUs:** 68HC05
    INC Counter   ;   Increment Counter

Addressing	Format	Bits	Cycles
Inherent - A	INCA	$4A	3
Inherent - X	INCX	$5A	3
Direct	INC Reg	$3A Adr	5
Index 0 Off	INC ,X	$7A	5
Index 8 Off	INC Off,X	$6A Off	6

Instruction 20.18 68HC05 inc operand instruction.

Instruction: "DEC Operand"   **Bits:** See Below

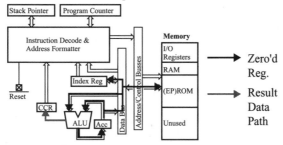

Execution:
Operand ← Operand - 1
Z ← (Operand - 1) == 0
N ← (Operand - 1) >> 7

Instruction Cycles: 3-6

Example: **MCUs:** 68HC05
    DEC Variable   ;   Count Down in a Loop
    BNE Label

Addressing	Format	Bits	Cycles
Inherent - A	DECA	$4A	3
Inherent - X	DECX	$5A	3
Direct	DEC Reg	$3A Adr	5
Index 0 Off	DEC ,X	$7A	5
Index 8 Off	DEC Off,X	$6A Off	6

Instruction 20.19 68HC05 dec operand instruction.

Instruction: "BIT Operand"   **Bits:** See Below

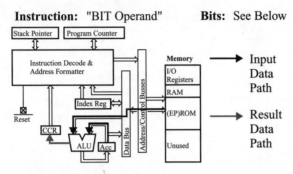

Execution:
Res ← Acc & Operand
Z ← (Acc & Operand) == 0
N ← ((Acc & Operand) & $080) >> 7

Instruction Cycles: 2-5

Example: **MCUs:** 68HC05
BIT $1   ;   Bit 0 is a Flag
BNE Label   ;   Branch if Bit 0 Set

Addressing	Format	Bits	Cycles
Immediate	BIT #val	$A5 val	2
Direct	BIT reg	$B5 Adr	3
Extended	BIT reg	$C5 HAdr LAdr	4
Index No Off	BIT ,X	$F5	3
Index 8 Off	BIT Off,X	$E5 Off	4
Index 16 Off	BIT Off,X	$C5 HOff LOff	5

Instruction 20.20 68HC05 tst operand instruction.

Instruction: "BIT Operand"   **Bits:** See Below

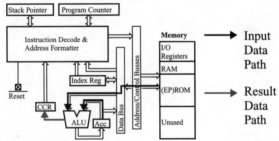

Execution:
Res ← Acc & Operand
Z ← (Acc & Operand) == 0
N ← ((Acc & Operand) & $080) >> 7

Instruction Cycles: 2-5

Example: **MCUs:** 68HC05
BIT $1   ;   Bit 0 is a Flag
BNE Label   ;   Branch if Bit 0 Set

Addressing	Format	Bits	Cycles
Immediate	BIT #val	$A5 val	2
Direct	BIT reg	$B5 Adr	3
Extended	BIT reg	$C5 HAdr LAdr	4
Index No Off	BIT ,X	$F5	3
Index 8 Off	BIT Off,X	$E5 Off	4
Index 16 Off	BIT Off,X	$C5 HOff LOff	5

Instruction 20.21 68HC05 bit operand instruction.

Instruction: "CMP Operand"   **Bits:** See Below

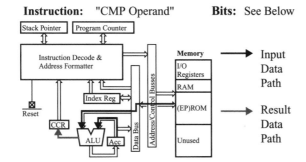

Execution:
Res ← Acc - Operand
Z ← (Acc - Operand) == 0
N ← ((Acc - Operand) & $080) >> 7
C ← (Acc - Operand) < 0

Instruction Cycles: 2-5

Example:
CMP 37   ; If Acc != 37 then Branch
BNE Label

MCUs: 68HC05

Addressing	Format	Bits	Cycles
Immediate	CMP #val	$A1 val	2
Direct	CMP reg	$B1 Adr	3
Extended	CMP reg	$C1 HAdr LAdr	4
Index No Off	CMP ,X	$F1	3
Index 8 Off	CMP Off,X	$E1 Off	4
Index 16 Off	CMP Off,X	$C1 HOff LOff	5

Instruction 20.22 68HC05 cmp operand instruction.

Instruction: "CMX Operand"   **Bits:** See Below

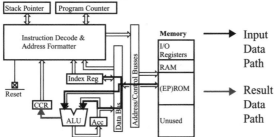

Execution:
Res ← X - Operand
Z ← (X - Operand) == 0
N ← ((X - Operand) & $080) >> 7
C ← (X - Operand) < 0

Instruction Cycles: 2-5

Example:
CMX 37   ;   If Index != 37 then
BNE Label ;   Branch

MCUs: 68HC05

Addressing	Format	Bits	Cycles
Immediate	CMX #val	$A3 val	2
Direct	CMX reg	$B3 Adr	3
Extended	CMX reg	$C3 HAdr LAdr	4
Index No Off	CMX ,X	$F3	3
Index 8 Off	CMX Off,X	$E3 Off	4
Index 16 Off	CMX Off,X	$C3 HOff LOff	5

Instruction 20.23 68HC05 cmx operand instruction.

20

MOTOROLA 68HC05

Instruction: "ASL/LSL Operand" **Bits:** See Below

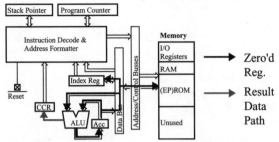

Execution:
Operand ← (Operand << 1) + 0
Z ← ((Operand << 1) + 0) == 0
N ← ((Operand << 1) + 0) >> 7
C ← Operand >> 7

Instruction Cycles: 3-6

Example: **MCUs:** 68HC05
  ASLA   ;   Acc = Acc * 2

Addressing	ASL Format	LSL Format	Bits	Cycles
Inherent - A	ASLA	LSLA	$48	3
Inherent - X	ASLX	LSLX	$58	3
Direct	ASL Reg	LSL Reg	$38 Reg	5
Indexed 0 Off	ASL,X	LSL ,X	$78	5
Indexed 8 Off	ASL Off, X	LSL Off, X	$68 Off	6

Instruction 20.24 68HC05 asl/lsl operand instruction.

Instruction: "ASR Operand"   **Bits:** See Below

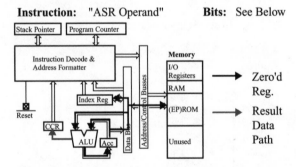

Execution:
Op ← (Op >> 1) + (Op & 0x080)
Z ← ((Op >> 1) + (Op & 0x080)) == 0
N ← ((Op >> 1) + (Op & 0x080)) >> 7
C ← Op & 1

Instruction Cycles: 3-6

Example: **MCUs:** 68HC05
  LDX #3   ;   Divide "Acc by 8
Loop:
  ASRA
  DECX
  BNE Loop

Addressing	Format	Bits	Cycles
Inherent - A	ASRA	$47	3
Inherent - X	ASRX	$57	3
Direct	ASR Reg	$37 Adr	5
Index 0 Off	ASR ,X	$77	5
Index 8 Off	ASR Off,X	$67 Off	6

Instruction 20.25 68HC05 asr operand instruction.

Instruction: "LSR Operand"   **Bits:** See Below

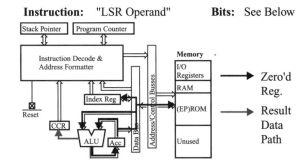

Execution:
Op ← (Op >> 1)
Z ← (Op >> 1) == 0
N ← 0
C ← Op & 1

Instruction Cycles: 3-6

Example: **MCUs:** 68HC05
LDX #3   ;   Divide Acc by 8
Loop:
LSRA
DECX
BNE Loop

Addressing	Format	Bits	Cycles
Inherent - A	LSRA	$44	3
Inherent - X	LSRX	$54	3
Direct	LSR Reg	$34 Adr	5
Index 0 Off	LSR ,X	$74	5
Index 8 Off	LSR Off,X	$64 Off	6

Instruction 20.26 68HC05 lsr operand instruction.

Instruction: "ROL Operand"   **Bits:** See Below

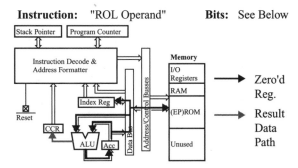

Execution:
Op ← (Op << 1) + C
Z ← ((Op << 1) + C) == 0
N ← Op << 6
C ← Op >> 7

Instruction Cycles: 3-6

Example: **MCUs:** 68HC05
CLC   ;   Shift 16 Bit Number by
ROL Reg   ;   1
ROL Reg+1

Addressing	Format	Bits	Cycles
Inherent - A	ROLA	$49	3
Inherent - X	ROLX	$59	3
Direct	ROL Reg	$39 Adr	5
Index 0 Off	ROL ,X	$79	5
Index 8 Off	ROL Off,X	$69 Off	6

Instruction 20.27 68HC05 rol operand instruction.

20

MOTOROLA 68HC05

Instruction: "ROR Operand"   **Bits:** See Below

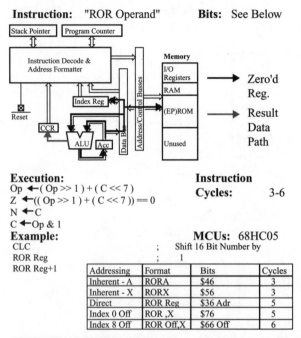

Execution:

$Op \leftarrow (Op \gg 1) + (C \ll 7)$

$Z \leftarrow ((Op \gg 1) + (C \ll 7)) == 0$

$N \leftarrow C$

$C \leftarrow Op \mathbin{\&} 1$

Instruction Cycles: 3-6

Example:

			MCUs: 68HC05
CLC	;	Shift 16 Bit Number by	
ROR Reg	;	1	
ROR Reg+1			

Addressing	Format	Bits	Cycles
Inherent - A	RORA	$46	3
Inherent - X	RORX	$56	3
Direct	ROR Reg	$36 Adr	5
Index 0 Off	ROR ,X	$76	5
Index 8 Off	ROR Off,X	$66 Off	6

Instruction 20.28 68HC05 ror operand instruction.

Execution Change Operators

There are quite a few different options available in the 68HC05 for changing program execution (both conditionally and nonconditionally). I've tried to break down the different types of execution change operations into three catagories. The first is a direct change to any location within the memory space. This can either be a jump or subroutine call. The second type of execution change is a conditional and direct jump to an offset from the current instruction pointer. This method of execution, in the classic sense, requires less program storage, although really takes the same number of instruction cycles as the direct changes to the program counter. The last type of execution change is the interrupt request (primarily software). This operation can be used to great advantage for providing a "BIOS" function for the application software. If you are familiar with IBM PC (8086) assembly language programming, the execution change operations in the 68HC05 should be very easy to understand.

Changing the PC directly (Instructions 20.29 and 20.30) has a surprising number of options, depending on where the new address is located and how it is to be accessed. The primary method of changing the program counter to a new address is either "direct" or "extended," in which the address to jump to is part of the instruction.

If an indexed address is used, the address specified in the instruction will get an 8-bit value that is added to the offset provided in the instruction. With this, table jumps can be implemented from anywhere in the 68HC05's memory space.

The "JSR" instruction (Jump to SubRoutine) works in exactly the same manner as the "JMP" instruction, except the program counter of the next instruction is saved on the stack. When the subroutine has finished executing, an "RTS" (Return from Subroutine -

Instruction 20.31) is executed and the address is retrieved from the stack and put into the Program Counter. The program then resumes execution from the address after the "JSR" instruction.

Branching consists of adding an 8-bit two's complement offset to the program counter at the instruction after the branch instruction's. The 8-bit two's complement number means that the new execution address can be -128 or $+127$ from the start of the next instruction. This probably sounds pretty complex (although it really isn't).

For example, in the following code (which carries out a 16-bit increment), I've added the address and instruction bits to show you how a branch to offset works:

```
Addr    $3C Reg+1   INC Reg+1   ;   Increment Low 8 Bits
Addr+2  $26 $02     BNE Skip    ;   Skip High 8 Bit INC if Low++ != 0
Addr+4  $3C Reg     INC Reg     ;   Increment High 8 Bits
Addr+6          Skip            ;   Execute the Next Instruction
```

As the first increment is executed, the zero and negative bits of the CCR are set/reset based on the state of the lower 8 bits of the 16-bit number. The zero bit is checked, and if it isn't set, then the "BNE" will add the offset (to "skip" which is "2") to the program counter of the next instruction (which is "addr+4") to get the correct address to be executed, which should be "Addr+6."

While this is very straightforward, the real fun comes when execution jumps to addresses above (or less than) the current address. For example, a simple 8-bit power-of-two function could be implemented as:

```
Addr                Power2      ;   Do Acc << X
Addr    $5D         TSTX        ;   If X == 0 then Don't ROL A
Addr+1  $27 $04     BEQ Skip
Addr+3              Loop        ;   Come Back Here for Each Loop
Addr+3  $48         ASLA        ;   Shift Acc up by 1
Addr+4  $5A         DECX        ;   Decrement the Power Counter
Addr+5  $26 $FC     BNE Loop    ;   Do Again?
Addr+7              Skip        ;   Finished, Return to Caller
Addr+7  $81         RTS
```

The first branch ("BEQ Skip") should be quite straightforward based on what I showed above. At the end of the "BEQ Skip" instruction, the program counter will be set to "Addr+3," if the Branch is to be executed, the program counter will have to be equal to "Addr+7." This means that 4 is simply used as the offset.

The second branch ("BNE loop") has the surprising offset of $FC. Actually, it shouldn't be that surprising when you realize that the offset is actually -4 (if you convert "$FC" to decimal, you'll find that it is actually "-4"). Because the program counter is at "Addr+7" at the end of the "BNE Loop" instruction and if the branch is to be taken, it has to be at "Addr+3," which is four addresses less.

Another example of this is implementing an endless loop. Because the program counter is pointing to the next instruction when the offest is added to it, you have reset the program counter to point to the start of the instruction looping back to itself. This looks like:

```
Addr    $20 $FE   BNE *              ;   Endless Loop
```

If you do a lot of hand assembly with the 68HC05 (especially during "patching" and debug of code), you'll become a real champ at counting backwards in hex.

For the most part, branching is used to execute conditionally. There are ten branch instructions (Instruction 20.33) that carry out branches after a variety of different conditions. All branch to offset take three instruction cycles.

The following table lists them, along with their complementary instructions (the condition is valid for the high-level statement "if Condition then Branch to Offset"):

```
                                         Complementary Instruction
Ins   Condition      CCR Bits            Ins   Condition      CCR Bits
BHI   A > B          C == 0 && Z == 0    BLS   A <= B         C == 1 || Z == 1
BHS   A >= B         C == 0              BLO   A < B          C == 1
BEQ   A == B         Z == 1              BNE   A != B         Z == 0
BMI   A < 0          N == 1              BPL   A >= 0         N == 0
BHCS  (A&$F)=(B&$F)  H == 0
```

Note that "BHS" is equivalent to "BCC," and "BLO" is equivalent to "BCS." The "BHS" and "BLO" mnemonics indicate the branch condition after a comparison. The "BCC" and "BCS" mnemonics indicate that the branch is to take place depending on the condition of the carry flag.

Like the operation of the 8-bit index register, you may be thinking that the 8-bit two's complement offset in the branch instruction is needlessly limited. Actually, by using the complementary instruction, you can create a jump instruction into anywhere in memory. Which is why I created the table above, to be able to relate complementary branches.

For example, if you were to create the assembly code for the statement:

```
if A > B then goto Label
```

and "Label" could be anywhere in memory, then the following code would be used:

```
Addr     $B6 A        LDA A       ; Start with "A - B"
Addr+2   $B1 B        CMP B
Addr+4   $23 $03      BLS Skip    ; Jump if Greater than (or
Addr+6   $CC $LH $LL  JMP Label   ;   branch around "JMP" if the
Addr+9                Skip        ;   Result is Less than/equals)
```

The branch instruction changes the program counter when the complementary function (i.e., "A <= B" is executed) to jump around the "JMP label" instruction. In the code above, "LH" and "LL" are the high and low bytes, respectively, of the address at "Label." This may seem like a clumsy method of carrying out a conditional jump, but many compilers just create this code and leave it (even if the code can be optimized down to a single branch).

Earlier in this chapter, I showed an example where the "brpl" and "brmi" instructions could cause problems (especially in repeating increment/decrement operations).

If you compare my table in Instruction 20.33 to a table in Motorola's 68HC05 instruction documentation, you'll notice that I've left out a number of branch instructions that Motorola considers important. I haven't really. I just don't consider them to be relavent to the branches above. These instructions (Instructions 20.34 and 20.35) poll the current interrupt state and input pin condition and allow conditional jumps and branches on the condition of the IRQ pin and the "I" bit of the CCR. I don't use these instructions too much because it is very risky using the interrupt mask bit to pass information (and for the most part, its condition is not unknown in code), and I can poll and branch based on the the IRQ pin using the "BRCLR" and "BRSET" instructions described below.

You may have also noticed that I have not yet discussed the branch always ("BRA" - Instruction 20.36) and branch never ("BRN" which is presented below). As you will see later in the chapter, I don't consider the "BRN" to be a useful instruction as a branch. Branch always is best suited for relocatable code. This is because there are several "JMP" options that take up as little space as the "BRA" instruction and take fewer instruction cycles to execute.

The branch to subroutine (BSR - (Instruction 20.32) instruction operates very similarly to the "JSR" instruction but uses an offset rather than an absolute address for the subroutine address. The full address of the instruction following "BSR" is placed on the stack, just as it is for the "JSR" instruction. The "RTS" instruction is used to return the instruction after the "BSR" instruction.

Processor execution of a software interrupt (Instruction 20.37) "SWI" instruction is identical to that of a hardware interrupt request, except that resetting the requesting hardware is not required. The ReTurn from Interrupt ("RTI") instruction (Instruction 20.38) is used for both hardware and software interrupts.

To carry through with the IBM PC analogy, I would consider the software interrupt to be best used as a "BIOS" (basic input/output system) interface for a relocatable program. Code could initiate a BIOS request through the use of an "SWI" instruction with the operation to be executed specified in the accumulator or index register. The advantages of doing this are that the BIOS function can be located anywhere in the 68HC05's memory map and can change without affecting the application code, and different hardware can be supported without changing the application code. An example of this would be setting up asynchronous serial handler BIOS code that would run in a variety of 68HC05s with and without SCI modules. In this case, the same application could run in a 68HC05J1A or a 68HC05C8 without change to the code.

A very significant advantage of the SWI instruction is that interrupts are masked after the instruction has executed. This allows time-critical code to be executed without fear of an interrupt screwing up the sequence or timing.

Another use of the software interrupt instruction would be in an RTOS. Using the "SWI" instruction instead of a subroutine call saves all the context information on the stack automatically and faster than if the contents of the registers was saved with individual instructions. In the RTOS I present in this book, I use the "SWI" instruction to make operating system requests.

Bit Operators

In the 6800 (the microprocessor that is the precursor to the 68HC05 and the other Motorola microcontrollers), there are no bit operations. I feel that this is actually quite a disadvantage when connecting a microprocessor or microcontroller to external hardware. To access individual bits or test conditions, multiple instructions are required, which both takes up space and takes extra cycles.

Fortunately, the 68HC05 instruction does have a number of bit-oriented instructions. This greatly eases the effort required to interface with external hardware (which may be a single switch or LED on an individual pin). Actually, this reminds me of a good point to make that I haven't made elsewhere. When selecting a compiler or an assembler for the 68HC05, make sure that it is specifically designed for the 68HC05; a 6800 (or 6802) assembler will not produce code that is usable by the 68HC05.

Instruction: "JMP Address"   **Bits:** See Below

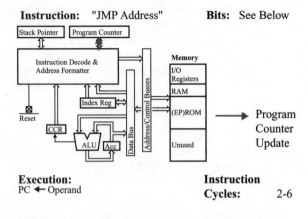

Execution:
PC ← Operand

Instruction Cycles: 2-6

Example: **MCUs:** 68HC05
JMP Label   ;   Jump to Label anywhere
:   ;   in Memory
Label:

Addressing	Format	Bits	Cycles
Direct	JMP Adr	$BC Adr	2
Extended	JMP Adr	$CC HAdr LAdr	3
Index 0 Off	JMP ,X	$FC	5
Index 8 Off	JMP Off,X	$EC Off	5
Index 16 Off	JMP Off,X	$DC HOff LOff	6

Instruction 20.29 68HC05 jmp operand instruction.

Instruction: "JSR Address"   **Bits:** See Below

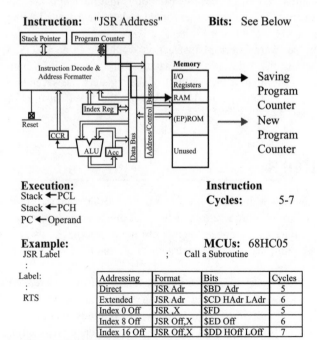

Execution:
Stack ← PCL
Stack ← PCH
PC ← Operand

Instruction Cycles: 5-7

Example: **MCUs:** 68HC05
JSR Label   ;   Call a Subroutine
:
Label:
:
RTS

Addressing	Format	Bits	Cycles
Direct	JSR Adr	$BD Adr	5
Extended	JSR Adr	$CD HAdr LAdr	6
Index 0 Off	JSR ,X	$FD	5
Index 8 Off	JSR Off,X	$ED Off	6
Index 16 Off	JSR Off,X	$DD HOff LOff	7

Instruction 20.30 68HC05 jsr operand instruction.

Instruction: "RTS"   **Bits:** $81

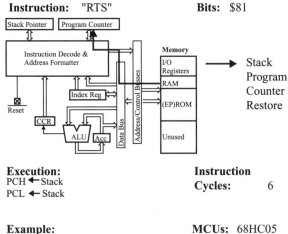

Execution:
PCH ← Stack
PCL ← Stack

**Instruction
Cycles:**   6

Example:
JSR Label   ;   Call a Subroutine
    :
Label:
    :
RTS

MCUs: 68HC05

Instruction 20.31 68HC05 rts instruction.

Instruction: "BSR Address"   **Bits:** $AD Addr

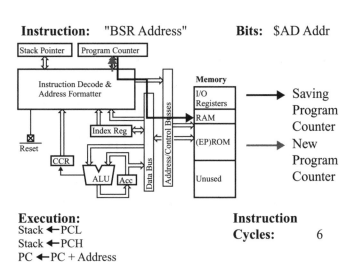

Execution:
Stack ← PCL
Stack ← PCH
PC ← PC + Address

**Instruction
Cycles:**   6

Example:
BSR Label   ;   Call a LOCAL
    :   ;   Subroutine
Label:
    :
RTS

MCUs: 68HC05

Instruction 20.32 68HC05 bsr operand instruction.

Instruction: "BMC/BMS Offset" **Bits:** See Below

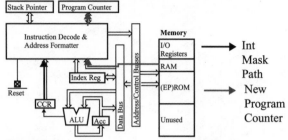

Int
Mask
Path
New
Program
Counter

Execution:
  if CCR.Bit(s) == Start
    PC ← PC + Offset

Example:
  BNE Label   ;   Local Jump to "Label" If the Zero
                   ;   Flag of the CCR is Reset

Instruction
Cycles: 3
MCUs: 68HC05

Instruction(s)	Bits	Branch Cond	Cycles
BCC/BHS Offset	$24 Offset	Carry == 0	3
BCS/BLO Offset	$25 Offset	Carry == 1	3
BEQ Offset	$27 Offset	Zero == 1	3
BHCC Offset	$24 Offset	Half == 0	3
BHCS Offset	$25 Offset	Half == 1	3
BHI Offset	$22 Offset	Zero + Carry == 0	3
BLS Offset	$23 Offset	Zero || Carry == 1	3
BMI Offset	$2B Offset	Negative == 1	3
BNE Offset	$26 Offset	Zero == 0	3
BPL Offset	$2A Offset	C == 0 || Z == 1	3

Instruction 20.33 68HC05 conditional branch instructions.

Instruction: "BIH/BIL Offset" **Bits:** See Below

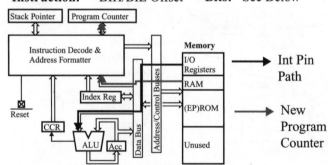

Int Pin
Path

New
Program
Counter

Execution:
  if Int.Pin == Start
    PC ← PC + Offset

Example:
  BIH Label   ;   Local Jump to "Label" If
    :   ;   Interrupt Pin is "HI"
  Label:

Instruction
Cycles: 3
MCUs: 68HC05

Instruction	Bits	Cycles
BIH Offset	$2F Offset	3
BIL Offset	$2E Offset	3

Instruction 20.34 68HC05 branch on interrupt pin state instructions.

Instruction: "BMC/BMS Offset"   **Bits:** See Below

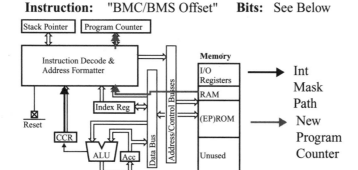

Int
Mask
Path
New
Program
Counter

Execution:
  if Int.Mask == Start
    PC ◄─ PC + Offset

Example:
  BMC Label   ;   Local Jump to "Label" If
  :   ;   Interrupt Mask is Enabled
  Label: ;   (Low)

Instruction
Cycles: 3

MCUs: 68HC05

Instruction	Bits	Cycles
BMC Offset	$2D Offset	3
BMS Offset	$2C Offset	3

Instruction 20.35 68HC05 branch on interrupt mask state instructions.

Instruction: "BRA Offset"   **Bits:** $20 Addr

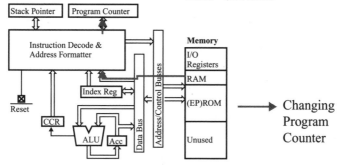

Changing
Program
Counter

Execution:
  PC ◄─PC + Offset

Example:
  BRA Label   ;   Local Jump to "Label"
  :
  Label:

Instruction
Cycles: 3

MCUs: 68HC05

Comments: Branching is from the start of the
next instruction - 128 to +127. "BRN"
(Branch Never - $21) is the opposite
to Branch Always (and is a 2 byte
and 3 cycle "nop").

Instruction 20.36 68HC05 bra offset instruction.

Instruction: "SWI" **Bits:** $83

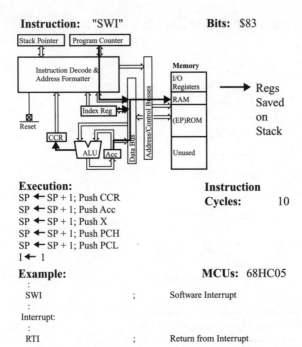

Regs
Saved
on
Stack

Execution:
SP ← SP + 1; Push CCR
SP ← SP + 1; Push Acc
SP ← SP + 1; Push X
SP ← SP + 1; Push PCH
SP ← SP + 1; Push PCL
I ← 1

Instruction Cycles: 10

Example:

    :
    SWI   ;   Software Interrupt
    :
    Interrupt:
    :
    RTI   ;   Return from Interrupt

MCUs: 68HC05

Instruction 20.37 68HC05 swi instruction.

Instruction: "RTI" **Bits:** $80

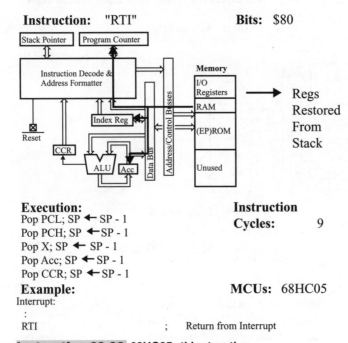

Regs
Restored
From
Stack

Execution:
Pop PCL; SP ← SP - 1
Pop PCH; SP ← SP - 1
Pop X; SP ← SP - 1
Pop Acc; SP ← SP - 1
Pop CCR; SP ← SP - 1

Instruction Cycles: 9

Example:
Interrupt:
    :
    RTI   ;   Return from Interrupt

MCUs: 68HC05

Instruction 20.38 68HC05 rti instruction.

The most basic bit operators are the bit reset and set instructions (Instructions 20.39 and 20.40). These instructions operate directly on individual bits in the first 256 memory locations of the 68HC05's memory space. Any register in the first 256 memory locations can be accessed. These two instructions can really be thought of as a read|AND/OR|write operation. For example, if the "BCLR" instruction was used to reset bit 5 of "Reg," the actual data operation is:

```
Reg = Reg & ( $FF ^ ( 1 << 5 ))
```

Which is to say, the register is read, ANDed with a mask in which every bit except for the one to be cleared (in this example bit 5) are ANDed with '1,' and then written back to the original memory location. Setting a bit is similar; after the byte is read, it is ORed with all bits reset except for the single bit to be set.

The "BRCLR" and "BRSET" instructions (Instructions 20.41 and 20.42) are used to cause program execution to branch on the state of a specific bit in a specific memory location (within the first 256 memory locations in memory).

In the diagrams showing the instructions, you should note that I show how the actual bits are generated. Like the bit set/reset instructions above, I have changed the way Motorola usually documents the instructions (each one actually being 8 different op-codes, one for each bit) and shown how the op-codes are calculated based on the bits.

The branch on bit conditions work like the branch instructions previously described. The offset to the instruction can be -128 to $+127$ from the instruction pointer at the following instruction.

20

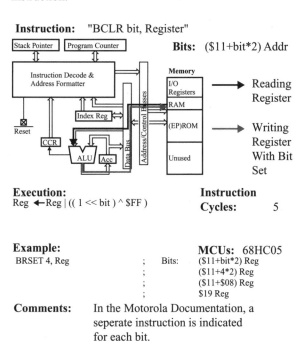

Instruction: "BCLR bit, Register"

Bits: ($11+bit*2) Addr

Reading Register

Writing Register With Bit Set

Execution:
Reg ← Reg | ((1 << bit) ^ $FF)

Instruction Cycles: 5

Example:
BRSET 4, Reg   ;   Bits:
                    ;
                    ;
                    ;

MCUs: 68HC05
($11+bit*2) Reg
($11+4*2) Reg
($11+$08) Reg
$19 Reg

Comments: In the Motorola Documentation, a seperate instruction is indicated for each bit.

Instruction 20.39 68HC05 bclr bit, register instruction.

Instruction: "BSET bit, Register"

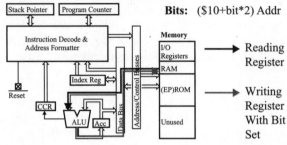

Bits: ($10+bit*2) Addr

→ Reading Register

→ Writing Register With Bit Set

Execution:
Reg ← Reg | (1 << bit)

Instruction Cycles: 5

Example:
BSET 7, Reg

MCUs: 68HC05

; Bits:	($10+bit*2) Reg
;	($10+7*2) Reg
;	($10+$0E) Reg
;	$1E Reg

Comments: In the Motorola Documentation, a seperate instruction is indicated for each bit.

Instruction 20.40 68HC05 bset bit, register instruction.

Instruction: "BRCLR bit, Register, Offset"

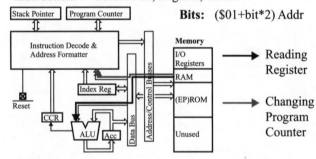

Bits: ($01+bit*2) Addr

→ Reading Register

→ Changing Program Counter

Execution:
if (Reg & ((1 << bit) ^ 0x0FF) then
PC ← PC + Offset

Instruction Cycles: 5

Example:
BRCLR 1, Reg, Label

MCUs: 68HC05

; Bits:	($01+bit*2) Reg Off
;	($01+1*2) Reg Off
;	($01+$02) Reg Off
;	$03 Reg Off

Comments: In the Motorola Documentation, a seperate instruction is indicated for each bit.

Instruction 20.41 68HC05 brclr bit, register, offset instruction.

Instruction: "BRSET bit, Register, Offset"

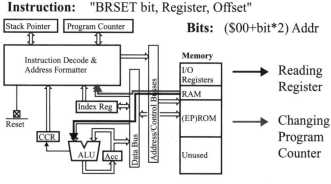

Bits: ($00+bit*2) Addr

→ Reading Register

→ Changing Program Counter

Execution:
if (Reg & (1 << bit) then
    PC ← PC + Offset

Instruction Cycles: 5

Example:
BRSET 2, Reg, Label   ;   Bits:

MCUs: 68HC05

;	($00+bit*2) Reg Off
;	($00+2*2) Reg Off
;	($00+$04) Reg Off
;	$04 Reg Off

Comments: In the Motorola Documentation, a
                seperate instruction is indicated
                for each bit.

Instruction 20.42 68HC05 brset bit, register, offset instruction.

Processor Control Instructions

There are a number of instructions available for controlling the 68HC05's processor and status registers directly. These instructions will be useful for providing critical timing I/O operations, reducing the microcontroller's power consumption, and accessing CCR bits. In a PC or workstation processor, many of the analogous instructions are never used (they are often used in the operating system, however), but in 68HC05 and other microcontroller's applications, they are critical.

The "nop" instruction (Instruction 20.43) does absolutely nothing, as you would expect. One byte of memory and two cycles are required to execute the instruction. There are two concerns that I have with the 68HC05 nop instruction. The first is with the bit pattern. I feel that a microcontroller should have two "nop" instructions, one with all the bits reset ($00) and one with all bits set (i.e., $FF). The reason for this is that nops can be put into EPROM and then have instructions programmed into them without having to erase the entire EPROM in the microcontroller. If you want to take out instructions, by clearing all the bits you will end up with a "nop" as well.

The second concern I have about the nop instruction as it stands is the two instruction cycles required to execute the instruction. This means that the actual granularity of the nop instruction is 4 clock cycles (with 2 clock cycles for each instruction cycle). To help make nop delays more precise, I use the "branch never" instruction ("BNE") as shown in Instruction 20.44 to provide 3 cycles of delays. Using a combination of "NOP"s and

"BNE"s, you can get down to one-instruction-cycle accuracy for any required delay of more than two instruction cycles.

Often in RTOSs, when all tasks are waiting for an external event, a dummy task is executed that just loops around forever, waiting for an interrupt to happen, and then a higher-priority task can execute. This task is usually implemented simply in three bytes:

```
DummyTask    ;  Execute ONLY when all other Tasks Waiting
  CLI        ;  Enable Interrupts
  BRA *      ;  Loop at this address
```

The asterisk (or "splat," "*") is used to indicate that the start of the current line is the address to jump to. So, in this case, the "BRA *" will become the opcode $20 $FE.

In the 68HC05, the "WAIT" instruction is perfect for this task (excuse the pun). Waiting for an interrupt request could be handled by a single "WAIT" instruction rather than creating a separate, simple task (such as shown above). (Instruction 20.45) When "wait" is executed, the clocks continue running (along with the timers and all peripheral I/O functions), so when an interrupt is requested, execution will jump directly to the appropriate interrupt vector. When "wait" executes, the instruction clock stops but restarts immediately upon a hardware reset or interrupt request.

"STOP" (Instruction 20.46) works similarly to "WAIT," but also turns off the microcontroller's oscillator. This means that peripheral interrupt functions except for the "IRQ" pin interrupt cannot execute after a "STOP" instruction is executed. If a hardware Reset or an

Instruction: "NOP"   **Bits:** $9D

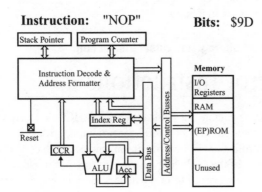

Execution:

Example:
NOP   ;   Do nothing for 2 cycles

Instruction Cycles: 2

MCUs: 68HC05

Comments: The "Nop" can be used for either
Saving space for "patching" in code
or providing critical timings. "BRN"
(Branch Never - $21) can be used
as a "NOP" and requires 3
Instruction Cycles (and 2 Bytes).

Instruction 20.43 68HC05 nop instruction.

Instruction: "BRN Byte"   **Bits:** $21 Byte

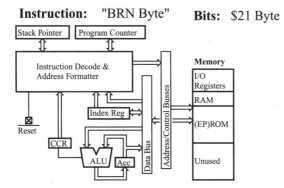

Execution:

Example:
BNE Byte

Instruction
Cycles: 3

MCUs: 68HC05
;   Do nothing for 3 cycles

Comments: The "BNE" (Branch Never) can be used as a 3 cycle "Nop" instruction to provide greater timing granularity to critical timing loops.

Instruction 20.44 68HC05 enop instruction.

Instruction: "WAIT"   **Bits:** $8F

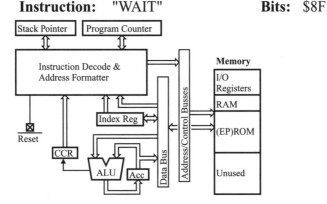

Execution:
I ← 0

Instruction
Cycles: N/A

Example:
WAIT

MCUs: 68HC05
;   Wait for Reset/Interrupt

Instruction 20.45 68HC05 wait instruction.

Instruction: "STOP"   **Bits:** $8E

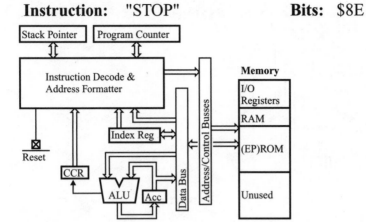

Execution:
I ← 0
Osc ← Stop

Instruction Cycles: N/A

Example: **MCUs:** 68HC05
STOP   ;   Wait for Reset/Interrupt

Instruction 20.46 68HC05 stop instruction.

Instruction: "RSP"   **Bits:** $9C

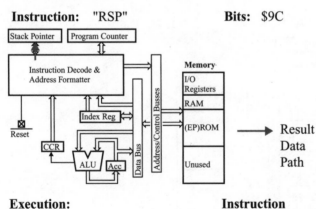

Execution:
Sp ← $FF

Instruction Cycles: 2

Example: **MCUs:** 68HC05
RSP   ;   Reset the Stack Pointer

Instruction 20.47 68HC05 rsp instruction.

Instruction: "CLC/CLI/SEC/SEI"   **Bits:** See Below

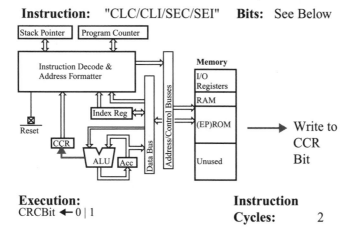

→ Write to
CCR
Bit

Execution:
CRCBit ◄— 0 | 1

**Instruction
Cycles:**   2

20

Example:
  CLI   ;   Enable Interrupts

MCUs: 68HC05

Instruction	Format	Bits	Cycles
Clear Carry	CLC	$98	2
Clear Int	CLI	$9A	2
Set Carry	SEC	$99	2
Set Int	SEI	$9B	2

Instruction 20.48 68HC05 CCR bit set/reset instructions.

"IRQ" is requested, then after the oscillator is restarted, 1920 cycles are waited for the oscillator clock to stabilize before the appropriate vector is retrieved and the code is executed.

If the stack pointer has to be reset for any reason (i.e., for starting a new task in a RTOS), the "RSP" (Instruction 20.47) should be used. This instruction sets the contents of the stack pointer to the top of the stack (address $FF).

The last category of processor control instruction is the CCR bit set/reset instructions (Instruction 20.48). These instructions are used to manipulate the CCR carry and interrupt bits, which cannot be accessed directly. In many applications, the carry bit is used to pass binary parameters (with care being taken to make sure that instructions that affect the carry bit are not used). The "CLC" and "SEC" instructions can be used for setting these values.

The interrupt flags can be set and reset using the "CLI" and "SEI" instructions. These instructions are used to enable and disable interrupts (when the bit is reset, interrupts are disabled). These instructions cannot be used to pass parameters simply because there are no branch-on-condition instructions that can access the interrupt bit of the CCR.

MOTOROLA 68HC05

68HC05 EXAMPLE APPLICATIONS

I have designed the 68HC05 applications presented here to run on one of the least-capable devices in the family, the 68HC05J1A. While there are many features available in higher-end 68HC05s, I felt that the "J1A" was well suited to the example applications (especially the RTOS) because built-in peripheral features are not required.

First Application

Developing the flashing LED and button-polling application was a very good experience for me because it went quite well right from the beginning and only required minor "tweaking" of the circuit and code that amounted to about a half hour of work to get it running properly. This was quite gratifying for me because my last experience with writing an application for a 6800 architected processor was in 1982 (and was my second assembly language programming class). This made me feel like my methods of approaching learning how to develop microcontroller applications were validated.

The circuit for this application should compare very closely with the circuits designed for the other microcontrollers, with two important differences (see Figure 21.1).

The first thing to note is the 1-megohm feedback resistor across the "Osc1" and "Osc2." While playing around with options, I was able to get the 68HC05 to run without the resistor. I found that it was most reliable (basically on start up) with it. For this reason, I would always recommend that the high-value feedback resistor is connected between "Osc1" and "Osc2."

The second difference is in my wiring the momentarily on switch ("SW" in Figure 21.1). In all the other applications, I have this switch wired to ground pulling down a resistor (external or internal) pulled up to Vcc. In the 68HC05 devices with an integrated pull-down that can be enabled, this simplifies the circuit by allowing you to implement it without a pull-up (or pull-down) resistor.

The code used for the application is also quite straightforward:

```
; AP1 - Blink an LED on Pin PA7 and Monitor Button on PB5
;
;  This program will blink an LED on Pin PA7 2x per second. Note, a
;   counter has been added to the interrupt Handler to slow down the
;   interrupt rate.
```

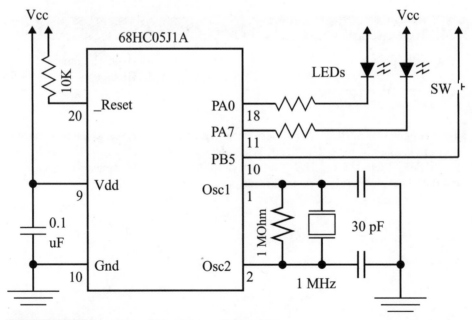

Figure 21.1 Flashing LEDs with a 68HC705J1A.

```
;
;   Myke Predko - 97.09.23
;
;   Hardware Notes:
;     68HC705J1A is Device Used
;     Running with a 1 MHz Crystal
;     Reset is pulled up using a 10K Resistor
;     PA0 is connected to a 220 Ohm Resistor and an LED Pulled up to Vcc
;     PA7 is connected to a 220 Ohm Resistor and an LED Pulled up to Vcc
;     PB5 is connected to a momentarily Open Switch connected to Vcc
;

;  Variables and Macros
count     equ  $C0                 ;  Counter for Toggling the Real Time LED

  PAGE
;  Mainline

 org rom
mainline
   clr    count                    ;  Clear the Counter
   clrx   ;  Clear X for Int to work Properly
   lda    #$80                     ;  Turn off LED1 Initially
   sta    porta
   lda    #$81                     ;  Make PA7/PA0 an Output
   sta    ddra
   lda    #$DF                     ;  Enable the Single Pull-Down Bit
   sta    pdrb
   lda    #$10                     ;  Short Real Time Clock
   sta    tscr                     ;    the Maximum Timer Delay
   cli    ;  Enable interrupts
;  Loop for the Timer Interrupt Handler/Poll the Input Bit
Loop

   brset  5,portb,High             ;  If Button is High turn ON LED

   bset   0,porta                  ;  Button low (not Pressed), LED OFF

   bra    Loop                     ;  Branch back to Loop

High                               ;  Button High, LED ON

   bclr   0,porta

   bra    Loop

  PAGE
;  Timer Interrupt Handler
timrint:
   bset   2,tscr                   .;  Reset Interrupt
   inc    count                    ;  Increment Counter before Test == 8
   lda    count                    ;  Does count == 8?
   cmpa   #8
   bne    ti_end                   ;   No, Skip Over the Code
   clr    count                    ;   Yes - Restart
   lda    porta                    ;  Toggle PA7 and LED
   eor    #$80
   sta    porta
ti_end
   rti

  PAGE
```

```
;   Reset/Interrupt Vectors

org $7F1
  db      $00                     ;   External Interrupts Disabled

org $7F8                          ;   Reset and Interrupt Vectors
  dw      timrint
  dw      mainline
  dw      mainline
  dw      mainline
```

The second instruction in the code clears the index ("X") register. This operation is really not required, but I put it in because the "ICS05J1A" simulator will flag an error when interrupts are used because it is reading and saving a register that isn't initialized. Simply clearing this register will eliminate this error.

At the end of the code, after I set up the timer interrupt vector to point to the "timrint" interrupt handler, note that I follow with three vectors pointing to the "mainline." This is probably confusing because the next two vectors following the timer interrupt are the "IRQ" pin and "software" interrupt handler vectors. I really just put in the two "dw mainline" statements to take up space before the reset vector location at $7FE.

I could just have easily changed the five lines to:

```
org $7F8          ;   Reset and Interrupt Vectors
  dw      timrint
org $7FE
  dw      mainline
```

Looking through the code, there shouldn't be anything that is hard to understand. If you have worked with other Von Neumann architected processors, the 68HC05 should not offer any surprises and may be something that seems intuitively familiar (especially with the stack that can have registers pushed on it).

Real-Time Clock and Thermometer Using "mykeRTOS"

When I decided to do the 68HC05's LCD clock/thermometer using the RTOS I developed for the book, I wasn't expecting any significant surprises or problems. From the previous sentence, you're probably thinking that I was just asking for trouble and, to some extent, I found it. To be fair, I didn't have major problems, but it was an interesting project.

The circuit itself was very straightforward (see Figure 21.2). There shouldn't be any surprises here. The 68HC05J1A was connected to the hardware quite simply, and you should be able to branch back between this design and the other microcontroller's LCD clock/thermometer quite easily.

When I started writing the software, I wanted to do some funky things with it, so I created quite a complex organization for the application's tasks (including ending tasks and letting others take their task information blocks). This actually worked out quite well with a few insignificant problems that were fixed in the simulator before burning a micro with anything. If you look at the source code on the CD-ROM, "RTOSAPC.ASM" will show how I created the application code (including shutting down the "application" task when it was no longer needed).

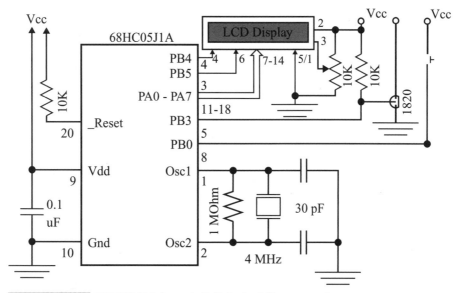

Figure 21.2 68HC05J1A-based digital clock/thermometer.

I was going to use the same code as a base when I added the DS1820 digital thermometer, but here's where I started running into problems. The first was space. At this point in time, I was running with "RTOS4.ASM." The primary difference between this RTOS and the final version ("mykeRTOS") is how some of the task requests work. They were changed to take up less space. The largest change made was to the "StartTask" RTOS request in which I changed from having to save the new task's address using the "SetA" and "SetX" requests before "StartTask." In the newer version, the lower address of the task to start is stored in the Index register when "StartTask" is initiated.

I also simplified the LCD task; as I originally wrote it, the task was well suited to providing a variety of generic operations (through messaging requests, its ability to write directly to the instruction and data registers of the LCD).

These requests in "LCDTask" as well as some other features of the application code were removed. One of the features that was taken away was the clever (at least I thought so) code for ending "Application" to make space for the (unfortunately named) "BUTTask."

The final block diagram for the application code is shown in Figure 21.3.

Writing the code for the DS1820 was not without its challenges as well. I ended up having quite a few problems properly timing up the 68HC05 to work within the DS1820's timing parameters. From this I discovered that the 68HC05 really isn't as fast as the other microcontrollers in handling individual bits, but much faster in processing bytes.

I was never able to output a valid "1" to the DS1820 from the 68HC05 running at 1 MHz. A "1" is a negative pulse between 1 and 15 usecs; at 1 MHz, the best I could do with the "bset"/"bclr" instructions was 24 usecs. This is why the application is designed with a 4-MHz crystal. While making this change, I was pleasantly surprised at how easy it was; the only code change I had to make was increasing the timer interrupt to interval by 4x (by changing the value written to "TCSR").

What was interesting was the 68HC05 ran the output character loop so quickly that an additional delay was required to meet the DS1820's specifications (after sending a bit, the

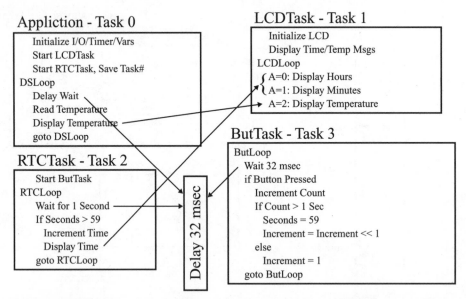

Figure 21.3 RTOS-based digital clock/thermometer application code block diagram.

line must be idle for at least 60 usecs). This specification would have been violated even if the 68HC05 were left running at 1 MHz.

This is an excellent example of what I mean when I say direct performance comparisons between the microcontrollers are meaningless and misleading. I could specify an application that was I/O bit intensive and a PIC would leave the 68HC05 in its dust. But, with an application that was byte-processing intensive, the 68HC05 would be much faster.

There are a couple of things to note in the DS1820 code. The first is the interrupt masking ("cli" instruction before accessing the DS1820). This is done to ensure that an interrupt doesn't spoil the single-line timing.

The second thing to look at is the three "nop"s that are commented out in the "GetDS" macro. When I originally coded this, I used a polling loop to wait for the DS1820 to let the line go high. This polling loop would not work with the "JICS" simulator. There was no way to simulate a pull-up (not to mention the DS1820—I did not use "UMPS" for any of the 68HC05 applications), so I avoided this with the three "nop"s, which take the same amount of cycles as the one "brclr" instruction executing once.

Now, the final application (known as "RTOSAP.ASM" on the CD-ROM) does work very well. If you go through the code, you'll probably make some observations about the application and RTOS code.

The first comment would be, if subroutines were allowed in the RTOS, then there wouldn't have been any code space issues. I would agree with this but point out that there would probably be variable space issues. Allowing subroutines would mean that more space would be needed for the task information block (which houses all the information required for each task), and there would be more effort required in the RTOS code to figure out where the bottom of the stack actually was.

Another observation that you might make is that the source is more complex than in a straight programming environment. On this point, I would have to disagree with you.

If you look at the task block diagram (Figure 21.3), it may seem quite confusing, but if you look at the pseudocode within each block, it's pretty simple. For example, for "BUTTask" (which is one of the more complex tasks in the application) the pseudocode is:

```
ButLoop
  Wait 32 msec
  if  Button Pressed
    Count++
    if Count > 1 Sec           ;  (if it's > 31)
      Seconds = 59             ;  Force a New Minute
      Increment = Increment << 1
    else
      Increment = 1
  goto ButLoop
```

Which should be easy to understand. The trick is to figure out what the tasks do and how they interrelate. This is really a change in the way you think when traditionally programming. With the RTOS, the timer interrupt is very simple and doesn't have to take into account how the different tasks have to interact around them. In this RTOS example, each task is separate and autonomous, which I think is actually much simpler.

After going through this, you might ask if this was a good demonstration application for use with this microcontroller and RTOS. The answer might be "no" because of the squeezing I had to do to get the code to work in the 68HC05J1A (which only has 1200+ bytes of control store space). But I would argue that it is actually a very good example application.

This application is actually much easier to develop and debug in "mykeRTOS" than if it were coded using traditional techniques. Not having the different functions interract is a really nice feature. Once one task is running and debugged, it can be brought in, accessed, turned off, or whatever to help isolate any problems with the other tasks. You should also note that being able to do this is well suited to a "bottoms-up" application development approach, such as I use in my applications.

68HC05 SUMMARY

The 68HC05 is radically different from the other microcontrollers presented in this book. This is not only in the architectural design of the processor but also in the wide variety of different devices available and Motorola's willingness to design a part specifically for an application.

One thing that I don't want to imply is that the 68HC05 is not as powerful in terms of instruction execution as the other devices presented here. I have to note that clock speed is only a single parameter of the function that determines the actual performance; the 68HC05 has some functions and instructions that make it much more efficient and faster than the other devices presented here.

While I should probably discuss performance comparison in a different chapter, there are a few points that I should make because it may seem that the 68HC05 is deficient when compared to other devices.

The first point is reiterating the point above: clock speed is not a very good indicator of overall performance. Overall performance is determined on the actual speed of being able to move data throughout the system, not just manipulating it in a processor. I have a 133-MHz Pentium laptop and a 133-MHz Pentium PC. Both of these devices should run applications in an identical fashion (both have similar amounts of memory and I run both in Super VGA mode, 800 by 640 pixels. The only real difference is that the PC has a 1.6-Gbyte hard drive and the laptop has 800 Mbytes of hard disk storage). But, the PC runs compilers about three times faster than the laptop.

The next point is the architecture. I have stated that the Harvard architecture is more efficient that the Princeton because two buses are used for instructions and data (and while an instruction is handling data the next instruction is being fetched), but there are applications where the Princeton architecture will run rings around the Harvard architecture. No microcontroller other than the 68HC05 is able to run a RTOS as efficiently as I've presented here. For the 8051 and AVR, the other two devices presented in this book that could be run under an RTOS, quite a bit of time and instructions are required for saving and loading the context registers during task switching.

The 68HC05's "flat" memory architecture allows handling data either saved in EPROM or RAM to be read in exactly the same way using the same instructions and hardware. This can be of particular advantage when implementing self-modifying code (such as the 16-bit "index" operation I showed earlier in this section), or one thing I think could be very useful is implementing a debugger/monitor program and then downloading an execution file into RAM and executing it and debugging it from there.

The Motorola microcontrollers have a bad reputation for not having specific part numbers available. This is exacerbated by the number of part numbers that Motorola advertises (over 180 at the time of writing the book) and the relatively few that are available "off the shelf." One of the things that I learned as I was researching this book was that most 68HC05 part numbers are developed for customers in special production runs. I hope this previous sentence hasn't turned you off to the Motorola devices because you think that you are a small customer to Motorola and you are unable to pay the NRE and carry the inventory of getting devices built for your application. If you want to use a 68HC05 for a specific application and you aren't sure if you are able to source a certain part number, contact your local Motorola office and see what it can offer.

When researching this book, I found that the 68HC05 software development tools were either poor and cheap (free) or extensive and expensive. This is a function of the length of time the 6800 architecture has been out on the market, with many low-end development tools available for free. This does not make it a very attractive for tool developers to construct 68HC05 tools for sale unless they can provide significant added value. The RAPID tools presented in this book (available with the 68HC70J1CS development kit) are competent but difficult to develop large applications with.

The only real deficiency that I would consider the 68HC05 line to have is the lack of true "ISP" capability. The 68HC05 devices seemed to be designed for using a custom programmer for application development (or an emulator module) and then when volume production is initiated, mask ROM parts are then used (Motorola has a high-speed mask programming capability). I would like to see a true ISP capability (with EEPROM program memory) added to the 68HC05 line, which would help stimulate the hobbyist market as well as give application designers an option of using 68HC05s and allow them to be upgraded easily in the field.

When choosing which microcontroller to use, I've heard a number of engineers state that they want the "best" device. This usually means that they want the most elegant design with the smallest code space required and the fastest execution speed. When thinking about these parameters, it may seem like the 68HC05 doesn't measure up to the other devices presented in this book. The 68HC05's advantage, compared to other microcontrollers, is its architecture, which many engineers originally learned assembly language programming and basic computer interfacing on. The Princeton architecture used with the 68HC05 also allows the development of applications on the 68HC05 that the Harvard-architected micro-controllers cannot.

Motorola 68HC05 Resources

My personal style for researching microcontrollers is to use the Internet for looking for information on the devices, along with manufacturer's information. Usually, I'm looking for introductory information on the devices and some hints on how to get started with it. I first did this with the PIC and was amazed at how much information, applications, and tools are available on the Web.

The 68HC05 was actually quite a disappointment in this area and really lags behind all the other devices I've presented in this book. To be fair, there are quite a lot of companies advertising products, but just about none of them provide FAQs, example applications, or tools that are easily found for the other devices. I think this is due to Motorola's philoso-phy of trying to interest primarily high-volume customers where a custom device is to be developed for them.

The lack of good non-Motorola sites is really a shame because it limits the critical mass that has made other devices such as the PIC so succesful (even though the 68HC05 is the easiest device for a "classically" trained programmer or engineer to start working with).

WEB SITES

The lack of good external sites is really offset by the information (both datasheets and application notes) and tools available on Motorola's site:

http://www.mcu.motsps.com/mc.html

This site includes datasheets for the different devices (as well as the enhanced devices (68HC11 and up), development tools, and searchable FAQs.

The best information site that I was able to find is:

http://www.oztechnics.com.au

LISTSERVERS

Motorola maintains a listserver for each of its microcontroller device families. To sub-scribe to the 68HC05/68HC08's, send a note to:

majordomo@www.mcu.motsps.com

with "subscribe mot-68HC05-68HC08" in the body of the message.

COMPANIES

As I went through the Web looking for good Web sites, I was surprised to see that the 68HC05 is second sourced by Harris.

Motorola

Motorola Semiconductor Product Sector
6501 William Cannon Drive West
Austin, Texas
http://www.mcu.motsps.com/mc.html

Harris

1-800-4-HARRIS (1-800-442-7747) ext. 700
http://www.semi.harris.com/

MICROCHIP PICMICRO

PICMICRO MICROCONTROLLERS

CONTENTS AT A GLANCE

The Microchip PICMicro is one of the rising stars in the microcontroller world. The PICMicros are some of the most efficient microcontrollers in terms of operating speed/instructions per clock cycle of any devices discussed in this book. In terms of features, Microchip has been astonishingly busy releasing new parts (over 40 in 1997). These devices have been colloquially known as the "PIC," but are known to Microchip, the manufacturer, as the "PICMicro."

While I call the PICMicro a "rising star," which implies that it has only recently been created, the architecture has actually been around for a very long time (actually longer than all of the microcontrollers discussed in this book except for the Motorola products). It was originally developed by General Instrument's chip manufacturing division. As part of corporate streamlining and prioritizing, the chip manufacturing division was "spun off" as "Microchip," which has been aggressively marketing the PICMicro and its line of serial EEPROMs.

This aggresive marketing and support is what attracted me to the PICMicro and allowed me to pursue this interest for a couple of years as a hobbyist before writing my first book, *Programming and Customizing the PIC.* The PICMicro is produced in many diverse "flavours," with just about every possible combination and permutation of features possible, which will allow you to decide on a device with exactly the right features for your planned application.

Low-End PICMicros

The low-end ("16C5x") range of devices are the "basic" level of the PICMicro family. While containing a "subset" of the instructions available in the high-range families, the low-end devices are pretty much source-code compatible with them. I would recommend that these devices should not be considered for new applications/learning about the PIC. The lack of interrupts, the smaller available RAM and control store, no advanced I/O, and no in-system programming will result in what I consider unnecessary difficulties in porting applications between device families. As probably the final nail in the low-end's coffin, midrange devices are available at the same or less price range and in the same packages as the low end.

Now, having said this, there are some low-end PICMicros to consider, and that's the 8-pin 12C5xx series. These devices allow up to six I/O pins with 512 or 1K instructions for small or simple applications. The 12C5xx series are probably the best small device interfaces available. I have seen applications using the 12C5xx parts for interfacing more complex processors to motors (with PWM outputs), LCDs, and sonar ranging equipment.

Midrange PICMicros

The midrange PICMicros are the true workhorses of the family. The midrange products really are a complete microcontroller line in their own right, with a myriad of different features. They use the same basic architecture as the low-end PICs; their major difference is the ability to handle interrupts.

The midrange devices have this range of "standard" features:

Interrupt/Subroutine Levels	8
Control Store	512 - 8K Instructions
File Registers ("RAM")	36 - 192 Bytes
Interrupt Sources	4 - 12
In-System Programming	
Timers	1 - 3

And, in terms of hardware options, midrange devices can have the following features:

Power	2.0 - 5.0 V
Package Types	Plastic OTP, Ceramic Window, SOIC, QFP
Operating Speeds	DC to 4 MHz to 20 MHz
Digital I/O Pins	13 - 33
Control Store Types	Mask Programmable, EPROM, EEPROM/Flash
A/D Options	Voltage Comparators, R-Ladder DACs, Integrating/Slope ADCs, PWM I/O
Serial I/O	SPI, I2C, Asynchronous
Other I/O	Direct LCD I/F, Parallel Slave Port

This wide range of options (along with in-system programming) gives the midrange PICMicros the advantage of being able to widely share code in a large variety of different situations. I will focus on these devices for this section of the book.

High-End PICMicros

The high-end PICMicros use 16-bit instructions and can access up to 64K words of address space. Each word is sixteen bits wide, so the high-end PICMicros (identified as "17Cxx") can actually access up to 128K bytes as program or data storage externally. This external I/O could also be memory mapped I/O devices similar to what I've shown in the 8051 example applications.

In terms of architecture, as well as supporting reading/writing control store, the 17Cxx devices also have a revised central processor core. This core allows access of all processor registers through different instructions (the low-end and midrange devices do not allow access of the accumulator like it is a register, as the 17Cxx does). This increases the flexibility of the devices and instructions to be usable in a wider variety of applications. The high-end PICMicros provide multiple interrupt vectors, instead of the midrange's single interrupt vector.

The high-end devices are primarily designed for interfacing with other digital devices. For this reason, the 17Cxx family does not have ADCs or features designed to allow interfacing directly with sensors (except through a bus) as do the midrange parts.

23

MICROCHIP PICMICRO

THE PICMICRO PROCESSOR ARCHITECTURE

The processor architecture discussion presented in this chapter focuses in on the midrange PICMicros, but it also applies to the low-end PICMicros. The major difference between the low end and the midrange is the inability of interrupt hardware in the low-end devices. The differences between the midrange and the high-end PICMicros are discussed at the end of this chapter.

THE CPU

The PICMicro processor is a true Harvard-architected CPU and can be thought of as simply an ALU with registers. There are a number of specific-use registers that control the operation of the CPU as well as I/O control registers and RAM registers that can be used by the user program for variable storage and interfacing to the peripheral hardware in the chip.

All addresses are explicitly defined in the instructions. In the register instructions, there are 7 bits reserved for the addresses. This means there are up to 128 addresses possible in the PIC. (Figure 24.1.)

In this discussion, there is one aspect of the PICMicro core I am not discussing, and that is the "w" register. The "w" register can be thought of as an accumulator or a temporary storage register.

Every arithmetic operation that takes place in the PIC uses the "w" register. If you want to add the contents of two registers together, you would first move the contents of one register into "w" and then add the contents of the second to it.

The PICMicro architecture is very powerful from the perspective that the result of any operation can be stored either in the "w" register, or back into the source register of the data. Storing the result back into the source effectively eliminates the need for an additional instruction for saving the result of the operation. This allows movement of results easily and efficiently.

This changes the processor diagram to Figure 24.2. The diagram shows the PICMicro architecture at its simplest level. Well over half of the instructions can be run only using this hardware.

The last parameter of an arithmetic register operation is used to specify the destination of the result. The destination of "1" stores the result back in the source register. The convention for putting the result back into the source register is to use the character "f" which is defined in Microchip's "MPASM" assembler. Specifying a destination of "0" or "w" will put the result into the "w" register.

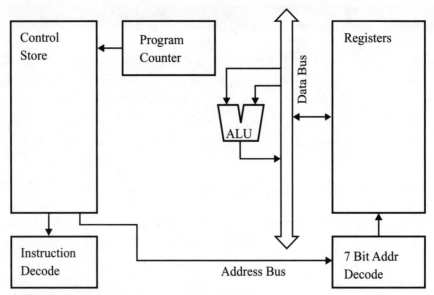

Figure 24.1 Basic PICMicro architecture.

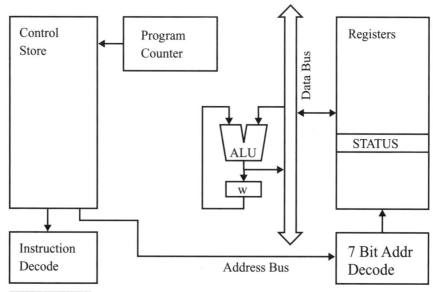

Figure 24.2 PICMicro architecture with w register.

To specify the destination of the value, in the instruction nmenonic the last instruction parameter is changed, i.e.:

```
addwf    FSR, w              ;  Add "w" to FSR and put result in
                             ;   "w"
iorwf    TMR0, f             ;  Inclusive OR "w" with TMR0 and
                             ;    Store Result in TMR0
```

Leaving the result in "w" is useful for instructions where you are comparing and don't want to change the source. It is also used in cases where the result is an intermediate value or the result is to be stored in another register.

If the destination is left off the end of the instruction, i.e.:

```
addwf    Reg                 ;  Add "Reg" to the contents of "w"
```

The microchip assembler (MPASM) and most others will interpret this to mean that the destination of the result is back into the source register (destination is "f" or "1").

THE STATUS REGISTER

The status register is the primary CPU execution control register used for controlling the execution of the program.

The actual register is broken up into three parts. The first part is the execution status flags ("z," "dc," and "c"). These 3 bits are the status of the program's execution. The zero flag ("z") is set when the result of an operation is zero (i.e., add, sub, clear, bitwise operations). The carry flag ("c") is set when the result of an addition operation is greater than 255 (0x0FF) or the result of a subtraction operation is greater than or equal to zero. The carry bit is meant to indicate that any higher-order bytes should be updated as well. The "digit carry" ("dc") is set when the least-significant

Bit	Label	Description
0	C	Carry Flag
1	DC	Digit Carry Flag
2	Z	Zero Flag
3	_PD	Power-Down Bit
4	_TO	Time-Out Bit
5	RP0	Odd/Even Register Bank Select
6	RP1	High/Low Register Banks Select
7	IRP	Index Register High/Low Register Banks Select

nybble (four bits) of the result is greater than 15 after an arithmetic operation (add or subtract).

These bits can be read from or written to and are updated according to the execution of each instruction. Note that these bits cannot be updated as part of an instruction. In *Programming and Customizing the PIC*, I presented the following macro:

```
ClearFlags Macro        ;  Clear the processor status flags
   movlw   0x0F8
   andwf   STATUS
   endm
```

The purpose of the macro was to clear all the processor status bits before executing an arithmetic instruction. But, the processor status flags cannot be updated as part of an instruction.

Instead, for this operation to work, the macro should have been:

```
ClearFlags Macro        ;  Clear the processor status flags
   movlw   0x0F8
   andwf   STATUS, w
   movwf   STATUS       ;  Write back to the STATUS register
   endm
```

With the status register storing the status of arithmetic operations, the PICMicro diagram now looks like Figure 24.3.

The next two bits in the status register indicate the mode in which the processor responded to execution start or wake up from sleep. The following table shows the values of the bits following different situations. The purpose of these two bits is for the application program to understand why the processor is at the initial program location.

The last set of bits is dependent on the type of processor used. For the low-end PICMicros (16C5x), these bits are used like the PCLATH registers in the mid and high-end PICMicros. This is described below in "The Program Counter" section.

For the midrange PICMicros, up to 128 register addresses (using 7-bit addressing) can be directly accessed in an instruction. Only 128 registers may seem to be quite a limitation to you (and it is). So the designers of the PICMicro decided to make 128 registers a "bank." Up to four banks (for 512 registers) can be available in the midrange PICMicros (typically only two are implemented). The banks are selected by the "RPx" bits in the STATUS register. This means our architecture is now as shown in Figure 24.4.

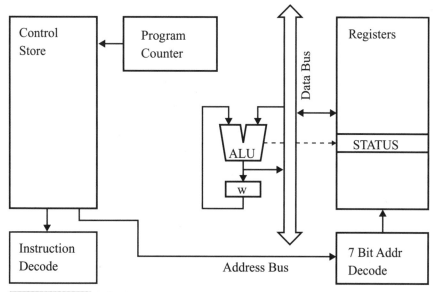

Figure 24.3 PICMicro architecture with STATUS regsiter.

_TO	_PD	Condition
1	1	Power-On Reset/_MCLR Reset During Operation
0	1	WDT Reset During Normal Operation
0	0	WDT Wake Up from Sleep
1	0	_MCLR Reset during Sleep or Interrupt Wake Up from Sleep

In some PICMicros, the file registers are "shadowed" between the banks while there are a number of PICMicros that provide separate RAM Registers in multiple banks. This may be an issue when deciding which type of PICMicro and what prewritten software you are going to use for an application. To avoid this issue, I try to stay in Bank 0 as a default and move to Bank 1 only when I have to access an array variable or hardware register located in bank 1 and then move back to bank 0 when I'm finished.

In case you're wondering, the PIC16C5X series of microcontrollers doesn't have a second bank (because these bits are used for selecting different control store address "pages" as opposed to file register banks). Having only one bank in the devices also means that the the "option" and "tris" registers (which are located in bank 1 of the midrange PICMicros) cannot be accessed directly by the low-end processor. To allow access to these registers, the "option" and "tris" instructions have been included, which allow you to write the contents of the "w" register into these registers.

To new users of the PICMicro series processors, changing file register banks can be a confusing aspect of the PICMicro architecture. This is complicated by the way addresses are implemented in the Microchip addressing convention. A bank 1 register has an address of 0x080 or greater (bit 7 of the address set indicating page 1 is to be used) while a bank 0 register has an address of 0x07F or less. This is really just a way of writing addresses. In

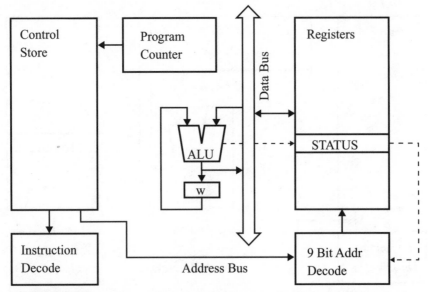

Figure 24.4 PICMicro architecture with register bank select.

this format the "RP0" can be thought of as bit 7 of the address. When you see an address that has this bit set, before accessing the register, the RP0 bit of the STATUS register must be set.

For midrange PICMicros with four banks implemented, the register addresses range from 0 to 0x01FF, with RP1 and RP0 used to select the current 128 address bank.

The "primary register" (status, INDF, FSR, PCL, PCLATH, and INTCON) addresses are the same for each type of PICMicro and show up at the same address in each register page. This is designed to allow code to be used between devices without having to change register addresses when the code is used on a different device. The basic two-bank register layout is shown in Figure 24.5.

REGISTER ADDRESSING

There are three different methods of getting and manipulating data in the PIC: immediate addressing, register direct addressing, and indirect addressing. Each of these modes is different, and their functions overlap each other in a variety of ways, but each is designed for a specific type of operation.

Immediate addressing means that the value to be used in an operation is part of the data. Using the immediate operations, the "w" register can be loaded with a specific value or modified by some operation using an explicit value. (Figure 24.6.)

What can you do with immediate addressing? It is used anytime you know exactly what value you want to use for an operation or load into a register.

To set up an I/O direction register with a specific pattern:

```
bsf     STATUS, RP0         ;  Move to Bank 1
movlw   0b011011101         ;  Make Bits 1 & 5 Output
movwf   TRISB ^ 0x080       ;  <- Make "TRISB" a Valid 7 Bit Address
bcf     STATUS, RP0         ;  Return to Bank 0
```

Addr.	Bank 0	Bank 1	Addr.
0x000	INDF	INDF	0x080
0x001	TMR0	OPTION	0x081
0x002	PCL	PCL	0x082
0x003	STATUS	STATUS	0x083
0x004	FSR	FSR	0x084
0x005	PORTA	PORTA	0x085
0x006	PORTB	PORTB	0x086
0x007	*	*	0x087
0x008	**	**	0x088
0x009	**	**	0x089
0x00A	PCLATH	PCLATH	0x08A
0x00B	INTCON	INTCON	0x08B
0x00C			0x08C
		PCON***	0x08C
0x020			0x0A0
0x07F			0x0FF

* - PORTC/TRISC
For Optional Port

** - I/O Registers

PCON*** - Power
Up Control
Register

■ - File
Register
Space

- - - - End of File
Register
Space

Figure 24.5 Midrange PICMicro registers.

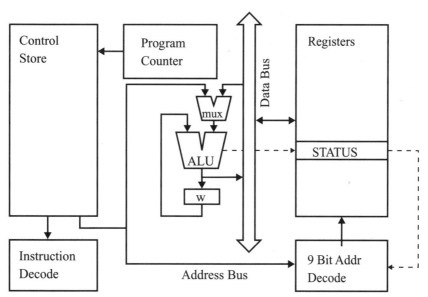

Figure 24.6 PICMicro architecture with immediate data passed from instructions.

Don't be confused by the XORing "TRISB" explicitly with 0x080. This is done because "TRISB" is equal to 0x086, which indicates that the register is at address 0x006 in bank 1. If "TRISB" were left with bit 7 of the address still set, a warning message "302" would be generated by MPASM. To avoid this, yet still have meaningful code, I toggle the high bit, which specifies the page the register is used on. The bit is toggled rather than cleared (using

24

"& 0x07F") so that if I make a mistake and try to put a bank 0 register in bank 1 (which has "RP0" set), the "302" message will alert me to the discrepancy and I can make the changes before I try to execute the code accessing a 7-bit register address in the wrong bank.

Accessing a register means that you are processing it through the ALU, and some result is placed in "w" or back in the register itself. The usual way to load the "w" register with the contents of a register is by using the "movf" instruction. This instruction works in a very similar manner to that of the other "w" register arithmetic instructions described in "PICMicro Instructions."

The following code loads the contents from a register and stores it into another one.

```
movf  Reg1, w       ;  Load the contents of the First Register
movwf Reg2          ;  Store them in the Second Register
```

Being able to explicitly address registers can be important, but there will be times when you want to access data indirectly and change the address arithmetically. The "INDF" and "FSR" registers are used to allow indexing or indirect addressing of data, allowing data to be kept and accessed as arrays.

The "INDF" register is a "pseudoregister" at address 0, which doesn't really exist. Accessing this register uses the "FSR" register for the address of the register you will actually be accessing. Our CPU diagram will now be updated to Figure 24.7.

For example, if you wanted to record a string of bytes coming into the PIC, this could be done explicitly with a number of variables, but this would be difficult to keep track of. Instead, a simple array of bytes could be used to allow access of the data. Individual bytes in the array could be accessed explicitly, but the whole string could be accessed sequentially using very simple programming logic.

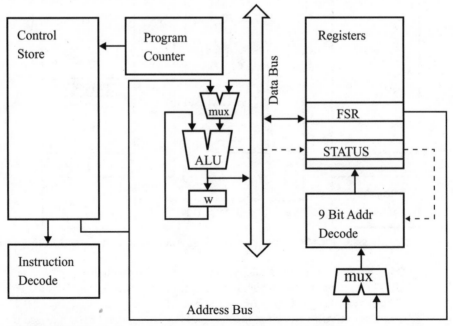

Figure 24.7 PICMicro architecture with indirect addressing.

In "c," an array is declared and accessed as:

```
char  Array[ 10 ]       ;        ;  Setup a 10 Digit Array
  Array[ i ] = 'a';              ;  Modify an Array Element
  j = Array[ i ];                ;  Read an Array Element
```

In PICMicro Assembler, this could be implemented as:

```
Array equ    Array_Start              ;  Define Address for Array Start

;  Array[ i ] = 'a';
  movlw      Array                    ;  Modify an Array Element
  addwf      i, w                     ;   Get Offset at "i" in the Array
  movwf      FSR                      ;  Store in the FSR
  movlw      'a'                      ;  Get the Character to Put in there
  movwf      INDF                     ;  Store in the Array

;  j = Array[ i ];
  movlw      Array                    ;  Read an Array Element
  addwf      i, w                     ;   Get Offset The same way as Above
  movwf      FSR
  movf       INDF, w                  ;  Get the Character and Store it.
  movwf      j
```

Looking at the preceding example, you can see that single-dimensional arrays can be implemented quite easily, as can multidimensional arrays. Multidimensional arrays are like single-dimensional arrays, but the index is arithmetically calculated from each parameter (i.e., the index for element 3, 5 in an 8-by-8 array (where the first element of each dimension is "1") would be 2 * 8 + 4).

As noted above, in the low-end PICMicro microcontrollers, the registers can only be accessed in one page. This means that the "RP0" bit in the status register is not used and, more importantly, you cannot directly access the "TRIS" and "OPTION" registers (which are typically in page 1 of the midrange PICMicro's register space).

There is one thing that I have to note with regards to the FSR register and indirect addressing. Even though the FSR register can access 256 different register addresses in two banks, it cannot be used to access 256 file registers contiguously (or as one array of 128 or more sequential addresses). The reason for this is the control registers contained at the first few addresses of each bank. If you try to wrap around a 128-byte bank, you will screw up your microcontroller's control registers, with disastrous results.

Another way of looking at how the "INDF" and "FSR" registers work is to consider a "standard" processor and its index instruction. For example, loading an accumulator from an index may have the instruction:

```
move  a, (Index)
```

The parentheses around "index" indicate that the contents of the register contain the address of the register whose contents we want to put in the accumulator ("a").

In the PIC, rather than using "INDF," we can think of the equivalent instruction being:

```
movf  (FSR), w
```

So instead of using "(FSR)," "INDF" is substituted and carries out exactly the same action as above (the contents of FSR is used as the address of the register to use as the source).

24

MICROCHIP PICMICRO

THE PROGRAM COUNTER

Understanding how to change the program counter can be one of the most difficult things you will have to learn with the PIC. Looking across the different family of devices, implementing "gotos" and "calls" will seem inconsistent and difficult to understand. Actually, these instructions work according to a similar philosophy, and once you understand it they really won't seem all that scary.

In all PICMicro devices, instructions take one instruction word or address. This is part of the RISC philosophy that is used for the design. There is not sufficient space in a "goto" or "call" instruction for the entire address of the new location of the program counter. This is because in the 14-bit (midrange) PICMicros, only 11 bits are available in the instruction for the new address. These 11 bits, which represent 2K instruction addresses, are known as a "page."

Typically, all the least significant bits are put in the instruction. The most significant bits are loaded from another register, called "PCLATH" everytime a "goto" or "call" instruction or a "computed goto" is executed. (Figure 24.8.)

While this form is used for all "gotos" and "calls," the method in how this works varies considerably between the three different PICMicro families. Below, I go through each of the families to explain how the "goto" and "call" instructions work.

But before I do that, I want to talk briefly about another method of changing the program counter. The lower 8 bits of the program counter are directly accessible by the program and can be used to implement simple tables or "computed gotos". In this operation, only the lowest 8 bits can be directly modified by the software, with the remaining bits coming from PCLATH.

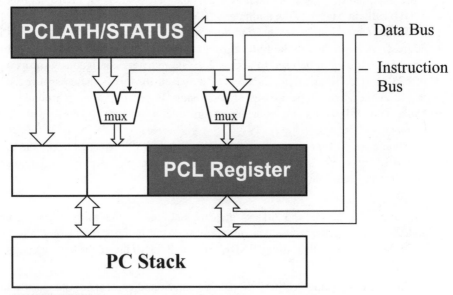

Figure 24.8 PICMicro program counter block diagram.

The Low-End 16C5x Family

The PICMicro 16C5x family of devices deviates slightly from the model shown above. That is because the 16C5x does not have a PCLATH register. Instead, the high-value bits are stored where the "RP" bits would be in the mid-range device's STATUS register. These bits are combined with the bits in the instruction to form the "goto Address."

The low-end PICMicros have a 512 address "page." The 16C5x "goto" and "call" instructions only provide 9 and 8 bits, respectively, of the addressing space. This means that directly, "goto" can access any address in the 512 address page and "call" can only access the first 256 addresses of the page.

To go beyond this (i.e., for the 16C57 part, which has 2K addresses), the "PA0" and "PA1" bits in the STATUS register must be set to the correct 512 address page you want the code to execute in. Once this is done, a "goto," "call," or computed "goto" is done with the PICMicro execution changing to the expected 512 address page when the lower bits of the program counter are changed.

Computed "gotos" work exactly the same as in the other PICMicros, with one important difference. Like call labels, the table and all its elements must be within the first 256 address of a 512 addresss page. This means that in the 1K instruction address 16C56, there are only two goto table segments that can be used (with a total of 512 elements), whereas in the midrange and high-end PICMicros, there isn't this limitation.

The Midrange 16Cxx Family

Because the midrange PICMicros have a 14-bit instruction length, quite a bit larger code space can be implemented in them (up to 8K) from the low-end devices. Because of this, the few simple bits in the STATUS register could not be used to follow the general rules outlined above quite closely. So the "PCLATH" register was created to provide this function.

With the 14-bit instruction size, 11 bits are specified in the "goto" and "call" instructions for the address. This means that the "page" size of the midrange PICMicros is 2K.

If you look through the list of PICMicro devices, you will see that most have 2K or less of control store which means that PCLATH will not be required except for Tables which are not in Page zero.

Running the "addwf PCL[, f]" instruction directly in the PICMicro can still only access up to 255 addresses in a table. However, unlike the low-end parts, data can be any size and located anywhere in memory.

For example, this is how a 700-element table would be implemented in the PICMicro at a random address (i.e., not at a 256 address boarder). "Table" is a subroutine that will return the correct element in "w."

```
Table                            ;  Return the Element at EntryHigh/Entry
   movlw      HIGH TableStart     ;  Calculate the PCLATH Value
   addwf      EntryHigh, w        ;  Add to high byte of the Element Number
   movwf      PCLATH              ;  Store in the PCLATH Register
```

```
    movlw      TableStart & 0x0FF
    addwf      Entry, w          ;  Calculate Offset in 256 Byte "Page"
    btfsc      STATUS, C         ;  If Carry Set, Increment 256 Byte "Page"
    incf       PCLATH
    movwf      PCL               ;  Jump to the Table Element

TableStart                       ;  The Table Starts Here
    retlw      Element_1         ;  Return the Element for Entry = 0
    retlw      Element_2         ;  Return the Element for Entry = 1
       .
       :
    retlw      Element_700       ;  Return the Element for Entry = 699
```

This is the basic code for a "computed goto." First PCLATH is set up with the correct high bits of the table entry's address, followed by calculating the correct offset of the lower 8 bits of the table entry's address. When calculating the lower 8 bits, if the sum is greater than 0x0FF, then PCLATH is incremented because the address is in the next 256-byte "page."

The High-End 17C4x Family

The high-range PICMicros, while similar in operation to the midrange, differ in one important aspect; parts of PCLATH are updated during a goto/call operation. During the "goto" and "call" instruction execution in the mid-range parts, PCLATH is never changed.

PERIPHERALS

In the architecture diagrams above, I haven't shown how the peripheral registers are set up in the PIC. In terms of blocks, the whole register set can be thought of as being architected exactly the same as a regular computer.

This is very analogous to how peripherals are wired to your PC's input/output bus and slots. The address bus is actually the bus shown as the short line in the previous architecture graphics. Each peripheral is actually a block that is hung on the address decode logic, data bus, and controlled by the instruction decode hardware. So, to create a new design with a new feature, the chip designer drops a new device onto the data bus and runs lines from the address decode logic.

Interrupts

In all PICMicros with interrupts, the "INTCON" register (located at address 0x0B in the PICMicro memory map) is the main source of interrupt control. The most significant bit ("global interrupt enable" or "GIE") is set to allow interrupt requests to execute. Upon entry into the interrupt handler, GIE is reset by the hardware before the interrupt handler begins execution. When the interrupt handler has finished, the GIE bit is set by the return from interrupt instruction ("retfie"). It is not recommended that GIE is set inside the interrupt handler. This may lead to unexpected execution within the PICMicro by way of nested interrupts.

The INTCON Register is defined as:

Bit	Label	Description
0	RBIF	Interrupt on PortB Input Change
1	INTF	RB0/INT Pin Interrupt Flag Bit
2	T0IF	TMR0 Overflow Interrupt Bit
3	RBIE	Interrupt on PortB Input Change Enable
4	INTE	RB0/INT Pin Interrupt Enable
5	T0IE	TMR0 Overflow Interrupt Enable
6		Enable Bit for Peripheral Interrupt
7	GIE	Global Interrupt Enable (Set to Allow Interrupt Handler Execution)

The next most significant bits are the interrupt enable flags. These bits are set to allow interrupts when their respective interrupt functions occur. As a pointer, in the PICMicro documentation, it is very easy to find the interrupt enable bits; the labels that are given to them all end in "IE." Along with the interrupt enable flags in "INTCON," there are the interrupt active flags, which are set when the expected interrupt conditions are met. It is important to note that these bits can be set even if either the GIE or interrupt enable bits are reset (which means that when these bits are set, an unexpected interrupt can occur).

It is very important to note that these bits must be reset before a return from interrupt ("retfie") instruction is executed. If the bits are not reset before the interrupt handler ends, then the interrupt handler will be requested again immediately following the execution of "retfie." Interrupt active Flags all have labels that end in "IF," while the interrupt enable flags all end in "IE."

Additional interrupt enable bits and interrupt active flags may be located in other registers throughout the PIC. This means that before setting GIE, you have to make sure that all the interrupt enable flags are in the correct state. This is made considerably easier by noting that all interrupt enable bits are reset upon power-up and to enable an interrupt, the IE bit must be set (= 1).

To explain the sequence of events for programming and handling interrupts, I've put in the following interrupt execute flow:

1. Initialize interrupt source hardware.
2. Enable interrupts.
   - Set GIE and IE of appropriate interrupt in INTCON.
3. Wait for the interrupt to happen.
   - This could be waiting for an interrupt in a loop or executing normally, and processing the data from the interrupt when required.
4. Interrupt request.
   - Wait for the current instruction to complete.

24

MICROCHIP PICMICRO

5. Handle interrupt request.
   - If "IE" flag NOT set for actual interrupt, goto 8.
6. Execute interrupt handler.
   - Start execution at address 4.
7. Reset interrupt controller and return from the interrupt.
   - Reset the interrupt active flag.
   - Set the expected IEs for the next interrupt.
   - Execute the "retfie" instruction.
8. Resume executing at instruction following "interrupted" one.

It is important to note that more than one interrupt source can have an interrupt pending at any time. Different interrupts can be handled by checking the appropriate interrupt active flag ("IF").

All interrupts for the midrange PICMicros start executing at address 0x004. As noted, the high-end PICMicros have multiple interrupt vectors to allow one interrupt source per vector.

Address	Priority	Interrupt Sources
0x0008	Highest	External Interrupt on RA0/INT Pin
0x0010	.	TMR0 Overflow
0x0018	:	External Interrupt on TOCK1
0x0020	Lowest	Peripherals (Controlled by PEIF Register)

Note that eight instructions are available for each interrupt type. This means that the high-end PICMicro, like the 8051, could handle an interrupt inside the 8 instructions and not affect any other sections of memory. In doing this, saving the "w" and STATUS registers is probably critical if instructions other than bit modifying instructions are used, leaving only three instructions (after also counting the "retfie" instruction) for servicing the interrupt.

The "interrupt latency" period is the time the hardware takes to acknowledge the interrupt, and the "processing time" is the number of instruction cycles the program takes to handle the interrupt. Reset the timer and return to the mainline. The latter value is found by using the simulator and understanding how long the program takes (basically finding it empirically). You could determine this by looking at your interrupt handler and counting the number of cycles you expect it to take, but determining the value by the simulator is the easiest and most accurate method I've found.

The interrupt latency cannot be arithmetically calculated. Instead, it typically takes three or four instruction cycles (with the GIE and appropriate "IF" bit set) in which the PICMicro is not executing any instructions.

Note that handling the interrupts involves saving and restoring the state of the mainline program. Care must be taken to ensure that the registers containing the execution status are restored before returning from the interrupt. And, just as importantly, the state of the interrupt handler must be set up correctly (i.e., correct page) before it can start executing. "Application Design" describes how this is done.

CPU PROGRAM COUNTER STACK

The CPU program counter stack is a simple way of storing where the program is executing when a subroutine is called, or an interrupt is serviced. When a program is going off somewhere for a while (a subroutine or interrupt), the current program counter value is saved before the program counter changes location. When execution is returned, the program counter is restored to its previous value.

The PICMicro stack does work differently from many other microprocessor and microcontroller architectures. Normally, registers and miscellaneous data can be stored on the stack as well as the program counter. This is not possible with the PICMicro microcontrollers. Only the program counter can be "pushed" on and "popped" off the stack.

The stack is also very limited (only 8 locations deep in the midrange PICMicros and above, only 2 locations deep in the low-range and 16 deep in the high-end PICMicros). This means that care must be taken to ensure that more than 8 calls can be done with the PIC. Actually, this is not an unreasonable limit if your software is not recursive.

If you've had any experience with any other microprocessors or microcontrollers, you probably feel that the PICMicro cannot compete with them in terms of data passing on the stack during subroutines. Actually, that isn't true. The PICMicro can use the "FSR" and "INDF" registers as a stack very efficiently. For example, say you wanted to write a routine that caused a specified delay. In compiled "C," this might look like:

```
push dlay
call dlay_routine
pop  nothing
```

In the PIC, this could be implemented with the following code:

```
movf  dlay, w
movwf INDF
incf  FSR
call  dlay_routine
decf  FSR
```

While an instruction or two extra is executed to implement a stack over other processor architectures, the FSR can be used as a very efficient stack pointer.

SLEEP

When the PICMicro isn't going to be used for a period of time in an application, you may want to put it to into a low-power mode called "sleep." This is done when the PICMicro isn't required to execute for a while and when it will be required to execute again is known well beforehand.

"Sleep" is used to reduce the amount of power your application uses by ensuring that the I/O pins are set to receiving nonchanging logic values (to prevent unwanted current flow, which results in increased power requirements), then just executing the "sleep" instruction.

During "sleep," if the PICMicro is driving the oscillator, it is turned off. The current state of all the registers are saved. Unless peripheral devices have their own clocks, they will stop running. The watchdog timer does continue to run, however, and when it times out, it will reset the PICMicro out of "sleep." The name "sleep" for the state really isn't a misnomer; the device is really not working until it is woken up in some way.

24

Waking up from sleep can be done a number of different ways, including toggling the reset pin, external interrupts, and the watchdog timer. TMR1, if available and run from an external crystal, can be used to wake the PICMicro up from sleep, but the other internal timers cannot wake the PICMicro up out of sleep (simply because they are turned off). Depending on how the PICMicro is woken up, the program will start at a different location.

One important thing to remember about sleep is how long it will take the PICMicro to get out of it. During sleep, all the major functions of the PICMicro are shut down (except for the watchdog timer) and this includes the oscillator. To ensure that the oscillator is stable after wake-up, 1024 oscillations will be counted before the PICMicro begins to execute again. This delay must be taken into account in your application. The PICMicro sleep/wake cycle looks like Figure 24.9.

Toggling _MCLR or waiting for a watchdog timer time-out will result in the PICMicro being reset and starting to execute at address 0. Since address 0 is also the address the PICMicro starts up at on initial power-up, the "_TO" and "_PD" bits must be checked to understand why the program is at the reset address. Using registers for this function is not recommended because at initial power up, they are at one or two indeterminate values, which may match the test values.

In some of the newer PICMicros, the "PCON" register can be used to differentiate the circumstances for a "Power-On Reset/_MCLR" Reset. This eliminates the need to set some file registers aside with a specific pattern loaded into them to be checked after reset to see if the PIC had been put to sleep.

External interrupts (pins or states) can be used to take the PICMicro out of sleep as well. There is one interesting aspect of this that should be noted. If the "GIE" bit is set,

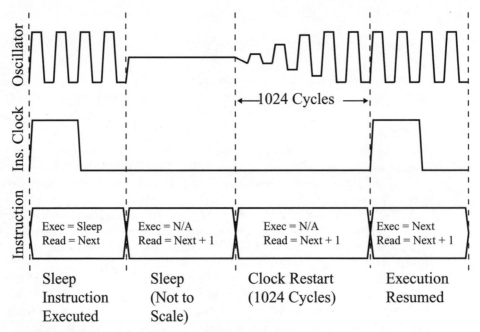

Figure 24.9 PICMicro sleep instruction execution.

Microcontroller
Mode

Extended
Microcontroller
Mode

Microprocessor
Mode

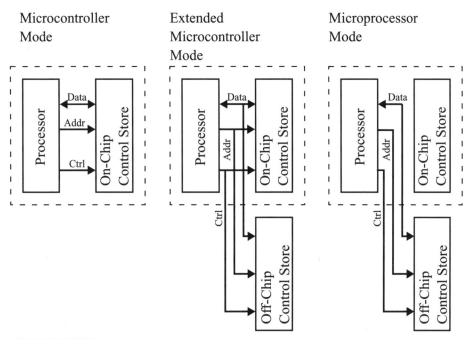

Figure 24.10 High-end PICMicro memory modes.

then the PICMicro will reset back to the interrupt handler address (0x004). If it's not, the PICMicro will continue executing the program where it stopped to go to sleep.

Actually, I lied. After an external interrupt, the PICMicro will execute the instruction after the "sleep" before doing anything else (i.e., jumping to the interrupt handler (Address 4)). Wake up from interrupt is similar to what is shown in Figure 24.9, but after the first instruction after sleep is executed, the interrupt handler is executed.

Because the instruction after sleep is always executed, it is recommended to always put in a "nop" instruction following the sleep instruction. By doing this, you won't have to think about how the PICMicro will be operating after wake up from sleep.

PICMICRO 17C4X ARCHITECTURE

The high-end PICMicros differ from the low- and midrange devices in two major respects. The first is the device's ability to interface via a microprocessor like external bus. The second (and probably more significant) difference is the inclusion of the "w" register in the register bank. Both these features make the 17C4x devices different from the other PICMicros in terms of software development and capabilities.

External Addressing

The high-end PICMicros can run in three different memory modes. (Figure 24.10.) The memory mode the PICMicro runs is selected by using the configuration fuses (which can be specified by the "_CONFIG" assembler instruction). These different modes give the 17C4x quite a bit of flexibility in regards to how the PICMicro is used. Irregardless of the memory mode used, the PICMicro register locations do not change.

24

MICROCHIP PICMICRO

The microcontroller mode means that the PICMicro runs exactly the same way as the other PICMicros. The control store is located inside the PICMicro, and no pins are used for interfacing. There is only one device protect mode, and that works with the microcontroller mode (the memory modes using external memory can't take advantage of this mode with external memory devices).

The extended microcontroller and microprocessor memory modes use I/O bits in the C, D, and E ports. These bits form a multiplexed address/data bus along with control signals. The typical method of wiring external devices is by using an address Latch as shown in Figure 24.11.

There are a few important things to note about this mode. The first is that the external address space is either less than 64K words (in extended microcontroller mode) or exactly 64K (in microprocessor mode). This means the PICMicro can access up to 128K bytes. Each byte can be read from or written by using the "table" commands. Because a write capability is included in the table commands, RAM can be used to provide extra storage space to the PIC.

Along with memory devices, other devices can be attached to the external memory bus. This means that typical microprocessor interface devices can be used with the PICMicro as "memory-mapped I/O." They are also accessed using the table read/write instructions.

REGISTERS

As noted elsewhere, the high-end devices use a different register model. (Figure 24.12.) This register model means that the PICMicro can transfer data to the execution registers much faster and more efficiently than in the mid- and low-range devices. If you were to take a program that appears in this book and assemble it for a 17C4x device, you'd find many errors, mostly centered around the use of the "movf" instruction (which doesn't exist for the 17C4x family).

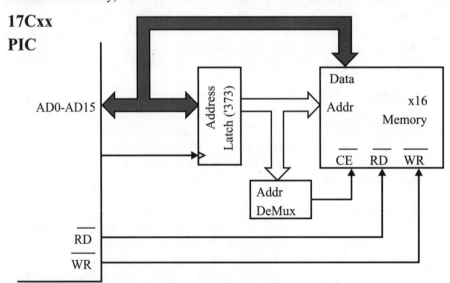

Figure 24.11 High-end PICMicro external memory wiring.

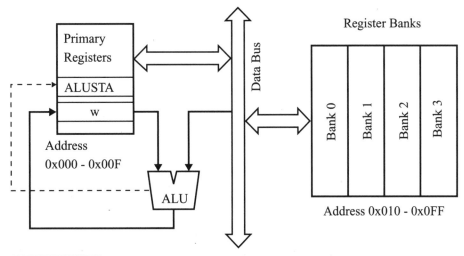

Figure 24.12 High-end PICMicro register block diagram.

This instruction doesn't exist in the high-end devices because of the ability to transfer data back and forth between the "p" (primary) and "f" (file) register set.

While this seems like a real blessing, there is one problem that you must be aware of. The high-end instruction set doesn't support the use of the

```
movf Reg, f
```

Which checks the value of "Reg" and sets the zero flag accordingly. This cannot be done in the high-end devices unless the register to be checked is in the primary set. Saving a value in "w" and checking another register may not be possible in the high-end processors. This is probably not a big problem for most applications, but it is something the programmer has to be aware of.

24

PICMICRO HARDWARE FEATURES

Different Types of PICMicros

Like all microcontrollers, new PICMicro devices are continually added to the family seemingly continuously, each with more features. As I go through this, I've tried to pick out the major product types and their features.

8-PIN PICMICROS

The recently introduced 8-pin PICMicros have become very popular in a very short order. These devices provide up to six I/O pins along with a variety of advanced features (including TMR0, a watchDog timer, ADC, and ISP).

The PIC12C5xx parts are essentially low-end devices with in-system programming capability. Also included is an internal RC oscillator (meaning no external pins are required to provide a clock to the PICMicro) and internal reset circuitry. These features allow the PICMicro to run with Vdd and ground and up to six I/O pins. They are currently available with 512 or 1024 instructions, which can be burned to EPROM via the midrange ISP protocol. The PIC12C67x parts, which were available in early 1998, use the midrange CPU architecture with built-in ADCs and have interrupt capabilities.

LOW-END PICMICROS

The low-end PICMicros consist of a basic processor core with no interrupt capability and a very small program counter stack. They do not have any of the advanced I/O features of the midrange PICMicros (i.e., built in ADCs, serial ports, microprocessor bus interfaces, etc.). Their big advantage is that they are very cheap (although this advantage is becoming less and less significant as time goes on and midrange devices become available in the same price ranges). Low-end PICMicros are identified as "16C5x."

Because of the lack of interrupts, the small program counter stack, a maximum program size of 2K, and no periperal functions (i.e., ADCs, serial interfaces, etc.), I tend to shy away from using these devices.

MIDRANGE PICMICROS

There is a lot of variety in the midrange of the PICMicro product line; there is a large range of features and functions that the user can choose from. Also, code can be transported across the line with very few changes required.

The devices can have anywhere from 13 to 33 I/O port pins, multiple timers, PWM I/O, asynchronous serial communication, directly controlled LCDs, EEPROM program store, and the list goes on and on. The basic midrange CPU consists of 35 instructions, with interrupts and an eight element deep program counter stack. The interrupt sources can be input pin states, timer overflows, serial data input, A/D completion, along with others. A maximum program size of 8K allows very complex applications. One of the more interesting devices PICMicros are designed for are LCDs. Using the PIC14C00 device, LCDs can be wired directly to the PICMicro without requiring any intermediate hardware.

The midrange devices are identified as "16Cmx," where "m" is the model and "x" is the device within the family. Except where noted, all the devices can run up to 20 MHz with 2.5 to 6.0 volts input. The models are as follows:

MODEL	CONTROL STORE	FILE REGISTERS	FUNCTIONS/COMMENTS
16C55x	512 - 2K EPROM	80 - 128	13 I/O Pins, TMR0
16C62x	512 - 2K EPROM	80 - 128	13 I/O Pins, TMR0, Analog Comparators
16C64x	2K - 4K EPROM	128 - 176	22 I/O Pins, TMR0, Analog Comparators
16C66x	2K - 4K EPROM	128 - 176	33 I/O Pins, TMR0, Analog Comparators
16C6x	1K - 8K EPROM/ROM	36 - 192	13 - 33 I/O Pins, TMR0, TMR1, TMR2, SPI, SCI
16C7x	512 - 8K EPROM/ROM	36 - 192	13 - 33 I/O Pins, ADC, TMR0, TMR1, TMR2, SPI, SCI
16C84	1K EEPROM/ROM	36	13 I/O Pins, TMRO, EEPROM, 10 MHz Max
16F8x	512 - 1K EEPROM/ROM	68	13 I/O Pins, TMR0, EEPROM, 10 MHz Max
16C9xx	4K EPROM	176	LCD Drivers, 25 I/O Pins, TMR0, TMR1, TMR2, SPI, 8 MHz Max, 3.0 V Min

HIGH-END PICMICROS

The 17Cxx devices are enhancements to the basic architecture used in the low-end and midrange PICMicros. Able to access up to 64K (16-bit) words of memory, they can provide complete system solutions rather than just traditional intelligent hardware control (as the other PICMicros typically do). The 17Cxx devices have 33 I/O pins, can run at up to 33 MHz, and have many of the bus interface options of the midrange parts (although no ADCs).

The CPU core allows for much more flexible internal data transfer and provides for multiple interrupt vectors for different interrupt handlers. These features allow much more efficient coding of applications. The 17Cxx has 55 instructions which are expanded from the midrange devices and reflect the increased functionality of the CPU core.

Device Packaging

The PICMicros come in a wide variety of packages. The best-known package is the 18-pin DIP, which has 9 pins to a side and 0.100" between pins and 0.300" wide. This is the package the 16F84 and many of the baseline low-end and midrange devices are available in.

There are a number of different packages available for the PICMicro. The encapsulants consist of black epoxy potting compound (and known as an "OTP" package) and the quartz window ceramic package (shown as a "J" type package in Figure 25.1).

Microchip Package Options*

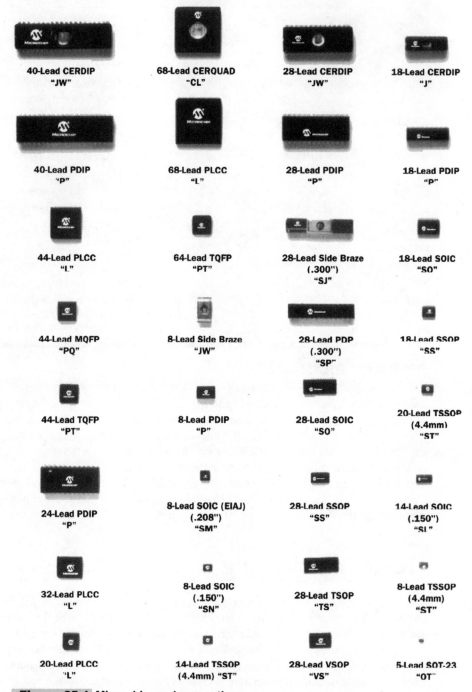

Figure 25.1 Microchip package options.

This is used with devices that have EPROM control store, which can be erased using ultraviolet light. The disadvantage of this package is its cost and the chance that the EPROM can be accidentally erased. After a device is programmed, the window should always be covered with an ultraviolet opaque sticker (an old metalized disk drive write protect sticker works well) to identify that it has been programmed and to help prevent unwanted erasures.

The package you decide upon will have a major impact on the finished application. But when prototyping, I highly recommend using "JW" or EEPROM parts, which will allow reprogramming.

Control Store Types

There are three different types of memory used for the "program memory" (following the convention of this book I tend to call "control store") of the PICMicro. They are, erasable programmable memory (EPROM), electrically erasable programmable memory (EEPROM also known as "double-EPROM" or "E-squared PROM"), and hardwired or read only memory (ROM). Each different type of memory offers advantages in different situations.

EPROM is the basic type of control store memory used in the PICMicro devices. Midrange EPROM (and EEPROM) PICMicros have the significant advantage of being able to be programmed with the PICMicro in the application after board assembly (due to their "ISP" control store). This can be done at either in circuit test (ICT), functional test, or at a dedicated programming station.

Currently, the only PICMicro devices which have EEPROM control store are in the 16?8x family, which offers the midrange processor with some advanced parallel I/O capabilities (i.e., timer overflow interrupt and interrupt on pin change) and functionality which is at a level between the low-end and the higher featured parts. Microchip now identifies its EEPROM parts with an "F" (for "Flash"). The original EEPROM part is the 16C84, which you will probably find many references to and which is a bit confusing when you look at current datasheets and catalogs and find it "obsoleted".

ROM-based control store means that the program has been built into the chip at the factory. While Microchip does provide mask ROM parts, it is their intention to be a source of primarily EPROM "OTP" microcontrollers to give their customers greater flexibility in parts that they offer.

Reset

The PICMicro microcontrollers are reset by a single pin, "_MCLR." When this pin is asserted (i.e., equal to a "0"), the PICMicro will be in a reset state. This means that all output drivers will be turned off and the local clock (driven by the PICMicro) is turned off.

The reset vector is the address the PICMicro's program counter is set to at the start of the program. This value is zero for the mid- and high-range PICMicros and the last address for the low-range PICs. For example, 0x01FF is the reset address of the 512 instruction 16C54.

The 8-pin PICMicros really start at the last address, but they appear to start up at address zero. This is because the internal RC oscillator's calibration value is stored in "w" as the last instruction in control store. When the program counter rolls over, as noted later in this chapter, if the internal RC is used, then the first instruction should save the value in "w" into the "OSCCAL" register. The calibration load is the instruction:

```
org     ControlStoreSize - 1  ;  Go to the Last Address in Control Store
movlw   Calibrate             ;  Store the Calibration Value in "w"
```

Reset is not to be confused with power up. On power up, most of the hardware register bits are set to specific values, and the remaining bits and the "file" (RAM) registers have unknown values. After a reset cycle, the remaining bits and the file registers are set to the values they were at before reset was active. By setting some file registers to a known, not easily repeatable state, a program can check to see whether or not the reset vector was executed by a power up or reset condition.

In most new PICMicros, the "PCON" register will provide this same function as setting file registers to a specific value.

Resetting a running PICMicro may be desired if the input voltage goes below a predetermined threshold ("brown-out"). Many newer PICMicros have brown-out detection and reset built into their reset circuitry. Other PICMicros will require a discrete brownout detector.

Normally in the PICMicro, reset delay circuitry is not required. This is because of the length of time the PICMicro can be programmed to power up (using the "PWRTE" bit in the configuration fuses). As discussed elsewhere, the optimal reset circuit is simply a pull up resistor attaching _MCLR to Vcc.

System Clock/Oscillators

The PICMicro can run with a wide variety of different system clocks. This adds a great deal of flexibility to your application's design. There are four types of oscillators used with the PICMicro: external resistor/capacitor (also known as "RC"), internal RC, crystal, and external. Each has advantages that can be exploited during application development.

"Resistor/capacitor" ("RC") oscillators use the time constant of a simple R/C network to provide a clock of an approximate frequency (typically 20% accurate). (See Figure 25.2).

Note that the OSC2 pin outputs 1/4 of the clock frequency (which is actually the instruction clock). This signal can be used to synchronize external devices to the PICMicro.

This 20% accuracy means that the RC clock circuit can only be used for applications where precise timing is not required. This leaves out applications where the PICMicro outputs serial data, audible tones, or interfaces with other parts. There still are a lot of applications where the RC clock is appropriate, but the RC clock should not be used in any applications that require precise timing.

Because of the nonlinear nature of the PICMicro OSC1 pin, there is no simple formula to be used for calculating the resistor and capacitor values. The datasheet for each PICMicro has suggested resistance and capacitance values for different frequencies.

The "internal RC" oscillator uses an internal resistor/capacitor circuit with a "calibration" value that is loaded as the first instruction. This value is normally programmed in at the factory and is saved as the first application instruction:

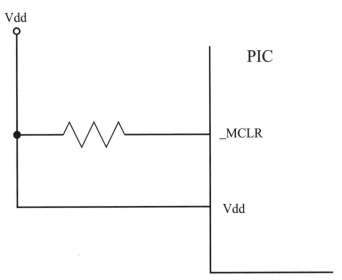

Figure 25.2 Simple PICMicro reset circuit.

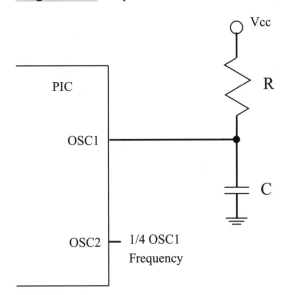

Figure 25.3 RC PICMicro oscillator circuit.

```
org 0                      ;   Beginning of the Application
   movwf   OSCCAL          ;   Save the Internal RC Oscillator Calibration Value
```

Before using an R/C oscillator, the PICMicro's configuration fuses must be set appropriately. Other clocking schemes include a low-power clocking mode ("LP" mode), standard megahertz-range crystals ("XT"), and high-speed clocks ("HS"). These three modes can accept either a crystal (or ceramic resonator) or an external clock source. The crystal clock circuit is typically as shown in Figure 25.4.

The external capacitor values (C1 and C2) can be found in the data sheets for the PICMicro and are unique to the device the same way that R and C are selected in the RC

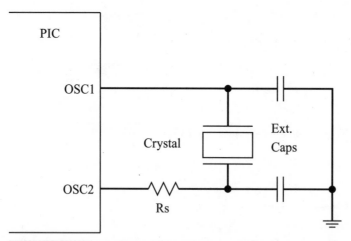

Figure 25.4 Crystal-based PICMicro oscillator circuit.

oscillator (above). Rs is a bit of a nebulous value and its inclusion is usually by empirically determined need and is in the hundreds of ohms.

A "ceramic resonator" can also be used in place of a crystal. You should take care if you're using a resonator with built-in capacitors. They may be at too high a level to allow the PICMicro to operate. With integral capacitors, the resonator may make the layout of your application simpler (with fewer parts) and potentially cheaper because the ceramic resonator typically costs the same as a crystal, but does not require the extra parts (capacitors) and vias of a crystal solution.

Another bonus is that a ceramic resonator is a lot more physically robust than a crystal.

The only downside to the ceramic resonator is in terms of timing resolution. Typically, a ceramic resonator is accurate within 0.5%, whereas a crystal with only 200 ppm (0.02%) accuracy is readily available. For most applications, this is not an issue, but for developing real-time clocks and such, a crystal with this accuracy (or better) should be used.

To determine how the configuration fuses for the oscillator should be set, as a rule of thumb, you can use the following:

TYPE	FREQUENCY RANGE
RC	0 to 4 MHz
LP	5 KHz to 200 KHz
XT	100 KHz to 4 MHz
HS (-04)	4 MHz
HS (-10)	4 MHz to 10 MHz
HS (-20)	4 MHz to 20 MHz

The system clock starts up at power on time, as shown in Figure 25.5.

If an external oscillator is used to provide the system clock to the PICMicro, then the LP, XT, or HS clock mode should be selected. The output of the external oscillator should be input to OSC1, with OSC2 being left unconnected ("floating"). OSC2 will output a signal at the same frequency as OSC1, but it is not within phase of the OSC1 signal. OSC2 should not be used to drive other devices.

If the clock driving OSC1 is required for other parts of a circuit, then it should be buffered and fanned out (with OSC1) to the other devices. (Figure 25.6.)

Hardware and File Registers

Like other Harvard-architected processors, the PICMicro has completely separate register and control store spaces. The register space is used for storing values used by the software (also known as "variables") and for locating the PICMicro hardware control registers. Along with the RAM and registers, there is a "w" register, which is used as an accumulator or temporary storage.

The registers are contained within a 128 (or 256 in the case of the high-range) address "bank." Each register contains up to 8 bits. These registers can be accessed via a number of different mehods in software. Typically, registers that control the hardware and are

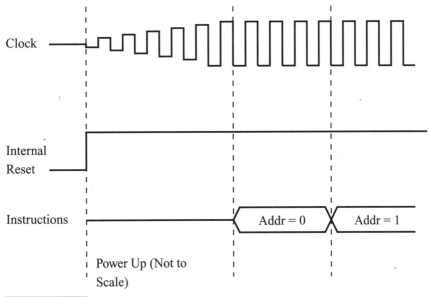

Figure 25.5 PICMicro power-up sequence.

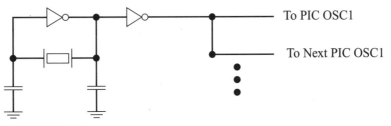

Figure 25.6 Clock circuit for fanning out external clock to multiple PICMicros.

only accessed during the initialization of the application are located in bank 1. This is an important note because it allows you to structure your initialization to set the bank select and reset it for execution of the program only once. (Figure 25.7.)

As I mentioned in the "PICMicro Architecture" chapter, I like to put array variables in bank 1 and general-purpose variables in bank 0. With this convention, I can go to bank 1 to initialize the hardware registers and then stay in bank 0 just about exclusively because the array variables, which are accessed by FSR, don't require the "RP0" of the STATUS register to be set.

The PICMicro hardware registers are all located at the same addresses across the families of devices and have the same variable names. This allows code to be reused easily between PICMicro part numbers. The PICMicro Processor registers ("STATUS", "INT-CON", "FSR", "INDF", "OPTION", "PCL", "PCLATH," and "INTCON") are all located at the same addresses within each register bank in the PICMicro. This allows the same access of the different registers, regardless of how the bank select bits are set. The hardware registers start at address zero within each bank, and the RAM registers are located immediately following them.

The low-end PICMicros only have one register bank. To access the registers which are typically located in bank 1 of the PICMicro (most notably the "TRIS" and "OPTION" registers), special instructions are used which transfer the contents of "w" to them directly. There is no way to read these registers back, so it is recommended that you keep a separate copy of these registers if you are going to use the values later.

As can be seen in Figure 25.8, I've lied a bit. The low-end devices do have different banks (addressed by bits 5 and 6 of the address), but the two registers ("OPTION" and "TRIS") that are located in "bank 1" of the midrange devices are not available in the reg-

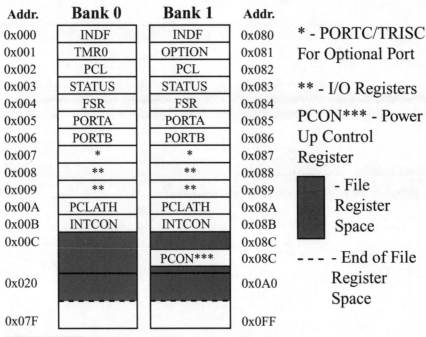

Figure 25.7 Midrange PICMicro registers.

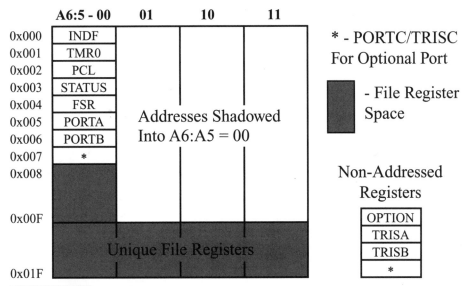

Figure 25.8 Low-end PICMicro registers.

ister memory map. Instead, they can only be written to (with the contents of "w") using the "OPTION" and "TRIS" instructions.

Also in the low-end devices, note that the addresses with bit 4 reset (equal to zero) are all common across the four banks, but the file registers with bit 4 set are unique to the different banks. This means that up to 64, the unique file registers can be present in the low-end PICMicros.

The "w" register is an intermediate register and is normally used as an accumulator or storage of temporary values. Except in the high-end devices, it is not directly addressable, but can be manipulated by various instructions. The "w" register can be the destination of all arithmetic instructions.

The high-end PICMicros, while behaving in a similar manner, are a bit more complex. This complexity comes from two sources. The first is the set of "primary" (or "p") registers, which are a subset of the complete register set. Staying in this vein is the location of the "WREG" register (which is the high-end's version of "w") which is not separate from the other registers (and can be accessed and written to like other registers). This location of "w" allows you to test/set/reset bits as you would in the other PICMicros. For this reason the high-end PICMicros can be considered to have a more "orthogonal" register set than the other PICMicro families.

The high-end PICMicro's basic architecture looks like Figure 25.9. The registers in banks 0 to 3 can be either hardware control registers or file registers.

CPU Program Counter Stack

The PICMicro's program counter stack is actually quite simple. It is a parallel load/unload LIFO ("last in/first out") memory which has the same number of bits as the program counter. (Figure 25.10.)

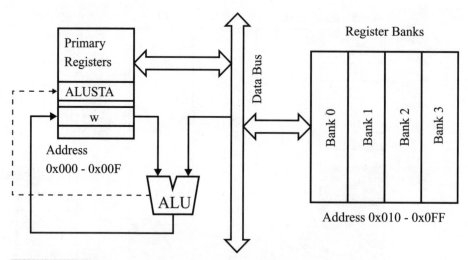

Figure 25.9 High-end PICMicro register block diagram.

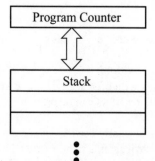

Figure 25.10 PICMicro program counter and stack.

There is no way to access the stack data. As noted elsewhere in the book, this means that the PICMicro cannot implement a real-time operating system or debug/monitor program. Now there are some programs available that will simulate a monitor program and RTOS, but they really don't meet the specifications of these types of applications.

While a monitor can, for the most part, be replaced by a hardware emulator, the loss of being able to do a full RTOS is, in my opinion, a serious deficiency in the PICMicro.

Interrupts

Implementing interrupts in the PICMicro is quite easy if you follow a few basic rules. Actually, the PICMicro behaves in a very straightforward manner when it comes to interrupts. I have repeated Figure 11, which I showed at the start of the book for handling interrupts, because it can be used directly in the PICMicro.

When creating an interrupt handler, the first thing that has to be done is saving the "context" registers. When execution jumps to address 4 (in the midrange PICMicros, in the high-end PICMicros, other addresses are used, based on the interrupt type) upon acknowledgment of an interrupt, only the program counter has been saved on the stack. This means that the other registers critical to the operation of the mainline have to be saved.

Typically, the code used to do this is:

```
org  4     ;  Address of the Start of the Interrupt Handler

IntHndlr
    movwf   _w              ;  Save "w"
    movf    STATUS, w       ;  Save "STATUS"
    bcf     STATUS, RP0     ;  Make Sure Execution in Bank 0
    movwf   _status         ;
    movf    FSR, w          ;  OPTIONAL - Save FSR if both Mainline and
    movwf   _fsr            ;     IntHndlr modifies/uses FSR
    movf    PCLATH, w       ;  OPTIONAL - Mandatory if > 2K of Control Store
    movwf   _pclath         ;     or Tables used in both Mainline and IntHndlr
    movlw   HIGH $          ;  OPTIONAL - Reset PCLATH (Mandatory if PCLATH
    movwf   PCLATH          ;     was saved above)
```

The labels starting with an underscore ("_") and have the register names in lower case are conventions that I use for context saving file registers. As the comments indicate, "FSR" is saved if it is modified and used in both the mainline and interrupt handler ("IntHndlr").

PCLATH is a bit more complex. Since it is used during "gotos"/"calls" over a 2K page boundary or for tables outside the first 256 addresses, then to be on the safe side, save PCLATH and set it explicitly for use in the interrupt handler.

Another consideration for PCLATH and the interrupt handler is that you may feel that it would be better to put the interrupt handler starting in memory somewhere else than address 4. I recommend against this practice because if you are working with a PICMicro that has more than 2K, you will (not "may") find that occasionally you will be executing in a higher page of memory and when the interrupt occurs, the "goto" the interrupt handler sends executes into an unexpected location (the "boonies"). This can be further complicated by updating PCLATH before executing the goto, which is a problem because this will most likely affect "w" and "STATUS," meaning that before the goto can be executed, the context register save must be completed. It is much simpler to just put the interrupt handler starting at address 4.

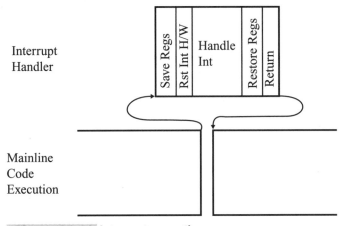

Figure 25.11 Interrupt execution.

The code above is for the most general case. Because I don't know which register bank will be active when the interrupt handler is invoked, I make the "_w" file register available at the same address in all the banks. After "w" has been saved and "STATUS" has been stored in "w," I explicitly make sure that bank 0 is selected for execution.

After the context registers have been saved, you have to determine what was the source of the interrupt. In the PICMicro, this is done by looking at the enabled interrupt active flags (these bits are usually located in "INTCON" or "PIR" registers, but for some features, they are located in other locations). If you have experience with PCs and their processors (which have a separate interrupt vector for each interrupt type), this probably sounds like a pretty onerous task trying to figure out which interrupt is active. To indicate that the interrupt has been handled, you must reset the appropriate "IF" bit.

In some of the PICMicro's peripheral devices, additional instructions will be required to make it ready to request another interrupt.

I put the "IF" reset code as early as possible in the interrupt handler in case another interrupt request comes in while servicing the current one. When the new interrupt request is made, it will be latched by the hardware, and when the current interrupt handler has completed and the global interrupt enable ("GIE") bit is set, the new interrupt will be serviced.

After all this, we are finally able to respond to the interrupt request. I think it's good practice to have the interrupt handler execute as quickly as possible so that pending an interrupt request doesn't experience any undue delay.

Once processing has completed, the context registers are restored and execution is allowed to return to where it was before the interrupt request was accepted. The code to do this is basically an inversion of the entry code with one important twist.

```
IntHndlrEnd                     ;  Return from the Interrupt
  movf       _pclath, w         ;  OPTIONAL - Restore PCLATH if it was
  movwf      PCLATH             ;   saved/changed in IntHndlr
  movf       _fsr, w            ;  OPTIONAL - Restore FSR if it was
  movwf      FSR                ;   saved/changed in IntHndlr
  movf       _status, w         ;  Restore the Status Register
  movwf      STATUS
  swapf      _w                 ;  Restore "w" without affecting the STATUS
  swapf      _w, w              ;   Register
  retfie                        ;  Return from the Interrupt
```

The "twist" is the two "swapf" instructions operating on "_w." The problem is to load "w" with the saved value without affecting the STATUS register bits (the zero flag is affected by the "movf" instruction). To avoid this problem, the "swapf" instruction (which doesn't affect any STATUS bits) which swaps the high for the low nybble is used, first to reverse the value in "_w" and then reverse it again as it is loaded into "w."

Timers

The timers available in the PICMicro are pretty middle of the road (compared to other microcontroller's timers) in terms of capabilities, but they do offer some features that will make developing applications easier and more efficient.

TMR0

The basic programmable timer available in all PICMicros is "TMR0," which is an 8-bit timer that has an optional prescaler. The prescaler, along with the clock divide by two

("/2") circuit can delay the incoming clocks by 2 to 256 times. This allows the timer to handle longer intervals/more events in a given period.

The circuit shown in Figure 25.12 indicates that there is a prescaler dedicated to TMR0. As will be seen in the "Watchdog Timer" subchapter below, this is not the case.

Note that even if the prescaler is not used, the input signal is still divided by two. This circuit is used to condition the incoming signal and ensure that it has a 50% duty cycle. For example, if a series of pulses at 1 MHz were input into "TOCK0," the divide-by-two circuit would condition them to a 500-kHz square wave signal at the input of TMR0 or the prescaler.

The "T0IF" bit is the interrupt request bit in INTCON and is set when TMR0 rolls over from 0x0FF to 0x000. T0IF is only available in PICMicros that have interrupts (i.e., the midrange and high-end devices). It would be nice to be able to poll it in the low-end device, though.

I typically use the instruction clock for the TMR0 source if I am implementing a specific delay. Normally I use a crystal or ceramic resonator for the clock, and this will allow TMR0 to be used for a providing a reasonably precise delay.

To calculate this delay, the first thing you will have to do is determine whether or not the prescaler will be required. This can be determined simply by calculating:

$$TMR0\_Count = Period / (2 * (4 / freq))$$

If the "TMR0_Count" value is greater than 256, then repeatedly divide it by two until it is less than 256.

For example, if you wanted to get a tenth of second delay in a PICMicro running at 1 MHz, the formula would work out to:

$$TMR0\_Count = Period / (2 * (4 / freq))$$
$$= 0.1 \text{ s} / (2 * 4 / 1{,}000{,}000 \text{ /sec})$$
$$= 12{,}500$$

This value is greater than 256, so the prescaler will have to be used.

By dividing 12,500 by 64, we end up with 195.3125, which is the value TMR0 will have to count to with a prescaler of 64 to delay 0.1 seconds at 1 MHz. Note that the actual Prescaler_Value will be 128 to take into account the clock divide by two at the input to TMR0.

The 0.3125 will be rounded off the TMR0_Count value and, if necessary for precise timing, will be made up by individual instruction cycles.

From this, we can make a general delay formula using TMR0 and the prescaler:

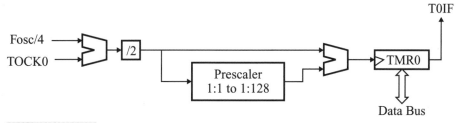

Figure 25.12 PICMicro TMR0 block diagram.

$$\text{Delay} = \text{TMR0\_Count} * \text{Prescaler\_Value} * 4 \, / \, \text{freq}$$

Normally, when this delay is up, we want TMR0 to interrupt the PICMicro's execution. This can be done by preloading TMR0 with a value that when added to "TMR0_Count" will cause the interrupt request bit T0IF to be set.

This is easy to do. TMR0 is initially loaded with the overflow value (256) minus the "TMR0_Count" value. So, to get a TMR0_Count value to interrupt after a specific delay, we can use the formula:

$$\text{TMR0\_Count} = 256 - \text{Delay} * \text{freq} \, / \, (\text{Prescaler\_Value} * 4)$$

Going back to the 0.1-second delay for a 1-MHz clocked PICMicro with the divide by 64 prescaler active, the intial TMR0 value can be calculated as:

$$\text{TMR0\_Count} = 256 - 0.1 \text{ sec} * 1{,}000{,}000 \text{ /sec} \, / \, (128 * 4)$$
$$= 256 - 100{,}000 \, / \, 1024$$
$$= 256 - 195$$
$$= 61$$

TMR1

TMR1 and TMR2 are optional timers that can be used to provide additional features to the PICMicro with very little processor overhead. TMR1 is designed for providing a real time clock that runs during sleep and can be used to provide a method of monitoring the current status of the external hardware.

TMR1 differs from TMR0 (and TMR2) in its hardware and clocking capabilities. TMR1 is a 16-bit timer that can be driven by an external clock (similar to the clock used to drive the PICMicro itself). Being a 16-bit timer, its prescaling requirements are much less than the other timers (a 16-bit timer will overflow in the same amount of cycles as an 8-bit timer with a 256 clock prescaler).

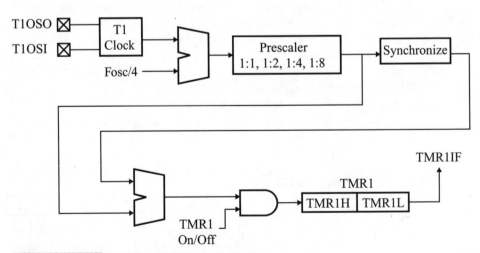

Figure 25.13 PICMicro TMR1 block diagram.

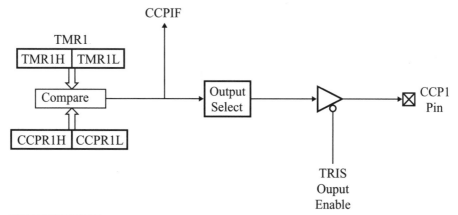

Figure 25.14 PICMicro TMR1 compare mode block diagram.

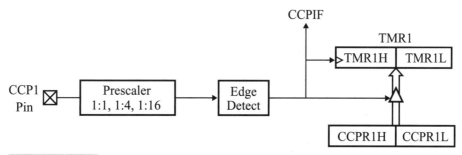

Figure 25.15 PICMicro TMR1 capture mode block diagram.

When the TMR1 clock is enabled, the two pins ("T1OSO" and "T1OSI," which are pins RC0 and RC1, respectively) are enabled as clock inputs able to run with a crystal up to 200 kHz. A 32.768-kHz watch crystal is often used to provide a real-time function on the chip. This clock will run during "sleep," except when synchronized clock input is used as input to TMR1.

The "synchronize" block is used to synchronize the external clock with the internal processor clock. To synchronize the clock with the internal processor, the clock is sampled at the second and fourth clocks of each instruction cycle (which will cause the timer to update at up to the internal processor clock speed). Synchronization should not be used if the PICMicro is to go to sleep and TMR1 is to be kept running (the synchronization will not pass any timing signals to TMR1 because the processor clock is not being distributed throughout the PICMicro even if it is being driven externally).

TMR1 can be used similarly to the 68HC055 clock, with interrupts either being requested when the timer has rolled over ("TMR1IF") or when a specified interval has been reached. This is known as "compare mode." Compare mode can be used to interrupt the PICMicro when the count has achieved a specific value. (Figure 25.14.)

The other enhanced mode for TMR1 is "capture mode," which saves the TMR1 value during an external event. (Figure 25.15.) The prescaler on the input allows multiple events to occur before the processor is interrupted.

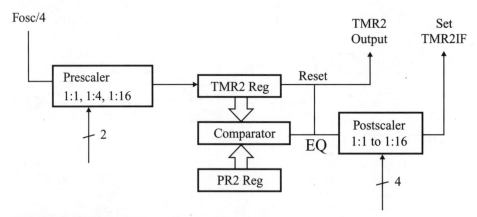

Figure 25.16 PICMicro TMR2 block diagram.

TMR2

The other optional timer available in some PICMicros is an 8-bit free-running timer that is reset when its internal value matches a preset value. The primary purpose of this timer is to provide a PWM output that can be converted into an analog voltage or used to control the speed of a DC motor. (Figure 25.16.)

TMR2 continually runs, and when it is at the same value as "PR2," a comparator resets TMR2 and the count up to the value in PR2 repeats. With enabling some additional hardware, TMR2 can be turned into a PWM output that runs independantly of the processor. (Figure 25.17.)

The primary function of TMR2 doesn't change (it continues to count up to PR2 and then reset), but while its value is less than the value in CCPR1H, the PWM output will be high. If CCPR1H is less than PR2, you can output a PWM signal with the output high while TMR2 is less than CCPR1H and low while it is greater than CCPR1H.

This PWM signal has up to 8 bits of resolution for both the period and duty cycle of the PWM signal. This means that the output is fairly coarse and really not that precise compared to other methods of PWM output. While this is okay for outputting a DC voltage or controlling a DC motor, it is not appropriate for devices like radio control servos, which require a very precise pulse that is a small fraction of the whole PWM signal.

WATCHDOG TIMER

Like most other microcontrollers, the PICMicro's watchdog timer ("WDT") is used to reset the PICMicro when the order of execution has been lost (and the timer has not been reset within a specific amount of time). In the PICMicro, the WDT is run by an RC oscillator and will time out in roughly 18 msecs. The operation of the WDT is controlled by a bit in the configuration register, enabled when the bit is written to when the device is programmed.

The WDT cannot be accessed, except to be reset (using the "CLRWDT" instruction). I like to think of the WDT as an 8-bit timer with the overflow causing reset (instead of an interrupt like the other timers). This means that the internal RC clock that drives the WDT is running with a period of approximately 70 usecs (or a frequency of 14.2 kHz), assuming the WDT is an 8-bit counter.

You're probably thinking that 18 msec isn't a very long interval for running a program in between having to execute "clrwdt" instructions. The same prescaler as TMR0 uses can be used to lengthen the WDT time out (up to 2.3 seconds when the prescaler is set to 128). The TMR0 circuit, with the WDT added, becomes the circuit shown in Figure 25.18.

The prescaler source select, the prescaler value, and the TMR0 source are all selected in the "OPTION" register. The default condition is to pass the WDT through the prescaler and set the prescaler value to 1:128. This means that if the WDT is inadvertently enabled, your PICMicro application will reset itself once every two-and-a-half seconds or so. If the prescaler is specified for TMR0 and the WDT is inadvertently enabled, then the PICMicro will look like it never boots up (although this can be checked by looking at OSC2 with an oscilloscope) because the WDT is resetting the PICMicro every 18 msecs.

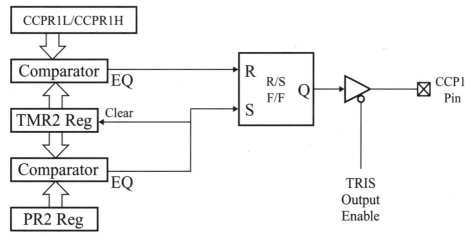

Figure 25.17 PICMicro TMR2 PWM mode block diagram.

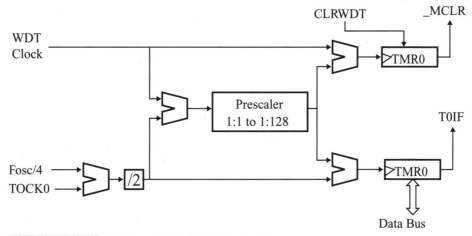

Figure 25.18 PICMicro TMR0/WDT block diagram.

If you're unfamiliar with the PICMicro, you might think that there is a very remote possibility of this happening. But with many home-brew programmers, where the configuration fuses have to be set manually, there is a good chance that this will happen. Like the code protect fuse (which makes many devices impossible to erase and reprogram), inadvertently enabling the watchdog timer will make your debug very difficult. For these reasons, I like to use a programmer and software that takes the configuration information out of the ".hex" file rather than explicitly set this myself in the programmer.

After reading about "sleep" mode and the watchdog timer and you're still not sure how they work together, I suggest that you read about "delay" and "power/execution control" in the chapter devoted to explaining the BASIC Stamp PBASIC functions. All but one of these functions use the WDT and "sleep" to provide definable delays and low-power operation for the Stamp, and understanding how they work will give you insight into the same functions in the PICMicro.

Built-in EEPROM

An interesting option available in EEPROM PICMicros is a bank of EEPROM memory available for use for data storage. This memory can be read very quickly but usually takes about 10 msec to write a byte into memory. This memory can be used as a RAM function, but more importantly, it can be used to store serial numbers, calibration data, user's setup, or any other information that would be useful to keep on hand when the power has been turned off the PICMicro.

Because the EEPROM data memory is not directly in the register map, to access a byte within the memory, the address and data have to be set up before the operation has started. This can be shown in the following code, which is used to read the EEPROM:

```
bcf     STATUS, RP0   ;   Data/Address Registers in Bank 0
movlw   EEPROM_Addr   ;   Load the EEPROM Address
movwf   EEADR
bsf     STATUS, RP0   ;   EEPROM Control Regs in Bank 1
bsf     EECON1, RD    ;   Initiate the Read
bcf     STATUS, RP0
movf    EEDATA, w     ;   Read the Byte at EEADR = EEPROM_Addr
```

Writing to EEPROM is carried out in a similar manner, but with one important difference: a special sequence has to be written to a pseudoregister "EECON2" to start the write operation. This sequence is used to make sure the EEPROM is not written to inadvertently (for this reason, in the code below, you'll note that I have turned off interrupts to make sure that the sequence, marked with "*" is not interrupted). The code to write a byte to EEPROM is:

```
bcf     STATUS, RP0   ;   Data/Address in Bank 0
movf    Data, w       ;   Load Data to Write
movwf   EEDATA
movf    Addr, w       ;   Load Address of Write
movwf   EEADR
bsf     STATUS, RP0   ;   EEPROM Control Regs in Bank 1
bcf     INTCON, GIE   ;   Disable Interrupts for Critical Code
bsf     EECON1, WREN  ;   Enable Writing
movlw   0x055         ;   * - Required Write Sequence
movwf   EECON2        ;   * - Required Write Sequence
movlw   0x0AA         ;   * - Required Write Sequence
```

```
movwf   EECON2          ;  * - Required Write Sequence
bsf     EECON1, WR      ;  * - Required Write Sequence, Start
bsf     INTCON, GIE     ;  Interrupts can now happen
btfsc   EECON, WR       ;  Poll "WR" waiting for Write to Complete
 goto   $ - 1
bcf     EECON1, WREN    ;  EEPROM Write Completed
```

At the end of this sequence, the byte will have been written into the EEPROM. Instead of the polling loop, an EEPROM write interrupt can be enabled which will interrupt the code when the write has completed.

As I was researching this book, I found a reference stating that if the EEPROM isn't being used in an application, the EEADR and EEDATA registers can be used as file registers. While this is certainly true (for both these two registers and other full 8-bit hardware data registers that are not being used), I would like to discourage this practice because with some registers, unwanted hardware operations may be initiated. I highly recommend that you do not use any registers for any purpose in the application other than what they are designed for.

Input/Output

Along with the digital I/O pins, the PICMicro has a number of I/O functions built in which will simplify the software effort required to interface to other devices. These functions are not available in all devices, although with the PICMicro, there are enough combinations and permutations to find a PICMicro that is well matched to the application's requirements.

PARALLEL SLAVE PORT

The parallel slave port feature of some PICMicros will allow you to interface a PICMicro easily to a microprocessor. This feature can be very useful to have if you are designing a system and you need a bused peripheral quickly (and don't have the time, money, or human resources to develop an ASIC).

When the parallel slave port is enabled, PORTD is devoted as an 8-bit read/write register (with the PICMicro writing values to be read by the microprocessor and it reading values written to the PICMicro). The operation of PORTD is controlled by the three control pins in PORTE. (Figure 25.19.)

If the PICMicro is to interrupt the "master" microprocessor, an I/O pin from PORTA, PORTB, or PORTC would be used to drive a microprocessor's interrupt request bit directly.

The only deficiency that I can see with this arrangement is the lack of additional registers for simplifying reading and writing multiple bytes or creating multiple features in the PICMicro. If this is to be implemented in the micro's parallel port mode, then either a communications protocol has to be designed for the 8-bit ports, or the external I/O pins have to be used for this feature (with the master microcontroller updating a parallel out port before writing/reading from the PICMicro).

SERIAL DIGITAL I/O

On some PICMicros, hardware has been provided to allow the PICMicro to communicate serially with other devices. While the serial interfaces described here can be emulated in

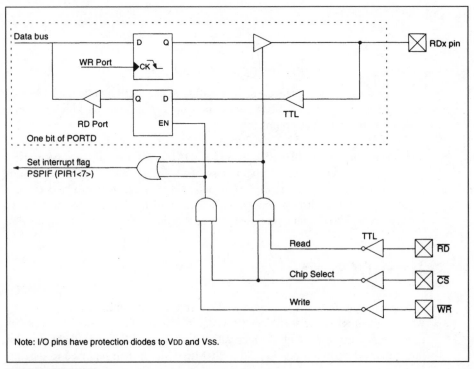

Figure 25.19 Parallel slave port implementation.

software on the PICMicros that don't have the hardware, this section will give you an idea of how the built-in serial communications hardware works.

SYNCHRONOUS SERIAL COMMUNICATIONS

The synchronous serial port ("SSP") module, available on midrange and high-end PICMicros, allows transfer of data along with a clock to implement a number of different protocols. The SSP has quite a complex block diagram (Figure 25.20).

The purpose of the SSP is to allow the PICMicro to behave as a SPI master/slave, an I2C slave, or an interface to an external synchronous serial I/O register (i.e., as is done in some of the example applications for the LCD data being driven by a serially loaded register).

In other microcontrollers, a synchronous serial controller can usually behave as an I2C master, the SSP does not have the circuitry necessary to generate the clock signals needed to master the I2C signals. If a I2C bus must be implemented, it can be done either by programming bits manually ("bit-banging") or by using the TMR2 output for driving the I2C clock and "fooling" the SSP that it is an I2C slave (when in fact you are using it to generate master's signals).

Microchip has recently released parts (the 17C5x family) which support full I2C mastering, but this has not been made available in midrange parts with the SSP. For this reason, if you want to get maximum performance out of synchronous serial parts (i.e., EEPROMs), then SPI should be used instead of I2C.

ASYNCHRONOUS SERIAL COMMUNICATIONS

The "SCI" (serial communications) or "USART" (universal synchronous/asynchronous receiver/transmitter) module is used to implement asynchronous serial communications in the PICMicro. The module really consists of two separate parts, a receiver and a transmitter, which are both driven by the user-programmable baud rate generator ("BRG").

As is implied in the "USART" name, synchronous data can be transmitted and received using the SCI. I have tended to shy away from this capability of the SCI module and used the SSP for this instead. (Figures 25.21 and 25.22.)

For the most part, the SCI module works exactly as expected and is quite intuitive in its operation. Data is transmitted once it has been written into "TXREG" and optionally interrupts the PICMicro when the data has been loaded into the "TSR" shift register (this will allow maximum speed transfer of a data string). Received data is placed into the RCReg and an interrupt request is initiated to indicate to the PICMicro that a byte has been received.

What may be a bit confusing is the operation of the BRG. The baud rate generator depends on an 8-bit register and an auxillary bit ("BRGH") for selecting the data rate to be used.

The formulas used to select the data rate are

```
Data Rate = Fosc / ( 64 * ( x + 1 ))   ;   If BRGH == 0
   x = Fosc / ( Data Rate * 64 ) - 1   ;   if BRGH == 0
```

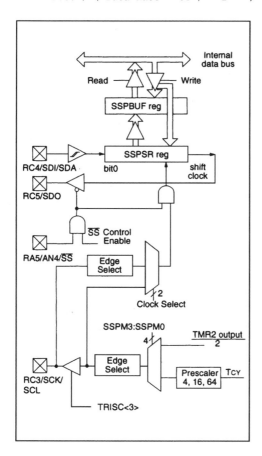

Figure 25.20 PICMicro SSP module SPI mode block diagram.

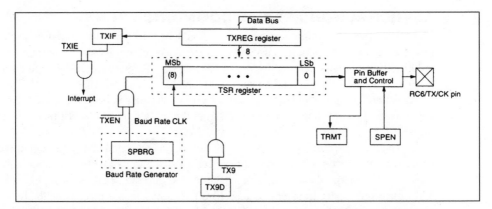

Figure 25.21 PICMicro SCI module asynchronous serial transmit module.

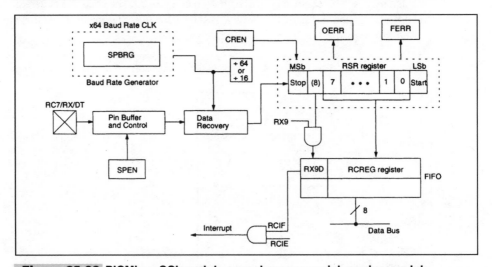

Figure 25.22 PICMicro SCI module asynchronous serial receive module.

```
Data Rate = Fosc / ( 16 * ( x + 1 ))    ;   If BRGH == 1
  x = Foxc / ( Data Rate * 16 ) 1        ;   if BRGH == 1
```

In early implementations of the SCI module, there could be problems if "BRGH" was set. To be on the safe side, you should keep BRGH reset. This is not a terrific hardship. At 10 MHz and BRGH reset, the PICMicro is able to send and receive from 1,200 to 76,800 bps.

The SCI can only receive/transmit data as positive logic. If you are receiving data from an RS-232 source and you are just using a current-limiting transistor to allow the PICMicro pins to handle the data, you'll find that the PICMicro's SCI will be unable to receive anything because the voltages will be inverted to what's expected. There is no circuitry internal to the PICMicro to invert the data.

ANALOG I/O

The 16C62x and 16C7x families of PICMicros have analog input and output capabilities. The method used for each family of devices is carried out differently. In the 16C62x family, a reference voltage is compared to, while in the 16C7x family, the actual voltage is read using a successive approximation algorithm.

Finding the best "general" analog input/output solution is difficult because of the varying requirements of different applications. The PICMicro analog I/O features will work in a variety of situations, ranging up to many audio frequency applications, but are not acceptable for very high speed situations.

16C62x—VOLTAGE COMPARISON

The 16C62x family of devices has an analog input voltage comparator circuit that can be used in a variety of different combinations of inputs, as well as rely on a voltage ladder DAC voltage output. Using a comparator is largely limited to applications that switch at a specific value (i.e., a thermostat responding to a temperature converted to voltage as either above or below a set point).

In the 16C62x, there are two comparators that can be operated in up to 10 different ways. The circuit used for a single 16C62x comparator can be represented as Figure 25.23.

There are two parts to this diagram that you should be aware of. The first is the input multiplexer ("I/P Mux"), which is used to select the inputs of the comparator. There are 10 different modes (including all the bit combinations) that the input multiplexers can work in to select the inputs for the comparators. (Figure 25.24.)

The second part of the comparator circuit to discuss is the voltage ladder and "16:1 Analog Mux." Like the input multiplexor, this is drawn very simply in Figure 25.23. The voltage ladder can produce voltages in two ranges.

If the "Vrr" bit of the "VRCON" register is set, the output voltage can be specified as a fraction of Vdd.

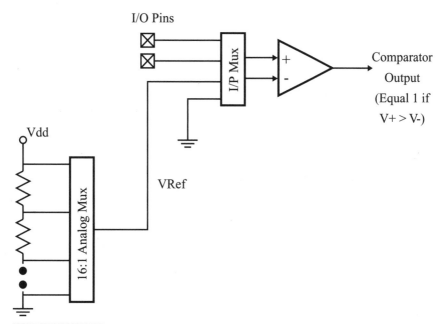

Figure 25.23 PIC16C62x voltage comparator block diagram.

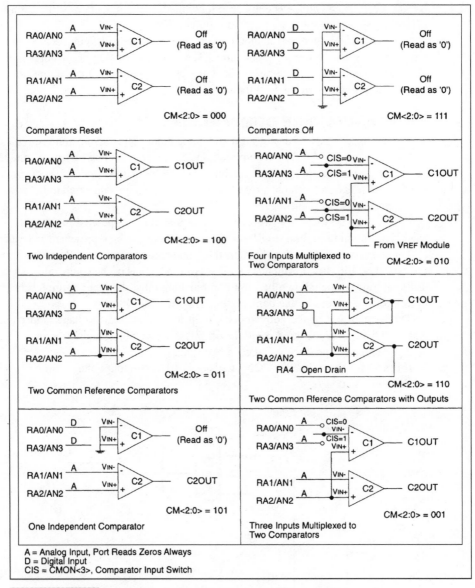

Figure 25.24 PIC16C62x voltage comparator I/O operating modes.

if Vrr == 1 then 2/3 Vdd >= Vout >= 0

if Vrr == 0 then 3/4 Vdd >= Vout >= 1/4 Vdd

As would be expected for a comparator, the response time is very fast (in the tens of nanoseconds) and can be typically polled for real time response or the output used to request a hardware interrupt.

The big disadvantage of the comparators is that they cannot be easily used for determining an input voltage level. A binary search routine could be used with the analog Vref.

For example, if you had an unknown voltage between 1.5 volts and ground on pin RA0/AN0 and Vdd was equal to 5.0 volts, the following code could be used to determine it:

```
Compare
   movlw     2              ;  C1 has RA0/ANO
   movwf     CMCON
   movlw     0x09F          ;  Use FSR to access VRCON rather than
   movwf     FSR            ;   changing RP0
   clrf      INDF           ;  Vref, is Not output and Start Low V
CompareLoop                 ;  Loop Here Until Vref > VIn (RA0)
   btfsc     CMCON, C1OUT   ;  If C1 High, then Input is at Gnd
    goto     CompareEnd     ;  End the Check
   incf      INDF           ;  Add 0.2V to Check
   goto      CompareLoop
CompareEnd                  ;  VRCon has the
```

Now there are more efficient methods of determining the voltage, but this method will show you how it can be done simply by increasing the voltage by 0.2 volts (Vdd / 24) until "VRef" is greater than Vin (at the RA0/AN0 pin). An obvious improvement to this algorithm is to use a binary search rather than just incrementing the VReg mux select.

16C7x—ANALOG INPUT

The 16C7x devices allow reading of analog voltages using an internal integrating ADC. The ADC can either use an internal voltage reference or an externally produced one to select the voltage range. The internal ADC voltage reference allows measuring voltages from 0 volts to Vdd.

Operation of the 16C7x's ADC is largely automatic, but there are a few considerations to be made when using the 16C7x parts. The first and probably most basic is that the I/O pins used for analog measurements are initially set to analog input mode on the PICMicro's power-up. In your software, one of the first things that has to be done is to set the appropriate pins to analog input. This is done by writing to ADCON1 (address 0x09F).

The next consideration is the "sampling" time available for the ADC. The ADC takes the voltage to compare to by using a capacitor (labelled "CHOLD" in Figure 25.25). "CHOLD" requires a certain amount of time to charge/discharge to the input voltage. This is done by closing switch "SS."

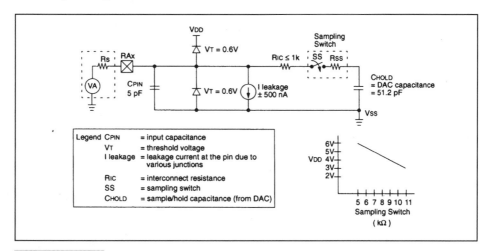

Figure 25.25 PIC16C7x ADC analog input model.

The length of time needed to allow the voltage on the capacitor to settle is given by the formula:

$$Tacq = \text{Amplifier Settling Time} + \text{CHOLD Settling Time}$$
$$+ \text{Temperature Coefficient}$$
$$= 5 \text{ us} + Tc + ((\text{ Temp - 25C }) * 0.05 \text{ us/C})$$

where

$$Tc = -\text{CHOLD} (\text{RIC} + \text{RSS} + \text{RS}) * \ln (1 / 512)$$

All of this is pretty complex, and I tend to avoid it wherever possible. If you can keep your source impedance to less than 10K and are operating at room temperature (25C), then an acquisition time of 15 usecs can be used safely (actually, the calculation works out to less than 12 usecs, so there is a good margin to make sure that the CHOLD capacitor is at the correct voltage).

Once the capacitor has the correct voltage, the ADC operation can be initiated. When doing this, a clock source has to be selected ("TAD"). This can be either run at 2, 8, or 32 times the instruction clock frequency or use an internal RC oscillator clock. Determining the correct value for the conversion is done using a table available in the device's datasheet (the parameters are not the same for all devices).

Typically, an analog comparison takes between 1.6 and 2.0 usecs to complete. This means that the entire ADC operation can take place in less than 20 usecs (which means the maximum sampling frequency is greater than 50 kHz).

The advantages of the 16C7X analog input measurement is that the measurement is totally internal to the workings of the PICMicro and independent of software. In the 16C62x family, if you are trying to measure a voltage, VRef has to be changed in software in some kind of algorithm to determine the correct Vin. The 16C7X analog-to-digital converters also have the advantage that voltages greater than Vdd can be measured. The disadvantages of this method of voltage measurement include the time required to have the circuit sample and hold the input voltage.

Configuration and ID Fuses

Something that sets the PICMicro apart from other microcontrollers is the use of the "configuration fuse register." This register is used to determine the oscillator type to be used, power up and reset options, external memory configuration, and control store protection. ID fuses are available to allow the user to indicate the device configuration or serial number.

The configuration fuses are located in control store in locations that the processor cannot normally access (for the low end they are located at address 0x0FFF, for the midrange they are located at address 0x02007, and for the high end they are located at address 0x0FE00 to 0x0FE0F) which means, except for the high end, they cannot be read during program execution.

Actually, what I've written here is pretty confusing. Before I try to straighten out what I've written above, I want to explain what kind of features are available in the configuration fuses. For each different PICMicro (including those in the same families), the configuration fuse bits (and states) are different, so unless you are going to use predefined definitions for the oscillator and other configuration (i.e., in an "include" device definition file, which I highly recommend), you should consult the datasheet for the PICMicro device.

The "RC" oscillator configuration selection is used for the RC oscillator network. The RC network is connected to the OSC1 pin, and OSC2 will output the instruction clock (the RC clock divided by four). "LP" is low power mode and is designed to run up to 100 kHz (normally a 32.678-kHz watch crystal is used for this mode). "XT" is the general-purpose oscillator and will take a crystal up to about 10 MHz. "HS" is meant for high speed applications that require greater than 10-MHz clock speeds. The speeds that I've quoted here are approximate, and the PICMicro part datasheets should be consulted for the correct options.

For Reset, many of the newer PICMicros have the capability to control the processor's reset internally ("MCLRE" used to disable the "_MCLR" pin and allow it to be used as an Input pin) or provide a power up timer ("PWRTE" specifies a 72 msec power up wait for the oscillator to stabilize and "OST" which waits an additional 1024 cycles to allow the clock to stabilize before allowing the processor to begin execution). Along with these options, some PICMicros have a "Brown Out" sense circuit (enabled by "BODEN") which will put the PICMicro into Reset when the voltage at _MCLR goes below 4.0 volts.

The control store memory (the application program) that has been burned into the PICMicro can be protected by using the "CP" bit. When enabled, if you want to read out the PICMicro's control store contents, they are read out XORed with the adjacent locations. This allows a programmer to compare to a known good program, but makes it virtually impossible for someone else to recreate the program.

Just a note about the "CP" bit. In newer EPROM devices, this bit is protected by a metal layer over the EPROM cell. This is to make it opaque to Ultra-Violet erasing light. This also means that if you have a JW (windowed) part that has this bit accidentally set, you may not be able to reprogram the control store. For this reason I recommend only using a programmer that takes the configuration bits from the object (hex) file and does not rely on the user setting or resetting the configuration bits manually.

The control store memory configuration in the high-end devices is specified by the configuration bits as well. These bits will select between microcontroller mode (only internal control store used), enhanced microcontroller mode (internal control store used along with external memory), and microprocessor mode (only external memory used).

As I mentioned in the paragraph describing the code protect bit, I want to reiterate that I highly recommend that a programmer is used that picks up the configuration bit values from the object file and are not programmed manually. While the worst thing that can happen is that the device cannot be reused, not correctly programming the configuration fuses can turn into a real pain because the device will not operate correctly. This is the number one problem that you will encounter as you begin working with the PICMicro; you'll be debugging a program and trying out a new version when everything stops working. The first thing you should check is the configuration fuses; chances are they've been programmed incorrectly.

The ID Fuses (located at addresses 0x0200 to 0x0203 for the low-end and at addresses 0x02000 to 0x02003 in the midrange) are used to store device serial number or code version information (usually in the form of a checksum). I generally don't play around a lot with these values (typically, they are loaded with the code checksum by the programmer) because they cannot be ready by the processor. The ID locations have a full twelve or fourteen bits available to be written to, but by convention only the bottom four bits are used. This means that the four ID fuse locations can be used to save 16 bits of information.

You may have noticed two things. The first is that I haven't talked about the address space from 0x02004 to 0x02006 in the midrange device and I haven't mentioned ID locations for the high-end devices. Addresses 0x02004 to 0x02006 can be used as additional ID fuses (the first 4 bits were specified to offer some level of compatibility with the low-end devices) or can be used to test the programmer function (i.e., make sure the part is properly seated in its socket) before programming any critical addresses.

The reason why I haven't mentioned ID fuses in the high-end devices is because they aren't implemented. ID values can be simply implemented in control store as data words and read by the processor using the "TABLRD" instruction.

Programming

A real cottage industry has developed in the design and sale of midrange PICMicro programmers. This can be attributed to the ease in which the devices can be programmed and the minimal circuitry and imprecise timings required. In my first book, *Programming and Customizing the PIC*, I jumped on the bandwagon and designed my own programmer. The midrange PICMicros use a simple synchronous serial protocol while the low- and high-end devices utilize a parallel protocol, which requires more hardware to program a device.

The synchronous serial protocol is available in both the midrange devices as well as the 8-pin devices (the "12Cxxx" family) and only requires five connections between the PICMicro and the programmer. (Figure 25.26.)

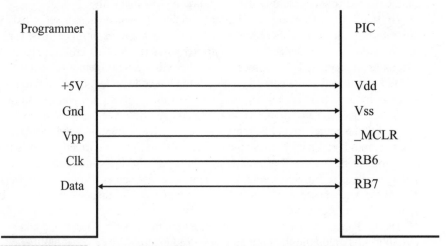

Figure 25.26 Midrange PICMicro serial programming interface.

All signals are at typical TTL/CMOS logic levels (0 to +5V) except for the _MCLR pin, which is driven with a 0 to +12 V (or more) voltage, which puts the PICMicro into programming mode. This simple connection for programming allows quite simple in-system programming ("ISP"). The data to be programmed into the control store is serialized (lsb first) with a command sent first.

The data stream looks like (for the 16F84) Figures 25.27, 25.28, and 25.29.

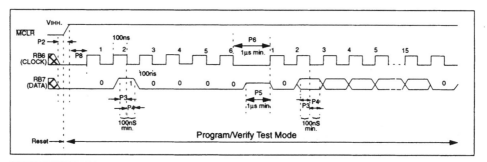

Figure 25.27 Midrange PICMicro serial programming load data command.

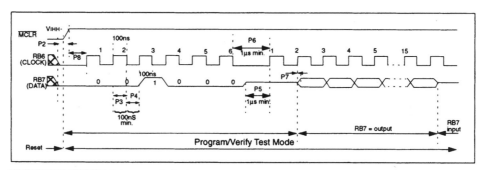

Figure 25.28 Midrange PICMicro serial programming read data command.

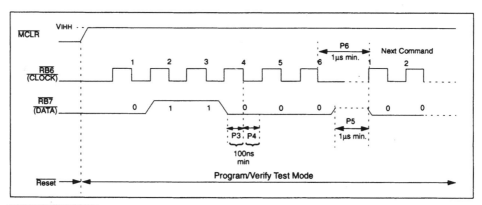

Figure 25.29 Midrange PICMicro serial programming increment address command.

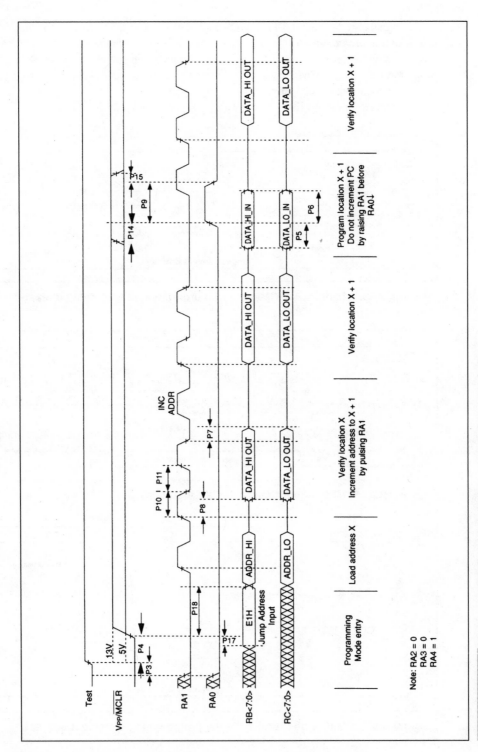

Figure 25.30 High-end PICMicro parallel programming waveform.

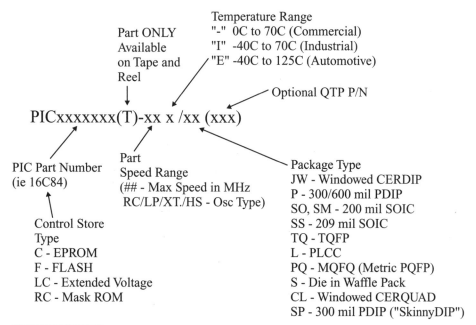

Figure 25.31 PICMicro part number definition.

The address of the data is not sent to as a command, but the PICMicro's internal program counter is used to keep track of the current address to program. If an address (or block of addresses) is not to be programmed, then the program counter is simply incremented.

When configuration data is to be sent, a special command is sent to set the program counter to 0x02000 (where the ID and configuration fuses are located). The low- and high-end devices use a parallel protocol in which the entire instruction (12 or 16 bits long) is transferred all at one time.

Like the midrange parts, the high-end PICMicro's internal program counter is used to keep track of the current address being written to. In Figure 25.30, you can see "RA0" being pulsed to increment the program counter. The configuration word of the low-end parts is located at the first location to be programmed, while for the high-end devices, the configuration word is made up of individual locations at the end of program memory (starting at 0x0FE00).

I just want to reiterate one last point on programming and the configuration word. In the PICMicro (especially with newer ones) when developing code, be very sure of what you are programming into the configuration word. If you accidentally program the code protect ("CP") bit, you may find that you are unable to erase it.

Ordering Information

Determining which part number to specify when ordering a PICMicro for an application or product is very consistent across the entire line. In Figure 25.31, please note that not all the options presented are available for each part.

PICMICRO APPLICATION DESIGN

CONTENTS AT A GLANCE

Power Input

System Oscillators and Clocks

Reset

Interfacing to External Devices
TTL/CMOS

Output Drivers

Interrupts

Application design for the PICMicros has been made a lot simpler by the robustness of the design and the attention to "real-world" operating conditions by the PICMicro developers. This means that developing applications for the PICMicro is fairly easy (which also means "cheap"). There are, however, a few rules that must be followed to ensure a successful and reliable application.

Power Input

In my own experimenting, I have found that PICMicros can handle a much wider range than they are rated at; I have run a PIC16C84 rated at 4.0 to 6.0V at 2.5V comfortably. But designing a product to run a 5-volt PICMicro at less than 5 volts for Vdd is definitely not recommended.

If you want to develop an application which uses battery (i.e., 2.5- to 3-volts) power, then you can use PICMicros designed for this voltage, or you can use a step-up power converter to provide 5 volts to the PICMicro.

But this doesn't mean that power can be taken for granted. The PICMicro requires a decoupling capacitor (0.1 uF) between Vdd and ground, because fairly large transients can be generated during high current output switching.

System Oscillators and Clocks

Along with a great deal of flexibility on power, the PICMicros can also use a number of different clocking schemes. These allow a great amount of flexibility in your application design and allow you to meet any specified requirements.

There are four different clocking modes. The first uses the charge/discharge cycle of a resistor/capacitor ("RC") network. The first type of oscillator/clock is best suited for low-cost applications where the actual timing is not critical (you can reasonably expect to be within 20% of the expected value with an RC oscillator). The target frequency is specified using the figures contained within the PICMicro datasheets. (Figure 26.1.)

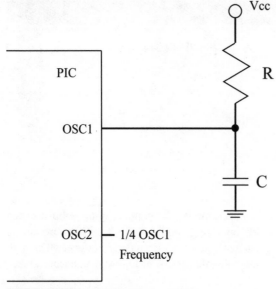

Figure 26.1 RC PICMicro clock.

Note: to ensure stable operation of the RC oscillator, the resistance value should be in the range 3K > R > 100K.

You will notice that I do not give a formula to allow you to specify the resistor and capacitor values for a given frequency. This is on purpose because a generalizing formula (like f = 2.2/RC) does not apply for the PICMicro because the charge/discharge path does not consist of only linear components. Instead, you should look at the data sheets for the PICMicro used in the application and use the recommended resistance and capacitance values for a given frequency from that.

Here is just such an example for the PIC16C84 data sheets:

C	R	FREQUENCY
20 pF	3.3K	4.68 MHz
	5.1K	3.94 MHz
	10K	2.34 MHz
	100K	250.16 kHz
100 pF	3.3K	1.49 MHz
	5.1K	1.12 MHz
	10K	620.3 MHz
	100K	90.25 kHz
300 pF	3.3K	524.24 kHz
	5.1K	415.52 kHz
	10K	270.33 kHz
	100K	25.37 kHz

There is no linear relationship between the capacitor and resistance values and frequencies.

The RC oscillator is optimal in applications where the timing is not critical but the cost is. If you wanted to use an RC oscillator (and the reasons for doing so would probably be focussed on the robustness of the oscillator compared to some of the other solutions), you could tune it for exactly the frequency you required. I would discourange this type of plan because the end result will not be very reproducible (imagine a modern, automated factory with dozens of people trying to match caps to resistors to PICMicros). If your application is going to see any kind of volume (say greater than one) and you require an accurate clock, you should look at the solutions below.

The 12Cxxx series of PICMicros (the 8-pin devices) contain internal RC clocks which can be used to drive the application. Typically, these clocks are accurate to 1-2%, using an internal "OSCCAL" register, loaded with a calibration that is set up when the part is tested at the factory. This method of providing the clocks has two advantages over more traditional methods. The first is that two pins are freed up and can be used for digital I/O, and the second is that the fewer parts will result in decreased application complexity and cost. Microchip has indicated that this feature will be available on future parts other than the 8-pin PICMicros.

26

MICROCHIP PICMICRO

The next step up from RC oscillators are "ceramic resonators," simple devices that give you much better accuracy than the RC (typically within 0.5% of the expected frequency). This accuracy will be good enough for most tasks that you require (including serial communications). The ceramic resonator has excellent mechanical durability, which makes it appropriate for applications that will be exposed to extreme environments.

The only designs in which a ceramic oscillator would be inappropriate is in applications where a very accurate timebase is required (i.e., a clock or something that plays music).

The clock that you are using must be identified before the PICMicro is programmed so the configuration fuses can be set. The RC oscillator uses its own specific configuration, while the other types of oscillators can use any of the three different specifications; the differentiator is the speed that is used.

Ceramic resonators are easy to set up and have a low part count. (Figure 26.2.)

Crystal oscillators provide the best in timing accuracy. These devices are still quite cheap and will give you outstanding accuracy. They are, however, a bit more finicky to set up (Figure 26.3).

Extreme care must be taken in using a crystal to ensure that the load capacitance for the circuit is correct. Compared to the other microcontrollers presented in this book, the PICMicro is quite particular about the actual value used in the circuit (the other devices presented here just require two 30-pF capacitors are the crystal pins). The following chart, taken from the PICMicro databooks, will give you an idea of what cap values should be used for different frequencies.

MODE	FREQUENCY	COSC1	COSC2
LP	32 kHz	33 - 68 pF	33 - 68 pF
	100 kHz	15 - 47 pF	15 - 47 pF
XT	100 kHz	47 - 100 pF	47 - 100 pF
	500 kHz	20 - 68 pF	20 - 68 pF
	1 MHz	15 - 68 pF	15 - 68 pF
	2 MHz	15 - 47 pF	15 - 47 pF
	4 MHz	15 - 33 pF	15 - 33 pF
HS	8 MHz	15 - 47 pF	15 - 47 pF
	10 MHz	15 - 47 pF	15 - 47 pF

As noted elsewhere, I have not had an application requiring Rs. If the PICMicro's oscillator doesn't start up reliably, you may want to experiment with an Rs value of 100 to 200 ohms.

Note: when checking the PICMicro clock signals, don't probe at OSC1, just OSC2.

The last type of clock that can be used for the PICMicro is a TTL clock. This can be provided from a specific oscillator "can," or from a convenient clock found in your circuit. In any case, only the OSC1 pin is used for hooking up the oscillator, which leaves OSC2 floating or unconnected.

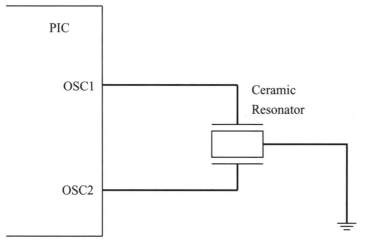

Figure 26.2 Ceramic resonator-based PICMicro clock.

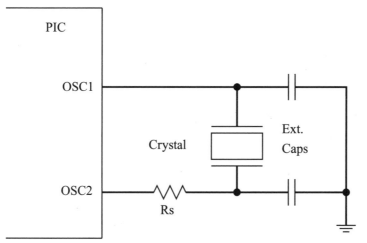

Figure 26.3 Crystal-based PICMicro clock.

Reset

Like power and clocking, reset can be very simple as well, as long as a few rules are observed. The _MCLR Line should be held low until power can be reasonably assumed to be good. There are a number of circuits that are good for doing this.

Using the built-in power-up timer may actually give you a chance to use no reset circuit at all! (Figure 26.4.)

The optional power-up timer (selectable in the configuration fuses) holds off the PICMicro reset for 72 milliseconds to allow power to stabilize. If you have an application with a very stable power supply (i.e., battery powered), you may want to forego using any type of reset circuit at all and just hold reset (_MCLR) to Vcc and let the PICMicro wait until the power is stable.

26

MICROCHIP PICMICRO

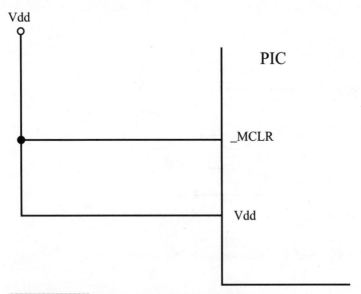

Figure 26.4 The simplest PICMicro reset circuit.

Even though _Reset can be connected directly to Vcc, I highly recommend putting a resistor pull-up between Vdd and _MCRL. (Figure 26.5).

This allows you to easily reset the PICMicro during debug by shorting _MCLR to ground (my tool of choice is a small screwdriver).

The power up sequence is shown in Figure 26.6.

If the resistor to Vdd reset circuit is used, the power-up reset timer "pwrte" (which causes a 72-msec delay between power up and the PICMicro running) bit in the configuration fuses should be set.

The _MCLR pin can also be driven by a standard TTL or CMOS driver for external control over the operation of the PICMicro. In some of the newer PICMicros, _MCLR is connected to brownout detection circuitry to simplify battery operation.

Interfacing to External Devices

In this section, I will discuss some basic types of interfacing and the rules that go along with them. The material will be at a very general level and can be applied to the other microcontrollers presented in this book.

TTL/CMOS

Obviously, interfacing to digital devices will be the simplest way of hooking up external devices to a PICMicro. The most basic way of doing this is moving the data in and out in a parallel or serial manner using the hardware provided in the PICMicro. This can be expanded for communicating directly with more than one peripheral device as required. There are a few rules for doing this.

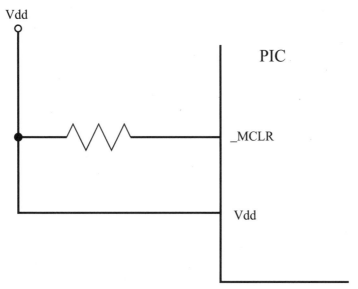

Figure 26.5 Typical PICMicro reset circuit.

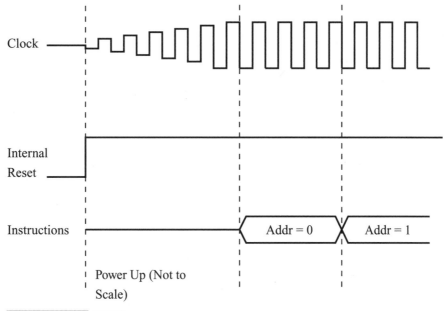

Figure 26.6 PICMicro power-up sequence.

Determining the type of bus is the first priority. A simple input or output bus can be accomplished easily. Implementing a bi-directional bus requires some arbitration rules for both input and output devices.

A parallel output bus is most easily implemented using device selects on the bused devices to address the device you want to talk to. This is similar to a "typical" microprocessor application after the addresses have been decoded.

26

MICROCHIP PICMICRO

Input from parallel devices can be done two different ways. The first is to use open collector drivers or switches pulling down to ground a pulled-up bus line. This is often known as a "dotted AND" bus (because when one or more devices try to drive the line active (low) then the line will go low, even if only one device is driving it). Using this type of bus does offer one significant advantage—multiple devices on one line can output data to the PICMicro simultaneously, making this type of bus particularly attractive for external interrupt sensing.

The second method of implementing the input bus is to use devices that have output that can be put in a high-impedance state. This means that when the PICMicro is ready to read from a particular device, it must indicate that it is ready for the device to drive the bus. The pin normally used on the peripheral device is called a "read" pin and is usually negatively active.

This method of inputting data is actually a simple processor bus, as shown in Figure 26.7 (with the PICMicro operating as an intelligent peripheral).

In implementing this type of input bus, there are a few things to watch out for. The first is you must make sure that all the devices on the bus can have their outputs put into a high-impedance ("high-Z") state. Any output drivers than can't go into a high-impedance state can result in "bus contention." The other important thing to check for is to make sure that all your devices can drive data for the length of time required by the PICMicro (and your software) to read it. This is important because some devices can only output data for a microsecond or two.

The code required to read a bus device would be:

```
bcf    CTL_PORT, _RD1   ;  Make the Read Bit Low
movf   DEV_PORT, w      ;  Read the Device Port
bsf    CTL_PORT, _RD1   ;  Turn off Device
```

Output Drivers

Creating a read/write (bidirectional) bus will involve using the instructions for the bus write and bus read (with High-Z drivers) with a few extra wrinkles. In the two unidirectional bus modes, the chip selects were used with the read/write pins on the peripheral devices. For a bidirectional bus, the chip select bits (usually negatively active) should be controlled independantly of the data bits and the read/write control bits.

I always return the PICMicro output port to "READ" (i.e., all the "TRIS" bits set) after completing a write. This will prevent any chance of bus contention due to the PICMicro driving the bus at the same time as one of the peripheral devices.

You may want to skip all this and use a high-end PICMicro (17C4x) in your application. The high-end series of PICMicros have an "extended microcontroller mode" and "microprocessor mode" in which peripheral devices could be put directly on an external PICMicro bus. These modes use a multiplexed address/data bus that complicates the design slightly.

This is a slightly different application than what is shown in the databooks. Putting peripheral devices on a processor's data bus along with memory devices is known as "memory-mapped I/O." You should note that in the diagram, the data bus only involves eight bits from each I/O device.

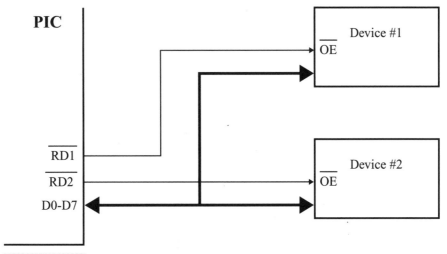

Figure 26.7 PICMicro parallel device interfacing.

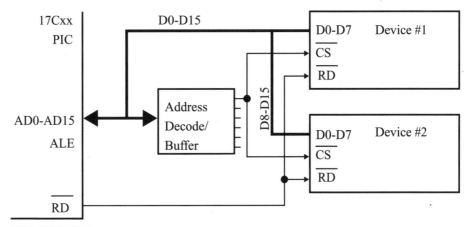

Figure 26.8 High-end PICMicro memory-mapped I/O.

Interrupts

In the previous chapter I explained in great detail how the interrupts in the PICMicro are implemented. In this chapter I will point out a few of the issues to consider when using interrupts with the PICMicro. The PICMicro has the most difficult interrupt subsystem of any of the devices presented in this book. It's not so much that the interrupts themselves are complex or difficult, it's just that they require a thorough understanding of how the architecture works before you try to implement interrupts. The gains in application performance, however, are well worth the effort of learning how to implement interrupts.

What I haven't talked about is nesting the interrupts. When an interrupt happens, the "GIE" (global interrupt enable) bit is reset. The bit is set back on (allowing interrupts to happen) after the "retfie" (return from interrupt) instruction is executed. It is possible to turn on the GIE interrupt during the execution of the interrupt handler. EXTREME care must be taken in making sure that the current interrupt status is not lost. The code presented in chapter titled "PICMicro Hardware Features," both for interrupt entry and exit will not be acceptable for this task. My recommendation in this case would be to use the index (FSR register) like a stack and save the important registers in a stack like fashion (using a different place for every interrupt entry). Doing this will allow the use of multiple invocations of the interrupt handler for the same interrupt.

Actually, my real recommendation would be to redesign your application to not require nested interrupts. The PICMicro is not an ideal architecture for doing this, and if it is required, you would probably be better off looking at the other microcontrollers presented in this book.

Interrupts, while being very useful programming constructs, can make your life much more difficult when you have time-critical code in your mainline (especially if you use a timer overflow to provide an RTC feature). If this is the case, you should disable interrupts before starting the time-critical code and re-enabling them as soon as it has been completed.

```
bcf    INTCON, GIE    ;   Disable Interrupts During Time-Critical Code
:                     ;   Minimum code Required for a function
bsf    INTCON, GIE    ;   Enable Interrupts
```

After interrupts are re-enabled, you shouldn't be surprised that the next instruction following the "bsf INTCON, GIE" is the interrupt handler. Interrupts will stay pending until the GIE bit is set, allowing them to execute. In a number of the applications shown in this book, having to turn off interrupts occasionally is often required to make sure that mainline code runs properly.

Please note that this code is not required inside the interrupt handler itself. In fact, if the GIE bit is enabled inside the interrupt handler, there may be a chance that you will have a nested interrupt (i.e., an interrupt that has begun processing while another is already executing), which would cause the context-saving registers to be lost.

To ensure this doesn't happen, the only instruction that should set "GIE" in the interrupt handler code is the "retfie" instruction.

MICROCHIP PICMICRO

DEVELOPMENT TOOLS

Like the other microcontrollers presented in this book, there are a multitude of vendors offering different tools for the PICMicro. I really haven't reviewed any of them for this book. This is not to say that I don't think there are good products from third parties (many of them are extremely good); I'm concerned that with publishing delays, I may not be able to accurately review the products and discuss the positive and negative aspects of them as they are when the book is published.

However, in this chapter, I will introduce you to the Microchip development tool offerings because they are a very complete line of development tools for the PICMicro that are very competent and have defined many standards for how the PICMicro is programmed (both in terms of instructions and device programming). Through these tools I will introduce how different tools generally work with the PICMicro and things to watch out for.

MPASM

Microchip's MPASM is a full-featured assembler available free of charge from the Microchip Web site (and the CD-ROM included in this book). MPASM is capable of generating code for all devices in the PICMicro line (including specifying configuration memory information), along with handling macros, conditional assembly, and outputting data for use by MPLAB. The capability to link object files has also been recently introduced by Microchip for MPASM and their "C" compiler.

If you were to print out the .pdf file that defines MPASM, you'd find that it runs about 100 pages long. As I present the characteristics of the assembler here, I will try to identify the most important statements and options available to help you become productive in writing MPASM source code.

I should point out that MPASM is available as an MS-DOS command-line executable program or a Windows GUI (able to run on all flavors of Windows and Windows emulators). This will allow you to develop programs on virtually any platform that supports MS-DOS or Windows execution.

Like most assemblers, MPASM takes data in a variety of formats. The first (and probably most important) consideration of numerics is what is the default radix (numbering system) used. In MPLAB, if nothing else is specified, the default radix is "hex" ("0" to "F"). I personally don't like this and I manually change this default in all my programs to "decimal" ("0" to "9") by using the "r" option in the "list" statement. For a PIC16F84, I use the following List statement:

```
LIST P=16F84, R=DEC        ;  Specify 16F84 and Decimal Numbers
```

The optional numbering systems are hexadecimal ("hex"), decimal ("dec"), and octal ("oct"). I use decimal because I find it easiest to think in decimal and then specify a different numbering system when appropriate.

Entering constants in different numbering systems can be done in the following ways:

NUMBERING SYSTEM	SYNTAX	COMMENTS
Decimal	D'###'	"0" - "9" is valid for Decimal Numbers
	.####	
Hex	H'##'	"0" - "F" ("f") is valid for Hex Numbers
	0x0##	
Octal	O'####'	"0" - "7" is valid for Octal Numbers
Binary	B'########'	"0" - "1" is valid for Binary Numbers
Characters	'#'	Any ASCII character Valid except for
		Special Cases (See below)

The special-case characters are the same as standard "C" "backslash" characters and and are defined as:

Character	Hex Value	Comments
\a	0x007	Bell (Alert)
\b	0x008	BackSpace
\f	0x00C	Form Feed
\n	0x00A	New Line
\r	0x00D	Carriage Return
\t	0x009	Horizontal Tab
\v	0x00B	Vertical Tab
\\	0x05C	BackSlash
\?	0x03F	Question Mark
\'	0x027	Single Quote
\"	0x022	Double Quote
\0##	N/A	Octal Number ("0" is Zero)
\x##	N/A	Hex Number

Strings can also be defined by placing the string inside double quotes (' " '). These will be discussed at greater length below with regards to the "dt" directive.

Another use for a string is to define a string in control store. The primary use of strings is to create a numbers of characters that will be used for a table. I will explain this later in this subchapter. A string can also be used to define data to be loaded into control store, but this is only really useful in the high-end (17Cxx) devices because each word consists of two bytes and can be read back using the table read and write instructions.

When creating a new PICMicro MPASM program, I use the following template initially:

```
 title "Program Name - Brief Description"
;
;   Initial Comments/Version information
;
;   myke predko - YY.MM.DD
;
;   PIC Connections
 LIST P=DEVICE, R=DEC

 INCLUDE "DEVICE.inc"  ;  Get the Microchip Device Standard Definitions
;   INCLUDE Standard Definitions
 ERRORLEVEL 0,-305      ;  Don't Print missing destination messages


;   Variables - Define Variables
 CBLOCK MemStart        ;  Define the Variables to be used
 ENDC

;   Mainline
 org 0

;   If Interrupt is use, put "int" label at address 4

 end
```

27

This template has all the most important features that are required in any PICMicro MPASM program. I should also point out that the comments and initial header is the format that I use for all my programming, not just for the PICMicro assembler.

The first line, the "title" assembler directive is used to identify the program in the listing file. In the listing file, the string in quotes is put at the top of each line in the file. For different sections of the program, the "subtitle" statement can be used to differentiate them. Because of MPLAB, I really don't feel I have much need to use or even save the listing file, but I make sure I put in a title line in case I do.

Along with the "title" directive, "page" is the only other assembler directive that I use with any type of regularity. "Page" will cause a "form feed" character to be placed in the listing file and a new page will be printed. This is very useful for putting subroutines and blocks of code in easily recognized parts of the code. There are a number of other directives for controlling the printing of the listing file (i.e., "NOLIST" and "LIST," which turn off and on the writing to the list file), but I really don't bother with them because they make formatting the listing file more complex, which is something that I really don't need when developing software.

The "LIST" directive is used to tell the assembler what the specified operating parameters and formatting options for the listing file are. In the template above, I just specify the PICMicro device and that I want to use decimal numbers by default. Other list parameters include the page length, tab, and other listing formatting options, the type of hex file output, setting the number of lines per page, enforce compatibility with previous (normally incompatible) versions, and control the message level. For the most part, I am happy with the defaults.

Many of these "LIST" options are available to you from the command line or the MPASM window. But I recommend not using any command line or window parameters. Instead, all desired operational parameters should be specified in the "LIST" directive in the source file so that they are repeated each and every time you assemble the source program.

The "ErrorLevel" directive is used to specify which errors, warnings, and messages are to be ignored. This directive should be used with care, in case legitimate errors or messages are masked (which could result in the program not working properly). Typically, I only use the "errorlevel 0, −305" statement, which suppresses the message when a destination isn't put on an instruction (in this case, the assembler defaults to ",f", which puts the result back in the source register). This isn't very critical because over the years, I have basically ignored adding ",f" or ",1" to the end of my instructions when I want to save the result in the source register; the exception is when I want to store the result in "w" and for that I always add ", w" to the end of each instruction.

Variables are defined easily in MPASM one or two ways. Variables in the PICMicro are really file register addresses. This means that they can be defined as constant equates:

```
i equ 0x0C                      ;  Define a Counter
```

While this works, I prefer using the "CBLOCK" command for defining variable addresses.

```
CBLOCK fileRegStart             ;  Define Variables at Start of file registers
i                               ;  Define a Counter
  END
```

Using "CBLOCK" is much simpler than defining (and maintaining) lists of equates (especially when you are defining, deleting, and adding variables), but there is one problem: using CBLOCK, only 8-bit variables can be defined. This means that you will have to define two variables for a 16-bit variable and it tends to become messier. For the previous example, if "i" was a 16-bit variable, the "CBLOCK" statement would become:

```
 CBLOCK fileRegStart    ;  Define Variables at Start of file registers
ilo, iHI                ;  Define a sixteen bit Counter
 ENDC
```

While this isn't a terrible hardship, I wish there were some way to identify a variable as 16 bits long in the CBLOCK statement.

If you are defining an array, then you should specify the starting address and then set the address passed to the CBLOCK statement to the address after the end of the array.

Comments (";") can be placed anywhere in the code, and everything to the right of the ";" character is ignored by the assembler.

At the end of the program, the "end" directive tells the assembler to ignore the rest of the source. "End" is not an optional directive and must be in each and every program.

Macros are a very useful aspect of MPASM for simplifying code development (and having to replicate sections of code). The general format for Macros is:

```
MacroName Macro Parameter[, ... ]        ;  Define the Macro
Local Labels                             ;   Define Labels inside the Macro

    :                                    ;   Instructions inside the Macro

    endm                                 ;  End the Macro Definition
```

Once the macro is defined, it is used to replace the line it is invoked on with the instructions and directives inside the macro. Labels used inside the macro should be defined first with the "local" directive. This will make the label specific to the macro and will not be used elsewhere in the program (even if it has already been defined in the mainline).

To simplify things, the "$" operator could be used instead of a label for the "goto" values. While I use it a lot in my PICMicro assembly programming, I don't necessarily agree with its use in other devices, where the instruction length may be different for different instructions.

```
Dlay    Macro    Count
  movlw  Count               ;  Save the Count Value for Counting Down
  movwf  i
  decfsz          i
  goto  $ - 1                 ;  If "i" != 0 then continue decrementing
 endm
```

While I tend to shy away from using a lot of esoteric MPASM extensions and directives (I try to stay as close to the instructions only shown in the data sheets), there is one enhancement to the assembler I do use a lot of and that's the "dt" directive. This directive will convert a number of constant parameters into a series of "retlw" instructions for implementing tables easily.

```
TableRead                           ;  Read the Table at the Index in "w"
  addwf          PCL
  dt             "Hello", 0
```

In the example above, the "TableRead" routine will be converted by the assembler to:

```
TableRead
  addwf          PCL
  retlw          'H'
```

```
retlw          'e'
retlw          'l'
retlw          'l'
retlw          'o'
retlw          0
```

The "dt" directive will allow you to implement string outputs easily without requiring a lot of useless instruction input. For the other microcontroller processors presented in this book, the "dt" directive is not required because tables can be defined as single bytes using the "db" directive.

Using conditional assembly, I can create code for debugging applications on a simulator without having to wait for long delays to execute:

```
ifndef Debug                       ;  If "Debug" Defined, don't Dlay 15 msecs
 call          Dlay5ms             ;  Wait 15 msec for LCD to power up
 call          Dlay5ms
 call          Dlay5ms
else
 nop                               ;  Put in 3 "nops" to keep addresses
 nop                               ;    constant
 nop
endif
```

In the example above, if the symbol "Debug" is defined, then three "nop" instructions replace the calls to delay 15 msec. I insert the three "nop"s to make sure that all the addresses below this section of code don't change between versions.

When I use code like this, I define the symbol from the command line (or the MPASM window). This is really the only case in which I specify parameters externally to the program. In the command-line version of MPASM, the "Debug" symbol is defined when MPASM is initiated by entering:

```
MPASM /dDebug Filename
```

In the Windows version of MPASM, these parameters are specified from a window. Figure 27.1 shows what this will look like when MPASM is invoked from MPLAB. Specific parameters can be entered into the "extra default options" space.

The first time you run MPASM, you will probably be amazed at the number of files produced. You probably thought that all that would be required to output would be a listing

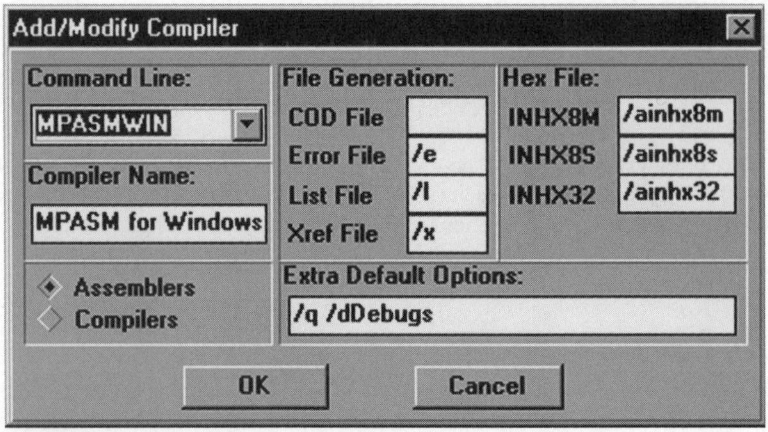

Figure 27.1 MPASMWin parameter window.

file and an object file used to program the device. Along with these two basic files, there is a ".err" and a ".cod" file. The ".err" is an error summary file.

The ".cod" file is a cross-reference file between the hex object file and the source so that symbolic debugging can be carried out by MPLAB or another symbolic debugger.

Recently Microchip has announced the capability of MPASM to create relocatable object files that can be linked together. Being able to create relocatable objects means that the libraries can be created and called from mainline routines.

While this is breaking topic a bit and deviating from exclusively discussing the Microchip development tools, I did want to mention some thoughts on the Parallax PICMicro assembler. In the "PICMicro Instructions" chapter, I introduce the Parallax PICMicro instruction set (which is designed to look like the i8051 instruction set). Like Microchip MPASM, the Parallax assembler is available free of charge and is used by a large number of people.

Personally, I feel that representing the PICMicro as an i8051 is undesirable. The reasons for this are primarily because STATUS registers and register contents can be changed unexpectedly. This prejudice also goes back to my experiences with IBM i8086 tools, which used different labels than the Intel standards, which meant that I ended up having to know two different instruction sets for the same processor. While I have never written code using the Parallax assembler, I fear that this is the case here as well; I would think that you will end up having to understand both the Parallax assembler and the Microchip PICMicro instruction set to truly understand what is happening in an application.

High-Level Languages

Of the processors presented in this book, the PICMicro's processor is the most difficult to develop a high-level language for. This is not to say that there aren't some very good compilers available, but they may seem high in price when compared to the compilers written for other devices. Much of this extra cost goes to the extra work required to write properly executing code for the PICMicro architecture.

In this subchapter, I will show some considerations in the development of high-level languages that must be taken into account when both choosing a compiler as well as what microcontroller to use. When I proofread this subchapter, I realized that many of the points that I have brought up here are not PICMicro specific but should be considered before choosing a compiler for any microcontroller.

I feel I can write about this with a reasonable amount of authority because of my experiences writing compilers for the PICMicro. From these experiences, I can discuss potential pitfalls to watch out for when developing your own compiler or choosing one already on the market. The first compiler I wrote was "C"-like with functions and produced MPASM-compatible source. The next compiler used a different syntax and produced INHX8M output (no explicit nesting cues like "{" and "}." Instead, the indenting of the source was used to select the current nesting level). In the last compiler (available on the CD-ROM with this book), I took great pains to make sure that all the different cases of midrange PICMicros were encompassed as well as providing a reasonable range of functions. Looking back at the compilers, the syntax of the language became simpler, but the capability of the created code became much more sophisticated. As well, I was able to think through how to implement different features and focus on what was most important for small embedded microcontroller applications.

The first major consideration of a high-level PICMicro language is determining how variables are stored. Most midrange PICMicros have file registers in bank 0 and bank 1. As part of this, a determination should be made on which bank is the "default" and which is the primary bank used by the compiler. Typically, I use bank 0 because the primary pin I/O data registers and peripheral function registers are located in this bank and, by keeping the variables in the same bank, there is no need to switch banks when accessing between I/O registers and file registers (which are used for reading and writing to external devices).

Going along with this philosophy is deciding where to put arrays. If the PICMicro has two banks, I always put arrays in bank 1. Typically, arrays are accessed using the "FSR" register, which can be up to 8 bits long and can access either bank 1 or bank 0 without having to change any operating control bits. Putting the arrays in bank 1 frees up bank 0 for single variables that can be accessed from the "default" state.

The last consideration of variables is how local (automatic) or temporary registers are implemented. In the compilers that I have written, I have placed them in an array and accesssed them either using explicit addresses or pseudo "push" and "pop" operations.

An example "push w" would be:

```
movwf INDF                    ;  Save the Contents of "w"
decf  FSR                     ;  Point to the next "stack" address
```

The disadvantages of this method are that the FSR must be used only for push and pop and it must be saved if arrays are to be implemented or if user assembler code is to use FSR. Because of this added complexity, in the latest compiler that I have written, I have virtually avoided using a "stack" altogether.

Following as a consideration for the compiler is how the current bank is kept track of. For example, setting up PICMicro I/O pins in "C" for an LCD could be done by:

```
PORTA = PORTB = 0;            //  Make Sure all I/O is Low


TRISA = TRISA & 0x018;        //  PORTA.0 = "E"
                              //  PORTA.1 = "RS"
                              //  PORTA.2 = "RW"

TRISB = 0;                    //  PORTB is Data Output
```

A simple compiler may produce the following code, which always keeps the PICMicro in bank 0.

```
clrf   PORTA                  ;  PORTA = PORTB = 0
clrf   PORTB

bsf    STATUS, RP0            ;  TRISA = TRISA & 0x018
movf   TRISA & 0x07F, w
bcf    STATUS, RP0
andlw  0x018
bsf    STATUS, RP0
movwf  TRISA & 0x07F
bcf    STATUS, RP0

bsf    STATUS, RP0            ;  TRISB = 0
clrf   TRISB & 0x07F
bcf    STATUS, RP0
```

But I would expect that a reasonably sophisticated compiler would produce the optimized code:

```
clrf   PORTA              ;   PORTA = PORTB = 0
  clrf   PORTB

  bsf     STATUS, RP0

  movlw 0x018             ;   TRISA = TRISA & 0x018
  andwf TRISA & 0x07F

  clrf   TRISB            ;   TRISB = 0
```

This second example takes half the number of instructions as the first (which obviously requires half as much control store and half as many instruction cycles to execute). Also, note that the compiled code leaves the processor executing out of bank 1, rather than returning to the default state (bank 0) after each access of a register in bank 1. When encountering either code for a bank 0 register or a "goto" or "call" instruction, then a "bcf STATUS, RP0" instruction could be inserted into the compiler's assembler output to return the processor back to the "default" bank.

The reason why I put the PICMicro back into the default bank before executing a "goto" or "call" is because at each label, there is a chance that each label can be accessed for several different locations. Making sure of the state before entering the location eliminates any concern about what bank the processor will execute in.

Another aspect of the PICMicro that complicates compiler design is the use of the "PCLATH" register and the inability to write directly to the full address space. This can make it considerably more difficult to implement something like the BASIC "if" statement:

```
if   i = 0 then Label
```

The most direct method of producing this code would be:

```
movf    i               ;   Set Zero Flag Depending on contents of "i"
btfsc  STATUS, Z
  goto  Label            ;   Goto "Label" if zero flag set
```

But if "Label" is in another code page (each code page is 2048 instructions in the midrange PICMicro), this code will force the compiler to add instructions.

Instead, my compilers have produced the following code for this case:

```
movf    i               ;   Set Zero Flag Depending on contents of "i"
btfss  STATUS, Z
  goto   Skip            ;   Skip Over Label Jump
  goto   Label           ;   Goto "Label" if zero flag set
Skip
```

With this code, I can add PCLATH modifiers easily, and if they aren't required, I can easily reduce the code to the example above.

Further complicating this is what happens in bit operations. The BASIC condition:

```
if   ( i & 0x080 ) == 0 then Label
```

Would be best compiled to:

```
btfss  i, 7             ;   Skip Next if Bit 7 of "i" is set
  goto  Label
```

But what would happen if "i" was located in bank 1, the "if" statement was located in page 0 (0-2047) and "label" was in page 1 (2048-4095)?

The code would probably look like:

```
bsf     STATUS, RP0
btfsc   i, 7            ;  Skip Next if Bit 7 of "i" is reset
 goto  Skip
bcf     STATUS, RP0     ;  Put the Code into Bank 0
bsf     PCLATH, 3       ;  Jump to Page 1
goto    Label
Skip
bcf     STATUS, RP0     ;  Go back to Bank 0 after all this
```

or (as I would prefer):

```
bsf     STATUS, RP0
movf    i, 0            ;  Get "i" for Compare
andlw   0x080
bcf     STATUS, RP0
btfss   STATUS, Z       ;  If i & 0x080 == 0 then Skip
 goto  Skip
bsf     PCLATH, 3
goto    Label
Skip
```

The reason why I would prefer the latter example is because the default bank has been selected before the jump, simplifying what has to be done before jumping to "label" (and making sure a known bank is selected upon finishing the instruction). To be perfectly honest, I prefer the latter way of implementing this instruction because it's easier for me to follow during the compiler development process and seems "cleaner."

Data (variable) size is another important consideration in PICMicro high-level languages. Most languages work with 8- and 16-bit data types. The larger and more varied the data types, the more complex the program becomes.

For example, the assignment:

$$a = b + c$$

could be coded as:

```
movf    b, 0
addwf   c, 0  movwf a
```

if all the variables are 8 bits. But if they are all 16 bits, the code becomes:

```
movf    b+1, 0          ;  Add the High Bytes together
addwf   c+1, 0
movwf   a+1
movf    b, 0            ;  Add the Low Bytes together
addwf   c, 0
movwf   a
btfsc   STATUS, C
 incf  a+1              ;  If Carry on Low Byte, Increment the Top
```

This becomes even more complex for 32 bits or when 8- and 16-bit values are mixed.

The last PICMicro processor quirk that will complicate the operation of a compiler is the "subtract" instructions.

This can be shown by:

$$a = b - c$$

In most compiler parsers, parameter scanning is done left to right. If this is done in the PICMicro, the code produced for this operation would be:

```
movf    b, 0
movwf   Temp[0]           ;   Store the value to have "c" taken Away From
movf    c, 0
subwf   Temp[0],0
movwf   a
```

For the compilers I have written, when I encounter a subtract operand, I reverse the order of the scan, so the code naturally becomes:

```
movf    c, 0
subwf   b, 0
movwf   a
```

How hardware registers are defined is an important aspect to how efficient a program executes. In "standard" "C," you cannot declare a variable to be at a specific address. Instead, you will have to define a register as a pointer to a specific address. If this has to be done, the compiled code will be considerably more complicated than if variable addresses could be defined explicitly with the variable declaration.

Built-in or linkable functions are something to be considered as well. For languages such as BASIC, there are a fair number of built-in functions. For this reason the BASIC compiled code may be much larger than you expect. Typically, I would only want a language that always had basic mathematical routines (including multiplication and division) and then linked in other routines as required.

Linkable functions are something to look at with a jaundiced eye. For a workstation or PC, they can make software development much easier. But in an embedded microcontroller where control store and other resources are at a premium, a complete suite of functions linked in may unduly restrict what the application can do. For this reason, you may want to use "canned" functions as little as possible, except for guides and examples of how to do things.

Now if the linker could only load in the functions that are required from the library, then this comment is obviously invalid.

The final consideration in choosing a compiler is what development tools it will work with. As I will show later in this chapter, "MPLAB" is really an excellent tool for developing software. For this reason, I highly recommend only looking at compilers that produce the ".COD" file which will allow symbolic debugging of the application.

There are a number of very cheap (and free) compilers available for the PICMicro. Most of these are designed specifically for the 16C84. Because the 16C84 (and the 16F84 follow-on) does not have any file registers in bank 1 and occupies one-half of a page of control store, developing a compiler for it avoids many of the issues presented above.

Right now, there are a lot of different compilers available for developing code on the PICMicro. The language of choice at the present time seems to be "C." These compilers range from free to about a thousand dollars. The higher the cost, the more extensive language features, support for built-in PICMicro features, and qualification that went into the compiler. A $100 BASIC compiler may be a good tool to use to begin working with the PICMicro (and using a 16F84). It is definitely not a good tool for developing code that can run on 16C74s or 17C44s. Because of this, I have to recommend that you research the various compilers and their current capabilities remembering the old adage:

"You get what you pay for and pay for what you get."

Microchip Application Development Tools

Like other microcontroller manufacturers, Microchip has a number of tools available for you to develop applications on their device. The Microchip tools are built around "MPLAB," which is an integrated development environment developed for Microsoft Windows/3.11 and Windows/95. "MPLAB," the assembler, and simulator are available free of charge from Microchip's Web site (and I have also included a downloadable version on the CD-ROM included in this book). (See Figure 27.2.)

MPLAB is a complete development environment that can be used to:

1. Develop and edit application source.
2. Simulate the application with external stimulus and modify internal registers.
3. Program a chip.
4. Provide a hardware emulator interface similar to the simulator.

MPLAB is a very sophisticated program that will make developing applications for the PICMicro much easier and much more efficient.

Along with MPLAB, Microchip also offers sophisticated secure control software in the form of "KeeLoq," which is an algorthim and PICMicro source for allowing external control of devices. Microchip also offers the "Fuzzy Tech" development system for simplifying the effort in developing fuzzy logic applications on the PICMicro.

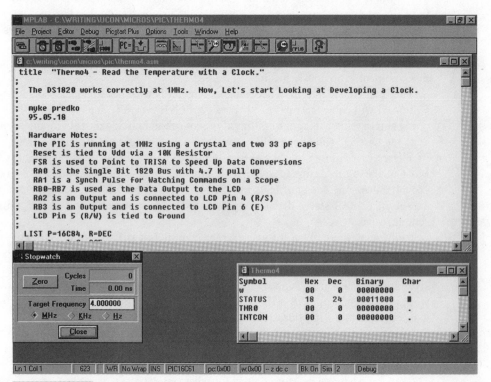

Figure 27.2 Microchip's MPLAB integrated development tool.

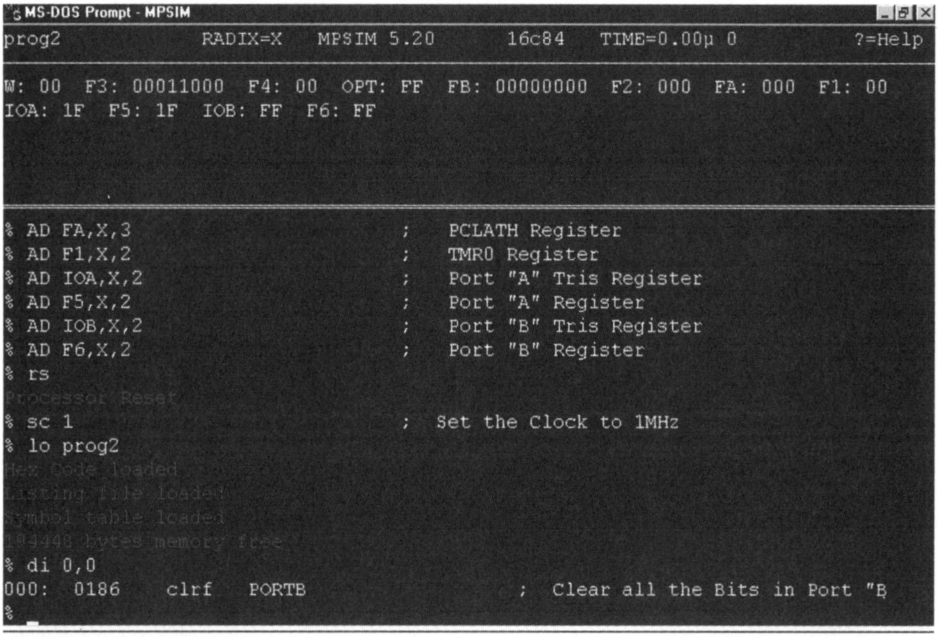

Figure 27.3 MPSIM operating screen.

MPSIM

"MPSIM" is a DOS command-line simulator for the PICMicro that is user configurable and takes the output of MPASM directly. Because MPSIM only requires the DOS command line, it may be preferred over MPLAB if you are running on an older (386 or less) PC or an emualated PC-DOS session. Personally, I much prefer "MPLAB" for application development and debug, but MPSIM does have some advantages over it in some respects.

Above I described MPSIM as being "user configurable." When you first read the documentation, you might feel as if I've exaggerated about this, but I can show you some tricks that I use to make debugging programs quite efficient and easier than is done in MPLAB.

Once invoked, MPSIM comes up the screen shown in Figure 27.3. The screen is broken up into three parts or "windows." The top part is a display of current simulated PICMicro status (including the software being run through the simulator, the PICMicro type and the current instruction count and elapsed time).

The "view window" is an area that is used to display user-specified registers. The registers and the format of the display are specified in the "MPSIM.INI," which I will describe in more detail below.

The bottom window contains a prompt for user-specified instructions as well as a display of the most current operations and their results.

When MPSIM is first invoked, it looks for a "MPSIM.INI" file. This text file is created by the user, and I use it to set up all the parameters used in the program. Here is an MPSIM.INI file I created some time ago:

```
;   MPSIM File for PROG2 - Turning on an LED
;
;   Myke Predko - 96.05.20
;
P 84                        ;   Use a 16C84
```

27

MICROCHIP PICMICRO

```
SR X                          ;  Hex Numbers in the Simulator
ZR                            ;  Zero the Registers
RE                            ;  Reset Elapsed Time and Step Count
DW D                          ;  Disable the wdt
V W,X,2                       ;  View the "W" Register
AD F3,B,8                     ;  Display: Status Register
AD F4,X,2                     ;    FSR Register
AD OPT,X,2                    ;    Option Register
AD FB,B,8                     ;    Intcon Register
AD F2,X,3                     ;    PCL Register
AD FA,X,3                     ;    PCLATH Register
AD F1,X,2                     ;    TMR0 Register
AD IOA,X,2                    ;    Port "A" Tris Register
AD F5,X,2                     ;    Port "A" Register
AD IOB,X,2                    ;    Port "B" Tris Register
AD F6,X,2                     ;    Port "B" Register
rs
sc 1                          ;  Set the Clock to 1MHz
lo prog2
di 0,0
```

In this file, I specify the device to be used, the default radix, the registers to be displayed, and the operating parameters. Any command that can be entered into MPSIM's user interface can be put into the MPSIM.INI file to simplify the initial state of the program. Along with the MPSIM.INI file, MPSIM produces the MPSIM.JRN file, which records all the keys entered in the simulation session. This can be useful for reviewing what was done to find a problem and will be discussed in more detail below.

Comments (after ";") are supported, but "whitespace" is not. If a blank line is put into the MPSIM.INI file, the previous instruction will be repeated. This is due to the user interface of MPSIM, which repeats the last instruction if the "Enter" key (which sends a carriage return character) is pressed. This feature is very useful when debugging a program and you are single stepping through it, but it is a pain if you are identifying registers to add to the display window.

One comment about setting up MPSIM.INI files. I try to use the same "header" in all files. This header consists of specifying the same basic registers each time MPSIM is used. These registers consist of the "w," STATUS, "FSR," "OPTION," "INTCON," and "TMR0" registers. I liken it to an airplane cockpit; on every instrument panel, there are six basic instruments; in my MPSIM screens, I always display the same basic registers in the same format.

The MPSIM instructions are:

Ins	Parameters	Comments
AB		Abort Session. The Journal file isn't changed
AD	Reg[,radix[,digits]]	Display the register in the "View" Window in the specified numbering system and the Number of Digits
		Numbering Systems: "X" - Hex "B" - Binary "D" - Digit
B	[address]	Set a Breakpoint at the current or specified address

	Reg Op Value	Set a Breakpoint when the "Reg Op Value" is true. Op: = - Equal > Greater than < Less than >= Greater than or equal <= Less than or equal != Not equal
BC	[addr	Reg]	Clear the Breakpoint. If no address or Register specified, all breakpoints are cleared.
C	[#break]	Continue executing from the current Program Counter. If "#break" is specified execution will execute through the specified number of breakpoints.
CK	pin, { hi, low }	-	Define a clock signal at a specific Pin. The clock is "hi" and "low" the specified number of cycles. The parameter "-" stops the clock.
DB		Display all the active breakpoints
DE	addr1, addr2	Delete Program Memory (Control Store)
DI	[addr1[, addr2]]	Display the Program Memory
DK	#, { Pin, State}	-	Define "Alt-F#" key to input the specified pin state as High, Low, Toggle, or Pulse ("H", "L", "T", or "P"). "-" turns off the "Alt-F#" key function.
DL	Symbol	Delete the Symbol
DM	[addr, addr2]	Display Program Memory numerically (not as instructions)
DP		Display all the Patches
DR		Display all the Registers
DS		Display the Symbol Table
DV	Reg	Delete Displayed Register in View Window
DW	[E	D]	Enable/Disable the WDT
DX		Display Current Trace Parameters. If in "Trace Mode," display the current state of the program's execution.
E	[addr]	Execute the program from either the current address or the specified one.

EE	addr	Modify EEPROM Data Memory. This is only appropriate for Micros which have EEPROM Data Memory.
EL	0 |1 | 2	Specify which Messages/Warnings/Errors are to be displayed during program execution.
F	Reg	Display the contents of the Register and prompt the user to change it.
FI	fn, addr, Reg[, n] |-	Input the next (or "n" specified) value in the file into the register.
FM	addr1, addr2, value	Fill unused program memory with the value.
FW	MC | EM | MP | RC256 | RC64 | RC | OSC	
		Specify the 17Cxx operating modes
GE	fn	Get the Filename and execute the instructions. This is a way of loading in a .INI file of commands.
GO		Reset the simulated PICMicro and begin executing.
GS	Symbol, value, type	Create a symbol of Type file ("F"), bit ("B"), label ("L") or literal ("K").
H		Display the Help Screen
IA	addr	Insert Assembly code starting at "addr"
IN	addr, instruction	Insert the Assembly Instruction at the specified address.
IP	[time | step]	Input stimulus acording to the "step" value in the Stimulus file.
IR	ALL | RAM | SFR	Randomize Register contents (either as "ALL" or the file or special function registers).
LJ		Load and execute the current Journal File. This is a method of repeating the instructions previously saved in the MPSIM.JRN file.
LO	fn	Load the .HEX and .COD file into MPSIM.
LR	fn	Load the register values
LS	fn	Load the external Symbol File
M	addr	Display the Program Memory starting at "Addr" and prompt the user to input changes. Entering "Q" will end the command. Entering "-" will move back and repeat the operation at the previous command.

NV		Everything is removed from the View Window.
O	fn	Output the patched .HEX file. *While I am including this command, I really don't recommend using it. I'm always very nervous of creating an object file that doesn't have any source to go with it.*
P	device	Select the PICMicro to be Simulated.
Q		End MPSIM and save the instructions in the Journal file.
RA		Restore the Patch Table, Symbol Table, and delete breakpoints.
RE		Reset the elapsed Time and Step Counters
RP		Restore the Program Memory to its original, unpatched condition.
RS		Reset the Simulated PICMicro.
SC	length	Specify the Instruction Cycle to be used in usecs.
SC	length	Specify the Instruction Cycle to be used in usecs.
SE	pin I port	Display the pin or port. The user is prompted to change the value.
SF	addr1, addr2, reg	Find the first useage of the specified register in program memory in the address range.
SI	addr1, addr2, ins	Find the first useage of the specified instruction in program memory in the address range.
SM	addr1, addr2, ins	Find the first useage of the specified instruction and display without symbolic information.

As seen in the example MPSIM.INI file above, after setting up the display and operational parameters, I load in a specific hex file and display the first instruction. After this, I usually load in the current file to execute and display the first instruction (which isn't done naturally by MPSIM).

When these instructions are entered during an MPSIM session, they are recorded in a file called "MPSIM.JRN" and this file can be used to help build an enhanced MPSIM.INI, which can be used to either help characterize a specific error or enable you to get to the location again very quickly after trying out a fix in the code.

For example, if after some time debugging, you discover that the defective code takes place five instructions after "Some_Label" in the code, the MPSIM.INI file could be enhanced by cutting and pasting the relevant lines from the journal file to the end of MPSIM.INI:

```
b "Some_Label"          ;  Put in Breakpoint at the instruction
e                       ;  Execute the program to the Breakpoint
ss                      ;  Execute five instructions to the problem
ss
ss
ss
ss
```

I haven't talked about stimulus files yet. These files are used by MPSIM and the MPLAB simulator to provide a repeatable input condition to the program to observe how a PICMicro will respond to these commands. An example file for testing a program's response to a button being pressed is:

```
!   TEST3.STI - Simulate a Couple of Key Presses
!
!   This File Is used for checking Button Read and Debouncing
!
!   Myke Predko
!
!   96.09.08
!
 STEP    RA3
    1      1       ! Make Everything High
  500      0       ! Now, Have the Button Pushed
 1000      1       ! Bouncing, Skip the Problem
 2000      0       ! Button Pressed Again
10000      1       ! Button is Released
```

The stimulus file consists of a set of states that start at a given step count. To get the correct step for a specific time, I use the formula:

$$\text{Step} = \text{Delay} \times \text{Frequency} / 4$$

The stimulus file can access any pin in the PICMicro (defined in the format "RA0" where "A" is the Port and "0" is the pin). "_MCLR" is used to represent the reset pin. The exclamation point ("!") character is used, commenting out everything to the right of it. White space can be used in a stimulus file.

While MPSIM is not a bad program, there is one major deficiency in it, in my opinion, and that's the lack of being able to display all the assembler instructions of the hex file. When I am debugging an application, I like to be able to see the "big" picture and see what is coming up. For this reason, I prefer the simulator in MPLAB to MPSIM.

MPLAB

MPLAB is one of the best integrated development environments available for any microcontroller. Along with containing an editor, assembler, and simulator, MPLAB can interface with the Microchip PICStart Plus Programmer and PICMaster Device Emulator. Optional high-level languages can be used for development with this tool as well. Lastly, MPLAB is capable of handling the application development, simulation, emulation, and programming of any PICMicro device, which means that only one version of MPLAB is required for all PICMicro application development needs.

The best part of MPLAB is that it is available free of charge from Microchip from their Web site (and a copy, current to the time of writing, is available on the CD-ROM that comes with this book).

The first time you see MPLAB operating (as in Figure 27.4), you will probably be turned off by the amount of complexity it has. But, after a while working with MPLAB, you should be able to set up a screen as you like it and become very proficient in developing applications with it.

MPLAB is written to work from Microsoft Windows 3.1(1) or Windows/95. While the software operations (editor, assembler, compiler, and simulator) will work under most other Windows emulators (i.e., Windows/NT or "SoftWin" for the Macintosh), the hardware peripherals (i.e., PICStart Plus and PICMaster) will not.

The MPLAB screen is broken up into four parts. The top line ("1") is a series of "pull-down" menus used to specify MPLAB operating parameters. The area ("2") below the top line is a "tool bar" consisting of a series of buttons that are used as quick controls to the operation of MPLAB. There are three or four different groups that can be selected, each one dedicated to a different function. I typically leave MPLAB set up with the simulator buttons (which are identified by the red and green "lights" at the left-hand corner of the selection). To select the different groups of buttons, the left most icon is clicked until the desired set of buttons comes up.

The center part of the screen ("3") consists of an area to load in operational windows (i.e., editors, memory displays, the stopwatch, or Watch Windows) and can be configured in any way that works best for you. As can be seen in Figures 27.3 and 27.4, I like to keep the different windows fully displayed.

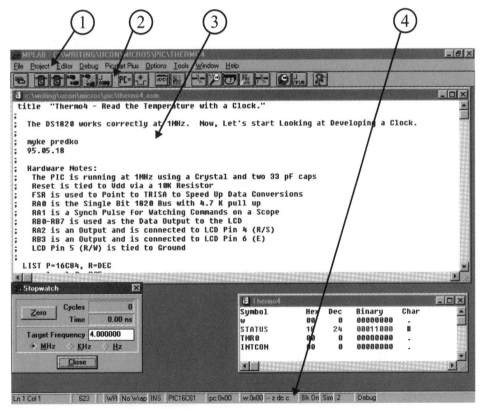

Figure 27.4 MPLAB function areas.

27

MICROCHIP PICMICRO

The bottom of the screen ("4") consists of a line indicating the current status of MPLAB. This status information consists of the current row/column of the active editing window, the PICMicro type, and the current (simulated or emulated) program counter, "w," and "STATUS" register contents.

Applications being developed under MPLAB are known as "projects," with each project consisting of the source files used for the application and the current MPLAB window settings. Creating a project is carried out by clicking on the "Project" pull-down menu and then clicking on "New Project" (this is typically identified as "Project" -> "New Project"). After this is selected, you will be prompted to specify the project's name followed by the names of the source files associated (which means they have to be assembled/compiled) with the project. The source files can be brought up in an editor window through "File" -> "Source."

Once you have loaded a source file, it can be edited using standard Windows GUI operations (i.e., to "cut" a marked section, the keystroke "Ctrl-X" is used). Multiple editing windows can be active at the same time. The editor accesses Window's clipboard so data can be passed between files and applications.

With the application source file created and edited, you can begin simulating the file after it compiles and assembles cleanly (compiler and assembler operations are specified under the "project" pull down). Before simulating a source file, it is imperative that you have the correct device specified. This is done by selecting "Options" -> "Development Mode" and then selecting the correct PICMicro for "Simulator Mode."

The window to select "Simulator Mode" ("MP-SIM") or "Editor Mode" looks like Figure 27.5.

As is implied by this window, you can select between having the simulator active or enter something called "Editor Mode." I always leave MPLAB with the simulator active ("Simulator Mode") except when I am modifying control store directly (this is something that's done quite a bit for 12C5xx's for their calibration value) or writing to an "F" device's EEPROM Data Memory.

Figure 27.5 MPLAB simulator device selection.

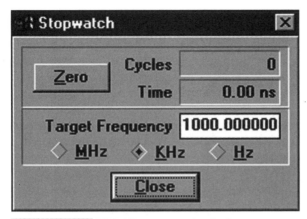

Figure 27.6 MPLAB stopwatch window.

While "Editor Mode" can be used for patching a device's control store, I really don't recommend using it for this purpose. Instead, during development, if you want to "patch" a device's code, I recommend making a copy of the current source and changing this and then reprogramming the device. I'm not a big fan of patching code directly; I've seen too many cases where somebody was patching firmware to try to fix a problem, fixed it, and then couldn't remember or recreate the changes made that fixed the problem so they could modify the source code.

There are two types of windows brought up to aid in debugging when using the simulator or the PICMaster. The first is the "stopwatch" window, which is used for keeping track of the current number of instruction cycles. Timing critical parts of applications can be checked over by setting the "target frequency" and then "zeroing" the count at the start of the code to be timed. (Figure 27.6)

The "watch" window is the other type of window dedicated to debugging applications. This is a special type of window that will display the current contents of registers (both hardware and file). When a watch window is created (clicking on "Window" - > "New Watch Window") you are prompted for selecting file register labels or addresses to be monitored during simulator execution. The watch window is shown circled in the bottom right-hand corner of Figure 27.7.

Adding variables to the end of the list in the watch window is done simply by clicking on the square in the upper left-hand corner of the window or pressing the "Insert" key (variables in the watch window are deleted by moving the cursor to the desired line and pressing "Delete"). If a 16-bit variable is to be displayed, enter "%%" after the variable name. Otherwise, the variable (or address) will be displayed as an 8-bit variable.

The MPLAB simulator uses the same format stimulus files as MPSIM. The stimulus files use events specified by the instruction count (which is displayed in the stopwatch). "Zeroing" the stopwatch will cause the data picked up from the stimulus file to start from the beginning.

When using the simulator (or PICMaster) and single stepping through an application, the current line is highlighted. If you are using a compiled language, you may want to also display the "program memory" contents (selected by clicking on "Window" - > "Program Memory") to see what the compiler produced for code at different locations or even the listing file. No matter what file is given precedence (the coloured bar at the top of the window), the highlighted bar will appear and allow you to follow what is happening.

27

MICROCHIP PICMICRO

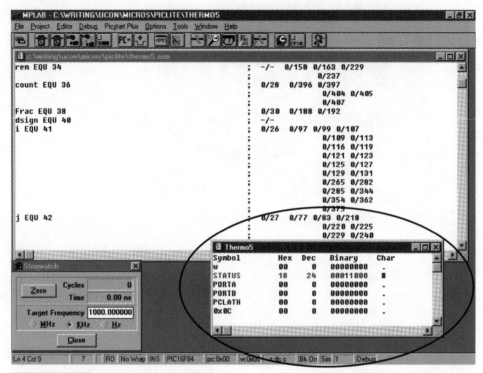

Figure 27.7 MPLAB watch window.

When programming in assembly language, I very rarely pull up the listing file or program memory display. There really isn't any reason to do this because the listing file adds line numbers, addresses, and op codes, which takes up space that could be used for instructions or comments. The program memory also has this information but doesn't have the symbolic (label) information. This is not to say that these files shouldn't be displayed when you are debugging high-level language applications, because you may want to look at what the compiler produced.

Breakpoints and "Run to Here" can be easily selected with the mouse. First the cursor is moved to the line you want to stop execution at (which is what both operations do). This is done by moving the mouse to the desired line and clicking the left mouse button. Next, the right button is pressed and the type of stop is selected. The "Trigger" and "Trace" options that you will see is to be used with the PICMaster emulator to specify when an operation (such as a code execution trace) is to begin operations.

One disappointing aspect of the MPLAB simulator is the speed it runs at. On my PC (a 133-MHz Pentium), the simulator executes about 300 PICMicro instructions per second. This means that a 0.1 second delay on a 4-MHz PICMicro will take over five-and-a-half minutes to execute on the simulator.

To try to avoid having to wait an unreasonable amount of time for delays and such, I will build in conditional code that is keyed to the presence/absence of pseudolabel (which is usually "Debug"). For example, if I had a delay with a 16-bit counter, I would write it as:

```
Dlay                        ;  Delay routine, Wait for hardware to be set up


  ifdef Debug
    movlw 1                 ;  Short Delay
    movwf Count
    movwf Counthi
  else
    movlw 77               ;  Unreasonably Long Delay
    movwf Count
    movlw 123
    movwf Counthi
  endif

  decfsz Count             ;  Delay Loop
   goto  $ - 1
  decfsz Counthi
   goto  $ - 3

  return
```

When this code is compiled and the "debug" pseudolabel is present, then "1" will be loaded into "Count" and "Counthi" and allows it to run very quickly. Otherwise, the full delay value is loaded into "Count" and "Counthi."

Looking at this, you're probably wondering why I just don't take out the code inside the "if" instead of making it run in a minimum number of cycles. The reason is because I want to have the same number of instructions in the debug code as in the application code. Differences in the size of the programs may result in problems when I want to change the operation of the code.

Once I have a program I have simulated and think will work, I burn it into a PICMicro microcontroller using the "PICStart Plus" programmer. This device is controlled by (and only works with) MPLAB. (Figure 27.8.)

The PICStart Plus control window looks like Figure 27.9. The PICStart Plus window is used for controlling the configuration fuses of the PICMicro. As I have said before, I highly recommend setting the configuration fuses in your program (using the "_CONFIG" directive) rather than setting them manually from this window.

A small hint: when you are ready to program a PICMicro, start up the PICStart Plus and then assemble/compile your code. When the assembly/compile completes, you'll see the configuration flags in the programmer window blink and go to the correct values. This will eliminate any chance of making an error in programming your part. The number-one error made when first starting out with the PICMicro is incorrectly setting the fuses, which means the device is apparently not executing the application because it is being reset by the WDT very quickly or the wrong oscillator type has been chosen.

When a PICMaster is connected to the PICMicro (via an interface card that is plugged into an ISA slot) it uses many of the same interfaces as the MPLAB simulator (and is selected in "Options" -> "Development Mode"). Along with the standard options, the PICMaster can be used to trace execution of the program based on specific conditions (i.e., "trace" or "trigger" points).

The PICMaster can be used to trigger external devices (i.e., oscilloscopes or logic analyzers) or can be used to trace the instruction execution flow. This is done by setting a "trace" point at a specific point in the program. Once this has finished executing, the "trace memory" can be examined to see how the program actually executed.

27

MICROCHIP PICMICRO

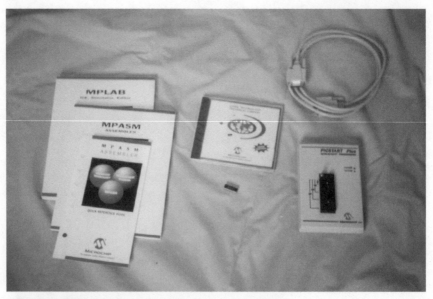

Figure 27.8 PICStart plus development system.

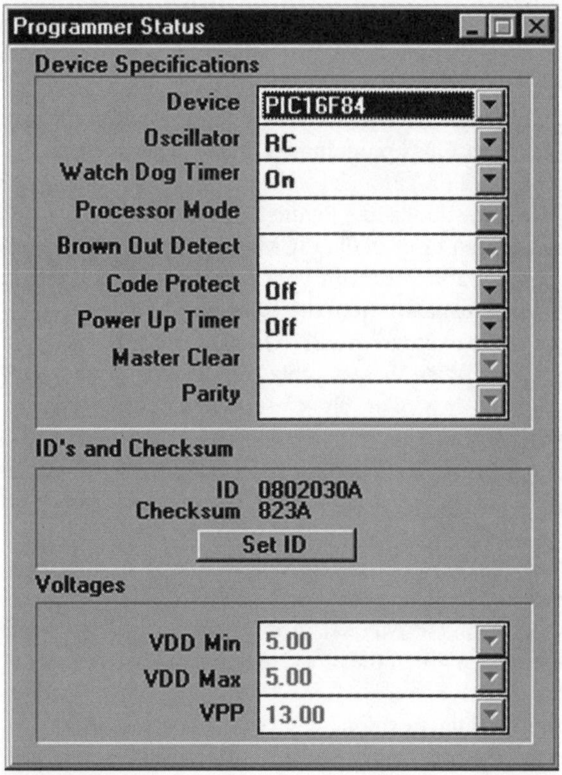

Figure 27.9 PICStart plus programmer control window.

In this subchapter, I've really done little more than explain the basic features of MPLAB as well as PICStart Plus and PICMaster. Like most well-written GUI programs, MPLAB is best learned over time and with experience. You can find your own shortcuts and preferred methods of operating the program. With the directions I've written here, you can at least get started with MPLAB and the PICStart Plus and PICMaster. I highly recommend printing out the .pdf files that will explain MPLAB and the hardware devices and going through them before attempting to use the products.

KEELOQ

Microchip's "KeeLoq"(TM) development system is a security algorithm for allowing control of hardware devices over media that can be monitored by third parties. My car's theft alarm uses a KeeLoq-equipped PICMicro in the locking/unlocking "fob" and in the car itself. The fob transmits a seemingly random number to the receiver and increments to a new (pseudo) random value for the next time a signal is to be sent.

Each fob/receiver combination has a unique linear feedback shift register to create a pseudo-random number based on a specific "seed" value. I like to think of the pseudo-random number generator like a wheel with a large number of points on it. When you are at any point on the wheel, you can figure out what is the next value as it rotates.

When the transmitter sends a signal, the receiver checks it against its wheel and responds if it is equal to the value at the next value on the wheel. If it isn't, the receiver marks the place and identifies the next point on the wheel. If the next time the transmitter sends a value and it matches the next expected value, then the receiver responds.

The reason for the receiver checking over the incoming signal and the chance that something is missed is because the transmitter's signal may be lost or garbled in the receiver (or, like me, you may have a small child that likes to push buttons—any buttons).

Now I have really simplified this and probably missed some very important points of how KeeLoq works. But this is okay because if you would like to use KeeLoq technology,

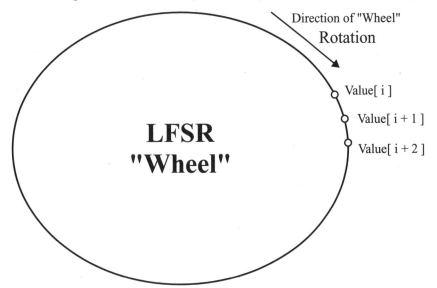

Figure 27.10 KeyLoq pseudorandom wheel.

you will have to sign a nondisclosure agreement with Microchip. KeeLoq is quite complex and is able to handle a number of different cases (such as sending different commands to the receiver) that I haven't discussed here.

FUZZY TECH

To help you develop your own fuzzy logic applications, Microchip has created "Fuzzy Tech." This tool will allow you to easily (and graphically) create fuzzy logic applications. Included in the kit is a simple demonstration board consisting of a resistive (ohmic) heater and a temperature sensor (thermistor). This demonstration board can be used to set up a first fuzzy logic application for a potentiometer (desired temperature setting), the temperature sensor, and the PWM heater output.

Fuzzy Tech creates MPASM-compatible output that can be integrated into the application code. The fuzzy-logic interface is only limited by the resources available in the PICMicro.

If you go through "Fuzzy Tech," you will discover that the rule generation still has to be done manually (although entered into the system through the Fuzzy Tech Microsoft Windows GUI) and then the system creates the output code. The application programmer is responsible for the interfaces to external hardware as well as any other functions to be put into the PICMicro.

"Fuzzy Tech" does not turn the PICMicro into a fuzzy logic device tailored to a specific application. Instead, it provides source code to be used as a fuzzy logic control for given inputs as an enhancement to the application.

THE PICMICRO INSTRUCTION SET

In this chapter I have primarily presented the midrange device's instruction set. Most of these instructions are common to the various PICMicro families, but there are some unique instructions for the 17C4X (high-end) architecture. These instructions are presented later in the chapter along with the Parallax PICMicro instruction set. The instruction bit definitions presented in this chapter are for the midrange PICMicros. If you are using the low- or high-end devices, then the proper bit patterns will have to be looked up in a Microchip datasheet, although the format of the instructions is similar between the different families.

Register Arithmetic Instructions

Register arithmetic operations (also known as "byte-orientated file registers operations" by Microchip) are the instructions used in the PICMicro to transfer data between registers as well as carry out mathematical operations on the data within the registers. This is a ten-dollar way of saying that these instructions move data around in the PICMicro as well as combine it arithmetically with other data.

If you first look through the PICMicro instruction set, you will probably be very surprised to see how limited it is (30-plus instructions are listed for the low- and midrange devices), but once you have experience with it, I think you'll be impressed with how powerful it is, and you will see that you are able to carry out a wide range of operations. Part of this flexibility is the ability to specify operation destinations. The PICMicro can often carry out operations in single instructions that would require two or more in traditional processors.

Part of the flexibility of the instruction set is the different ways in which registers can be accessed. The instructions described in this section can read and write all the registers in the PICMicro. Register addresses are specified in the instruction itself as a 7-bit number. Therefore, data can only be accessed within the current bank ("RP0" and "RP1" are used to specify the current bank). Data can also be addressed by the "FSR" (index) register by accessing "INDF" pseudoregister (at Address = 0). The PICMicro is unusual in that indexed addressing uses exactly the same format as direct addressing—the register address specified activates the indirection hardware.

The "movf" instruction is used to set the zero flag according to the contents of the register and can be used to load the "w" register with the contents of the specified register. (Instruction 28.1.)

This may seem like a weird way of describing the instruction, but it is actually quite accurate in what the instruction does. Like the other register arithmetic operations, the result of "movf" can be stored in the "w" register.

But if the "movf" instruction is specified with putting the source back into its register (i.e., a "movf reg, f" instruction), what is it actually doing? It's loading up the value from the register, checking it in the ALU to see if it is equal to zero and then putting the value back. So, in this way, I think of the primary function of "movf" as being used to set the zero flag. The secondary function of the instruction (because this is optional) is to load "w" with the contents of the source register.

The "movwf" instruction is used to store the contents of the "w" register into the specified file register. If the register is "INDF," then the destination will be the address pointed to by the "FSR" register. No status bits are affected during the execution of the instruction. (Instruction 28.2.)

The PICMicro processors have instructions which can be used to explicitly clear various registers. The "clrf reg" instruction places zero in the specified register. "clrw" places zero in the "w" register.

One thing to remember about the clearing and "movf" instructions is that they also set the zero flag. This may cause problems for you, if you are trying to maintain a status for later program execution. For this reason, you should plan on only using the carry flag as a passed status between routines, becuase it is affected by fewer instructions than the zero flag. (Instructions 28.3 and 28.4.)

The arithmetic operation that probably first comes to mind is addition. In the PICMicro, addition is carried out in a very straightforward manner, with the result produced as expected. (Instruction 28.5.)

All the operation bits are affected by the operation. The zero flag is set if the result ANDed with 0x0FF is equal to zero. The carry flag is set if the result is greater than 0x0FF (255).

The digit carry flag is set when the sum of the least significant four bits (also called a "nybble") is greater than 0x0F (15).

For example, if you had the code:

```
movlw  10      ;  Add  0x00A to 0x00A
movwf  Reg
addwf  Reg, w  ;  Put the Result in "w"
```

The "w" register would contain 20, "Reg" would still have 10 and the zero and carry flags would be reset (equal to zero) and the digit carry flag would be set.

Subtraction in the PICMicro is something that you should look over and understand thoroughly before you use it. (Instruction 28.6.)

Looking at the instruction sheet, you'll probably be completely confused about the operation of "subwf." The best way to explain subtraction in the PICMicro is to note that it is not subtraction at all. Instead, it is adding a negative value to the source.

So, instead of "subwf" being:

$$\text{Destination} = \text{Source} - \text{"w"}$$

It is actually:

$$\text{Destination} = \text{Source} + (\ -\ \text{"w"}\ )$$

The negative "w" term of the equation above is done by substituting the "2's" complement negation formula:

$$\text{Negative} = (\ \text{Positive} \wedge 0x0FF\ ) + 1$$

This means that the subtraction formula above now becomes:

$$\text{Destination} = \text{Source} + (\ \text{"w"} \wedge 0x0FF\ ) + 1$$

I find that when I am using the instruction it helps to remember this formula, because I can easily understand what "subwf" is doing and predict how it will behave.

Remembering this formula also helps me to understand how the carry flags work. Looking at the instruction (above), the carry and digit carry flags probably run counterintuitively to what you expect (and may have experienced with other processors).

For example, what happens when you subtract 2 from 1 in the PICMicro. I.e.,

```
Source       = 1
"w"          = 2
Instruction  = subwf Source, w
```

To try and understand it, we use the formula above and plug in the values for "source" and "w" getting:

$$w = 1 + (\ 2 \wedge 0x0FF\ ) + 1$$

Following it through, we get:

$$w = 1 + (\; 0x0FD \;) + 1$$
$$w = 1 + 0x0FE$$
$$w = 0x0FF$$

This is what we expect. But note that the carry flag would not be set, which is NOT what we expect from a typical processor. In a "true" subtract instruction, you would expect that the carry flag would be set in this example (typically "carry" becomes "borrow" in other microprocessors).

Now, for the same example, where:

$$\text{Source} = 2$$
$$w \quad = 1$$

We can follow the formula:

$$w = 2 + (\; 1 \; ^\wedge \; 0x0FF \;) + 1$$
$$w = 2 + (\; 0x0FE \;) + 1$$
$$w = 2 + 0x0FF$$
$$w = 0x0101$$

0x001 (0x0101 & 0x0FF) is actually stored in "w." But note that in this case of subtracting a lower value from a higher value, the carry flag (and, possibly, the digit carry flag) is actually set!

For this reason, after a "subwf," "sublw," or adding a negative number, I like to refer to the carry flag as the "positive" flag instead of a "borrow" flag.

If you look at the explanation of the instruction, it should now make a lot more sense.

The bitwise operations "andwf," "iorwf," and "xorwf" allow you to do the basic logical operations on the bits of a register. Probably the "and" and "xor" operations will be familiar to you, but Microchip has elected to call the "or" as "inclusive or" (i.e., "ior"). This works the same way as the traditional "or" you are familiar with. (Instructions 28.7, 28.8, and 28.9.)

The contents of the register specified are operated on with the contents of the "w" register. The zero flag in the status register is set or reset depending on the condition of data following the operation.

If you wanted to check the contents of a register, you could load "w" with zero and then XOR it with the contents of the register to check. If the contents were the expected value, the result would equal zero and the zero flag of the STATUS register would be set.

For example, jumping to a specific location if PORTB is equal to 0x0A5 would be accomplished by:

```
movlw    0x0A5      ;   Get the Check Value
xorwf    PORTB, w   ;   XOR it with the Expected Value
btfsc    STATUS, Z  ;   Do we Have a Match?
 goto    PORTB_A5   ;   ·Yes, Execute the Specific Code
```

The "comf" instruction is used for inverting all the bits in the source register. Following a bit in the footsteps of the "subwf" instruction, I want to note that this instruction does NOT negate a number (in 2s complement format). (Instruction 28.10.)

A negative can be produced using the "comf" instruction knowing that:

$$\text{Negative} = (\text{Positive} \wedge 0x0FF) + 1$$

The "comf" instruction is equivalent to XORing a value with 0x0FF. So to negative a file register:

```
comf    Reg
incf    Reg
```

Or if the result should be in "w" and the source not touched, the code would be:

```
comf    Reg, w
addlw   1
```

This sequence will only work with PICMicros that are able to execute the "addlw" instruction (namely the mid and high-range PICMicros).

The "swapf" instruction exchanges the nybbles in a file register. As with the other instructions in this section, the destination of this exchange can either be the "w" register, or the source register itself. What truly makes this instruction special, however, is the fact that none of the status flags (carry, digit carry, zero) are affected. This last feature makes "swapf" useful in some circumstances. (Instruction 28.11.)

From strictly a data movement point of view, the "swapf" instruction can be used for two purposes. The first is to allow the application program to store two digits in a single file register, swapping between the digits depending on which one you want to work on. The second is to do a fast four-position shift (either left or right, depending on which nybble you AND with 0x0F the result with afterward).

I often use "swapf" to separate a byte into two nybbles (4 bits each) for displaying. For example, to output a byte in hex format, the following code would be used:

```
swapf   Byte, w     ;  Get the High Nybble
andlw   0x00F
call    PrintHex    ;  Print It out

movf    Byte, w
andlw   0x00F
call    PrintHex    ;  Print the Low Nybble
```

One of the most useful things the "swapf" instruction can do for you is make sure that status registers are not changed when loading "w." This takes advantage of the fact that "swapf" does not change the current status register contents after execution. (This is typically used in the restoring of the context registers before returning from an interrupt).

The rotate instructions are useful for a number of reasons. Their basic function of rotate is to move a register 1 bit upward and downward, with the least significant value being loaded from the carry flag, and the most significant value put into the carry flag. (Instructions 28.12 and 28.13.)

The rotate instructions can be used for doing multiplication and division on a value with powers of 2. This can also be done on 16-bit values. The following example shows how to multiply a 16 bit number by 4:

```
bcf     STATUS, C   ;  Clear the Carry flag before Rotating
rlf     Reg, f      ;  Shift the Value over (mul by 2)
rlf     Reg + 1, f
bcf     STATUS, C   ;  Now, Repeat to Multiply by 2 again
rlf     Reg, f
rlf     Reg, f
```

Other uses include shifting data in or out serially and positioning a byte so individual bits can be tested.

Increment ("incf") and decrement ("decf") are used to change the value in a register by 1. (Instructions 28.14 and 28.15.)

Following the completion of an increment/decrement, only the zero flag is changed. You may have expected the carry flag to change state (if the value goes over 0x0FF for inc or below 0 for dec), but that isn't the case.

This means that incrementing or decrementing a 16-bit number isn't quite as straightforward as you might expect. Actually, I should change that. The 16-bit decrement isn't as straightforward as you would expect.

The 16-bit increment can be done by:

```
incf    Reg, f          ;  Increment the Low Byte
btfsc   STATUS, Z       ;  Are we at 0?  (Low = 256)
 incf   Reg + 1, f      ;  Yes, Increment the high
```

Because the zero bit is set when the low byte is equal to 0 (or 256, or any multiple of 256), we know when to increment the high byte of the 16-bit number.

The decrement isn't quite so simple. If a value reaches zero during a decrement, then all you've got is zero, and zero does NOT indicate that the high byte should be decremented. Therefore, you must actually use an instruction that changes the carry flag after the low-byte decrement to ensure that you know when to decrement the high byte. This is done by subtracting one from the low byte, rather than decrementing it, like so:

```
movlw   1               ;  Load "w" Register with Sub Value
subwf   Reg, f          ;  Subtract it from the Low Byte
btfss   STATUS, C       ;  Is the Carry Bit Set?
 decf   Reg + 1, f      ;  No-we rolled over, decrement High Byte
```

Along with the bit test instructions (described below), there are two other instructions that skip on a given instruction. They are the increment/decrement skip if the result is equal to zero. (Instructions 28.16 and 28.17.)

These two instructions work exactly the same as the incf and decf instructions in terms of data processing. One is added or subtracted from the source register. This value is then stored either in "w," or back in the source register. The important difference to these instructions is that if the result is equal to zero following the increment/decrement, the next instruction is skipped.

This means that decfsz and incfsz can be used for loop control operations. Actually, I should say that "decfsz" is normally used for loop control. The code example below shows how a loop can be repeated 37 times with very little software overhead:

```
movlw   37              ;  Load the Count Register
movwf   LoopCounter
Loop                    ;  Repeat for each iteration of the loop
  .
  :
decfsz  LoopCounter, f  ;  Decrement the Count Register
 goto   Loop            ;   If not == zero, loop again
                        ;  Continue on with the Program
```

This code can be used anywhere a loop is required, and, as you can see, the overhead is only four instructions (and is three instruction cycles per loop).

While "incfsz" is not as readily usable as "decfsz," it can be used to create a very "tight" timing loop to get a 16-bit delay value.

```
Loop                        ;  Timing Loop Return
    incfsz    Count         ;  Increment the Least Significant Byte
    incf      Counthi       ;   Inc Most Sig Byte if Least != 0
    btfsc     PORTn, Bitn   ;  Jump Out of Loop if conditions are met
    goto      Loop
    movf      Counthi, w    ;  Now, Get Correct Value for Most Sig
    subwf     Count, w      ;   Byte of the Count
    movwf     Counthi
```

In "loop," the least significant byte of the count is incremented each time through. The most significant byte is incremented if the result of incrementing the least significant byte does not equal zero.

This means that the most significant byte is equal to the count of the least significant byte minus the value in the most significant byte (which can be thought of as having the value of the least significant byte minus the most significant byte).

This little snippet of code only uses five instruction cycles (or 20 clock cycles) per loop and is the minimum 16-bit timing code that you can produce for timing an event. One (potentially serious) drawback of using this block of code is that there is no way to escape if there is an overrun (i.e., the event doesn't end in 64K $\times$ 5 instruction cycles). Despite this, this loop is an extremely efficient method of providing a 16-bit event timing with only five instruction cycle granularity (or possible error).

A couple of notes on these two instructions: If you are using them on processor registers, care should be taken to ensure that the hardware registers are capable of reaching zero. In the PIC16C5x (baseline) series of PICMicros, the FSR contains bits which can never be zero (are always equal to 1). These registers after any instruction will never reach zero, which means that they would never skip the next instruction.

As well, these instructions do not affect any status flags (zero would probably be expected). This means that you may want to put a "bsf STATUS, Z" after the instruction following the incfsz/decfsz instruction.

For example, in a loop:

```
    decfsz    Count         ;  Decrement the Count Value
    goto      Loop          ;   Jump back to Loop if Count != 0
    bsf       STATUS, Z     ;  Set Zero Flag to Indicate Loop End
```

Immediate Arithmetic Operators

The immediate arithmetic operators use explicitly specified values for the operations. These values are actually part of the instruction.

The "movlw" instruction is used to load "w" with a constant value. (Instruction 28.18.) The "movlw" instruction does not change any status registers during its execution.

The "addlw" is used to add an immediate value to the contents of the "w" register. (Instruction 28.19.) "Addlw" changes the zero, carry, and decimal carry flags in exactly the same way as the "addwf" instruction.

The "sublw" subtracts the value in "w" from the literal value. (Instruction 28.20.) This sounds confusing, and it is.

Instruction: movf Register, [w|f]   **Bits:**

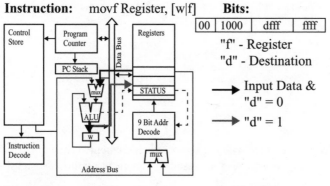

| 00 | 1000 | dfff | ffff |

"f" - Register
"d" - Destination

→ Input Data &
    "d" = 0

⇒ "d" = 1

Execution: d ← [f]   **Instruction**
                 Z ← [f] & 0x0FF   **Cycles:**   1

Example: **MCUs:** Mid-Range
movf STATUS,   w   ;   w = STATUS

Note: Zero Flag is Set/Reset according
            to contents of "Register".

Instruction 28.1 PICMicro movf register[, w|f] instruction.

Instruction: movwf Register   **Bits:**

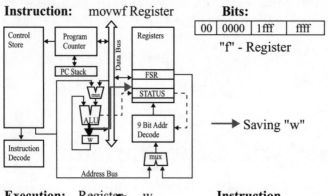

| 00 | 0000 | 1fff | ffff |

"f" - Register

→ Saving "w"

Execution: Register ← w   **Instruction**
                                            Cycles: 1

Example: **MCUs:** Mid-Range
movwf STATUS   ;   Restore STATUS

Instruction 28.2 PICMicro movwf register instruction.

Instruction: clrw

Bits:

00	0001	0000	0011

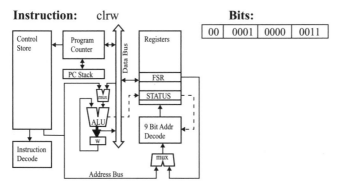

Execution: w ← 0
              Z ← 1

Instruction Cycles: 1

Example: **MCUs:**   Mid-Range

clrw   ;   w = 0

Note: Zero Flag is Always Set for "clr"
           instructions.

Instruction 28.3 PICMicro clrw instruction.

Instruction: clrf Register

Bits:

00	0001	1fff	ffff

"f" - Register

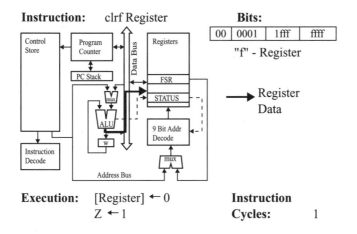

→ Register
   Data

Execution: [Register] ← 0
              Z ← 1

Instruction Cycles: 1

Example: **MCUs:**   Mid-Range

clrf Register   ;   Register = 0

Note: Zero Flag is Always Set for "clr"
           instructions.

Instruction 28.4 PICMicro clrf register instruction.

Instruction: addwf Register, [w|f]   **Bits:**

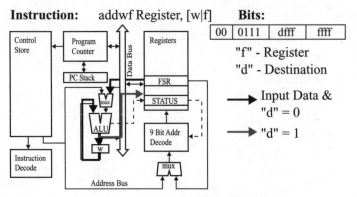

00	0111	dfff	ffff

"f" - Register
"d" - Destination

→ Input Data &
    "d" = 0

→ "d" = 1

Execution: $d \leftarrow w + [f]$

$Z \leftarrow (w + [f]) \ \& \ 0x0FF$

$C \leftarrow (w + [f]) > 0x0FF$

$DC \leftarrow ((w \ \& \ 0x0F) + ([f] \ \& \ 0x0F)) > 0x0F$

Instruction Cycles: 1

Example: **MCUs:** Mid-Range

```
movlw  7
addwf  Reg,  w  ;      w = Reg + 7
addwf  Reg,  f  ;    Reg = 2*Reg + 7
addwf  Reg      ;    Reg = 3*Reg + 14
```

Instruction 28.5 PICMicro addwf register[, w┊f] instruction.

Instruction: subwf Register, [w|f]   **Bits:**

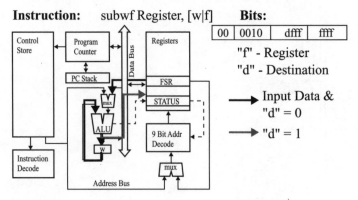

00	0010	dfff	ffff

"f" - Register
"d" - Destination

→ Input Data &
    "d" = 0

→ "d" = 1

Execution:

$d \leftarrow w + (Reg \char`^ 0x0FF) + 1$

$Z \leftarrow w \ \& \ 0x0FF$

$C \leftarrow w > 0x0FF$

$DC \leftarrow w > 0x0F$

Instruction Cycles: 1

MCUs: Mid-Range

Example:
```
movf Reg,   w   ;   Reg2 = Reg2 - Reg
subwf Reg2
```

Instruction 28.6 PICMicro subwf register[, w┊f] instruction.

Instruction: andwf Register, [w|f]   **Bits:**

00	0101	dfff	ffff

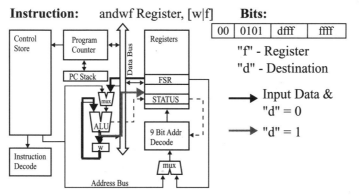

"f" - Register
"d" - Destination

→ Input Data &
   "d" = 0

→ "d" = 1

Execution: d ← w & [f]   **Instruction**
                 Z ← (w & [f]) & 0x0FF   **Cycles:**   1

Example: **MCUs:**   Mid-Range
movlw 7
andwf Reg,   w   ;   w = Reg & 7

Instruction 28.7 PICMicro andwf register[, w⎮f] instruction.

Instruction: iorwf Register, [w|f]   **Bits:**

00	0100	dfff	ffff

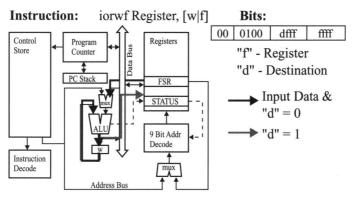

"f" - Register
"d" - Destination

→ Input Data &
   "d" = 0

→ "d" = 1

Execution: d ← w | [f]   **Instruction**
                 Z ← (w | [f]) & 0x0FF   **Cycles:**   1

Example: **MCUs:**   Mid-Range
movlw 7
iorwf Reg, w   ;   w = Reg & 7

Instruction 28.8 PICMicro iorwf register[, w⎮f] instruction.

Instruction: xorwf Register, [w|f]   **Bits:**

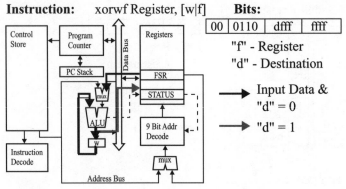

00	0110	dfff	ffff

"f" - Register
"d" - Destination

→ Input Data &
   "d" = 0
→ "d" = 1

Execution: d ← w ^ [f]   **Instruction**
                  Z ← (w ^ [f]) & 0x0FF   **Cycles:**   1

Example: **MCUs:** Mid-Range
movlw 7
xorwf Reg, w   ;   w = Reg ^ 7

Instruction 28.9 PICMicro xorwf register[, w|f] instruction.

Instruction: comf Register, [w|f]   **Bits:**

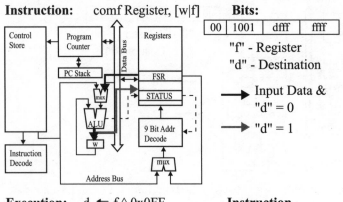

00	1001	dfff	ffff

"f" - Register
"d" - Destination

→ Input Data &
   "d" = 0
→ "d" = 1

Execution: d ← f ^ 0x0FF   **Instruction**
                  Z ← (f ^ 0x0FF)   **Cycles:**   1

Example: **MCUs:** Mid-Range
comf Register, w   ;   w = - Register
addlw 1

Instruction 28.10 PICMicro comf register instruction.

Instruction: swapf Register, [w|f] **Bits:**

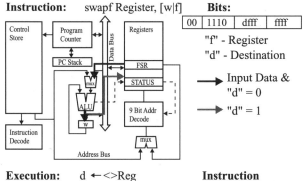

00	1110	dfff	ffff

"f" - Register
"d" - Destination

→ Input Data &
"d" = 0

→ "d" = 1

Execution: d ← <>Reg

Instruction Cycles: 1

Example: **MCUs:** Mid-Range

swapf _w ; Restore "w"
swapf _w, w ; without affecting
; the Zero Flag

Note: "swapf" is ofen used for outputting
nybbles of a byte or moving data
without affecting the Zero Flag.

Instruction 28.11 PICMicro swapf register[, w¦f] instruction.

Instruction: rlf Register, [w|f] **Bits:**

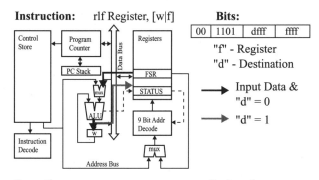

00	1101	dfff	ffff

"f" - Register
"d" - Destination

→ Input Data &
"d" = 0

→ "d" = 1

Execution:

Instruction Cycles: 1

Example: **MCUs:** Mid-Range

rlf Register, w ; Jump if Bit 7
btfsc STATUS, C ; of "Register"
goto Label ; is Set.

Note: The "Execution" Graphic Above is
for "d" = 1.

Instruction 28.12 PICMicro rlf register[, w¦f] instruction.

Instruction: rrf Register, [w|f]

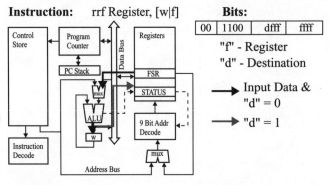

Bits:

00	1100	dfff	ffff

"f" - Register

"d" - Destination

➡ Input Data &
   "d" = 0

→ "d" = 1

Execution:

C ➡ Register

**Instruction
Cycles:** 1

Example:

```
rrf       Register,   w    ;  Divide
movwf     Divisor          ;  "Register" by
                           ;  2.
```

MCUs: Mid-Range

Note: The "Execution" Graphic Above is
for "d" = 1.

Instruction 28.13 PICMicro rrf register[, w|f] instruction.

Instruction: incf Register, [w|f]

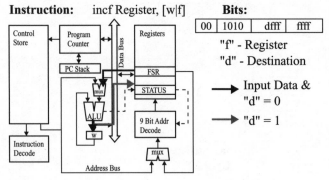

Bits:

00	1010	dfff	ffff

"f" - Register

"d" - Destination

➡ Input Data &
   "d" = 0

→ "d" = 1

Execution: $d \leftarrow f + 1$
$Z \leftarrow (f + 1)\ \&\ \text{0x0FF}$

**Instruction
Cycles:** 1

Example:

```
incf  Counter          ;  Counter++
```

MCUs: Mid-Range

Instruction 28.14 PICMicro incf register[, w|f] instruction.

Instruction: decf Register, [w|f]   **Bits:**

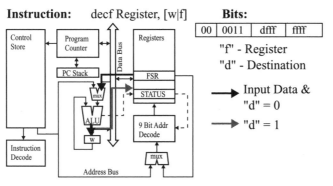

00	0011	dfff	ffff

"f" - Register
"d" - Destination

➡ Input Data &
   "d" = 0

→ "d" = 1

Execution: d ← f - 1   **Instruction**
            Z ← (f - 1) & 0x0FF   **Cycles:**   1

Example: **MCUs:**   Mid-Range
decf Counter   ;   Counter--

Instruction 28.15 PICMicro decf register[, w|f] instruction.

Instruction: incfsz Register, [w|f]   **Bits:**

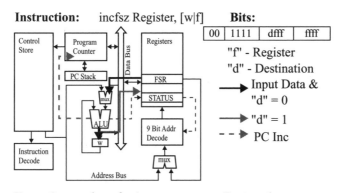

00	1111	dfff	ffff

"f" - Register
"d" - Destination

➡ Input Data &
   "d" = 0

→ "d" = 1

--→ PC Inc

Execution: d ← f + 1   **Instruction**
            PC ← (PC + 1) &   **Cycles:**   1/2
                 (d | 0)

Example: Loop   **MCUs:**   Mid-Range
        incfsz   Count
        incf   Counthi
        btfsc   Port, Bit
        goto   Loop

Note: "incfsz", as used above, can be used
        to time events.

Instruction 28.16 PICMicro incfsz register[, w|f] instruction.

Instruction: decfsz Register, [w|f]   **Bits:**

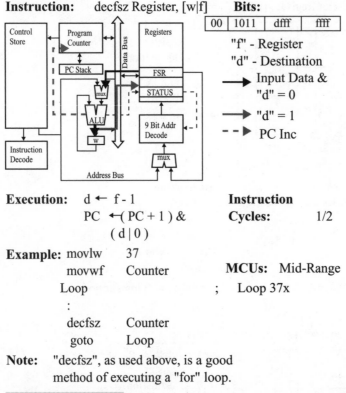

| 00 | 1011 | dfff | ffff |

"f" - Register
"d" - Destination

→ Input Data &
   "d" = 0

➤ "d" = 1

- - ➤ PC Inc

Execution: d ← f - 1
        PC ← (PC + 1) &
          (d | 0)

Instruction Cycles: 1/2

Example: movlw   37
        movwf   Counter
        Loop
          :
        decfsz   Counter
        goto   Loop

MCUs: Mid-Range

;   Loop 37x

Note: "decfsz", as used above, is a good
      method of executing a "for" loop.

Instruction 28.17 PICMicro decfsz register[, w|f] instruction.

I feel that the way this instruction, like "subwf," would make the most sense is if the literal value was subtracted from the value in "w." But the PICMicro architecture does not support this. The best way of thinking of this instruction is to visualize what happens in your mind. It looks like:

$$w = literal - w$$

and not

$$w = w - literal$$

which is what I indicated above would be the most intuitive.

With the derivation used for "subwf," "sublw" is actually:

$$w = literal + (w \wedge 0x0FF) + 1$$

"Sublw" changes the flags in exactly the same manner as "subwf."

Because this instruction works in a way that I find to be nonintuitive, I try to avoid using it except to negate the value in "w" by using the instruction "sublw 0."

```
sublw   0    ; Negate Value in "w"
```

There is one little trick you may want to do if you have to subtract an explicit value and that is to add the negative of the value.

For example, say you want to create the code to do the following:

$$w = w - 47$$

This could be:

```
movwf   Temp        ;   Save the Value in "w"
movlw   47          ;   Get the Subtraction Value
subwf   Temp, w     ;   Subtract it from the Original "w"
```

If you are using a PIC16Cxx (Not the low end devices) you can use:

```
addlw   0 - 47      ;   Add the Negative Value
```

If you are using a PIC16C5x (the low end, which doesn't have this instruction) and want to negate the contents of "w," here is an interesting little snippet of code that came up on the PICLIST one day:

```
addwf       Reg, w          ;   "w" = "w" + Reg
subwf       Reg, w          ;   "w" = Reg - "w"
                            ;   "w" = Reg - ("w" + Reg) ("addwf Reg, w)
                            ;   "w" = Reg - "w" - Reg
                            ;   "w" = - "w"
```

The result in "w" will be the negative of what was in there before. "Reg" will never be changed.

The "addlw" and "sublw" instructions are not available in the low-end (16C5X) devices.

The bitwise immediate operations ("andlw," "iorlw," "xorlw") carry out the bitwise logic operations directly on the contents of the "w" register. (Instructions 28.21, 28.22, and 28.23.)

These operations, like the register address bitwise operations only set the zero flag in the status register, depending on the result. The result is stored back in "w," with no opportunity to store the result in a register during the instruction. Executing the instruction "iorlw 0" is a good way of determining whether or not the value in "w" is equal to zero or not (following the instruction, the zero flag will be set/reset appropriately).

The "retlw" instruction is useful for subroutines that return a condition as well as a table (which is described elsewhere). The instruction loads "w" with an immediate value before executing a return from subroutine. (Instruction 28.24.)

The "retlw" instruction can replace the two statements:

```
movlw       Value           ;   Get the Value to Put in "w"
return
```

The "retlw" instruction is the only subroutine return available to the low-end (16C5X) devices. (Instruction 28.18.)

Execution Change Operators

Before attempting to use a "goto" or "call" instruction, it is imperative that you understand how they work. If you haven't done so, go back and read about the program counter in the "PICMicro Architecture" chapter. The "goto" and "call" instructions can behave strangely in some circumstances, and the program counter will not end up with the correct destination address.

Instruction: movlw Literal

Bits:

| 11 | 0000 | LLLL | LLLL |

"L" - Literal

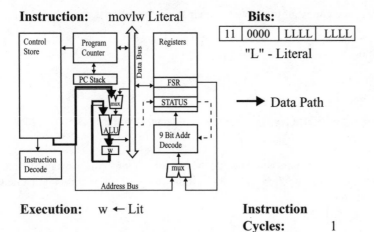

→ Data Path

Execution: w ← Lit

Instruction Cycles: 1

Example:

movlw   w, 77   ;   w = 77 Decimal

MCUs: Mid-Range

Instruction 28.18 PICMicro movlw literal instruction.

Instruction: addlw Literal

Bits:

| 11 | 111x | LLLL | LLLL |

"L" - Literal

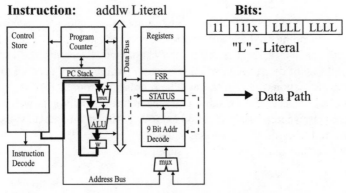

→ Data Path

Execution: w ← w + Lit
Z ← (w + Lit) & 0x0FF
C ← (w + Lit) > 0x0FF
DC ← ((w & 0x0F) + (Lit & 0x0F)) > 0x0F

Instruction Cycles: 1

Example:

movf   Reg,   w
addlw   7   ;   w = Reg + 7
addlw   -13   ;   w = (Reg + 7) - 13

MCUs: Mid-Range

Instruction 28.19 PICMicro addlw literal instruction.

Instruction: sublw Literal

Bits:

11	110x	LLLL	LLLL

"L" - Literal

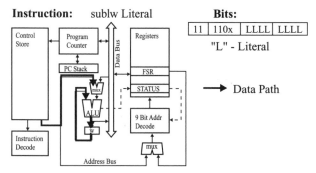

→ Data Path

Execution: w ← w +(Lit^0x0FF)+1   **Instruction**
                 Z ← w & 0x0FF   **Cycles:**   1
                 C ← w > 0x0FF
                 DC ← ((w & 0x0F) > 0x0F

Example: **MCUs:** Mid-Range
movf   Reg, w
sublw 0   ;   w = -Reg

Note: "addlw -Lit" should be used instead
            of "sublw" for subtracting a Negative
            Literal from "w".

Instruction 28.20 PICMicro sublw literal instruction.

Instruction: andlw Literal

Bits:

11	1001	LLLL	LLLL

"L" - Literal

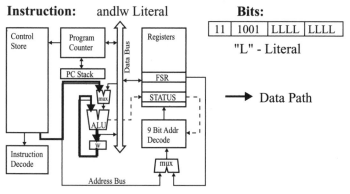

→ Data Path

Execution: w ← w & Lit   **Instruction**
                 Z ← (w & Lit) & 0x0FF   **Cycles:**   1

Example: **MCUs:** Mid-Range
movf   Reg,   w
andlw   7   ; w = Reg & 0b000000111

Instruction 28.21 PICMicro andlw literal instruction.

Instruction: iorlw Literal

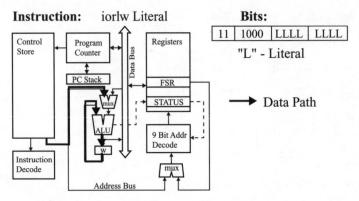

Bits:

| 11 | 1000 | LLLL | LLLL |

"L" - Literal

➤ Data Path

Execution: w ← w | Lit
Z ← (w | Lit) & 0x0FF

Instruction Cycles: 1

Example:
movf   Reg,   w
iorlw   7   ;   w = Reg | 0b000000111

MCUs: Mid-Range

Instruction 28.22 PICMicro iorlw literal instruction.

Instruction: xorlw Literal

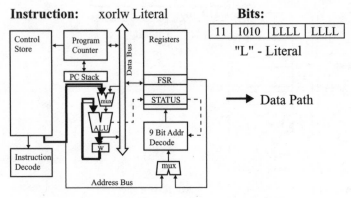

Bits:

| 11 | 1010 | LLLL | LLLL |

"L" - Literal

➤ Data Path

Execution: w ← w ^ Lit
Z ← (w ^ Lit) & 0x0FF

Instruction Cycles: 1

Example:
movf   Reg,   w
xorlw   7   ;   w = Reg ^ 0b000000111

MCUs: Mid-Range

Instruction 28.23 PICMicro xorlw literal instruction.

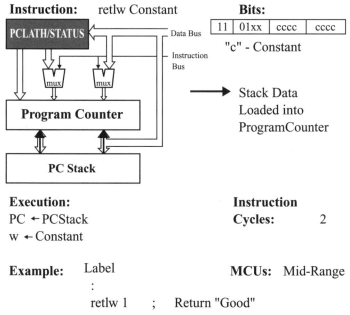

Instruction: retlw Constant

Bits:

| 11 | 01xx | cccc | cccc |

"c" - Constant

Stack Data
Loaded into
ProgramCounter

Execution:
PC ← PCStack
w ← Constant

**Instruction
Cycles:** 2

Example: Label
     :
    retlw 1 ; Return "Good"

MCUs: Mid-Range

Instruction 28.24 PICMicro retlw literal instruction.

The reason for the unusual actions taken during the "goto" or "call" instructions is that in the PICMicro instruction set, all instructions are the same length. This means that the address size could be larger than what the instruction has available bits for.

Both "goto" and "call" can be explicitly defined within a device specific "page" (256/512 addresses for the low-end, 2K addresses for the midrange, and 8K addresses for the high-end). If the label to goto or call is outside the page, the PCLATH register (or appropriate STATUS bits, for the low end) must be set with the correct page information.

For example, jumping between pages in the mid-range PICMicros can be accomplished by:

```
movlw    high Label         ;  Interpage "goto"
movwf    PCLATH
goto     Label
```

In this snippet of code, the PCLATH register is updated with the new page before the "goto" instruction is executed. This forces the PC to be loaded with the correct and full "label" address when "goto" is executed. (Instruction 28.25.)

"Call" works almost exactly the same way as "goto," except the pointer to the next instruction is stored on the program counter stack. (Instruction 28.26.)

In the PIC16C5x family, subroutines to be called can only start in the lower 256 addresses of each 512 address page. This is because the bit definition for the instructions don't allow access to the full 9-bit "page."

There are three different types of return statements in the midrange and high-end PICMicros (as noted above, the 16C5X can only execute the "retlw" instruction). Each one of these takes the value from the top of the hardware stack and puts it in the program counter. These addresses are used to return from subroutines or an interrupt.

I should note that if a "return" instruction is specified in low-end MPASM source code, a "retlw 0" instruction (which loads 0 into the accumulator) will actually be used. There will not be an error for using this instruction that doesn't exist in the low-end PICMicro architecture.

The simple "return" statement returns the stack pointer to the address pointed after the call to subroutine. No registers or control bits are changed. (Instruction 28.27.)

"Retfie" is used to return from an interrupt. Actually, it works identically to "return," except that the "GIE" bit in the interrupt control register is set during the instruction. This allows waiting interrupts to execute immediately following the execution of the instruction (this simplifies the interrupt handler to execute different interrupts sequentially, rather than having to provide a check before ending the handler to make sure nothing is pending and if there is, to handle them). (Instruction 28.28.)

Microcontroller Control Operators

There are only two instructions which are used to explicitly control the operation of the processor. The first, "clrwdt," is used to reset the watchdog counter. The second, "sleep," is used to hold the PICMicro in the current state until some condition changes and allows the PICMicro to continue execution. Following these instructions, "OPTION" and "TRIS" are used to copy the contents of "w" into the bank 1 registers.

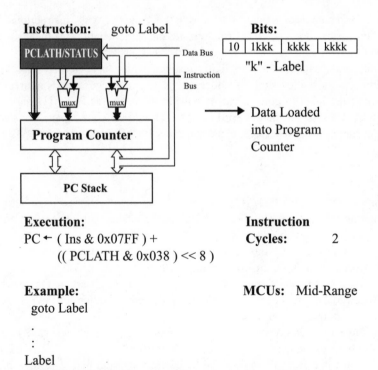

Instruction: goto Label

Bits:

10	1kkk	kkkk	kkkk

"k" - Label

Data Loaded into Program Counter

Execution:
PC ← (Ins & 0x07FF) +
      ((PCLATH & 0x038) << 8)

Instruction Cycles: 2

Example:
  goto Label
  .
  :
Label

MCUs: Mid-Range

Instruction 28.25 PICMicro goto label instruction.

Instruction: call Label

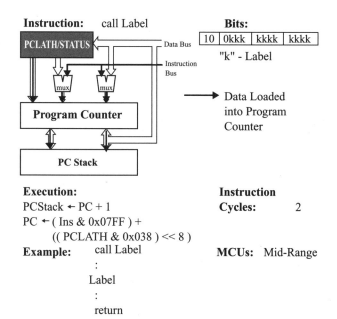

Bits:

| 10 | 0kkk | kkkk | kkkk |

"k" - Label

Data Loaded
into Program
Counter

Execution:
PCStack ← PC + 1
PC ← (Ins & 0x07FF) +
    ((PCLATH & 0x038) << 8)

**Instruction
Cycles:**   2

Example: call Label
          :
          Label
          :
          return

MCUs: Mid-Range

Note: "Call" is limited by the depth of the
        PC Stack (8 in mid-range PICs)

Instruction 28.26 PICMicro call label instruction.

Instruction: return

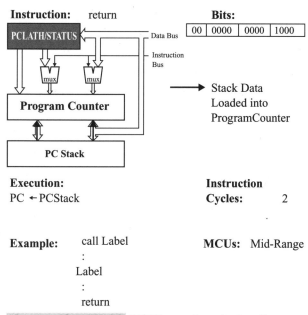

Bits:

| 00 | 0000 | 0000 | 1000 |

Stack Data
Loaded into
ProgramCounter

Execution:
PC ← PCStack

**Instruction
Cycles:**   2

Example: call Label
          :
          Label
          :
          return

MCUs: Mid-Range

Instruction 28.27 PICMicro return instruction.

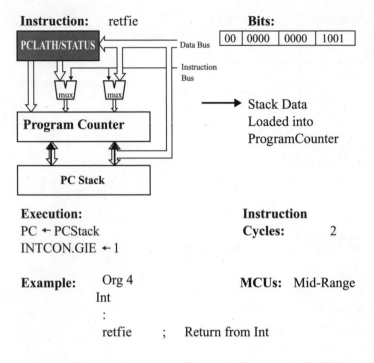

Instruction: retfie

Bits:

00	0000	0000	1001

Stack Data
Loaded into
ProgramCounter

Execution:
PC ← PCStack
INTCON.GIE ← 1

Instruction Cycles: 2

Example:
```
        Org 4
        Int
        :
        retfie    ;    Return from Int
```

MCUs: Mid-Range

Note: Interrupts are Active after executing this Instruction

Instruction 28.28 PICMicro retfie instruction.

The "clrwdt" (Instruction 28.29) clears the watchdog timer (and the TMR0/WDT prescaler if it is used with the watchdog timer) resetting the interval in which a timeout can occur. The purpose of "clrwdt" is to reset the PICMicro if execution is running improperly and not resetting the WDT as expected. To help ensure "clrwdt" is not executed at an inappropriate time, the application should only have one "clrwdt," and this should only be called by executing through one path (i.e., every time an operation has completed and the queue for the next one is about to be checked).

There are two purposes of the "sleep" instruction (Instruction 28.30). The first is to shut down the PICMicro once it has finished processing the program. This prevents the PICMicro from continuing to run and screwing up the other hardware in the application. Using the PICMicro in this manner presumes that the PICMicro is only used for a certain aspect of the application's execution (i.e., initialization of the hardware) and will no longer be required in the application.

The second purpose of the "sleep" instruction is to provide a method of allowing the PICMicro to wait for a certain event to happen. The PICMicro can be flagged of this event in one of three ways. The first is a reset on the _MCLR pin (which will cause the PICMicro to begin executing again at address 0), the second is if the watchdog timer wakes up the PICMicro, and the third method is to cause wakeup by some external event (i.e., interrupt). Using "sleep" for any of these methods will allow you to eliminate the need for wait loops and could simplify your software.

Waking up from sleep will take a minimum of 1024 clock cycles before the PICMicro resumes execution. This means that "sleep" is not appropriate if the PICMicro has to respond quickly to an external input.

The PIC16C5x devices only have one register page (no extra pages) and therefore do not have any way of directly accessing registers which are normally in page 1 (i.e., the "option" and "tris" registers). To allow you to access these registers, the PICMicro instruction set has the "option" and "tris" instructions. Both instructions write the contents of the "w" register directly into the appropriate register. This means that you are unable to read back the contents of these registers.

The "option" instruction (Instruction 28.31) is quite straightforward, but the "tris" instruction does merit some discussion. In almost all PICMicro microcontrollers, there are more than one I/O port; you're probably wondering how the tris registers are accessed using the "tris" instruction. (Instruction 28.32) In the "tris" instruction, the port to be used is specified (with a numeric value of 5 to 7 or the port name (i.e., "PORTA")) in the instruction.

To write the contents of "w" into "TRISB," the instruction would be:

```
tris    PORTB
```

These last two instructions are currently available in all the midrange PICMicro devices, but are only necessary for the (low end) PIC16C5x devices. Use of these instructions in the midrange PICMicros (which have multiple pages) is not recommended by Microchip because the instructions may not be available in future versions of the PICMicro.

"Nop" means no operation (Instruction 28.33); when executed, the processor will just skip through it, nothing will change. "Nop"s traditionally are used for two purposes. The first is to provide time synchronizing code for an application. The second is to provide space for "patch" code.

This is usually done by replacing the "nop" with a patch instruction. In the PICMicro, it is inconvenient to use "nop"s in this manner. This is because of the way the programmable memory used in the PICMicro works. In EPROM (and EEPROM) technology, when the memory is ready to be programmed (i.e., "cleared") all the cells are set (= "1"). During programming, the zeros are added to make the various instructions.

Why this makes it a problem for the PICMicro is that the "nop" instruction is all zeros. This means that an instruction cannot be burned out of a "nop."

But, there is a method of providing space in the code for patches. This means that the code loaded into the PICMicro can be modified without having to erase the device (which can take a while for an EPROM device) and then reload the code. To do this, the reverse of making instructions from "nops" is used.

For example, you may put the following code in your 16C84 program to provide patch code space:

```
goto    $ + 5           ;  Skip Over four patch addresses
addlw   0x0FF           ;  Instruction with all bits set
addlw   0x0FF
addlw   0x0FF
addlw   0x0FF
```

To enter some patch code, all the "1"s in the first "goto" instruction can be turned to "0"s, making the instruction into a "nop." The "addlw 0x0FF" are used because they have all the bits set. The construct above will allow you up to add up to four instructions without having to reassemble your code.

As in the example above, all midrange PICMicros use "addlw 0x0FF" to make sure all the bits are set at a program address. Low-range PICMicros use "xorlw 0x0FF" and the high-range uses "call 0x01FFF" to achieve the same effect.

Because the "nop" instruction, in the PICMicro, consists of all the bits set to zero, instructions can be programmed out very easily, allowing deleting sections of code without resorting to erasing and reprogramming an entire device (which might not be possible in the case of an OTP part).

Bit Operators

Bit setting and resetting is done by the "bcf" and "bsf" instructions, respectively. These instructions can be thought of in two ways. (Instructions 28.34 and 28.35.)

In traditional programming (Von Neumann), there are instances of ANDing or ORing a value with a constant when only one bit is affected. This can be modelled very easily using the "bcf" and "bsf" instructions.

Instruction: clrwdt

Bits:

00	0000	0110	0100

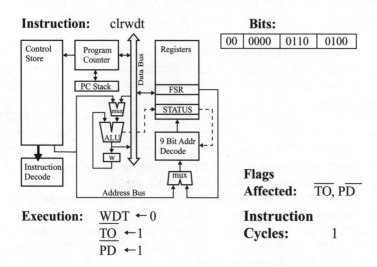

Flags Affected: $\overline{TO}$, $\overline{PD}$

Execution: $WDT \leftarrow 0$
$\overline{TO} \leftarrow 1$
$\overline{PD} \leftarrow 1$

Instruction Cycles: 1

Example:
clrwdt   ;   WDT = 0/Reset

MCUs: Mid-Range

Comments: Only one "clrwdt" instruction should be in the program.

Instruction 28.29 PICMicro clrwdt instruction.

Instruction: sleep

Bits:

| 00 | 0000 | 0110 | 0011 |

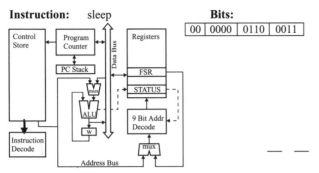

Execution: $\overline{TO} \leftarrow 1$
$\overline{PD} \leftarrow 0$
Oscillator Off

**Instruction
Cycles:**   N/A

Example: **MCUs:** Mid-Range
sleep   ;   Sleep and Wake
nop   ;   up on Int
                               ;   Condition.

Note: "nop" should ALWAYS follow "sleep"
Instruction.

Instruction 28.30 PICMicro sleep instruction.

Instruction: option

Bits:

| 00 | 0000 | 0110 | 0010 |

"f" - Register

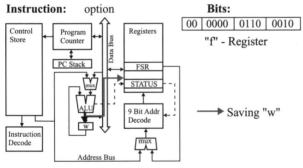

Saving "w"

Execution: Option ← w

**Instruction
Cycles:**   1

Example: **MCUs:** Mid-Range
movlw 0x0D7   ;   Setup TMR0 with
option   ;   Prescaler

Note: "Option" has been included to provided
compatibility with Low-End PICs.

Instruction 28.31 PICMicro option instruction.

Instruction: tris PORTn   **Bits:**

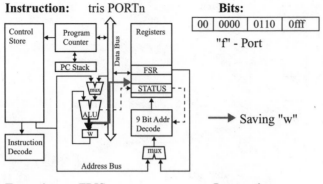

00	0000	0110	0fff

"f" - Port

Saving "w"

Execution: TRISn ← w   **Instruction**
                                 Cycles: 1

Example: **MCUs:**   Mid-Range

```
movlw  0x0FE      ;   Setup PORTB.0 as
tris   PORTB      ;     Output
```

Note: "tris" has been included to provided
            compatibility with Low-End PICs.

Instruction 28.32 PICMicro tris PORTn instruction.

Instruction: nop   **Bits:**

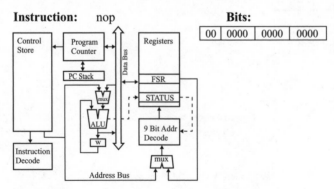

00	0000	0000	0000

Execution: **Instruction**
                                 Cycles: 1

Example: **MCUs:**   Mid-Range

```
nop               ;   Waste one cycle
```

Instruction 28.33 PICMicro nop instruction.

For example, if you want to AND a value with 0x07F. Normally this would be done by:

```
movlw   0x07F              ;  Load in the Value for ANDing
andwf   Reg, f             ;  And it to get a single value
```

But in the PICMicro, this can be simply done by one instruction:

```
bcf   Reg, 7               ;  Reset Bit Seven of the Register
```

ORing works with the "bsf" (bit set) in an analogous way. Any bit in the register space that is writeable can be handled this way. These instructions can be used to great advantage in situations where you only want to change one bit in a register (such as in the status register).

In using these instructions, not only is the operation carried out in one instruction cycle rather than two, but the operation can be carried out guaranteeing that no other bits in a register are affected.

This is not quite true. As I explained in "PICMicro Architecture," the use of "bsf" or "bcf" may not be appropriate with I/O ports. This is because of the inadvertent changes that can take place with the register output latches after executing this instruction (writing back the state that was read, not the one written to the output latches).

The PICMicro architecture doesn't use jump on condition instructions. Instead, there are a number of instructions that allow skipping the next instruction in line. (Instructions 28.36 and 28.37.) As noted above, "decfsz" and "incfsz" can be used for loop control. What I wanted to talk about here is actually controlling the execution of the program.

Program execution control is carried out by use of the two instructions which allow the program to skip the next instruction if a certain register-bit condition is met. In a traditional architecture, jumps and branches are controlled by status-register conditions. This can be done in the PICMicro as well by using the bit-skip instructions and accessing the status register.

For example, if you wanted to jump if the zero flag was set to zero ("jz" in Intel i86 parlance), the following PICMicro code would be used:

```
btfsc STATUS, z           ;  Skip next instruction if zero bit is reset
  goto label              ;  Zero bit was set, goto the specified location
```

This can be continued for "JC" (jump on carry), "JNZ," and so on. Bit skip instructions are useful in a variety of cases, from checking interrupt active flag bits to seeing if a number is negative (checking the most significant bit) to checking the status of a bit "flag." At the end of the chapter, I have included a list of the built-in MPASM "extensions" with their PICMicro equivalents.

High-End (17C4X) PIC Instructions

If you are using the high-end PICMicros (17Cxx), you'll probably notice that I haven't explained several of the instructions used for these processors above. (The 17CxX instruction set has 55+ instructions, whereas the low and midrange devices have just more than 30).

There are three types of enhanced 17Cxx instructions: additional arithmetic instructions, data movement instructions, and table read and write instructions. I won't go through the additional arithmetic instructions because they behave in a very similar manner to the

Instruction: bcf Register, Bit

Bits:

01	00bb	bfff	ffff

"f" - Register
"b" - Bit

→ Data Path

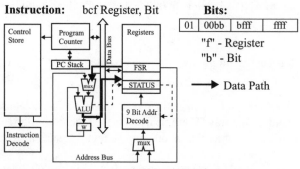

Execution: Register ← Register & (0x0FF ^ (1 << Bit))

Instruction Cycles: 1

Example:
bcf   PORTB,   3 ;   Clear Portb.3

MCUs: Mid-Range

Note: Using bcf/bsf is not recommended for I/O Ports (as in the Example Above).

Instruction 28.34 PICMicro bcf register, bit instruction.

Instruction: bsf Register, Bit

Bits:

01	01bb bfff ffff	

"f" - Register
"b" - Bit

→ Data Path

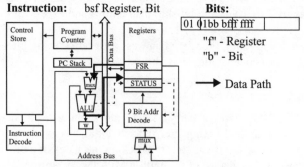

Execution: Register ← Register |

Instruction Cycles: (1 << Bit)

Example:
bsf PORTB, 3 ; Set Portb.3

MCUs: Mid-Range

Note: Using bcf/bsf is not recommended for I/O Ports (as in the Example Above).

Instruction 28.35 PICMicro bsf register, bit instruction.

Instruction: btfsc Register, Bit

Bits:

01	10bb	bfff	ffff

"f" - Register

"b" - Bit

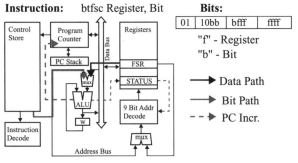

→ Data Path

→ Bit Path

- - → PC Incr.

Execution: PC ← (PC + 1) &
Reg &
(1 << Bit)

Instruction Cycles: 1

Example: **MCUs:** Mid-Range

btfsc   STATUS,   Z ;   Jump if Equal
 goto   Label   ;   to Zero

Note: The bit skip instructions work are the
basic method of branching after
comparison.

Instruction 28.36 PICMicro btfsc register, bit instruction.

Instruction: btfss Register, Bit

Bits:

01	11bb	bfff	ffff

"f" - Register

"b" - Bit

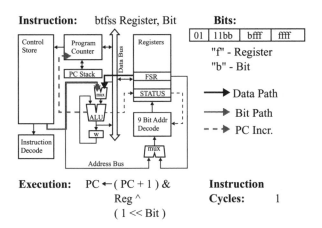

→ Data Path

→ Bit Path

- - → PC Incr.

Execution: PC ← (PC + 1) &
Reg ^
(1 << Bit)

Instruction Cycles: 1

Example: **MCUs:** Mid-Range

btfss STATUS, Z ;   Jump if Not
 goto   Label   ;   Equal to Zero

Note: The bit skip instructions work are the
basic method of branching after
comparison.

Instruction 28.37 PICMicro btfss register, bit instruction.

instructions explained above. They simply provide enhanced function (for example the 8x8 bit multiplication) to the high-end PICMicros over the low-end and midrange devices.

Data movement instructions replace the "movf" instruction in the other PICMicros. The two instructions "movfp" and "movpf" are used to pass data back and forth between the primary registers and the file register banks. (Instruction 28.38.)

High-end table instructions are really beyond the scope of this book. Simply put, these instructions allow accessing a large table in program memory (essentially breaking the barrier between control store and data space). This program memory typically consists of RAM chips wired to the PICMicro using the diagram in "architecture," but it can also be memory-mapped I/O devices, passing back and forth data 8 bits at a time. To do this, the other 8 bits of the 16-bit transfer cannot be active at the same time (to avoid any opportunity for bus contention).

To carry out table reads and writes, first set up the pointer to the address of the table. This is followed by a 16-bit transfer between the PICMicro (using the "table latch" registers) and the external device. (Instruction 28.39.)

The 17C4X, for the most part, behaves like the other PICMicros but does have some features that improve its usability and allows more complex operations.

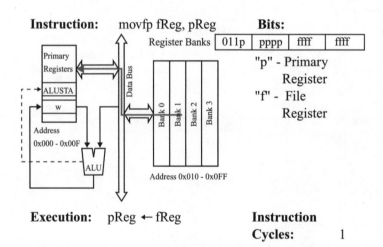

Instruction: movfp fReg, pReg   **Bits:**

Register Banks | 011p | pppp | ffff | ffff

"p" - Primary Register
"f" - File Register

Execution: pReg ← fReg

Instruction Cycles: 1

Example: **MCUs:** Hi-End
movfp   PORTB,   w ;   = "movf PORTB, w"
                     ;   In Low-End/Mid-
                     ;   Range

Notes: The High-End PICs use "movfp" and "movpf" are analogous to "movf" and "movwf" in the Low and Mid-Range.

Instruction 28.38 High-end PICMicro movfp freg, preg instruction.

Instruction: tablwt t, i, f   **Bits:**

| 1010 | 11ti | ffff | ffff |

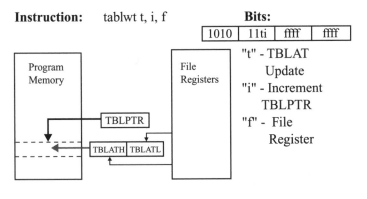

"t" - TBLAT
   Update
"i" - Increment
   TBLPTR
"f" - File
   Register

Execution: if t == 0   **Instruction**
          TBLATL ← fReg   **Cycles:**   1
      else
          TBLATH ← fReg
          ProgMem ← TBLAT   **MCUs:** High-End
      if i == 1
          TBLPTR++

Example:
movfp PORTB,   w   ;   = "movf PORTB, w"

                    ;   In

Note: The High-End PICs use "movfp" and
       "movpf" are analogous to "movf" and
       "movwf" in the Low and Mid-Range.

Instruction 28.39 High-end PICMicro tablwt t, i, f instruction.

MPASM Extensions

The Microchip supported "MPASM" assembler has a number of special instructions used to make coding the PICMicros easier. The instructions for the low-end and midrange are as follows:

INSTRUCTION	DESCRIPTION	CYCLES	STATUS FLAGS AFFECTED	ACTUAL PICMICRO INSTRUCTIONS
bz Label	Jump if Z Flag Set	2-3	None	btfsc STATUS, Z goto Label
clrc	Clear Carry Flag	1	Carry	bcf STATUS, C
clrdc	Clear DC Flag	1	Digit Carry	bcf STATUS, DC
clrz	Clear Zero Flag	1	Zero	bcf STATUS, Z
lcall Label	Call the subrtn in another Page	2-4	None	Dependant on PICMicro and Label Address

INSTRUCTION	DESCRIPTION	CYCLES	STATUS FLAGS AFFECTED	ACTUAL PICMICRO INSTRUCTIONS
lgoto Label	Goto the Label in another Page	2-4	None	Dependent on PIC PICMicro and Label Address
movfw Reg	Move Reg into w	1	Zero	movf Reg, w
negf Reg	Reg = -Reg	2	Zero	comf Reg
				incf Reg
setc	Set Carry Flag	1	Carry	bsf STATUS, C
setdc	Set DC Flag	1	Digit Carry	bsf STATUS, DC
setz	Set Zero Flag	1	Zero	bsf STATUS, Z
skpc	Skip if Carry	1	None	btfss STATUS, C
skpdc	Skip if DC	1	None	btfss STATUS, DC
skpnc	Skip if No Carry	1	None	btfsc STATUS, C
skpndc	Skip if No DC	1	None	btfsc STATUS, DC
skpnz	Skip if No Zero	1	None	btfsc STATUS, Z
skpz	Skip if Zero	1	None	btfss STATUS, Z
subcf Reg, d	If Carry, Decf the Reg	2	Zero	btfsc STATUS, C
				decf Reg, d
subdcf Reg, d	If DC, Decf the Reg	2	Zero	btfsc STATUS, DC
				decf Reg, d
tstf Reg	Set Zero Flag if Equal to Zero	1	Zero	movf Reg

Parallax PICMicro Instruction Set

Parallax Inc. has written a very popular assembler for the Microchip PICMicros. "PASM" (as it is known) uses an assembler language that is similar to i8051 instructions. The assembler also supports MPASM (standard Microchip) instruction formats as well.

Some of these instructions are designed specifically for the low-end PICMicros (they have been noted). If you're working with a midrange PICMicro, these instructions MUST NOT be used.

You should note that many of these mnenonics result in multiple PICMicro instructions with unexpected changes to the STATUS and "w" register. I find it a major problem to keep track of what is happening with the "mov" instruction extensions to allow full access to the PICMicro instruction set (see below).

The big advantage of PASM instructions is that it makes some instructions more "orthoganol" or able to access registers in a variety of different ways. Another advantage is that the PICMicro may seem more accessible if you are familiar with the i8051. Some people like these instructions because the destination (back into the file register or into "w") is more explicitly defined in the instructions. In many ways, the Parallax PICMicro Instruction Set is similar to the enhanced instructions that Microchip has developed (and is presented above) and like the Microchip enhancements can only be used effectively if they are well and truly understood.

PASM is available from the Parallax Web site.

- Literal Instructions
fr - File Register

PASM DATA INSTRUCTION	INSTRUCTIONS DESCRIPTION	CYCLES	CONTEXT RESOURCES AFFECTED	ACTUAL PICMICRO INSTRUCTIONS	
CLR Parm	ClearParameter				
"W"	w=0	1	Zero	clrw	
fr	fr=0	1	Zero	clr	fr
WDT	WDT=0	1	_TO,_PD	clrwdt	
MOV Parm	Move Data				
"W, #"	w = #	1	None	movlw	#
"W, fr"	w = fr	1	Zero	movf	fr, w
"W, /fr"	w = fr ^ 0x0FF	1	Zero	comf	fr, w
"W, fr-W"	w = fr+(w^0x0FF)+1	1	Z, C, DC	subwf	fr, w
"W, ++fr"	w = fr + 1	1	Z	incf	fr, w
"W, —fr"	w = fr - 1	1	Z	decf	fr, w
"W, >>fr"	w = fr >> 1	1	Carry	rrf	fr, w
"W, <<fr"	w = fr << 1	1	Carry	rlf	fr, w
"W, <>fr"	w = NibSwap fr	1	None	swapf	fr, w
"fr, W"	fr = w	1	None	movwf	fr
"!Port, W"	TRIS = w	1	None	TRIS	Port
"!Port, #" TRIS = #		2	w	movlw	#
				TRIS	Port
"!Port, fr" TRIS = fr		2	w, Zero	movf	fr, w
				TRIS	Port

- Literal Instructions
fr - File Register

PASM DATA INSTRUCTION	INSTRUCTIONS DESCRIPTION	CYCLES	CONTEXT RESOURCES AFFECTED	ACTUAL PICMICRO INSTRUCTIONS	
"OPTION, W" OPTION = w		1	None	OPTION	
"OPTION, #" OPTION = #		2	w	movlw	#
				OPTION	
"OPTION, fr" OPTION = fr		2	w, Zero	movf	fr, w
				OPTION	
"fr, #"	fr = #	2	None	movlw	#
				movwf	fr
"fr, fr2"	fr = fr2	2	Zero	movf	fr2, w
				movwf	fr
ADD Parm	ADD two Values				
"W, fr"	w = w + fr	1	Z, C, DC	addwf	fr, w
"fr, W"	fr = w + fr	1	Z, C, DC	addwf	fr, f
"fr, #"	fr = fr + #	2	w, Z, C, DC	movlw	#
				addwf	fr, f
"fr, fr2"	fr = fr + fr2	2	w, Z, C, DC	movf	fr2, w
				addwf	fr, f
SUB Parm	Subtraction				
"fr, W"	fr = fr+(w^0x0FF)+1	1	Z, C, DC	subwf	fr, f
"fr, #"	fr = fr+(#^0x0FF)+1	2	w, Z, C, DC	movlw	#
				subwf	fr, f
"fr, fr2"	fr=fr+(fr2^0x0FF)+1	2	w, Z, C, DC	movf	fr2, w
				subwf	fr, f
AND Parm	Bitwise AND				
"W, #"	w = w & #	1	Zero	andlw	#
"W, fr"	w = w & fr	1	Zero	andwf	fr, w
"fr, W"	fr = w & fr	1	Zero	andwf	fr, f
"fr, #"	fr = fr & #	2	w, Zero	movlw	#
				andwf	fr, f
"fr, fr2"	fr = fr & fr2	2	w, Zero	movf	fr2, w

- Literal Instructions
fr - File Register

PASM DATA INSTRUCTION	INSTRUCTIONS DESCRIPTION	CYCLES	CONTEXT RESOURCES AFFECTED	ACTUAL PICMICRO INSTRUCTIONS	
OR Parm	Bitwise Inclusive OR				
"W, #"	w = w | #	1	Zero	iorlw	#
"W, fr"	w = w | fr	1	Zero	iorwf	fr, w
"fr, W"	fr = fr | w	1	Zero	iorwf	fr, f
"fr, #"	fr = fr | #	2	w, Zero	movlw	#
				iorwf	fr, f
"fr, fr2"	fr = fr | fr2	2	w, Zero	movf	fr2, w
				iorwf	fr, f
XOR Parm	Bitwise Exclusive OR				
"W, #"	w = w ^ #	1	Zero	xorlw	#
"W, fr"	w = w ^ fr	1	Zero	xorwf	fr, w
"fr, W"	fr = fr ^ w	1	Zero	xorwf	fr, f
"fr, #"	fr = fr ^ #	2	w, Zero	movlw	#
				xorwf	fr, f
"fr, fr2"	fr = fr ^ fr2	2	w, Zero	movf	fr2, w
				xorwf	fr, f
DEC Parm	Decrement Register				
"fr"	fr = fr - 1	1	Zero	decf	fr, f
INC Parm	Increment Register				
"fr"	fr = fr + 1	1	Zero	incf	fr, f
NEG Parm	Two's Complement Negation				
"fr"	fr = 0 - fr	2	Zero	comf	fr, f
				incf	fr, f
NOT Parm	Bitwise Complement				
"W"	w = w ^ 0x0FF	1	Zero	xorlw	0x0FF
"fr"	fr = fr ^ 0x0FF	1	Zero	comf	fr
TEST Parm	Test Parm Equal to Zero				
"W"	Z = (w == 0)	1	Zero	iorlw	0
"fr"	Z = (fr == 0)	1	Zero	movf	fr, f

- Literal Instructions
fr - File Register

PASM DATA INSTRUCTION	INSTRUCTIONS DESCRIPTION	CYCLES	CONTEXT RESOURCES AFFECTED	ACTUAL PICMICRO INSTRUCTIONS
RR Parm	Rotate Register to Right			
"fr"	fr = fr >> 1	1	Carry	rrf fr, f
RL Parm	Rotate Register to Left			
"fr"	fr = fr << 1	1	Carry	rlf fr, f
SWAP Parm	Swap Nybbles of Register			
"fr"	fr = <>fr	1	None	swapf fr, f
CLRB fr, bit	fr.bit = 0	1	None	bcf fr, bit
SETB fr, bit	fr.bit = 1	1	None	bsf fr, bit
CLC	Carry = 0	1	None	bcf STATUS, C
STC	Carry = 1	1	None	bsf STATUS, C
CLZ	Zero = 0	1	None	bcf STATUS, Z
STZ	Zero = 0	1	None	bsf STATUS, Z
ADDB fr, bit	fr = fr + Bit	2	Zero	btfsc fr, bit
				incf fr, f
SUBB fr, bit	fr = fr - bit	2	Zero	btfss fr, bit
				decf fr, f
MOVB fr.b, fr2.b2	Move Bit	4	None	btfss fr2, b2
				bcf fr, b
				btfsc fr2, b2
				bsf fr, b
MOVB fr.b, /fr2.b2	Move Invert	4	None	btfsc fr2, b2
				bcf fr, b
				btfss fr2, b2
				bsf fr, b
NOP	Do Nothing	1	Nothing	nop
SLEEP	Put PICMicro to Sleep	N/A	_TO, _PD	sleep
LSET Addr	Jump Setup	0-2	PA0, PA1	bcf/bsf STATUS, PA0

* - Low End Instruction, bcf/bsf of STATUS PAx Bits Address Dependent

- Literal Instructions
fr - File Register

PASM DATA INSTRUCTION	INSTRUCTIONS DESCRIPTION	CYCLES	CONTEXT RESOURCES AFFECTED	ACTUAL PICMICRO INSTRUCTIONS	
MOVSZ Parm	Skip if Result = 0				
"W, ++fr"	w = fr + 1	1/2	w	incfsz	fr, w
W, —fr"	w = fr - 1	1/2	w	decfsz	fr, w
INCSZ fr	w=fr+1, if Z Skip	1/2	w	incfsz	fr, f
DECSZ fr	w=fr-1, if Z Skip	1/2	w	decfsz	fr, f
SB fr, bit	Skip if Bit Set	1/2	None	btfss	fr, bit
SNB fr, bit	Skip if Bit Reset	1/2	None	btfsc	fr, bit
SC	Skip if Carry Set	1/2	None	btfss	STATUS, C
SNC	Skip if C Reset	1/2	None	btfsc	STATUS, C
SZ	Skip if Zero Set	1/2	None	btfss	STATUS, Z
SNZ	Skip if Zero Reset	1/2	None	btfsc	STATUS, Z
CJA fr, #	if fr > #	3/4	w, C, DC, Z	movlw	#
	Skip_Next			addwf	fr, w
				btfss	STATUS, C
CJA fr, fr2	if fr > fr2	3/4	w, C, DC, Z	movf	fr, w
	Skip_Next			subwf	fr2, w
				btfss	STATUS, C
CJAE fr, #	if fr > #	3/4	w, C, DC, Z	movlw	#
	Skip_Next			subwf	fr, w
				btfss	STATUS, C
CJAE fr, fr2	if fr > fr2	3/4	w, C, DC, Z	movf	fr2, w
	Skip_Next			subwf	fr, w
				btfss	STATUS, C
CSB fr, #	if fr < #	3/4	w, C, DC, Z	movlw	#
	Skip_Next			subwf fr, w	
	btfsc STATUS, C				
CSB fr, fr2	if fr < fr2	3/4	w, C, DC, Z	movf	fr2, w
	Skip_Next			subwf	fr, w
				btfsc	STATUS, C

- Literal Instructions
fr - File Register

PASM DATA INSTRUCTION	INSTRUCTIONS DESCRIPTION	CYCLES	CONTEXT RESOURCES AFFECTED	ACTUAL PICMICRO INSTRUCTIONS	
CSBE fr, #	if fr <= #	3/4	w, C, DC, Z	movlw	#
	Skip_Next			addwf	fr, w
				btfsc	STATUS, C
CSBE fr, fr2	if fr <= fr2	3/4	w, C, DC, Z	movf	fr, w
	Skip_Next			subwf	fr2, w
				btfss	STATUS, C
CSE fr, #	if fr == #	3/4	w, C, DC, Z	movlw	#
	Skip_Next			subwf	fr, w
				btfss	STATUS, Z
CSE fr, fr2	if fr == fr2	3/4	w, C, DC, Z	movf	fr2 w
	Skip_Next			subwf	fr, w
				btfss	STATUS, Z
CSNE fr, #	if fr == #	3/4	w, C, DC, Z	movlw	#
	Skip_Next			subwf	fr, w
				btfsc	STATUS, Z
CSNE fr, fr2	if fr == fr2	3/4	w, C, DC, Z	movf	fr2 w
	Skip_Next			subwf	fr, w
				btfsc	STATUS, Z
JMP Parm	Jump to Address				
"addr9"	PC = 9 Bit Address	2	None	goto	addr9
* - Low End Instruction					
"PC+W"	PC = PC + Offset w	2	Z, C, DC	addwf	PCL, f
"W"	PC = w	2	None	movwf	PCL
CALL addr8	Call Subroutine	2	None	call	addr8
* - Low End Instruction					
RET	Return & w = 0	2	w	retlw	0
SKIP	Skip Over Next Ins	2	None	btfss	FSR, 7
* - Low End Instruction, Bit 7 of FSR is always Set					

- Literal Instructions
fr - File Register

PASM DATA INSTRUCTION	INSTRUCTIONS DESCRIPTION	CYCLES	CONTEXT RESOURCES AFFECTED	ACTUAL PICMICRO INSTRUCTIONS	
LJMP addr	LSET before JMP	2-5	PA0-PA2	bcf/bsf STATUS, PAx	
				:	
				goto	addr
* - Low End Instruction					
LCALL addr	LSET before CALL	2-5	PA0-PA2	bcf/bsf STATUS, PAx	
				:	
				call	addr
* - Low End Instruction					
RETW 'String'	Table Return	2	w	retlw	'S'
				etlw	't'
				retlw	r'
				etlw	'i'
				retlw	'n'
				retlw	g'
IJNZ fr, addr9	Increment/Jump	2/3	None	incfsz	fr, f
				goto	addr9
DJNZ fr, addr9	Decrement/Jump	2/3	None	decfsz	fr, f
				goto	addr9
JB fr, bit, addr9	Jump on Bit	2/3	None	btfsc	fr, bit
				goto	addr9
JNB fr, bit, addr9		2/3	None	btfss	fr, bit
				goto	addr9
JC addr9	Jump on Carry	2/3	None	btfsc	STATUS, C
				goto	addr9
JNC addr9	Jump on !Carry	2/3	None	btfss	STATUS, C
				goto	addr9
JZ addr9	Jump on Zero	2/3	None	btfsc	STATUS, Z
				goto	addr9

| # - Literal Instructions | | | | | |
| fr - File Register | | | | | |

PASM DATA INSTRUCTION	INSTRUCTIONS DESCRIPTION	CYCLES	CONTEXT RESOURCES AFFECTED	ACTUAL PICMICRO INSTRUCTIONS	
JNZ addr9	Jump on !Zero	2/3	None	btfss	STATUS, Z
				goto	addr9
CJA fr, #, addr9		4/5	w, C, DC, Z	movlw	#
if fr > #				subwf	fr, w
goto addr9				btfss	STATUS, C
				goto	addr9
CJA fr, fr2, addr9		4/5	w, C, DC, Z	movf	fr, w
if fr > fr2				subwf	fr2, w
goto addr9				btfss	STATUS, C
				goto	addr9
CJAE fr, #, addr9		4/5	w, C, DC, Z	movlw	#
if fr >= #				subwf	fr, w
goto addr9				btfss	STATUS, C
				goto	addr9
CJAE fr, fr2, addr9		4/5	w, C, DC, Z	movf	fr2, w
if fr >= fr2				subwf	fr, w
goto addr9				btfsc	STATUS, C
				goto	addr9
CJB fr, #, addr9		4/5	w, C, DC, Z	movlw	#
if fr < #				subwf	fr, w
goto addr9				btfss	STATUS, C
				goto	addr9
CJB fr, fr2, addr9		4/5	w, C, DC, Z	movf	fr2, w
if fr < fr2				subwf	fr, w
goto addr9				btfss	STATUS, C
				goto	addr9
CJBE fr, #, addr9		4/5	w, C, DC, Z	movlw	#
if fr <= #				addwf	fr, w
goto addr9				btfss	STATUS, C
				goto addr9	

- Literal Instructions
fr - File Register

PASM DATA INSTRUCTION	INSTRUCTIONS DESCRIPTION	CYCLES	CONTEXT RESOURCES AFFECTED	ACTUAL PICMICRO INSTRUCTIONS	
CJBE fr, fr2, addr9		4/5	w, C, DC, Z	movf	fr, w
if fr <= fr2				subwf	fr2, w
goto addr9				btfsc	STATUS, C
				goto	addr9
CJE fr, #, addr9		4/5	w, C, DC, Z	movlw	#
if fr == #				subwf	fr, w
goto addr9				btfsc	STATUS, Z
				goto	addr9
CJE fr, fr2, addr9		4/5	w, C, DC, Z	movf	fr2, w
if fr == fr2				subwf	fr, w
goto addr9				btfsc	STATUS, Z
				goto	addr9
CJNE fr, #, addr9		4/5	w, C, DC, Z	movlw	#
if fr == #		subwf	fr, w		
goto addr9				btfss	STATUS, Z
				goto	addr9
CJNE fr, fr2, addr9		4/5	w, C, DC, Z	movf	fr2, w
if fr == fr2				subwf	fr, w
goto addr9				btfss	STATUS, Z
				goto	addr9

EXAMPLE PICMICRO APPLICATIONS

CONTENTS AT A GLANCE

The most common PICMicro used by beginners is the PIC16F84 (because the EEPROM control store allows fast program updates without an ultraviolet erasing step). This is an 18-pin DIP that can be programmed by an astonishingly large variety of programmers. The PIC16F84 has a 14-bit PICMicro (midrange) processor with interrupts. This part is primarily used to show how the PICMicro works.

Most documentation available in books and on the 'net give the 16C84 as the most common device for beginners. The 16C84 was "obsoleted" in 1997 and the 16F84 has taken its place. The two devices are virtually identical, except for some differences in the configuration register and the 16F84 has more file registers available. The programming specifications of the 16F84 are identical to the 16C84.

First PICMicro Application

To create code to show how the PICMicro could be powered up and execute a program, the following circuit was created on a prototyping system. (Figure 29.1.)

For the first program, I wanted to get one of the LEDs to flash at a speed that was visible to me (i.e., not require an oscilloscope to observe the output). Also, I wanted this flashing to be caused by a timer-initiated interrupt (so that in the final version, the button sensing could execute in the mainline and not be affected by the flashing LED).

The clock frequency is 1 MHz, which means the instruction clock is actually running at 250 kHz. The maximum TMR0 delay that I can put in (with the prescaler set to 256 and used for TMR0 input) is 65,536 instruction clocks. This means that the LED would flash on and off at a rate of about two times per second.

With this design point, "Prog1" was written:

```
title  "PROG1 - Flash an LED."
;  This is the First PIC Program. The purpose is to Flash an LED.
;
;  myke predko
;  95.05.17
;
;  Hardware Notes:
;    The PIC is running at 1MHz using a Crystal and two 33 pF caps
;    Reset is tied to Vdd via a 10K Resistor
;    RB0 is an Output and is connected to an LED with a 220 Ohm Resistor
;      in Series to Vdd
;
  LIST P=16C84, R=DEC
  errorlevel 0,-305
  INCLUDE "c:\mplab\p16c84.inc"

;  Common Declares
```

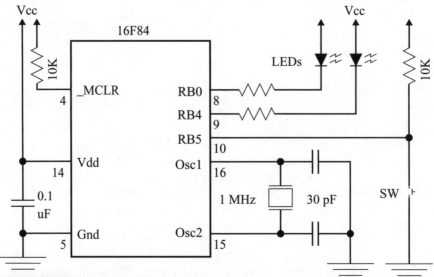

Figure 29.1 Flashing LEDs with a PICMicro.

```
;  Register Usage
 CBLOCK 0x00C
_w, _status                    ;  Context Registers to Save
Count
 ENDC


 PAGE
 __CONFIG _CP_OFF & _XT_OSC & _PWRTE_ON  & _WDT_OFF
                ;  Note that the WatchDog Timer is OFF
;  Code for Prog1

  org    0

  goto        Mainline        ;  Skip Over the Interrupt Handler

  org 4

Int                           ;  Interrupt Handler
  movwf       _w              ;  Save Context Registers
  movf        STATUS, w
  movwf       _status

  bcf     INTCON, T0IF        ;  Reset the Interrupt

  movlw       1               ;  Flip RB0
  xorwf       PORTB

  movf        _status, w      ;  Restore the Context Registers
  movwf       STATUS
  swapf       _w
  swapf       _w, w
  retfie

Mainline
  bsf         STATUS, RP0
  bcf         TRISB & 0x07F, 0 ;  Enable RB0
  movlw       0x0D7           ;  Enable the Timer
  movwf       OPTION_REG & 0x07F
  bcf         STATUS, RP0

  bcf         PORTB, 0

  clrf        TMR0            ;  Enable/Reset the Timer

  movlw       0x0A0           ;  With Interrupts
  movwf       INTCON

  goto        $               ;  Loop Around Forever

end
```

If this program were blocked out in pseudocode, it would look like:

```
RB0 = Output               ;  Enable RB0 as an Output


Prescaler = TMR0           ;  Setup the Timer
Prescaler = 256
TMR0 = 0

TMRInterrupt = Enabled
```

```
    While 1 == 1                    ;  Loop in the Mainline Forever

TMRInt          ;  Timer Interrupt

  TMRInterrupt = Reset

  RB0 = RB0 ^ 1                     ;  Toggle the Output Pin

  Return from Interrupt
```

"Prog2," the completed first application, builds on this but really only modifies the mainline slightly. In pseudocode the mainline would be changed to:

```
  RB0 = Output                     ;  Enable the LED Outputs
* RB4 = Output

  Prescaler = TMR0                 ;  Setup the Timer
  Prescaler = 256
  TMR0 = 0

  TMRInterrupt = Enabled

  While 1 == 1                     ;  Loop in the Mainline Forever
*   if RB5 == 0                    ;  Button is Low
*     RB4 = 0
*   else
*     RB4 = 1

* - Code Added Relative to "Prog1"
```

As you can see, the only differences between Prog2 and Prog1 is the additional code used to poll the momentary on button ("SW" in Figure 29.1) and pass the value through to LED2.

```
title   "PROG2 - Flash an LED and Show Button Input."
;
;  This is a continuation of the First PIC Program. The purpose is to
;   Flash an LED and poll a switch and when it's low, Light a Second
;   LED.
;
;  myke predko
;  95.05.17
;
;  Hardware Notes:
;   The PIC is running at 1MHz using a Crystal and two 33 pF caps
;   Reset is tied to Vdd via a 10K Resistor
;   RB0 is an Output and is connected to an LED with a 220 Ohm Resistor
;    in Series to Vdd
;   RB4 is an Output and is connected to an LED with a 220 Ohm Resistor
;    in Series to Vdd
;   RB5 is connected to a 10K Resistor Pull-Up and a Switch Pulling to
;    Ground
;
  LIST P=16C84, R=DEC
  errorlevel 0,-305
  INCLUDE "c:\mplab\p16c84.inc"

;  Common Declares

;  Register Usage
  CBLOCK 0x00C
_w, _status                        ;  Context Registers to Save
```

```
        Count
         ENDC


         PAGE
         __CONFIG _CP_OFF & _XT_OSC & _PWRTE_ON  & _WDT_OFF
                                ;  Note that the WatchDog Timer is OFF
      ;  Code for Prog1

         org     0

         goto      Mainline      ;  Skip Over the Interrupt Handler

         org 4

      Int                        ;  Interrupt Handler
         movwf     _w            ;  Save Context Registers
         movf      STATUS, w
         movwf     _status

         bcf       INTCON, T0IF  ;  Reset the Interrupt

         movlw     1             ;  Flip RB0
         xorwf     PORTB

         movf      _status, w    ;  Restore the Context Registers   movwf    STATUS
         swapf     _w
         swapf     _w, w
         retfie

      Mainline

         bsf       STATUS, RP0
         movlw     0x0EE         ;  RB0/RB4 are Output Enabled
         movwf     TRISB & 0x07F
         movlw     0x0D7         ;  Enable the Timer
         movwf     OPTION_REG & 0x07F
         bcf       STATUS, RP0

         bcf       PORTB, 0

         clrf      TMR0          ;  Enable/Reset the Timer

         movlw     0x0A0         ;  With Interrupts
         movwf     INTCON

      Loop                       ;  Loop Around Here to Poll the Input Bit

         btfsc     PORTB, 5      ;  Handle the Switch Input Bit
          goto     SetBit        ;   Bit is Set

         bcf       PORTB, 4      ;  Switch and (now) LED Low

         goto      Loop

      SetBit                     ;  Set the Bit

         bsf       PORTB, 4

         goto      Loop


         end
```

As I try to do with all the software I write, I looked through this program for areas to improve. The most glaring area that can be improved upon is passing the switch input bit to the LED output bit.

In the code above, the code is at the level of what I would expect from a good optimizing compiler "C" for the source:

```
if (( PORTB & 0x010 ) == 0 )
  PORTB = PORTB & 0x0DF;
else
  PORTB = PORTB | 0x020;
```

But this could be handled differently without using an "IF" statement; the code could be:

```
PORTB = ( PORTB & 0x0CF ) | (( PORTB {{ 1 ) & 0x0DF );
```

I realize that this seems like a real mess, but in the PICMicro, this could be coded as:

```
rlf      PORTB, w    ;  Shift PORTB by 1 and Put into "w"
andlw    0x020       ;  Isolate the Input Bit
bcf      PORTB, 5    ;  Turn off the LED bit
iorwf    PORTB       ;  If SW is high, move it to the LED
```

Which is a bit simpler (requires fewer instructions) and always takes the same number of cycles (in the original code, setting or resetting the LED output took different paths, which take a different number of cycles). But if the bit is to be left high, it will actually go low for an instruction cycle, which is a problem in this application because the LED will partially light (we will be esentially be outputting a PWM signal to it). Also, this solution changes the "w" register and zero flag, which the original solution does not. So, with what initially looked like a promising way to improve on some code may actually be less desirable than the original method.

But without experimenting and trying out different things, you'll never really understand what is possible.

Digital Clock/Thermometer

When I started this book, I had just finished reviewing the galley proofs of *Programming and Customizing the PICMicro Microcontroller* and was feeling pretty good about my knowledge about the PICMicro. This example application was done shortly after starting this book and turned into a really humbling experience for me. The problem was with the setting up the real-time clock.

Like the digital clock/timer applications I created for the other microcontrollers in this book, I wanted to use a beginner's device. The PICMicro I selected was the 16F84, which contains the basic 14-bit PICMicro core (which has interrupts), a single 8-bit timer (TMR0) with prescaler, and EEPROM control store. A 1-MHz crystal was used to provide timing for the application.

(The circuit I designed for this application is shown in Figure 29.2.)

With this, I was able to get the interface to the DS1820 operating quite simply. One of the things that made it much easier was the use of "RA4," which is an open-drain I/O. This pin was put into "output" mode and only driven low when the PICMicro is communicatng with the DS1820. In the PICMicro applications directory, this program is "Thermo5."

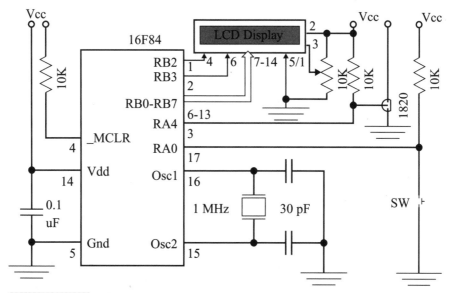

Figure 29.2 PICMicro-based digital clock/thermometer.

The real-time clock was run from the interrupt handler and would wait 50,000 cycles (which, with four clock cycles per clock "tick" worked out to 200 msec or one-fifth of a second). Once the counter had reset itself, the interrupt handler would reload the counter and wait another fifth of a second. The interrupt handler is very simple:

```
Int                           ;  Interrupt Handler
  movwf        _w
  movf         STATUS, w
  movwf        _status

  bcf          INTCON, T0IF   ;  Turn Off the Interrupt Request Bit

  call         Dlay64         ;  Delay 72 Cycles to Get 80 Cycles with 195
  call         Dlay8          ;   Timer "Ticks"

  movlw        TMRStart       ;  Now, Wait 50,000 Cycles
  movwf        TMR0

  movf         _status, w
  swapf        _w
  swapf        _w, w
  retfie
```

The mainline consisted of a basic loop and would monitor TMR0 and increment a sub-second counter everytime TMR0 was reset. Once the sub-second counter reached five, a second counter was incremented and if it equalled 60, a minute counter would be incremented and the new time would be displayed.

The "Dlay8" and "Dlay64" subroutines are simple routines to delay 72 instruction cycles to make sure the interrupt timer delayed 50,000 cycles. They use the characteristic subroutine overhead of the PICMicro to provide a specific number of timing delays. The routine(s) to develop the delay is:

```
Dlay64                              ;   Delay 64 Instruction Cycles
  call        Dlay32
Dlay32
  call        Dlay16
Dla816
  call        Dlay8
Dlay8
  call        Dlay4
Dlay4
  return
```

"Dlay4" is the basic unit and requires four cycles (two for the original "call" instruction and two for the "return" instruction). "Dlay8" uses these four cycles as well as calling "Dlay4" itself. The longer delays are built off from this as well. This is a very efficient method of providing a set number of instruction cycle delays and ensuring that the timer (and prescaler) is reset at the correct time interval.

With a stack that is only eight nested routines deep, it may be possible to "blow" the stack if too many nested subroutines are called (i.e., using this method, a maximum 512-cycle delay can be implemented from the mainline). This method, while seemingly very simple, actually took quite a bit of work to make sure the timings were precise (this was confirmed on the MPLAB simulator).

Because I had worked quite a bit with the PICMicro and I had not yet worked with the Dallas Semiconductor thermometer (and its one-wire interface), I initially focused in on the LCD and DS 1820 interface. I was able to implement this with little problem. The source I used to develop the DS 1820 interface is in "Thermo3." The software interface to this device went very smoothly.

After the LCD and thermometer interfaces were written, I then wrote the real-time clock software, using the assumption of interrupting the PICMicro every 50,000 cycles as shown above. After I got this written and started running the application, I immediately noticed that I had a problem. The clock seemed to be losing time at quite a healthy rate.

In fact, the clock was losing 30 or 40 seconds per hour. When I worked it out, I found the clock had an error up to 12,500 ppm.

This error was caused by how I designed the timer and how the PICMicro operates. The design and the PICMicro were incompatible because of three reasons.

The first was in how long interrupts take to be responded to. An interrupt handler can begin to execute three or four instruction cycles after the request has been received. When I wrote this code, I timed it for an interrupt "latency" (number of cycles needed to respond to the interrupt request) of three cycles. This means that occasionally, an extra cycle would be taken responding to the request.

The second problem with the design being absolutely accurate in terms of timing is what happens during a two-cycle instruction (i.e., a "goto" or "call"). If the interrupt is ready to execute during the instruction, it will have to wait an extra cycle for the instruction to complete. This extends the maximum interrupt latency by another cycle.

The last design incompatibility was that when the PICMicro was sending pulses to the DS1820 (either as a read or a write) to ensure that the timing was correct, I would disable interrupts. If an interrupt request came in during a read or write to the DS 1820, the request would be delayed by some length of time. To try to eliminate this, I moved the DS1820 temperature read to when the timer value was reset. This did help eliminate this incompatibility quite a bit, but I still had an error on the order of thousands of PPM (which would be different for different times, depending on when the interrupt occurred).

A new strategy appeared while I was doing research on the 68HC05. In some models of the 68HC05, there is a 16-bit counter without any prescaler (as described in the 68HC05 section). Looking at this problem from the 68HC05's perspective, I redesigned my code to allow the timer to mimic the 68HC05's and never require a reload by setting the prescaler to 256 and letting an interrupt happen every 65,536 instruction cycles. The interrupt handler became:

```
Int
   movwf      _w                    ;   Context Register Save
   movf       STATUS, w
   movwf      _status

   bcf        INTCON, T0IF          ;   Reset the Interrupt Flag

   incf       Frac3                 ;   Add 64K to the Count

   movf       _status, w            ;   Restore the Context Registers
   movwf      STATUS
   swapf      _w
   swapf      _w, w
   retfie
```

With this code, when the timer counter overflowed, the interrupt handler would reset the interrupt request and add 64K to a 24-bit counter ("Frac1" through "Frac3"). In the main-line, when at least a second had gone by (bit 2 of Frac3 is set, indicating that the interrupt handler had executed approximately four times, resulting in a total in the 24-bit counter of at least 250,000), 250,000 (which is 1,000 clock cycles or one second) is taken away from the 24-bit counter and the seconds are updated.

With this type of interrupt handler, the interrupt request always happens at the same time (after 65,536 instruction cycles) and if the interrupt request occurs at a time when it cannot be serviced immediately, the timer and prescaler continue to count after the overflow has occured. Since I can guarantee that the interrupt will be serviced before the next time the counter overflows, there isn't any concern that a timer overflow will be lost.

After implementing this clock (in source "2Thermo1" through "2Thermo4"), I found my timing problems went away completely and my timing error was about a hundred PPM (which is what I expected with the particular crystal being used with the hardware). Also, the code required to implement this type of real-time clock was simpler than the original code and did not require the same amount of effort to determine proper timings of the original method.

When you look at the source code for this application, you'll note that the "Thermo" series was written a couple of months before the "2Thermo" series. In real-life, you'll very rarely get an opportunity such as this to rethink and redo an application as I was able to here, but the lesson is to look at other devices and see what you can learn from them that is applicable in the current (or future) applications.

PICLite Language and Digital Clock/Thermometer Application

Something that has really turned into a part-time hobby for me is to write compilers for the PICMicro. The PICMicro is an interesting device to develop compilers for because of how differently the processor is architected. I'm interested in developing the best language for the PICMicro because I don't feel that assembly is the best way to develop applications, but most high-level languages do not take advantage of all the features available in the PICMicro. My ultimate goal is to develop a high-level language that could be used for all 8-bit microcontrollers.

The features that have to be considered when developing a PICMicro compiler are:

1. The ability of the result of an operation to be stored in the "w" register or the source register.
2. The limited contiguous RAM memory (which is only about 100 bytes per bank).
3. The limited index resources.
4. PCLATH and jumping within code pages (and implementing data tables in control store).

Reading this, you might think that the PICMicro is more difficult to develop a compiler for than other microcontrollers, but I would rather say, it is different from the other devices. Each microcontroller presented in this book has its own quirks, which makes writing a compiler difficult.

My first compiler was a "C" compiler for the 16C84. After doing this, one of the things I concluded was that "C" is not well suited for microcontroller applications. This is because of its reliance on large integer values, pointers, and data structures, which are difficult to implement in microcontrollers. "C" is also poorly suited for implementing registers at specific memory locations as well as interrupt handlers at specific addresses. For the latter reasons, I found that there is generally a lot of assembly-level programming that has to be added to microcontroller "C" applications, which really defeats the purpose.

My next compiler was a structured language with the ability to embed assembler and define variables and functions at specific addresses. This was a real improvement over the "C"-like language, but I still had the problem of keeping track of the index pointer, especially with array variables. The only real concern I had with it was how I implemented tables. It turned out that only up to 251 table elements could be implemented for a single "table" data type. Actually, I was very happy with this language, but it was only written for the 16C84. At this time, my sophistication with the PICMicro was growing and I was starting to use devices like the 16C73A, which have more than one page of control store and more than one shadowed bank of file registers.

The third version of the compiler that is presented in this book is a nonstructured language able to generate code for the whole midrange PICMicro family (except for devices which have four banks of file registers). I went with the nonstructured language because I wanted to add a comprehensive macro processor to add the structured features of the language.

"PICLite" is a very simple language designed for the midrange (14-bit core with bank 0 and bank 1 registers) family of PICMicros. Currently, the output is assembler and is executed from a PC-DOS command line. Once the assembler has been created cleanly, it can be run through MPASM (version 1.40 or greater). Assembler can be written in line without any special headings.

This language is simpler than "BASIC," but (I think) well organized and optimized. Source programs can be of any size and are not limited in any way (other than your PC's hard drive space).

Eight-bit ("byte" data type) and 16-bit ("word" data type) variables and arrays are supported, but registers (defined as specific addresses) can only be an 8-bit variable. For assignment statements, I have kept to "C" conventions if possible.

PICMicro interrupts are supported and are simple to implement. At the end of the main-line code, placing the label "int:" will cause an interrupt header to be inserted in the code and the code following will be the interrupt handler. At the end of the program, the interrupt return is placed.

This language was developed as a result of a discussion in the PICLIST. If you have any more ideas for the language, please let me know via the list.

PICLITE LANGUAGE DEFINITION
Command Line Options:

```
[D:][Path]FileName[.Ext]    - Disk/Path Source File is In
.                           - Debug Enable (Don't Delete .~tm File)
!                           - No Response (No Printing out of Results)
/C                          - Produce MPLAB Files
```

Invocation is:

```
PICLIte [D:][Path]FileName[.Ext] [.] [!]
```

Output is:

```
FileName.lst               - Listing File
FileName.asm               - MPASM Format Assembler File
FileName.~tm               - Debug/Temporary File (for Language Debug)
```

Language Defintion:
Address Labels (Case Sensitive):

```
Label{:}                       - The Label Starts in the first column of the
                                 line (all other Instructions have to start
                                 in a column other than the first one).
                               - The colon (":") at the end of the label is
                                 optional for program labels, but
                                 mandatory if a program statement
                                 (ie "A = B + C") is on the same line.
```

Variable/Constant/Register Declaration:

```
Label{[Array]} DataType {= InitValue}
                               - Arrays only on "byte" or "word"
                               - InitValue ONLY on byte/word and NO ARRAYS
                               - Must be in the first column
```

Data Types (Case Insensitive):

```
= value                    - Constant Value
byte                       - file Register
word                       - two file Registers in Intel Format
@ addr @ addr              - Hardware Register/Defined
                           - Addr 2x for Shadowed Registers
                           - Registers @ addresses >= 0x02000 will be
                             14 bits long
                           - Registers @ addresses >= 0x02000 will be
                             calculated during compilation cannot use
                             Register or Variable Values.
```

Label Declaration:

```
Label{[Array]} DataType {= InitValue}
                               - Arrays only on "byte" or "word"
```

```
                              - InitValue ONLY on byte/word
                              - Array InitValue can be string or single
                                value
                              - if single value, each array element is
                                loaded with the value
                              - Must be in the first column
```

PICMicro Hardware Specifications:

```
type PIC_Type                 - PIC Specification (ie "PIC_Type" = "16F84")
{s}memory Start:End           - "s" means "shadow"/Bank 0 in Bank 1
size                          - "n" Instructions in Control Store
```

While these statements can be put in the source, I have created some ".def" files that contain this information for specific PICMicros.

Currently supported devices are:

- 16F84
- 16C71

Constant Formats:

```
0x0####                       - Hex Number
0b0########                   - Binary Number
###                           - Decimal Number
'c'                           - Characters
'\r'                          - Carriage Return (Standard "C" Backslash
                                Data types supported)
"St","ring"                   - String Data, Values concatonated with comma
                                (",")
```

Assembler instructions are inline in Microchip format:

```
                              - All 16Cxx instructions supported (including
                                "OPTION" and "TRIS")
                                - "retfie" is a valid instruction, but it
                                  is not recommended to be used unless
                                  context registers are properly restored
                                  before "retfie"
                              - if "goto" or "call" is preceeded by PICLITE
                                Statements then PCLATH will be set up
                                before Instruction.
                              - if "goto" or "call" is preceeded by a 16Cxx
                                instruction then PCLATH will be NOT be set
                                up before the Instruction.
                              - "w" and "STATUS" Registers can be
                                accessed like any others
                              - Language Instructions *can* modify
                                "STATUS", "FSR", "PCLATH" so writing to
                                these registers MUST be done with care
                              - NOTE: When Array Index Used in Language,
                                contents of the FSR will be changed
                              - Only Constant Array Indexes can be used
                                within Assembler Instructions that access
                                Array Variables
```

Language Operations:

Assignment Statements:

```
Label = Label ¦ Constant { Operator Label ¦ Constant ... }
      = Expression
```

Operators (in Descending Order of Priority):

"+"	- Addition
"-"	- Subtraction (Negation if Unary)
"*"	- Multiplication
"/"	- Division
"//"	- Modulus
"<<"	- Shift Left
">>"	- Shift Right
"&"	- Bitwise AND
" | "	- Bitwise OR
"^"	- Bitwise XOR
"=="	- Compare Values, Return 1 if Equals
"!="	- Compare Values, Return 1 if Not Equals
">"	- Compare Values, Return 1 if Left Greater
">="	- Compare, 1 if Left Greater or Equal
"<"	- Compare Values, Return 1 if Left Less
"<="	- Compare, 1 if Left Less or Equal
"&&"	- Logical AND
"| |"	- Logical OR

- Division and Modulus Code taken from
  Microchip AN617

Brackets:

```
"(", ")"                    - Used to Establish Order of Operations
"[", "]"                    - Array Index
```

Language Keywords:

```
if Expression then Label - If Expression != 0 Jump to Label

;                            - Comment, Everything to Right ignored

file [D:][path]FileName.ext - Load File and Insert Source

int:                        - Start of Interrupt Code
                            - Everything After "int:" will be put into
                              the Interrupt Handler
                            - Interrupt Code *can* call goto/call into
                              Mainline and visa-versa
```

Assembler Keywords and Identifiers:

```
"$"                              - Current Address in Program
"dt"                             - Define Table
```

Configuration Fuses (at 0x02007) Definitions:

"CONFIG_BASE"	- Variable located at 0x02007 (and defined in the ".DEF" files zipped with PICLite.exe) that contains the Configuration Fuse Values
CONFIG_BASE = Parm1 & Parm2...	
	- CONFIG_BASE can be assigned using the predefined operating parameters or constants
	- Standard Configuration Values. NOTE: These values are different for different PICMicros
CP_OFF CP_EN	- Code Protect On/Off
PWRTE_DIS PWRTE_EN	- Power Up Write Timer Enable/Disable
WDT_EN WDT_DIS	- Watchdog Timer Enable/Disable
RC_OSC HS_OSC XT_OSC LP_OSC	- Oscillator Type Definitions

With the language, I was able to repeat the digital clock/thermometer application using the language instead of assembler.

The code below is the resulting PICLite code that I developed (I used the usual development process and the final code is the fifth application developed):

```
;   Thermo5 - Implement a Read Time Clock/Thermometer
;
;   This Application runs a clock on an LCD screen and shows the
;    temperature from a DS1820.
;
;   myke predko
;
;   Started: 97.09.05
;   Updated:
;
;   Hardware:
;   The PIC is running at 1 MHz using a Crystal and two 33 pF caps
;   Reset is pulled up to Vdd via a 10K Resistor
;   RB0-RB7 is the LCD Data
;   RA0 - is a Pull Up, pulled down to ground to set the time
;   RA2 - LCD Pin 4 (R/S)
```

```
;   RA3 - LCD Pin 6 (E)
;   RA4 - Pulled up and used to communicate with DS1820
;   LCD Pin 5 (R/W) is tied to ground
;

file 16F84.DEF                          ;   Get the 16F84 Register Definitions

;   Variable Declarations

i byte
j byte
count    word
SP[ 9 ] byte                            ;   Values Returned from the DS1820
Frac     word = 0                       ;   Current Fraction of a Byte
FracHi   byte = 0                       ;   High Byte of 24 Bit Count Value

uDlay    byte = 0b000000001             ;   When Updating Once Per Second, # of
Minutes
Seconds byte = 0                        ;   The Current Time
Minutes byte = 0                        ;    Initialize to 12:00AM
Hours    byte = 0

E = 3                                   ;   LCD Control Bits
RS = 2

DSBit = 4                               ;   DS 1820 Control Bit

;   Mainline for Thermo5

   PORTA = 0x010                        ;   Make Sure DS1820 Line is High
   PORTB = 0

   TRISA = 1                            ;   RA0 is the Button input
   TRISB = 0                            ;   PortB is the Data Output
   OPTION_REG = 0x0D7                   ;   Enable the Timer

;   Initialize the LCD
   call    Dlay5                        ;   Wait 15 msec for the LCD to Reset
   call    Dlay5                        ;    Internally
   call    Dlay5

   PORTB = 0x030                        ;   Set the LCD for 8 Bytes/2 Lines
   call    SendINS
   call    Dlay5

   call    SendINS                      ;   Repeat a few times to Lock in
   call    SendINS

   PORTB = 0x038                        ;   Two Line LCD
   call    SendINS
   PORTB = 0x010                        ;   Turn Off the Display
   call    SendINS
   PORTB = 0x001                        ;   Clear the LCD RAM
   call    SendINS
   PORTB = 0x00C                        ;   Enable the Display
   call    SendINS

;   Now, Put in the Header Messages

   j = 0                                ;   Put in the First Message
   call    SendINS
```

```
       PORTB = 0x0c0                    ;  Move the Cursor to the Second Line
       call    SendINS

        j = 1                           ;  Put in the Second Message
        call    SendMSG

;   Enable Interrupts

        INTCON = 0x0A0                   ;  Enable the Timer Interrupt

        goto    DispTime                ;  Display Time before Updating

;   Loop Here waiting for 1 Second Timeouts and

Loop:

        call    DS_Reset                ;  Get the Current Temperature
        i = 0x0CC                       ;  Read DS w/o ROM Command
        call    SendDS
        i = 0x044                       ;  Initiate Temperature Conversion
        call    SendDS

        call    Dlay160                 ;  Wait 500+ usec for Temperature
        call    Dlay160                 ;   Conversion
        call    Dlay160

        call    DS_Reset                ;  Now, Read the Value
        i = 0x0CC                       ;  Read DS w/o ROM Command
        call    SendDS  i = 0x0BE       ;  Read the Scratchpad plus CRC
        call    SendDS
        call    Dlay160
        call    GetDS                   ;  Get the Nine Bytes from the
        SP[ 0 ] = i                     ;   Scratchpad
        call    Dlay160
        call    GetDS
        SP[ 1 ] = i
        call    Dlay160
        call    GetDS
        SP[ 2 ] = i
        call    GetDS
        SP[ 3 ] = i
        call    GetDS
        SP[ 4 ] = i
        call    GetDS
        SP[ 5 ] = i
        call    GetDS
        SP[ 6 ] = i
        call    GetDS
        SP[ 7 ] = i
        call    GetDS
        SP[ 8 ] = i

        call    DS_Reset                ;  Reset the DS1820

        PORTB = 0x0C6                    ;  Now, Put in the Temperature
        call    SendINS

        if ( SP[ 1 ] & 1 ) == 0 then DispTemp

        SP[ 0 ] = 0 - SP[ 0 ]           ;  Negative Temperature, Convert it

        PORTB = '-'                     ;  Indicate that it was Negative
```

```
       call    SendCHAR

DispTemp                               ;  Display the Positive Temperature

   SP[ 0 ] = SP[ 0 ] / 2               ;  Get the Actual Temperature in Celsius

   if SP[ 0 ] <= 99 then DispTens ;   Don't Display Over 100C

   PORTB = '1'
   call    SendCHAR

DispTens                               ;  Display the Tens Value

   if SP[ 0 ] <= 9 then DispOnes

   PORTB = (( SP[ 0 ] / 10 ) // 10 ) + '0'
   call    SendCHAR                    ;  Send the Tens Value

DispOnes                               ;  Disply the Ones Value
   PORTB = ( SP[ 0 ] // 10 ) + '0'
   call    SendCHAR

;  Now, See if the Time should be updated

UPDTime                                ;  #### Update the Time

   if ( FracHi & 0x04 ) == 0 then Loop  ;  Nothing to Display

   if ( PORTA & 1 ) != 0 then CheckTime  ;  Is the "Set" Button Being
                                      ;    Pressed?

   Minutes = Minutes + uDlay - 1   ;  Update the Number of Minutes

   Seconds = Seconds + 60          ;  Update the Number of Seconds

   uDlay = (( uDlay << 1 ) + 1 ) & 0x03F  ;  Update the Number of Seconds

   goto    IncTime                 ;  Now, Increment the Time

CheckTime:                             ;  Reset uDlay

   uDlay = 1

IncTime:                               ;  Now, See if we are to Redisplay Time

   if Frac >= 0x0D090 then IntTimeSkip
      FracHi = FracHi - 1          ;  Do the Carry for FracHi
IntTimeSkip:

   Frac = Frac - 0x0D090
   FracHi = FracHi - 3

   Seconds = Seconds + 1

   if Seconds < 60 then Loop       ;  Haven't Updated the Next Minute

   Seconds = 0

   Minutes = Minutes + 1           ;  Increment the Minutes

   if Minutes < 60 then DispTime
```

```
   Minutes = 0

   Hours = Hours + 1

   if Hours < 24 then DispTime

   Hours = 0        \

DispTime:                            ;  Display the Time on the LCD

   PORTB = 0x086                     ;  Display the Current Time   call SendINS

   j = Hours
   if j <= 12 then DispTimeHoursSkip
     j = j - 12

DispTimeHoursSkip

   PORTB = ' '
   if ( j < 10 ) && ( j != 0 ) then DispTimeNoTens
     PORTB = '1'
DispTimeNoTens:
   call    SendCHAR
   PORTB = ( j // 10 ) + ( 2 * ( j == 0 )) + '0'
   call    SendCHAR                  ;  Note that "12" is also Counted for...

   PORTB = ':'
   call    SendCHAR

   PORTB = ( Minutes / 10 ) + '0' ;  Now, Display the Minutes
   call    SendCHAR
   PORTB = ( Minutes // 10 ) + '0'
   call    SendCHAR

   j = 3
   if Hours > 11 then DispTimePM
     j = 2
DispTimePM:
   call    SendMSG

   goto    Loop                      ;  Finished displaying the Time

;   DS 1820 Subroutines

GetDS:                               ;  Read the DS 1820

   j = 8                             ;  Loop Around her 8x to get the value

GetDSLoop:

   bcf     PORTA, DSBit              ;  Toggle the DS Comm line to see what reply
is
   bsf     PORTA, DSBit

   nop      /                        ;  Follow Original Code to Read Bit

   bsf     STATUS, C
   btfss   PORTA, DSBit              ;  Is it still High?
    bcf    STATUS, C                 ;    No, Store a Zero

   rrf     i                         ;  Add the Bit to the Count
```

```
     call   Dlay4                        ;  Now, Delay 8 Cycles before Next Request
     call   Dlay4
     decfsz j
      goto  GetDSLoop

     return

SendDS:                                  ;  Send a Command to the DS 1820

  j = 8

SendDS_Loop:                             ;  Loop Here to Send each Bit

  bcf    PORTA, DSBit                    ;  Send out the Bit
  btfsc  i, 0                            ;  Sending a 1?
   bsf   PORTA, DSBit                    ;   Yes...

  rrf    i

  call   Dlay4                           ;  Delay 12 Cycles for the "0"
  call   Dlay4
  goto   $ + 1

  bsf    PORTA, DSBit                    ;  Make sure the Line is High

  decfsz j
   goto  SendDS_Loop

     return

DS_Reset                                 ;  Reset the DS 1820

  bcf    PORTA, DSBit

  call   Dlay160                         ;  Go down for 500 usec
  call   Dlay160
  call   Dlay160

  bsf    PORTA, DSBit                    ;  Now, Put it High

  call   Dlay160                         ;  Delay for at least 1 msec
  call   Dlay160
  call   Dlay160
  call   Dlay160
  call   Dlay160
  call   Dlay160

     return

SendINS:                                 ;  Send the Instruction in PORTB

  bcf    PORTA, RS                       ;  Set the RS Bit

  bsf    PORTA, E                        ;  Toggle the data out
  bcf    PORTA, E
  call   Dlay160                         ;  Wait 160 usec for Most commands
  if ( PORTB & 0x0FC ) != 0 then SendINS_End
    call Dlay5                           ;  Have to wait 5 msec for the
                                         ;   Instruction

SendINS_End:                             ;  All finished, End the Routine
    return
```

```
    SendCHAR:                         ;  Send the Character in PORTB

      bsf     PORTA, RS               ;  Set the RS Bit

      bsf     PORTA, E                ;  Toggle the data out
      bcf     PORTA, E

      call    Dlay160                 ;  Wait 160 usec for Most commands

      return

    SendMSG:                          ;  Send the Message to the LCD

      i = 0                           ;  Clear the Offset to "Table"

    SendMSG_Loop1:
      if j == 0 then SendMSG_Loop2    ;  If "j" == 0, then "i" is index to
        call  MsgTable                ;    Correct Msg

        iorlw 0                       ;  Was "0" returned?
        btfsc STATUS, Z
          decf j                      ;  Yes, Decrement "j"

        i = i + 1
        goto SendMSG_Loop1            ;  Try the Next Character

    SendMSG_Loop2:
        call  MsgTable                ;  Get the Current Character at "i"
        movwf PORTB
        i = i                         ;  Force "call SendCHAR" to PICLite
        call  SendCHAR
        i = i + 1
        call  MsgTable                ;  Are we at the End of the Message?
        iorlw 0
        btfss STATUS, Z
          goto SendMSG_Loop2

      return                          ;  The Message has been output to LCD

    MsgTable:                         ;  The Table of Messages

      movlw Table >> 8                ;  Set Up PCLATH before changing PCL
      movwf PCLATH

      movf  i, w                      ;  Get the Value for "i"
      ADDLW Table & 0x0FF
      btfsc STATUS, C                 ;  Increment PCLATH if Appropriate
        incf PCLATH

      movwf PCL                       ;  Now, Jump to the Table Address

    Table:
      dt    " Time: ", 0              ;  ASCIIZ Messages
      dt    " Temp: ", 0
      dt    "    ", 0
      dt    " PM", 0

    ;  Delay Routines

    Dlay4                             ;  4 Cycle to Return
```

```
        return

Dlay160

    count = 13
    decfsz count
      goto  $ - 1

        return

Dlay5

    count = ( 256 * 2 ) + 160
    decfsz count
      goto  $ - 1
    decfsz count + 1
      goto  $ - 3

        return


Int:                              ;  Interrupt Handler

    bcf     INTCON, T0IF

    FracHi = FracHi + 1           ;  Increment the Counter by 64K x 4
                                  ;    usecs

;   End of Interrupt Handler

;   End Thermo5.PIC
```

29

This language is not at the level you would expect for a commercial product, but it is a very useful compiler and a language that will incorporate most midrange PICMicro features. I'm pleased at how well assembler can be integrated in with the language.

One of the features that I do like about this compiler is the use of the index register ("FSR") only for array variables. In the previous compilers that I have written, the FSR register was used for implementing a stack for execution operation. For "PICLite," I referenced individual file registers rather than using the FSR like a stack and pointing to a value.

This compiler is not at a final product level. Before I would expect it to be working at a level where I could expect money for the product, I would want to have added the macro processor for allowing structured constructs (such as "if" - "else" - "endif" and "while" - "endwhile"). Actually, one of the reasons why I haven't added the macro processor is because I would like to rewrite the compiler (the fourth version) to allow functions, rather than a mainline and an interrupt handler.

PICMICRO SUMMARY

30

Of all the devices I've presented in this book, I probably like the PICMicro the best. Now the cynical reader may feel that I like the PICMicro the best because I wrote my first book about the PICMicro (which places it in a special place in my heart). Actually, I have pretty good feelings about all the devices. The 6800 was the first microprocessor I learned to program, I worked a lot with the 8048 and 8051 after I left university, I like the AVR because its architecture is well designed for writing a high-level language compiler, and I like the Stamp because it was my introduction to the PICMicro.

The reason why I like the PICMicro really stems from the elegance of the design. Compared to the other microcontrollers, the PICMicro is very simple. This simplicity does have its price, however, in the ways that certain applications and programs have to be written. Of all the devices presented in this book, the PIC is the one that is the most difficult to sit down and start writing software for.

The simplicity of design is reflected in the instruction set, only 35 instructions, each one instruction cycle long, except when the program counter is not just incremented.

The two hardware features I appreciate most with the PICMicro are the ease of programming for the midrange parts, and I really like the internal oscillator of the 12C50x parts and I'm looking forward to when it is available on more PICMicros.

If I were to look at the things I would do differently in the PICMicro, the list would probably be pretty short. The two things I would change (or would like to see changed) are eliminating the two cycles required for gotos, calls, and returns, and modifying the stack hardware to make real-time operating systems possible in the PICMicro.

Changing the goto/call/return statements to one instruction cycle would make timing applications dead easy. There would be almost no need to insert "nops" or "Goto $+1s" in the code to make different branches of the same loop execute exactly the same way, irregardless of the path taken.

I feel that the PICMicro's inability to access the stack to be a major liability in being able to develop RTOSes (which are very useful in many applications). When I originally thought of this, I was thinking about putting in a method of reading and writing to the program counter stack, but as I thought about it, I realized that putting in an array of stacks would be the most efficient method of doing this. The idea would be that each task would have its own stack that would be selected in the RTOS kernal before a "retfie" instruction was executed to let it resume execution.

I realize the PICMicro architecture may seem strange and difficult to work with (especially if you're familiar with Von Neumann-architected processors), but after time I think you'll find that the PIC is a very efficient, easy-to-program, and easy-to-interface-to device.

PICMicro Resources

The PICMicro really has a lot of Web resources available for it. From hints to development systems and compilers to programmers and applications, there really isn't a better 'net-supported device.

PICMICRO WEB SITES

As I said above, a lot of the best resources for the PICMicro can be found on the Web. Here are my favorite eight Web sites, with some notes on what you can find. You may find other sites that you like better. I would appreciate it if you would let me know.

Microchip's Web site:

http://www.microchip.com

Containing:

- PICMicro datasheets and application notes.
- PICMicro FAQs.
- Microchip serial EEPROM datasheets and FAQs.
- PICMicro development tools (MPASM, MPSIM, MPLAB, etc.).
- Web resources.
- Microchip distributors and manufacturer's reps.

The "GNUPIC" Archive
http://www.execpc.com/~rdmiller/gnupic/
Containing:

■ Freeware assemblers/compilers/simulators with source.

Eric Smith's PIC Project Page:
http://www.brouhaha.com/~eric/pic
Containing:

■ Eric's projects.
■ "Tips and tricks."
■ PICMicro Web resources.

Ormix's English Home Page:
http://www.ormix.riga.lv/eng/index.htm
Containing:

■ PICMicro resource information.
■ Development (programmer) software.
■ Programmer schematics.
■ List of in-circuit emulators.
■ Kits and development boards.
■ Applications.

Fast Forward's Home Page (Administered by Andy Warren):
http://www.geocities.com/SiliconValley/2499
Containing:

■ The "Embedded Systems Answer Line," containing a list of questions and answers
  about the PICMicros (and other Microcontrollers).

David Tait's PIC Resource Page:
http://www.man.ac.uk/~mbhstdj/piclinks.html
Containing:

■ David Tait's programmer and software information.
■ List of PICMicro resources and products.

DonTronics Home Page (Administered by Don McKenzie):
http://www.dontronics.com
Containing:

■ Don's meeting place for designers and programmers.
■ PICMicro information and product references.
■ SIMM stick information.

Parallax Inc. Home Page:
http://www.parallaxinc.com
Containing:

■ PICMicro products and application notes.
■ Basic Stamp information and application notes.
■ Information on connecting to Parallax-run PICMicro and Stamp lists.

30

MICROCHIP PICMICRO

LISTSERVERS

The PICLIST is an Internet listserver that distributes PICMicro-related e-mail to a subscriber list. To join the list, send an e-mail note to: "listserv@mitvma.mit.edu" with the words "subscribe piclist" in the first line of the body (not the subject line).

To get off the list, send an e-mail note to: "listserv@mitvma.mit.edu" with the words "unsubscribe piclist" in the first line of the body.

One note about the PICLIST: while it is a terrific technical resource, it can be overwhelming with the volume of mail it generates (often 100+ email messages per day). Initially, you may want to monitor the PICLIST through list archives rather than subscribe.

The list archive is available at:

http://www.iversoft.com/piclist/

Parallax offers a listserver for the PICMicro (and BASIC Stamp) as well. You can subscribe to this by going to the Parallax Web site ("http://www.parallaxinc.com") and following through "Links" to the listserver request.

Microchip

Microchip Technology Inc.
2355 West Chandler Blvd.
Chandler, AZ 85224-6199
Tel: (602)782-7200
Fax: (602)899-9210
http://www.microchip.com

ATMEL "AVR"

THE AVR MICROCONTROLLER

Atmel's AVR is one of the new kids on the block in terms of microcontroller design and architecture. The AVR's processor design is described as a "high-performance and low-power RISC architecture" that is Harvard type, and certainly one of the device's strong points is its fast program execution. It runs with a single clock cycle per instruction cycle.

The AVR probably has the most versatile processor of any microcontroller presented in this book. This means that when developing an application, a bit more effort should be put

Figure 31.1. AVR 8515 in a PLCC package and a 1200 in a DIP package.

into planning data and register storage than you would normally do with the other microcontrollers. This versatility has made the device easy to program for both assembly language application developers as well as compiler creators.

As I write this, only the 8515 and 1200 devices are available. The 1200 is a "low-end"
device, which is a significantly cut-down version of the AVR RISC architecture. The 8515
contains the full AVR architecture and many of the features that will be available in the
family as more devices become available.

The major selling points of the AVR line are the exclusive use of EEPROM for control
store, in-system programmability and an extensive instruction set with an ability to run
most instructions in one clock cycle.

AVR PROCESSOR ARCHITECTURE

CONTENTS AT A GLANCE

After you have read the first section of this book, you probably feel like Harvard and Von Neumann architectures are quite straightforward and easily definable (after going through the 68HC05, this has probably been reinforced in your mind). But there are a number of different architectures that don't truly fit these models.

If you look at the AVR documentation, you'll see something like Figure 32.1. Although it is quite complex, you can trace through the various buses (lines in the diagram) and feel like you have a good idea of how bits and bytes flow through the processor. But there are a number of subtleties that are not readily apparent that I will explain.

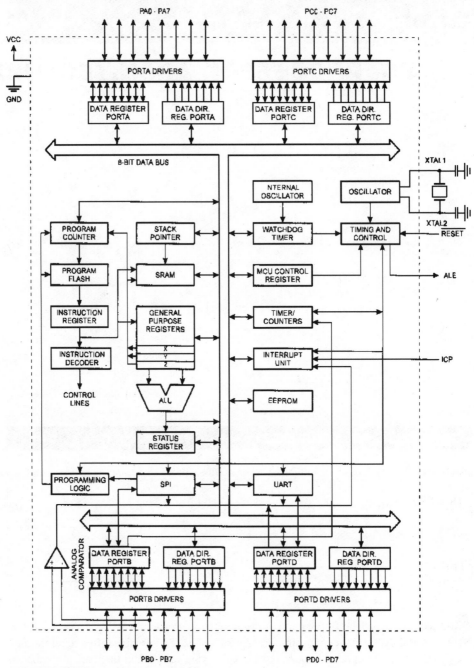

Figure 32.1 AVR 8515 block diagram by Atmel.

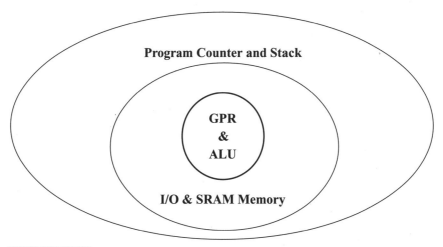

Figure 32.2 AVR processor architecture register priorities.

Like the subtleties in any processor, the AVRs stem from the philosophies that were used in designing the processor. As I went through the architecture, I discovered that the AVR is designed from the centre registers outwards, which can be shown graphically as Figure 32.2.

This philosophy has resulted in a processor that is very efficient at processing data. Not readily obvious in the previous two diagrams is how the AVR architecture has been optimized to take the best aspects of the Harvard and Princeton architectures to allow very fast and efficient software execution.

General-Purpose Registers and ALU

This simple general-purpose register/ALU core can execute 91 of the 120 instructions available within the AVR. Each one of these instructions uses the contents of the general-purpose registers ("GPRs") to carry out the operations. (Figure 32.3.)

Within this core, there are two types of instructions that can be executed. The arithmetic operations can operate on the contents of the GPRs, and the execution change instructions can only allow program execution to jump (but not call or save the current program counter) to another location inside the program. Later in this chapter, I will expand and explain how the program counter is actually implemented.

There is only one addressing mode for the GPR and ALU and that is register direct and is simply specifying the address of the register to be used. Either one or two registers can be specified by the instruction.

For example, adding two registers together and putting the result back into the first register is accomplished by using the "add" instruction:

```
add A, B
```

which can be written mathematically as:

$$A = A + B$$

or graphically as Figure 32.4.

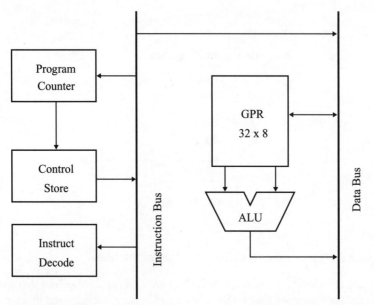

Figure 32.3 AVR general-purpose register and ALU block diagram.

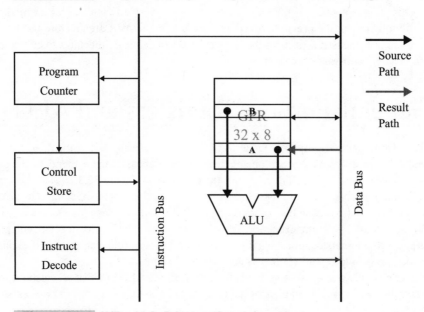

Figure 32.4 AVR add A, B instruction data paths.

A single register can be used in an instruction if a second parameter is not required (as in the complement instruction) or the second parameter is specified as part of the instruction. In the latter case, data is transferred from the "instruction bus" to the "data bus."

Adding a constant from a register is accomplished by:

```
adiw A, Const
```

which is:

$$A = A + Const$$

and shown graphically as Figure 32.5.

With this basic core, the program counter is assumed to increment after each instruction has been read in or be changed to a new value through the "jmp" ("Jump" or "goto") instruction (Figure 32.6).

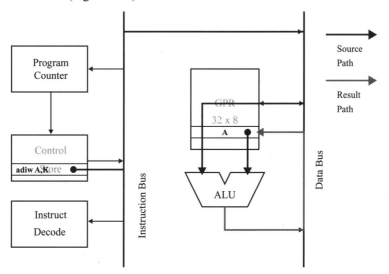

Figure 32.5 AVR adiw A, const instruction data paths.

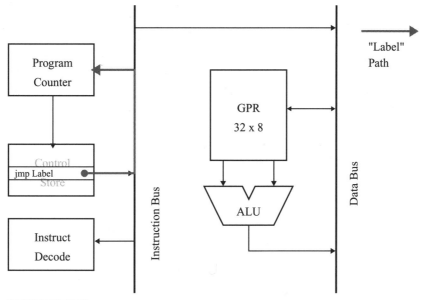

Figure 32.6 AVR jmp label instruction data paths.

32

ATMEL AVR

The STATUS Register

The first time you look at the AVR processor documentation and read through the "STATUS" register definition, you may be overwhelmed with all the bits available within it and their seemingly complex functions.

With the STATUS register, the AVR architecture becomes Figure 32.7.

The STATUS register becomes part of the I/O space (which is described in the subchapter below) and will record the state of the arithmetic operation. The bits are defined as:

BIT	ID	DESCRIPTION
0	C	Carry/Borrow Flag
1	Z	Zero Flag
2	N	Negative Flag
3	V	Two's Complement Overflow Flag
4	S	Sign Flag
5	H	Half Carry/Borrow Flag
6	T	Temporary Bit
7	I	Global Interrupt Enable

The most basic flag in the STATUS register is the "zero flag." This bit is set when the result of an operation is zero. When I go through the instructions, you should look at how many instructions modify this flag. This makes it a very inappropriate flag for passing parameters. Instead, the carry flag is a better choice (and traditional with many other applications and processors) and the "temporary bit" would be the best choice because of its ability to pass single bit values.

Like most microcontrollers and microprocessors, the "carry/borrow flag" is updated after an addition or subtraction. It is also used as a temporary MSB/LSB for rotate and shift instructions (this is also quite common in many microcontrollers).

The carry flag is set in addition if the result is greater than $FF while in subtraction, if the result is less than zero, then the carry flag is set.

The "half carry" flag is set after an addition or subtraction operation takes place, and the least significant nybble has to carry or borrow from the upper nybble.

For example, if you were adding "7" to a register that was loaded with "9":

```
add R16, R17    ;  R16 = 9, R17 = 7
```

Registers R16 contains 7, and when it's added to R17 (which contains 9), the result will be $10, which cannot be contained in the lower nybble. In this case, the "H" flag of the STATUS register would be set. If "A" contained a value less than 10, then the "H" flag would be reset.

Like all half carry/borrow flag implementations reviewed in this book, this bit is changed by a hex least significant digit carry/borrow. It doesn't change based on the decimal result. But if you are checking for a decimal carry, the half bit can be used with the

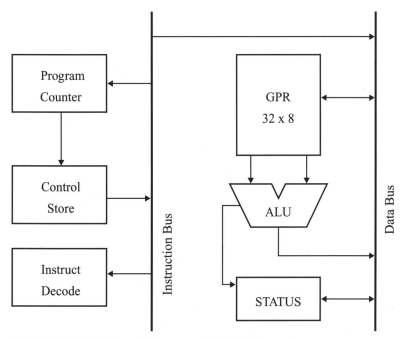

Figure 32.7 AVR architecture with STATUS register.

immediate add instruction as I've shown above. Adding "6" to a decimal value will set the Half Flag if the value is equal or greater to 10.

The "negative," "overflow," and "sign" flags may seem quite complex if you look at how they are set/reset in the arithmetic instructions. But they're actually very logical and straightforward to understand what they do and how they do it. These bits should only be checked after an addition/subtraction that may use or produce a negative two's complement number. As I go through each flag, please note that as I go along, each flag uses the results placed in the previously explained flags.

The "negative" flag is set when bit 7 (the most significant) bit of the result is set. When the most significant bit is set, it often notes that the result is negative. I should point out that the negative bit will be set when the result of a logical bit operation has the most significant bit set. In this case the negative bit should not be used for anything other than an indicator that the most significant bit was set after the operation (which may be required in some cases).

The "overflow" ("V") flag is somewhat more complicated than the other bits presented so far. (I was going to say that "overflow" is a bit more complicated, but that really is a terrible pun.) The "V" flag is set when adding or subtracting 2 two's complement numbers and the result is outside the valid two's complement range (for 8 bits it's -128 to $+127$).

When adding 2 two's complement numbers, the "V" flag will be set when the positive sum (or result) is greater than 127 or the negative sum is less than -128. The purpose of this bit is to provide an indication when the result is an invalid two's complement.

If you are thinking about what I've just written, you might be thinking that the result is a valid two's complement number. It just can't fit within the 8 bits of the register, and you'd be right. To help remedy this situation, the "sign flag" is used to resolve the situation. The "S" flag combines the results from the "N" and "V" flags to determine whether or not the result is positive or negative and, if the "V" flag is set, come up with a 9-bit two's complement number (as the result of adding or subtracting two 8-bit two's complement numbers).

After an operation that adds or subtracts two's complement numbers if the "V" flag is set, then the result is 9 bits long, with the most significant bit (the sign bit) being the "S" flag and the 8 bits of the result being stored in the 8-bit destination register.

The "T" bit is a temporary bit primarily used to store values from the "BST" and "BLD" instructions or used to pass single-bit parameters. While the "T" bit is not changed by any operations, it should be saved (along with the other STATUS bits) when an interrupt handler or subroutine is executed that could change the value.

The last flag is the global interrupt enable ("I"). When set, interrupt requests will be processed. When reset, interrupt requests will be left pending until the bit becomes set.

I/O and SRAM Addressing

Understanding how the general-purpose registers and how SRAM are accessed can be quite confusing. This is especially true when the low-end devices (i.e., the 1200) are lumped in with the "full" AVR devices (i.e., the 8515). In this subchapter, I will explain the "true" AVR memory and register architecture and then introduce the low-end device's differences.

How memory, general-purpose registers, and I/O registers are implemented in the AVR is really the only confusing aspect of the design. Or maybe it's just me.

What I find confusing is the two different ways these data areas can be accessed. The first method is to access each data area directly and uniquely. This direct access is the primary method of interfacing used by the arithmetic instructions. The other method of accessing combines the three register and memory areas (along with an external memory map) to create an unified "data address space." (Figure 32.8.)

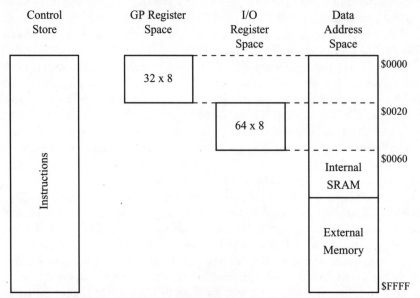

Figure 32.8 Full AVR processor architecture memory spaces.

The "I/O registers" is a 64-byte block that contains the processor operation registers as well as the I/O interface registers. "In" and "out" are the instructions used to pass data between the GPRs and the I/O registers.

The "internal SRAM" is a block of RAM which is used for variable storage. These bytes are accessed using the data address space "load" and "store" instructions (which can also access the GPRs and I/O registers as "data address space" locations).

The last area in the "data address space" is "external memory." All of the remaining 64K "data address space" can be set up as external SRAM (or memory mapped I/O devices). I will talk about setting up external memory in a later chapter.

While each device has different registers, there are a number that are common and at the same addresses in the "I/O register" space:

The other registers have I/O function registers, which are unique to the device and its hardware.

ADDRESSES

I/O	Data	RegName	Description
$3F	$5F	SREG	STATUS Register
$3E	$5E	SPH	Stack Pointer - High Byte
$3D	$5D	SPL	Stack Pointer - Low Byte
$3B	$5B	GIMSK	Interrupt Mask Register
$3A	$5A	GIFR	Interrupt Flag Register
$35	$55	MCUCR	Microntroller Control Register

32

ATMEL AVR

As I pointed out in the previous subchapter, for arithmetic instrucions, only the general-purpose registers are accessed, and their addresses are the same whether or not they are accessed through the GPR space (using the arithmetic instructions) or the data address space (using the "load"/"store" instructions).

The I/O registers can be accessed either via the "in"/"out" instructions in I/O space or using the "load"/"store" instructions in data address space. If the "load"/"store" instructions are used, the $20 (32 decimal) starting address (after the general-purpose registers) has to be added to the absolute addresses (this is shown in the table of common I/O registers above).

The "internal SRAM" and "external memory" can only be accessed through the data address space using the "load"/"store" instructions using absolute addresses. If external data is to be read, then the transfers will take one or two more execution cycles than if internal RAM was being accessed.

The "load"/"store" instructions are also enhanced by the use of index registers. In the GPR area, the last 6 registers can be used as 3 16-bit index registers, which can load data from either the data address space or program memory. These indices are known as "X" (Address $1A-$1B), "Y" (Address $1C-$1D) and "Z" (Address $1E-$1F).

The "Z" index can be used to read single bytes from control store as well. This allows tables to be implemented in control store.

From this, the AVR block diagram becomes Figure 32.9. In this block diagram, I have shown an "address bus" which is used to address registers and RAM. The address can be provided by a number of sources, reflecting that addresses can be specified explicitly in the instruction or use an index register.

For the low-end devices (notably the 1200), there are no SRAM and no instructions for accessing the GPRs and I/O registers reside in a single "data address space." (Figure 32.10.)

With the three data areas separate and none of them consolidated into a "data address space" the I/O registers can only be accessed by the "in" and "out" instructions, and the "load"/"store" instructions are virtually unused.

The low-end AVRs also only have one index register ("Z" located at $1E-$1F in the general-purpose register area). This index register can be used to access data either in the GPRs or the control store.

Program Counter and Stack

You will probably be surprised to find out that I have gone through 90% of the AVR architecture. The only really significant issue left to discuss is the program counter and how the stack is implemented. The stack implementation is a major differentiator between the low-end AVRs and the other devices.

In the low-end AVRs, the stack is a LIFO RAM added to the program counter. When a subroutine is called or an interrupt request executed, the contents of the program counter is pushed onto the stack. (Figure 32.11.)

In the 1200, this stack is only three entries deep. This means that you can have a maximum of three nested subroutines or two nested subroutines along with an active interrupt handler. This is quite a significant reduction in the capabilities of the microcontroller.

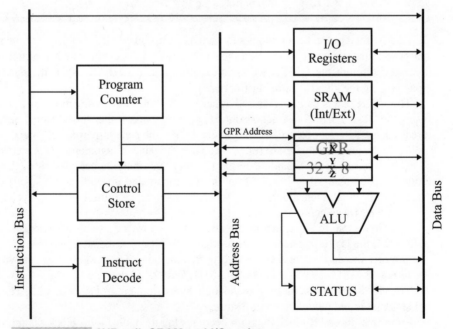

Figure 32.9 AVR wtih SRAM and I/O registers.

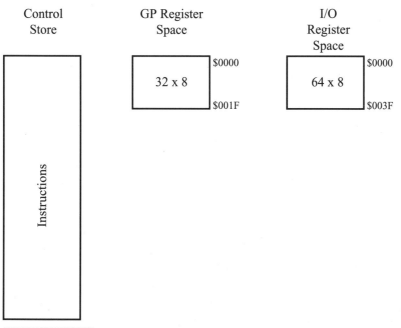

Figure 32.10 Low-end AVR processor architecture memory spaces.

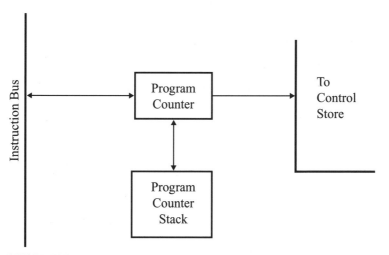

Figure 32.11 Low-end AVR processor program counter stack.

For the 1200 and other low-end AVRs, my block diagram is shown in Figure 32.12.

This stack restriction is not present in the other AVRs because they use the internal SRAM (and, possibly the external memory) for stack data storage. (Figure 32.13.)

This design allows all the RAM available in the AVR to be used for the stack. Being able to use a large amount of RAM for the stack allows a number of significant advantages in developing applications that I will review later in this section. The final block diagram for the AVR now becomes Figure 32.14.

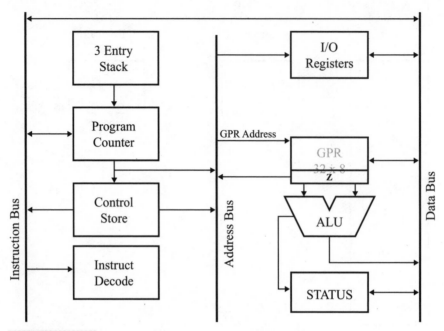

Figure 32.12 Low-end AVR block diagram with stack.

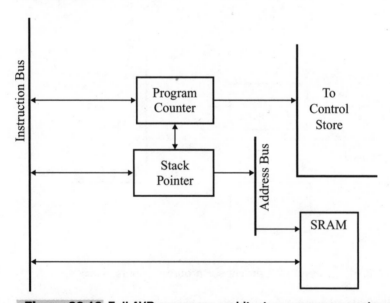

Figure 32.13 Full AVR processor architecture program counter stack.

With this, I am really finished with my discussion on the AVR architecture. Like for the other microcontroller processors, if you go back to the start of this chapter and compare my block diagram to Atmel's, you're going to notice that they are nothing alike. Even if you look at the simplified block diagram in the AVR documentation, you'll see that there is very little similarity between my block diagram and this one.

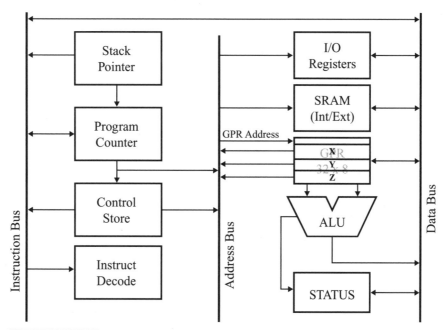

Figure 32.14 Full AVR processor architecture with stack pointer.

Now I'm probably worrying you; you now have three block diagrams for the devices and none of them look very much alike. Which one do you trust?

You should trust the one that makes the most sense to you. The block diagrams I have created for this chapter reflect my understanding of the architectures and how the instructions operate in them.

So, what happened here?

What you're seeing is one person's (my) interpretation of how the microcontroller is laid out. I don't have any special understanding or knowledge of how the die is laid out. What I have done is gone through the instructions and addressing modes and tried to understand how they work together. As you will see in the AVR instructions chapter, the final architecture that I have come up with (Figure 32.14) will execute all the instructions and I will use it to demonstrate both the addressing modes and the instruction data paths.

Interrupts

Interrupts in the AVR are more of an application-specific issue than an architectural one. I make this statement because it is very possible to write an interrupt handler that makes absolutely no changes to the context information (the stack, STATUS, and other registers) and some in which all the 32 GPRs and some of the special-purpose registers are saved.

In terms of what happens inside the processor during an interrupt, it is very simple; if an interrupt request is pending and the "I" flag of the STATUS register is set, then the address of the next instruction is stored on the stack and execution jumps to the appropriate interrupt vector address. When the interrupt request is acknowledged and execution jumps to the vector, the "I" flag is reset to prevent any interrupts from occurring inside the interrupt handler.

The STATUS register's "I" flag is set at the end of the interrupt handler when the "reti" instruction is executed. It can also be set inside the interrupt handler (after the context registers are saved) to allow nested interrupts. As many nested interrupts as there is room on the stack for the program counters and context register can be executed in the midrange and above AVRs. This is not true for the low-end AVRs, where the limited stack (three positions) will very quickly run out in nested interrupt or subroutine situations.

Data Addressing Modes

As you go through the AVR instructions chapter, you'll probably be amazed at the number of different data addressing modes available within the full AVR architecture. I wanted to give you a better idea of how the AVR processes instructions and how the instructions access the GPRs, I/O registers, and SRAM.

The most basic method of accessing data is directly to a general-purpose register. Typically, five bits are provided in the instruction, which allows any of the regisers to be accessed.

In an instruction that just accesses one GPR directly, the block diagram looks like Figure 32.15.

A typical instruction uses this for operating on one register (i.e., increment, decrement, negate, clear, etc.). Some of these instructions repeat the address in the instruction bits twice.

Two register instructions operate in much the same way:

In these instructions, the destination register ("D") is also be the first source (or first parameter).

```
  add R0, R1
Actually executes as:
```

$$R0 = R0 + R1$$

These previous two addressing modes are known as register direct. (Figure 32.16.)

A data parameter can also be defined as part of the instruction. In other microcontrollers, this is known as an "immediate" instruction. I would call it "immediate register direct" in the AVR. (Figure 32.17.)

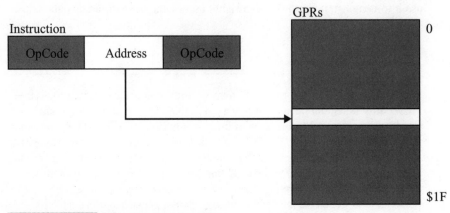

Figure 32.15 AVR direct addressing.

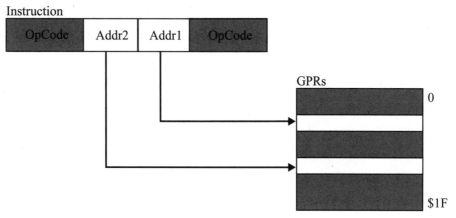

Instruction

Figure 32.16 AVR direct addressing to 2 GPRs.

Instruction

OpCode	Imm	Addr	Imm

Figure 32.17 AVR immediate addressing.

A good example of this type of instruction is "ORI." I wanted to bring this type of instruction to your attention for one very important reason. Because there are only 4 bits available for the register address, you can typically only access the most significant 16 GPRs. This obviously will have some impact on how you specify your working registers. In fact, I would recommend that the "working registers" are kept in the high 16 GPRs ($10 to $1F).

The last form of direct addressing accesses the entire memory map using a second word for a 16-bit address:

In this type of instruction, data is passed to/from the GPRs to the entire memory set. There are two things to point out with these instructions. The first is, again only the high 16 GPRs can be accessed, while the second is, these instructions are not available in the low-end AVRs (i.e., 1200). This means that in the low-end devices, the "in" and "out" instructions are used as a two register direct instruction to pass data between the GPR and I/O register sets.

The last type of data accessing is the indirect instructions. If you've looked at the AVR data sheets already, you'll have seen that five diagrams are used to represent the single diagram shown in Figure 32.18.

Figure 32.18 only shows the register indirect addressing and not the "predecrement" and "postincrement" options of the instructions.

The basic register indirection instructions uses the contents of the index register as the address to access. This is a very similar method to the index modes available in most other microcontrollers. I should point out that this is the only mode available in the low-end AVR (with only the "Z" index register available to access the GPRs and not the GPRs and I/O registers as a combined register space).

In this mode the index register value is not changed. A positive offset value can be added to the register indirection to get the actual address (this is known as "data indirect

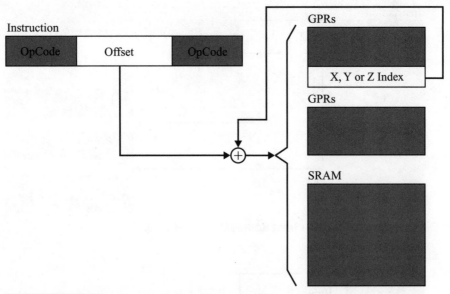

Figure 32.18 AVR indirect addressing to GPR/data memory.

with displacement"). The offset can be 0 to 63 and is added to the index value. I would see this instruction type best suited for implementing a pointer to a data structure with the off-set pointing to the appropriate element of the structure. The resulting address is not saved.

Some other register indirection modes are the "data indirection with predecrement" and "data indirection with post-increment." In these instructions, the index value is changed as part of the instruction (either before or after the data access). The (very significant) advantage of these types of instructions is their ability to simulate a stack, but with the added feature that they can also be used as indexes to data structures. This makes the AVR very well suited to developing compilers for languages with "automatic" variables.

When you read through the Atmel AVR data sheets, you'll see that they go on to show how control store data can be accessed, as well as providing the necessary explanation of how the program counter is changed. I've left this for the "AVR Instruction" chapter because these actions are much more instruction specific (although they do use the concepts introduced here).

AVR HARDWARE FEATURES

CONTENTS AT A GLANCE

The first impression I got when I saw the AVR 1200's data sheet was that this was a device that I would consider a later generation from the other devices in this book. Many of the features that are available show improvements over the same features available in the other devices reviewed in this book and have, for the most part, taken the best features of the different devices. This is not to say that every hardware feature will work so simply that a single instruction is all that's required to use a feature, but instead it's the next step in improving the internal resources of a microcontroller.

Packaging

The packaging for the AVR is very simple (especially when you compare it against the multitudes of different packages available for the 8051, 68HC05 and PIC); Atmel only currently provides plastic packaging and standard package types. (Figure 33.1.) The pin layout makes the devices almost (except for "reset") pin compatable with the 8051.

The "PDIP" packages are plastic DIPS with 0.100" (100 mil) spacing between lead centres. The SMT parts have 0.05" lead spacing.

While the AVR is very straightforward, the one thing I would like to bring to your attention is how the "PLCC" (for the 8515) part is implemented. If you look that the 8515's pin definitions, you'll see that the pins are defined exactly the same as the PDIP version, although with the inclusion of "no connect" pins at the middle of each side.

This is a really nice and thoughtful feature. You may not have a lot of experience with SMT, but I personally hate working with PTH prototypes and find that SMT versions of the parts have a radically different pin out, along with extra Vccs and grounds. With this layout philosophy, SMT production cards can be derived from PDIP prototypes with a minimum of fuss and rewiring.

System Clock

For the most part the AVR system clock (or oscillator) seems quite straightforward, but there are a few things to know for specifying the application speed or programming the

1200
(PDIP/SOIC/SSOP)

_Reset	Vcc
PD0	PB7 (SCK)
PD1	PB6 (MISO)
XTAL2	PB5 (MOSI)
XTAL1	PB4
PD2 (INT0)	PB3
PD3	PB2
PD4 (T0)	PB1 (AIN1)
PD5	PB0 (AIN0)
Gnd	PD6

8515 PDIP

PB0 (T0)	Vcc
PB1 (T1)	PA0 (AD0)
PB2 (AIN0)	PA1 (AD1)
PB3 (AIN1)	PA2 (AD2)
PB4 (_SS)	PA3 (AD3)
PB5 (MISO)	PA4 (AD4)
PB6 (MISO)	PA5 (AD5)
PB7 (SCK)	PA6 (AD6)
_Reset	PA7 (AD7)
PD0 (RXD)	ICP
PD1 (TXD)	ALE
PD2 (INT0)	OC1B
PD3 (INT1)	PC7 (A15)
PD4	PC6 (A14)
PD5 (OC1A)	PC5 (A13)
PD6 (_WR)	PC4 (A12)
PD7 (_RD)	PC3 (A11)
XTAL2	PC2 (A10)
XTAL1	PC1 (A9)
Gnd	PC0 (A8)

Figure 33.1 AVR 1200 and 8515 PDIP packages.

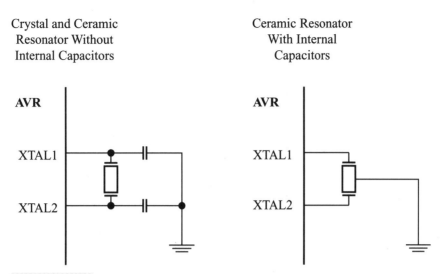

Figure 33.2 AVR crystal and ceramic resonator system oscillator wiring.

device (which requires a working oscillator). Also, there are some issues that will affect how you develop software for the application.

The first issue that you have to be cognizant of with the AVR is the instruction timing; most microcontrollers require multiple clock cycles, but the AVR uses one clock cycle per instruction cycle. This means that when timing an application, your job is simplified somewhat because most instructions execute at the speed of the system clock.

The AVR can use three different system clock sources; a crystal or ceramic resonator, an external clock, or an optional internal RC oscillator. The typical frequency range for the AVR is 0 to 16 MHz. I should point out that coupled with the single clock cycle per instruction cycle, the AVR really screams (especially at 16 MHz).

Now, is it fair to say that a 1-MHz AVR is equivalent to a 2-MHz 68HC05, a 4-MHz PIC, or a 12-MHz 8051? Definitely not.

It's not fair to compare because the different architectures operate differently and I wouldn't be surprised if you wrote PIC, 8051, and 68HC05 applications that all ran faster than the AVR, even with a slower clock. This is why I am always hesitant to say one architecture is "Best" and runs faster or more efficiently than any of the others.

Crystals and ceramic resonators can be simply connected to the AVR as shown in Figure 33.2.

If one of these circuits is used, do not drive other devices from either one of the "XTAL" pins.

The AVR can be driven by an external clock signal by driving the "XTAL1" pin. If you are going to use one clock with multiple AVRs, I recommend that you use the circuit shown in Figure 33.3.

The last method of driving the AVR system clock is to use an internal RC oscillator. This feature is currently only available on the 1200 and provides a 1-MHz clock. This feature is selected as a configuration fuse when the part is parallel programmed. The internal RC oscillator cannot be selected while serially programming the part.

33

ATMEL AVR

To Multiple
AVRs

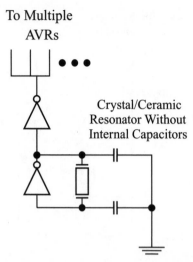

Crystal/Ceramic
Resonator Without
Internal Capacitors

Figure 33.3 AVR external crystal oscillator source.

A few points about the RC oscillator; the first is, you can only expect a 10% tolerance for this clock (which means it cannot be used for any applications that require any kind of timing accuracy). The fact that the internal RC oscillator can only be enabled during parallel programming may limit its usefulness in some situations—although to mitigate this, Atmel has made the "1200A" available, which has the internal RC oscillator enabled at the factory.

Timers

The AVR's programmable timers/counters, while being somewhat different in implementation to the counters available in the other microcontrollers, do provide all of the features required for microcontroller operation.

The source to the timers/counters can either be the instruction (CPU) clock or an external clock. The internal CPU clock can be prescaled or used directly; the clock source and prescaling is selected by an multiplexer. (Figure 33.4.)

The "CSxn" bits are located in the timer control register ("TCCR0"). In the AVR 8515, which has two timer/counter circuits, there are two of these multiplexer circuits—one for each of the timers. In the 1200, there is only one multiplexer circuit and timer. The timer itself increments on the rising edge of the input signal. This is why the inverted external pin clock input is available. I should point out that the external clock is sampled on the rising edge of the CPU clock.

Timer0 is a pretty simple 8-bit timer that can be read from or written to (turning off the clock is accomplished by selecting the "grounded" input at the clock multiplexer) with a maskable interrupt on counter overflow. (Figure 33.5.)

Timer1 is much more complex and can carry out pulse timing as well as time PWM output from the AVR. (Figure 33.6.) This timer can work in the same manner as Timer0 (and taking into account that Timer1 is 16 bit, while Timer0 is 8 bits wide) but its real power is using the extra functions as an event or PWM timer.

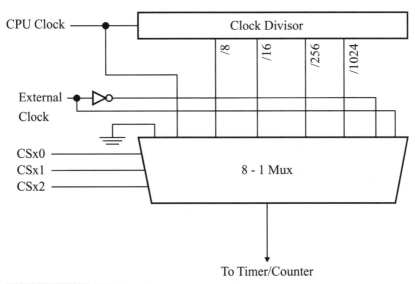

Figure 33.4 AVR timer/counter prescaler.

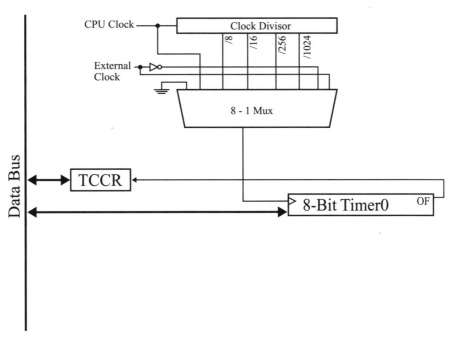

Figure 33.5 AVR Timer0 block diagram.

33

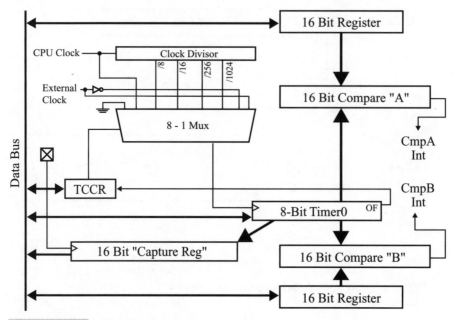

Figure 33.6 AVR Timer1 block diagram.

As an event timer, Timer1 will save (capture) the timer value at an arbitrary instant (which is defined by the change in the capture input pin). This "capture input pin" is run through a "noise canceller," which waits for a debounced signal to come through. If you are measuring an input pulse (by changing the edge select between captures), you shouldn't be worried about this debounce because it will be constant for both the leading and trailing edges of the pulse.

There are two PWM modes that are available in Timer1. The first mode causes interrupt requests when the compare "A" and "B" values match the current timer value. Also, when Timer1 matches the value in the compare "B" 16-bit register, the timer can be reset, restarting the PWM signal.

The output with code executing at the transition points is shown as Figure 33.7. Note that the Interrupt handlers are only two instructions long; for the compare interrupts, there are no "IF" flags which need to be reset.

The second PWM mode is to use the PWM to output (on Pin OC1A) a PWM signal (eliminating the need to provide code to handle the signal output). In this mode, the timer counts up to a "top" value, and when CmpA or CmpB is matched, the OC1A pin is toggled to a new state. When the timer reaches the "top" value, it begins to count down and the cycle is repeated.

In Figure 33.8, the Timer1 value is represented as a triangle wave, which is the numeric value in Timer1 at an instant in time. The Compare Value is the CmpA or CmpB value.

WATCHDOG TIMER

The AVR's watchdog timer consists of a separate timer with its own 1-MHz oscillator that when enabled will count for a specified period of time, and if it overflows without a "WDR" instruction to reset it, the microcontroller will be reset. (Figure 33.9.)

The watchdog timer is enabled by setting the "WDE" bit of the watchdog timer control register ("WDTCR"). The value in "WDP0" to "WDP2" determines the length of time before the watchdog timer resets the microcontroller.

WDP2	WDP1	WDP0	TIME OUT PERIOD
0	0	0	16 msec
0	0	1	32 msec
0	1	0	64 msec
0	1	1	128 msec
1	0	0	256 msec
1	0	1	512 msec
1	1	0	1.024 sec
1	1	1	2.048 sec

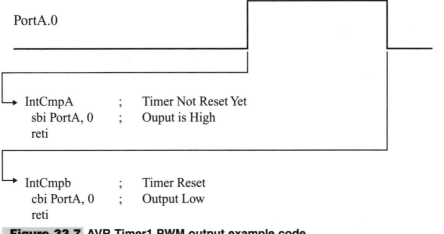

Figure 33.7 AVR Timer1 PWM output example code.

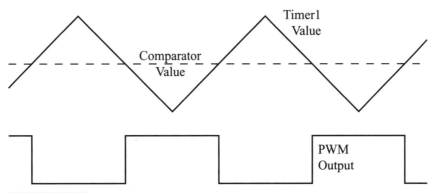

Figure 33.8 AVR PWM Timer1 values.

33

ATMEL AVR

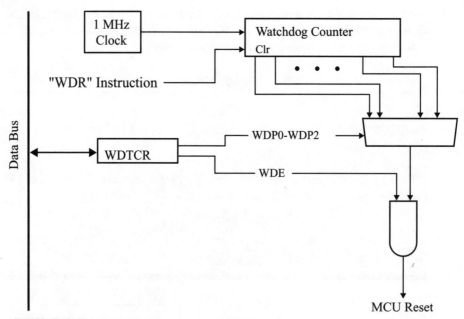

Figure 33.9 AVR watchdog timer block diagram.

In the AVR 1200, the watchdog timer can be shut off by simply resetting the WDE bit. In the 8515, there is an additional bit, the "WDTTOE," which must be set no more than four cycles before the WDE is disabled. This can be accomplished by the following code:

```
sbi     WDTCR, WDTTOE     ;  Enable the resetting of the WDT
cbi     WDTCR, WDE        ;  Turn off the WDT
```

The WDTTOE bit and its operation is designed to prevent a program from inadvertently turning off the watchdog timer. Like similar operations in other microcontrollers where the timing is critical for the operation, before executing the code above, interrupts should be globally disabled during its execution to make sure that an interrupt request isn't executed after the "sbi" instruction.

If you are planning on enabling the watchdog timer from somewhere other than the start (power up/reset) of your application, then before setting "WDE," you should reset the watchdog timer (using the "WDR" instruction). This will make sure the watchdog timer is in a known state before its processor reset is enabled and you don't get an inadvertent reset before it's expected.

Parallel Input/Output

When I first looked at the 8515's data sheet, I was surprised by all the different diagrams for the parallel I/O pins. There are literally 15 different diagrams showing how each pin works with the different I/O functions. As I go through the pin operation here, I just want to focus in on the basic pin I/O and not the enhanced features (which will be described later in the chapter), which looks like Figure 33.10.

This should give you an idea of how the pins work. With each block of pins (known as a "port bit") there are three I/O address associated with them: the I/O port value, the data direction ("1" for the bit to be output, "0" for a bit to be input), and a read value for the actual pin value. Along with this, there is the capability to enable a pullup in input mode, and there are a few pins that can cause an interrupt by their state.

Reading back a value can either be done at the I/O pin (look at the actual I/O value) or at the output of the "port register." Where the output value is read can be quite an important issue for an I/O pin; if a pin is overdriven or accidentally shorted to ground or Vcc, the output state will never change. Having a method to compare the contents of the output port and seeing what is actually at the pin could be important in some situations.

While the pins work similarly to other microcontrollers' pins, there should be one difference from the other device's pins that should be fairly obvious. This difference is that the internal pin pull up is not controlled by a separate register bit.

Instead it uses a combinatorial circuit to enable the pin's pull up (which is only active when the I/O pin is in "input" mode). In Figure 33.11, I show how the AVR is set to read a button pulling down the pin to ground:

Serial I/O

The AVR's SPI and UART serial ports work very similarly to the serial I/O ports available in other microcontrollers. The SPI is capable of serially transferring data to another AVR

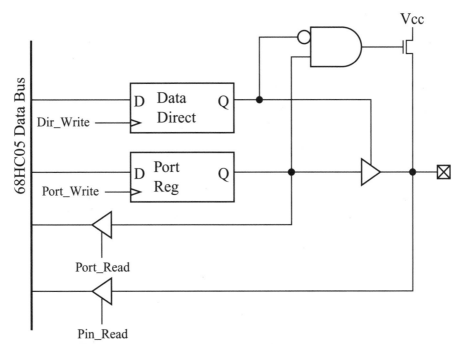

Figure 33.10 AVR parallel I/O pin block diagram.

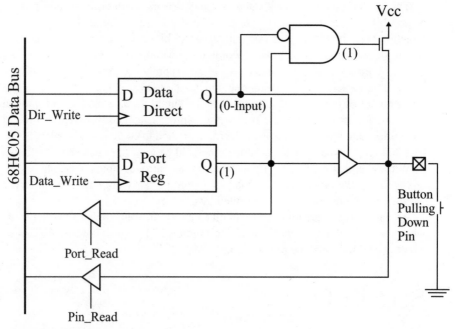

Figure 33.11 AVR parallel I/O pin with pull-up active.

or a parallel in/out shift register. Complex synchronous protocols (i.e., I2C or CAN) are not available as hardware options for the AVR.

UART

Asynchronous serial data can be transmitted and received in full duplex mode through the UART module in the higher-end AVRs (i.e., the 8515). The AVR's UART works very similarly to other microcontroller's UARTs in that it does not have the same capabilities to manufacture a parity bit.

The baud rate generator is at the heart of the UART. It is a programmable counter that provides a 16 times clock to the UART's transmitter and receiver. The count value to be put into the "UART baud rate register" ("UBRR") is:

```
UBBR = f / ( 16 * Data_Rate) - 1
```

Like other data rate generators, the value should be checked for the error rate (actual data rate to the desired data rate) before using the specified crystal and UBRR value.

The baud rate generator's output is 16 times the actual data rate to allow the receiver to sample the incoming line and find the approximate halfway point of the bit stream.

The UART's receiver block diagram looks like Figure 33.12. In this circuit, the "edge detect" logic determines whether or not a low encountered on a line is actual data or a "glitch." If it's data, it determines the middle of the bit and specifies when the "RX shift register" should start polling the incoming data bits.

The "edge detect" hardware also updates the "UART status register" ("USR") when a byte has been received or if there is an error condition like the RX register is overwritten (i.e., data has been received before the previously received data in the RX register has been read) or a framing error (data is coming in at a different size of data rate than what's expected—this is usually determined by a missing "stop bit"). Receiving data and resetting the receiver is accomplished by reading the RX Register ("UART data register"—"UDR").

If you guessed that the UART's transmitter was not more than a shift-out register, you'd be correct (see Figure 33.13). The output control allows data to be shifted out, or an idle bit of "1" to be sent. The sending of a character is simply accomplished by writing a byte to the "UDR" (which is the "TXHolding Register" in Figure 33.13).

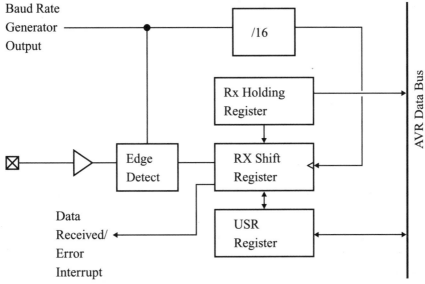

Figure 33.12 AVR serial receiver block diagram.

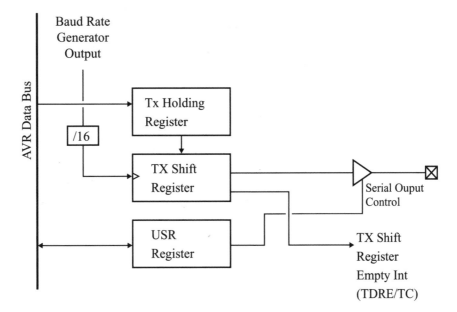

Figure 33.13 AVR serial transmitter block diagram.

Like other UARTs, the AVR's "TX Holding" register can be loaded while another character is being shifted out. Keeping the TX Holding register loaded as soon as the shift register is loaded and the previous character is being shifted out will give you the maximum data output rate (i.e., the start bit of a data byte running right after the stop bit of the previous byte).

SPI

While the "SPI" port is available on all AVRs for serial ("ISP") programming (which is described later in this chapter), it is only available on some devices for interfacing with external devices. In these devices, the "SPI" works very similarly to the 68HC05's SPI port. (Figure 33.14.)

The four pins of the SPI are used to interface with external devices. For example, having an AVR master and AVR slave communicate together would be implemented as Figure 33.15. With the master initiating the data transfers, note that the SCK pin has changed from output to input in the "slave" device.

To enable the SPI hardware, the "SPE" bit of the "SPI control register" ("SPCR") must be set. Inside this register, the master mode can be selected, but if the "_SS" pin is pulled low, then the SPI will only run in slave mode.

The "SPR" bits of the SPCR are used to specify the data transmission speed in the master. One important aspect to note on this is that an external clock cannot be used with the master and there are only four different instruction clock divisors available. To get a particular, very fast speed, you may have to change the speed the AVR runs at.

Data transfers are initiated in the master by writing to the SPI data register ("SPDR") and polling (or waiting for an interrupt) on the "SPIF" bit of the "SPI status register" ("SPSR") to determine when the transfer has completed.

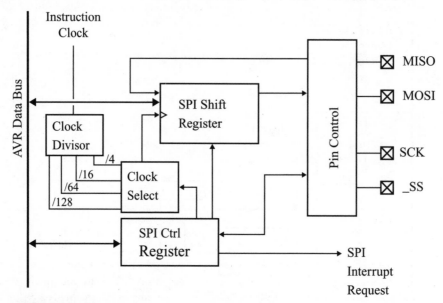

Figure 33.14 AVR synchronous serial I/O port.

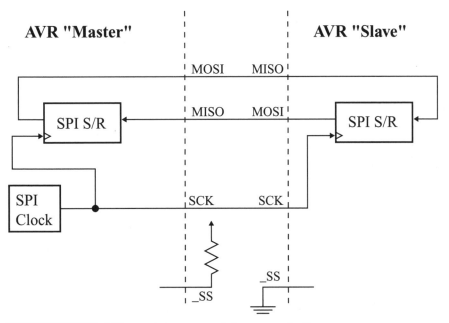

Figure 33.15 AVR synchronous serial communication.

Analog Input/Output

At the present time, the analog I/O capabilities of the AVR microcontrollers is limited to a built-in analog voltage comparator. The comparator in the AVR gives you the ability to not only compare to a reference voltage, but measure pulse widths using a built-in timer.

The comparator may seem to be a bit more complex than you might expect. (See Figure 33.16.) The output of the comparator is high when the voltage at the positive input (pin "AIN0") is greater than the voltage at the negative input (Pin "AIN1"). This output can be used to drive a number of different interrupt options as specified in the "analog comparator and status register" ("ACSR"):

ACIS1	ACIS0	INTERRUPT TYPE
0	0	Interrupt on Comparator Output Toggle
1	0	Interrupt on Comparator Output Fall
0	1	Interrupt on Comparator Output Rise

Or the "ACO" bit of the ACSR can be polled to read the actual value of the comparator output.

In low-power applications, you may want to turn off the comparator. This is done by setting the "ACD" bit of the ACSR. Before you turn on or off the comparator, interrupts should be masked (by resetting the "ACIE" bit in ACSR) to ensure that there are no spurious interrupt requests from the comparator hardware.

33

ATMEL AVR

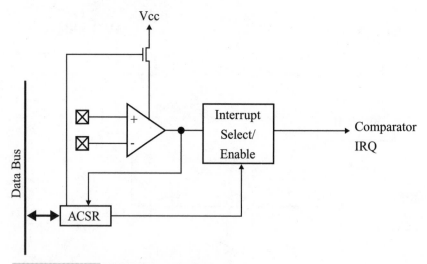

Figure 33.16 AVR voltage comparator.

In the AVR8515, the current timer/counter1 enable pin can be connected to the comparator output, and the point in time when the output rises or falls can be captured by setting the "ACIC" bit of ACSR. In this function, the width of a pulse entered into the comparator can be measured (this is also possible for the "ICP" pin, but using the comparator allows capturing or pulses at different voltage levels than the standard I/O pin).

To measure a TTL/CMOS level pulse using the compator/timer combination, the output of a simple voltage divider (using two 10K resistors) can be connected to the negative input of the comparator (pin AIN1).

Configuration

In the AVR, there are two types of configuration bits. The "fuse" bits are used for selecting the operating mode of the AVR, while the "lock bits" perform a similar function to the lock bits of the 8051. While not as structured as the "configuration fuses" of the PIC, these bits do allow you to specify the programming and operating functions of the AVR.

The "fuse bits" vary from device to device. In the 1200, "RCEN" when set is used to enable the internal RC oscillator (and ignore any external oscillators). The "SPIEN" bit, when reset, is used to allow serial (ISP) programming of the device. In all 1200s, the "SPIEN" bit is shipped reset and the "RCEN" bit is also reset (although you can order 1200As, which are shipped with this bit set).

The 8515 has the "SPIEN" bit as well as the "FSTRT" bit, which will allow a short start-up time (i.e., if an external oscillator is used as the clock) instead of the typical 16-msec power-up interval.

The "fuse bits" cannot be accessed during serial programming. They must be set or reset during parallel programming.

The "lock bits" are used to deny access to the AVR's EEPROM control store. When lock bit 1 is programmed, additional programming of the flash is not allowed and when lock bit 2 is programmed, the AVR's EEPROM cannot be read back.

EEPROM Data Memory

Reading and writing the EEPROM data memory in the AVR is quite simple and reliable. My only suggestion for Atmel would be to put the EEPROM memory in the data space (above the I/O registers) so that data could be read directly from the AVR's memory map. This isn't something I'd necessarily recommend for other devices (i.e., the PIC) because they don't have the large register/variable space of the AVR.

Accessing the EEPROM is done through a register-indexed address with the address stored in the "EEAR" register(s). If there are more than 256 bytes of EEPROM (as in the 8515) then there are two address registers ("EEARH" for the high byte of the address and "EEARL" for the low byte). These registers must have the correct address before a read or write can complete.

Writing to the AVR's EEPROM data memory is done by:

1. Wait for the "EEWE" bit of the EEPROM control register ("EECR") to be reset.
2. Updating EEAR with the correct address (optional).
3. Updating the EEPROM data register ("EEDR") with the correct value (optional).
4. Setting the "EEMWE" bit in the EECR. This can be done using the "SBI" Instruction. This bit is not available in the 1200.
5. Within 4 clock cycles of 4, the "EEWE" bit of the EECR is set to start the EEPROM write. The EEPROM write takes 2.5 to 4 msecs.

The purpose of the "EEMWE" bit in the 8515's EECR is to provide a hardware interlock to make it more difficult for a register that is running amok to accidentally put data in the EEPROM.

Reading from the EEPROM is similar:

1. Wait for the "EEWE" bit of the EECR to be reset.
2. Update the EEAR register(s)(optional).
3. Set the "EERE" bit of the EECR.
4. Read the value in EEDR.

The EEPROM write has to be complete before the software can attempt to read a byte.

Something that you should be aware of (although probably not critical to the operation of your software) is that after the "EERE" bit is set, the CPU is halted for two cycles while the data is fetched from the EEPROM memory. This means that the SBI EECR, EERE instruction (which initiates the read operation) actually takes three cycles instead of one.

Programming

The AVR is unusual because it can be programmed two different ways, using a parallel or serial protocol. For most production, the parallel mode is used because it is the fastest way of doing it and can access all the features of the AVR. The serial protocol is designed for use in manufacturing for programming the parts after the AVR has been soldered to the board.

33

ATMEL AVR

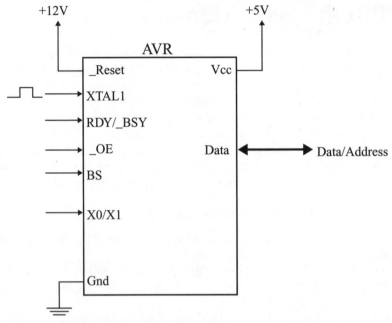

Figure 33.17 AVR parallel programming connections.

PARALLEL PROGRAMMING

The basic programming mode for the AVR is similar to what's used for the 8051. (See Figure 33.17.)

The control lines on the left side of the diagram above are for controlling the programming of the chip. Before any programming action can take place, the appropriate command has to be loaded in first. When the command is loaded in, the XA1/XA0 bits are set to 1/0 to indicate that the data bits are a command byte. The command byte bits are defined as:

BIT	DESCRIPTION
0	EEPROM type to Access (0 - Control Store/1 - Data)
1	Read from Control Store/Data
2	Read Lock and Fuse Bits
3	Read Signature Bits
4	Write Control Store/Data EEPROM
5	Write Lock Bits
6	Write Fuse Bits
7	Erase Chip

The "lock bits" are used to prevent additional code from being burned into the AVR after the device has been programmed or prevent unauthorized reading of the code loaded into the device. The lock bits can only be reset when an "erase chip" command is executed. The fuse bits are used to control the operation of the AVR (such as a short power-up or using the internal RC oscillator). The fuses can only be loaded during parallel programming.

The control bits are actually quite self-explanatory. The "XA1"/"XA0" bits are used to control the programming mode. "00" is an address load, "01" is a data load and "10" is used to load a command. I should point out that all commands are four bytes long. If the command needs less than four bytes (i.e., "Erase Chip" really only requires one byte), then the "XTAL1" line is still toggled four times for the instruction to execute (or the "_OE" line is toggled to read the data).

The "_OE" and "WR" bits are used to input/output data. The "BS" bit specifies whether or not the high or low byte of the control store is being accessed.

With all the bits combined, I can show that to program an instruction byte, the waveform shown in Figure 33.18 is used.

From Figure 33.18, all of the operations of the different pins should be pretty obvious. To "load" control store, the XA1/XA0 pins are set and the command $10 is output onto the data bits. Notice that when sending the address low/high that the BS bit follows the "physical address" with least significant byte first followed by the most significant.

Reading a byte from control store or EEPROM follows the conventions established for the write as is shown in Figure 33.19.

Every AVR is equipped with three "signature" bytes, which are read out as three consecutive reads after command $08 is sent to the AVR.

SERIAL PROGRAMMING

A I noted above, serial downloading of the EEPROM is designed to be implemented when the AVR is soldered into the circuit. The electrical hook up of the part to be programmed is actually quite simple. (Figure 33.20.)

Data is transmitted to and received from the device to be programmed using a synchronous serial protocol. (Figure 33.21.)

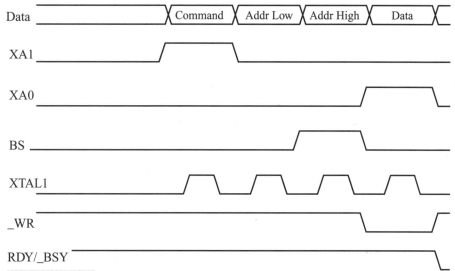

Figure 33.18 AVR parallel programming write.

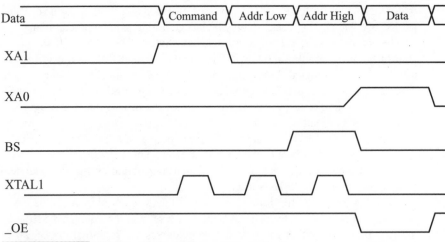

Figure 33.19 AVR parallel programming read.

Figure 33.1 is not to scale. The crystal oscillator should be running at about 1 MHz (although a 1200 or other AVR with a built-in RC clock that has been enabled by a parallel programming could be used instead). The high part of the clock should be more than four clock cycles long (greater than 4 usec with a 1-MHz clock) and the low longer than one clock cycle.

Programming commands require four bytes and are described in the following format:

INSTRUCTION	BYTE 1	BYTE 2	BYTE 3	BYTE 4
Programming Enable	1010 1100	0101 0011	xxxx xxxx	xxxx xxxx
Chip Erase	1010 1100	100x xxxx	xxxx xxxx	xxxx xxxx
Read Program	0010 B000	Addr High	Addr Low	Data Read
Write Program	0100 B000	Addr High	Addr Low	Data
Read EEPROM	1010 0000	xxxx xxx0	Addr	Data Read
Write EEPROM	1100 0000	xxxx xxx0	Addr	Data
Write Lock Bits	1010 1100	111x x21x	xxxx xxxx	xxxx xxxx
Read Device Code	0011 0000	xxxx xxxx	xxxx xxbb	Code at "bb"
("B" - 0 for Low Byte/1 for High Byte)				
("1" - Lock Bit 1, "2" Lock Bit 2)				

There are a few things to watch for when programming the AVR. The first is that to bring up the AVR in serial programming mode, at power up the _RST and SCK pins must be held low for 20 msec before starting. If the AVR's memory is not blank, then the "chip erase" command has to be executed after power up, then wait for 10 msec and make reset high and repeat the power up into serial programming mode.

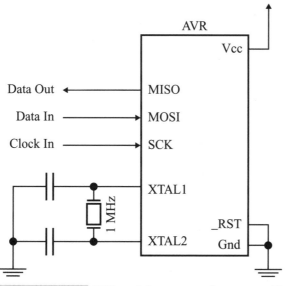

Figure 33.20 AVR serial programming connections.

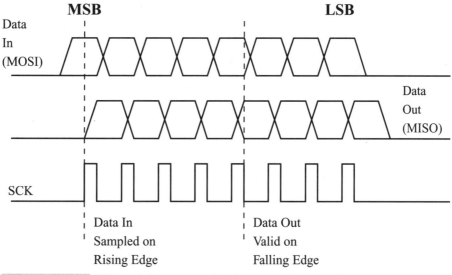

Figure 33.21 AVR serial programming byte transfer waveform.

33

ATMEL AVR

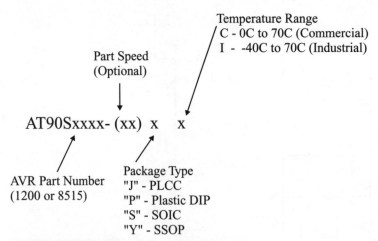

Figure 33.22 AVR part number definition.

The data EEPROM memory does not have to be erased. This is because the control store is "flash" (which means it has a single erase feature) and not EEPROM, in which each byte is erased automatically as the first action of the programming cycle.

The last thing to watch for in AVR serial programming (and, in my mind, the most important) is that there is no way to poll the EEPROM and program memory flash to find out when the write operations have completed. In your software, you will have to put in delays for the writes (10 msec for control store erase and 4 msec for EEPROM and control store data writes).

Ordering Information

Atmel knows the AVR as the "AT90Sxxxx" (where "xxxx" is the AVR part number). The "AT89Sxxxx" is the Atmel line of i8051 compatible parts (I made this mistake when I first ordered some Atmel parts). The ordering instructions for the 1200 and 8515 are as shown in Figure 33.22.

AVR APPLICATION DESIGN

CONTENTS AT A GLANCE

Power Input

Reset

Interrupts

Real-Time Operating Systems

In-System Programming

When I look at the AVR datasheets, I can see a number of features that reflect the relative youth of the device compared to other devices. Atmel was able to design the AVR from a "clean sheet" of paper, and in doing it they have been able to design the part by taking into account the best features of other devices out on the market. This is reflected in how the AVR has been designed for interfacing with other elements of an application.

Power Input

The AVR power input is very simple, like all microcontrollers in this book—just positive 5 volts and ground with a decoupling capacitor is all that's required. The AVR is nice to work with because of the wide voltage range available on all devices (2.7V to 6.0V) which makes battery operation easy to implement (for using two to four radio or NiCad batteries).

One of the features I really like in the AVR is its ability to be parallel (not serially) programmed without +12 volts applied to it. I'll discuss in-system programming later in this chapter. I wanted to point out this capability here because it could affect your decision on which device to use in a certain application (i.e., one where the AVR could be programmed on the board).

In terms of power consumption, the AVR's require a few mA in active mode to 100s of uA in "Sleep" mode.

Reset

The "_Reset" pin on the AVR is internally pulled up, which eliminates the need to provide a pullup to Vcc. In fact, for most application debug (where you're going to reset the AVR a lot to observe its behavior), a simple pushbutton switch, pulling _Reset to ground is all that's required. When the application is in a product, you will probably run with _Reset left floating (nothing connected to it). (Figure 34.1.)

Power up in the AVR is very typical for a microcontroller/microprocessor and can either be controlled externally or by Vcc (using the internal pull up). If the AVR is to power up using Vcc, the internal waveform sequence will look like Figure 34.2.

In Figure 34.2, "POR" is a circuit used to delay the AVR's operation until Vcc has stabilized. A Schmidt trigger starts the circut, which then starts a 3-msec delay ("Tpor" in Figure 34.2). Once this delay has finished the timeout circuit waits for the built in oscillator to stabilize before allowing the code to begin execution ("Tout" in Figure 34.2). This timeout delay is nominally 15 msecs but can be reduced to 1 msec if an external oscillator is used with the AVR.

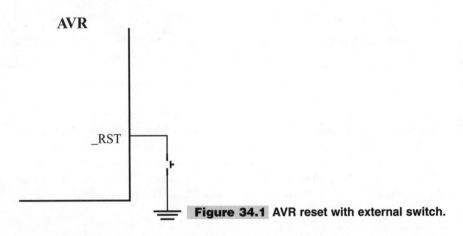

AVR

_RST

Figure 34.1 AVR reset with external switch.

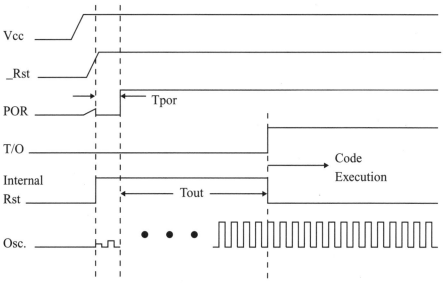

Figure 34.2 AVR boot timing diagram.

If the _Reset pin is pulled low for two clock cycles during program execution, the oscillator continues to run and the program is reset back to zero. When the _Reset line is allowed to return to a "high," program execution restarts at address zero.

Interrupts

Implementing interrupts is quite easy in the AVR, although you should have their execution planned out. You are able to execute an interrupt handler in just a few instructions or run interrupts in a very complex application.

An example of a three-instruction interrupt handler for the 1200 timer could be:

```
TmrInt                          ;   Set Bit When Timer Overflow
  cbi     TOV0, T1FR
  set                           ;   Set the "T" Flag of SREG
  reti
```

Now, this assumes that the "T" flag is available for indicating that the interrupt has taken place (and is being polled in the mainline). Actually finding an instruction that doesn't change the SREG flags is a bit of a challenge (because if they change the flags, then the context information of the mainline is lost). The reason why the 68HC05 doesn't have to worry about this is because it saves its status register (the "CCR") during the interrupt acknowledgment process, so changing the CCR bits isn't an issue. The 8051 doesn't have to worry about this because the status register ("PSW") does not have a "zero" flag.

If you are changing the status register in the interrupt handler, then you have to save it first. The simplest way of doing this is to reserve a general-purpose register for saving SREG during interrupts.

A more generic timer interrupt would now look like:

```
TmrInt                  ; Execute Code On Timer Overflow
   in    R0, SREG       ; Save the Status Bits

     :                  ; Execute the Interrupt Handler Code

   out   SREG, R0       ; Restore the Status Register
   reti
```

The next obvious extension to this is if you don't have a GPR available, the code would become:

```
IntHandler              ; Handle a Generic Interrupt
   push  R16            ; Save Registers Used in the Interrupt Handler
   push  R17
   in    R16, SREG      ; Save the Status Bits
   push  R16

     :                  ; Execute the Interrupt Handler Code

   pop   R16            ; Restore the Status Bits
   out   SREG, R16
   pop   R17            ; Restore Registers Saved for Interrupt Handler
   pop   R16
   reti
```

I should point out that the "push" and "pop" instructions could be substituted for "ld" and "st" using the predecrement/post-increment options on the index registers.

The (full) AVR uses a RAM stack which means nested interrupts can be implemented quite easily (just as in the 68HC05). After the interrupt handler has begun execution and the context registers are saved, an "SEI" instruction can be executed to allow other interrupts to take over execution of the AVR processor.

I should comment on interrupt handlers for the low-end (i.e., AVR 1200) devices. Because of the very short stack (only three entries on the 1200) and no RAM (just GPRs), you will have to plan how the interrupt handler is going to work very carefully. Personally, I would keep at least three GPRs available at all times (five, if the "Z" index registers are going to be used in the interrupt handler) for saving the mainline's context registers. I would not allow nested interrupts and avoid calling subroutines from within the interrupt handler (and to avoid calling subroutines wherever possible from the mainline as well). Implementing interrupts with these features is not very difficult and will prevent problems (namely a blown stack) later on.

Real-Time Operating Systems

If you've gone through the 68HC05's discussion on implementing an RTOS (and "mykeRTOS"), you'll probably realize that the full AVR architecture could be used to implement an RTOS quite easily. With the wide range of data storage options with all data (and pointers) being accessible by software, the actual RTOS code will be quite simple.

Now, having said all this, there are a number of decisions to be made in how the RTOS is going to operate and how data is saved. Because the AVR has a large number of registers that can be accessed for most instructions, there are a couple of strategies for using the registers in an RTOS.

The first method is to partition the thirty two GPRs into task blocks. Only two registers are required to execute all the arithmetic instructions (except for immediate operations). This means that conceivably up to 15 tasks could be implemented (in this scheme, I would hold back two registers for temporary registers for the RTOS and an index register for the task's use (although when using the index register in a task, the interrupts would have to be disabled to prevent the contents from being lost if a hardware interrupt changed the task execution)). For this scheme, RTOS request parameters would have to be passed on the stack or in the index register.

This GPR allocation, while supporting a large number of tasks, is not what I would consider optimal. Instead, if I were going to use the 32 registers to save the parameter information, I would probably set it up to use four registers per stack with the remaining four registers as index values. With this method, a stack area has been allocated to the task.

The GPRs would look like:

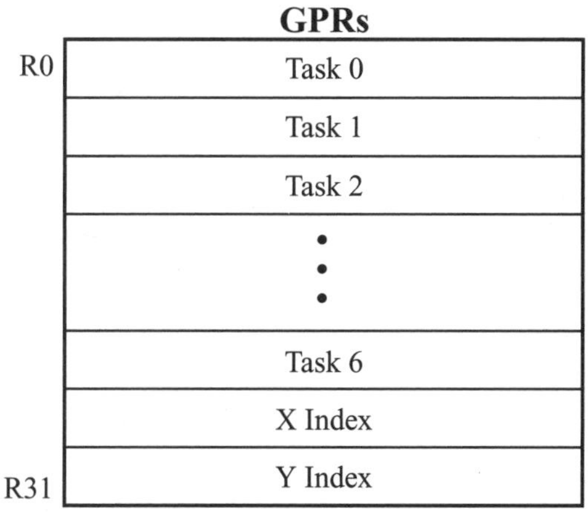

Figure 34.3 Example AVR GPR usage for an RTOS implementation.

and would allow up to seven tasks.

Another issue would be in handling immediate values. Rather than putting all the registers in the task sub-blocks together, I would put one register in the first 16 GPR addresses and the others elsewhere in the 32-GPR addresses. Doing this would allow both two GPR arithmetic as well as immediate arithmetic operations. To avoid confusion, I would probably define the registers used for each task rather than determining them arithmetically (i.e., task n uses "n" times four to get the offset of the task block information).

The code for this RTOS model request would be:

```
RTOS
  cli                        ;  Disable Interrupts
  st Parm0, R30              ;  Save the Request Information
  st Parm1, R31
  push      R28              ;  Save the Index Information
  push      R29
  in        R28, SREG        ;  Save the Task's SREG Information
  push      R28
  ld        R30, CurTask     ;  Have Index Point to the Task Block in SRAM
  ld        R31, CurTask+1
  in        R28, SPL         ;  Save the Stack's Stack
  in        R29, SPH
  st Z+,    R28
  st Z+,    R29
```

```
:                           ;  Execute the RTOS request

ld R30, CurTask             ;  Restore the Task's Stack
ld          R31, CurTask+1
ld          R29, -Z         ;  Get the Stack Information
ld          R28, -Z
st          SPL, R28
st          SPH, R29
pop         R28
out SREG, R28               ;  Restore the Task's Status Register
pop         R29
pop         R28
ld          R30, Parm0      ;  Get the Message Info for the Task
ld          R31, Parm1
reti                        ;  Return and enable Interrupts
```

This code takes up 26 instructions of overhead which is really impressive (and will result in a very fast RTOS request handling/task switch).

The more traditional way of saving all the registers is also possible, but this has the drawback that a lot of the available SRAM will be taken up saving task-context registers (i.e., in an AVR with 512 bytes of SRAM, a minimum of 32 bytes will be required for each task, which means a maximum of 12 tasks could be supported using this method). Another drawback would be the amount of time required to save and restore all the registers each time an interrupt or task switch is encountered. I played around with writing such an interface and found that it took 83 instructions, which is over three times more than the code above.

One thing you should have noticed is my explicit use of the "cli" and "reti" in the RTOS routine. The AVR does not have a software interrupt instruction, so the "I" bit in the Status SREG is not automatically masked. Instead, an RTOS subroutine must be called and in it interrupts are disabled and SREG is saved.

The AVR is ideally suited to have code run under an RTOS. Like my RTOS application in the 68HC05, some time must be spent planning how the RTOS and tasks are to be implemented.

As you've read through this sub-chapter, you're probably thinking that RTOS are pretty loose in terms of what is involved in developing them. This isn't the case at all. The important points to cover when designing an RTOS are:

1. Providing an interface for tasks to make requests of the RTOS.
2. Providing a consistent mechanism for saving the task information whether an RTOS request is made or a hardware interrupt request is encountered.
3. Having a messaging system able to pass information between tasks.

That's really it. How you implement it is up to you; the advantage of the AVR is the many different ways in which an RTOS can be implemented. I hope that in this sub-chapter I have introduced you to a number of different ways of carrying out the job and not relying on traditional methods which may not be the most efficient in the AVR.

In-System Programming

Using serial programming mode, the AVR can be programmed while in an application circuit. This mode requires the power and clock connections of the application to allow the programming mode to run. (Figure 34.4.)

Connections

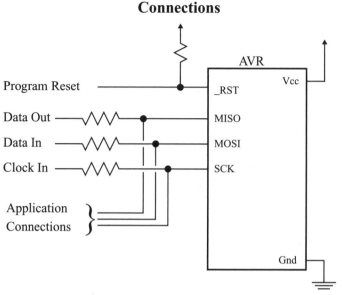

Figure 34.4 AVR in-system programming connections.

In Figure 34.4, I have placed terminating resistors in line of the programming pins to make sure that if the programming circuitry is holding the pins at a different level from the applications, the value at the pins will not be changed or be in contention.

This is not true for the reset line. In this circuit, I have normally pulled the line high and the programmer can pull it low to put the AVR into serial programming mode. The control for "_Reset" is really an open collector output.

With this circuit, would I use it with an application? Actually, I would—although I would probably connect the AVR to the programmer via a five-pin IDC connector (for Ground, _Reset, MISO, MOSI, and SCK), rather than looking at using something like a DB-25 to connect the application directly to a PC's printer port (as is done with some current AVR programming designs).

AVR DEVELOPMENT TOOLS

CONTENTS AT A GLANCE

Because of how recently the AVR has been made available, there are not a lot of tools available for the microcontroller. Despite this, Atmel has made sure there is a complete line of tools available for the AVR, and some manufacturers have begun to make software and hardware tools available to the user.

Assemblers

The great flexibility in the AVR architecture means that some thought has to be put into organizing which registers are used and how they are used. As you've probably gathered, the AVR has a great deal of orthogonality. Because of this, some planning and register defining is required.

I've found that in most "typical" microcontroller applications, very few actual variables are required. This is especially true if there are hardware functions (i.e., timers, serial ports, etc.) that can make the applications easier. This means that the 32 "general-purpose registers" will be able to handle the majority of programming needs that application mainlines have.

Reading the previous sentence, you're probably thinking that I slipped something in there, and I have. If you are writing an application that uses interrupts, then you have to start thinking about that planning that I mention above.

When implementing interrupts in the AVR, you have to make a conscious decision about what the context registers are that you want to save before executing the interrupt handler functions. Because the AVR can mathematically access any of the 32 registers in the GPR set, the "context registers" that must be saved can be surprisingly minimal.

For example, in an application that uses two interrupt handlers that may be nested, I might partition the 32 GPRs as shown in Figure 35.1.

This partitioning will allow the interrupt handlers to operate without having to save any of the mainline's registers (because the interrupt handlers use a completely different set of GP and index registers). The only register that should be saved in this example is the STATUS register (and it will be placed in the "Saved SREG" segment in each interrupt handler register block). By partitioning the GPRs in this manner, an interrupt handler can simply be:

```
Int

    LD SREG_Save, SREG    ;   Save the Interrupted Code's STATUS Register

        :                 ;   Process and Reset the Interrupt Request

    ST SREG, SREG_Save    ;   Restore Interrupted Code's STATUS Register

    RETI                  ;   Return to where Interrupt took place
```

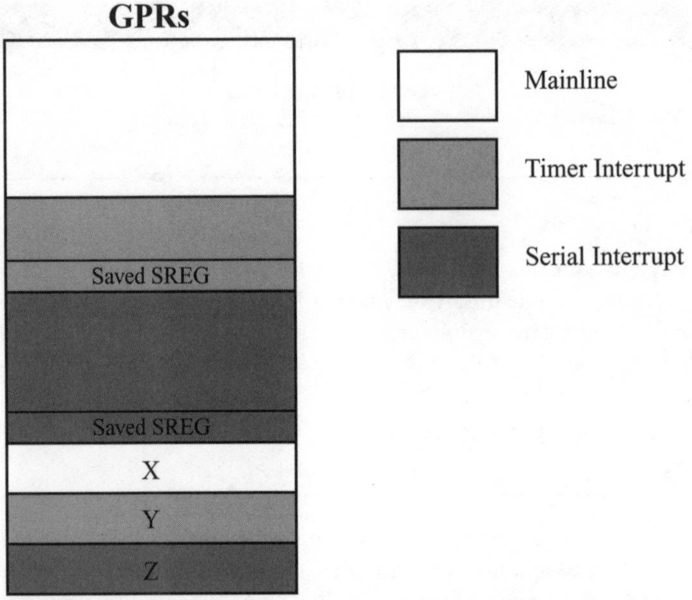

Figure 35.1 AVR mainline/Interrupt GPR allocation.

Personally, I don't like loading multiple registers from SRAM and trying to keep track of them. I find this confusing and difficult to follow. Instead, I only load the GPRs from SRAM as they are required and then save the result when I'm finished.

I've put this in more for your awareness than anything else. This goes back to my IBM 370 assembly programming experiences, where I found it very difficult to keep track of what register had what. So in my AVR assembly programming, I tend to keep only the most-used variables in the GPR and then load SRAM variables when they are required.

To avoid the problem of keeping the GPRs straight, you can define them with other labels:

```
#define i R16            ;  Define the Counter as "R16"
```

High-Level Languages

35

Atmel has very strongly stated that the AVR architecture is well suited to running code efficiently from a compiler. My initial thoughts on this was that it wasn't; the separation of the GPRs and SRAM would cause inefficiencies, and the limited number of GPRs would not allow for very efficient code execution.

As I thought about this and looked at my own compiler efforts with the PIC, I realized that there are some features in the AVR architecture that would make developing an efficient compiler comparatively easy compared to the other microcontrollers I'm writing about in this book. My comments in this subchapter are based on my personal style of compiler writing and may not be all that accurate compared to better compiler technologies available.

In most compilers, a stack function is used to evaluate expressions. For example:

$$A = B + C$$

as a series of stack operations would be:

```
push B
push C
add              ;  Pop Previous two Stack Elements, Add Together and
                 ;    Push Result back onto the Stack
pop  A
```

The reason why a stack is used is because it can be used to queue up data for complex operations. In the other architectures, this is possible but cumbersome because there are no registers available for easy pushing and popping of values and accessing the stack.

For example:

$$A = B + (C * D)$$

Would be represented as:

```
push B
push C
push D
mul
add
pop  A
```

For the AVR, if "A," "B," "C," and "D" were all in SRAM (or GPRs, it doesn't matter which with the "LD" (load) instruction), the code generated by the compiler to execute this would be:

```
ld    R0, B        ;  "push B"
push  R0
ld    R0, C        ;  "push C"
push  R0
ld    R0, D        ;  "push D"
push  R0
call mul           ;  There isn't a built-in "multiply" instruction
pop   R0           ;  Pop result of the multiplication
pop   R1           ;  Pop "B"
add   R0, R1       ;  "add" Top two Stack Elements
push  R0           ;  Store the Result back on the Stack
pop   R0           ;  Pop off the Stack Result and Store in "A"
st    A, R0
```

With this, an optimizing compiler should recognize the redundancy of pushing and popping values, so the code would become:

```
ld    R0, B
push  R0
ld    R0, C
ld    R1, D
call mul
pop   R1           ;  Retrieve "B"
add   R0, R1
st    A, R0
```

This can be further improved if the compiler has a certain number of registers available for each statement. The code could be further reduced to:

```
ld    R2, B
ld    R0, C
ld    R1, D
call mul
add   R0, R2
st    A, R0
```

The example above uses "global" (available everywhere in the program) variables. If the language the compiler is written for uses "automatic" (just available in the current routine) and passed parameters, the AVR is very well suited to handle this in an almost ridiculously simple manner.

Automatic variables would be handled as either one of the index registers (and use the "load"/"store" instructions with the predecrement/post-increment options which, allow them to emulate a stack) or the stack "push" and "pop" instructions. Personally, I would lean toward handling them with the index registers and stack emulation options.

If you were writing a "C" compiler for the AVR and you had the code:

```
main()
{

  :

  A = Complex( B, C, D );     //  "A =  B + ( C * D )" is Used Often,
                              //    put in a Routine

  :

} /*  End main  */
```

```
int Complex( int V1, int V2, int V3 )
{                           //  Handle the Complex Operations

int i;

    :

    return( V1 + ( V2 * V3 ));   // Return the Complex Operation

}  /*  End Complex  */
```

What would the compiled (and optimized) AVR code look like?

Before the call to "complex" would be made, one of the index registers would be identified as the "data stack" and the other would be a "base pointer." When data is pushed onto the data stack, the index pointer would be incremented to point to the next stack element. When the routine was called, the base pointer would be updated to point to the current location.

So, to carry out the "C" code above with "X" used as the "data stack" pointer and "Y" used as the "base pointer," the AVR instructions could be generated as:

```
main                                  ;  Mainline routine

    ldi    R0, DataStackStart & 0x0FF  ;  Initialize Data Stack Register to
    st     X, R0                       ;    the start of the Data Stack
    ldi    R0, DataStackStart >> 8
    st     X + 1, R0

    :

    ld     R0, B                       ;  Put Parameters on the Data Stack
    st     (X)+, R0
    ld     R0, C
    st     (X)+, R0
    ld     R0, D
    st     (X)+, R0
    call Complex                       ;  Now, Call the Subroutine
    ldd    R0, (X)-4                    ;  Get the Returned Value
    sbi    X, 4                         ;  Restore the Data Stack
    sbci 0                              ;   It's a 16 Bit Number

    :

Complex                               ;  Now Execute "Complex" Routine

    addiw  X, 1                         ;  Make Space for "i"

    mov    (X)+, Y                      ;  Save the Current Base Pointer
    mov    (X)+, Y+1

    mov    Y, X                         ;  Save the Current Stack as the
    mov    Y+1, X+1                     ;   Base Pointer

    :

    ld     R2, (Y)-5                    ;  Get "V1" or "B"
    ld     R0, (Y)-4                    ;  Get "V2" or "C"
    ld     R1, (Y)-3                    ;  Get "V3" or "D"
    call mul
    add    R0, R2
    std    (Y)-6, R0                    ;  Store Result as the Return Value
```

```
mov    X, Y                          ;  Restore Stack to Where we Started
mov    X+1, Y+1

sbi    1                             ;  Take away space used for "i"
sbci 0

ret
```

In this example, when the "B + (C * D)" operation is finally executed, the same number of instructions (and the same amount of space) is used, as when this operation was used with global variables in the mainline. This ability is what makes the AVR so powerful for use with a compiler; data can be manipulated in multiple formats without a major impact on the amount of RAM required or the space used.

The index registers also allow the easy use of pointers. With "X" as the "data stack pointer" and "Y" as the "base pointer," "Z" is left for reading tables in control store or for a general-purpose pointer.

In the previous example, the stack pointer could also be used, but when accessing the parameters in the "data stack," the value of the stack pointer will have to be saved in "X," "Y," or "Z" so the offset in the stack can be found. Simply using one of the other index registers with the "LDD"/"STD" instruction with increment is much simpler.

As you read this, you might be thinking to yourself that this is somewhat interesting (at least I hope you think this is at least somewhat interesting), but because you only program in assembly, it's of little use to you. I have gone through this level of detail to show you how automatic variables and stack-oriented arithmetic expressions could be quite simply implemented in assembly language programming without having to keep very complex operations straight.

Development Tools

For the applications presented in this book, I used the free AVR assembler and simulators available from Atmel and the "AT89/90 Series Flash Microcontroller Starter Kit," which consists of a programmer, a sample 1200 part, and software for developing AVR applications (including a CD-ROM of the part datasheets). For less than $100, this really is a great package to use for developing AVR applications. The programmer will handle all Atmel 8051 parts (i.e., the AT89S2051) and AVRs in both 20- and 40-pin DIP packages. (Figure 35.2.)

Like other development kits presented in this book, the Atmel "starter kit" is run from Microsoft Windows or the MS-DOS command line. What is unusual about the package is the lack of a complete integrated environment. The assembler, simulator, and programmer are all separate programs under Windows and not a true "IDE." Even though the packages are not integrated together, the simulator and programmer can quickly reload the assembled program files.

The Atmel assembler, known as "wavrasm" is a typical Windows editor with an integrated assembler. In Figure 35.3, I have shown the window that pops up after assembly is complete. Any errors that are encountered can be "double clicked" to jump to the error in the source file.

Once you have a syntactically correct application source, you can simulate it before burning a part. Atmel offers two tools for this. The first, "wavrsim," is a windows-based

Figure 35.2 AT89/90 series flash microcontroller starter kit.

35

ATMEL AVR

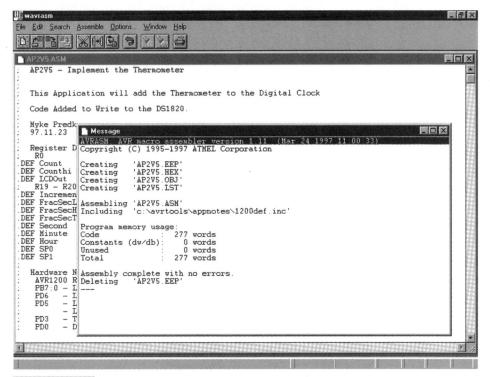

Figure 35.3 Atmel's wavrasm screen.

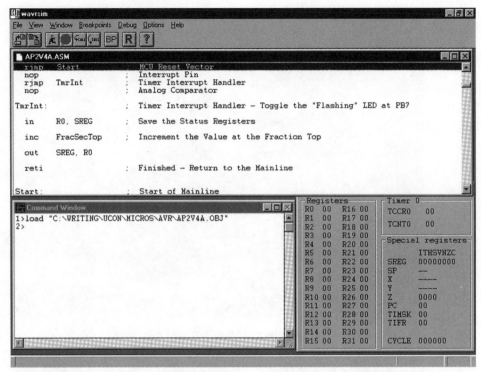

Figure 35.4 Atmel's wavrsim screen.

simulator that loads the ".obj" file for the application and allows you to step through it, debugging the application. (Figure 35.4.)

The largest deficiency I found with this program is that the I/O registers cannot be monitored (other than "TCCR0" and "TCNT0" for Timer0 and some of the interrupt mask registers). An user-definable register display (such as UMPs register windows or MPLAB's watch windows) would really be useful (and would have been very useful for this application). After a problem has been found with an application and it has been corrected and reassembled, the ".obj" file can be reloaded very quickly from the "files" menu with the virtual microcontroller reset, and you an continue executing from there.

"AVRStudio" (Figure 35.5) is a Windows/95 or Windows/NT enhancement to "wavrsim." AVRStudio can display I/O registers (as shown in Figure 35.5), which is an improvement over wavrsim, but for the most part it works very similarly to the original simulator.

When the application has been written and debugged on the simulator, then it's time to burn it into a microcontroller. This is done using the programmer provided in the "starter kit" and a Windows screen for loading the .hex file (which is in Intel format). (Figure 35.6.)

When the program operation has completed, the device will begin to execute. Using the IDC connectors, the AVR can be wired into a prototype circuit, or use the built-in LEDs and pushbuttons.

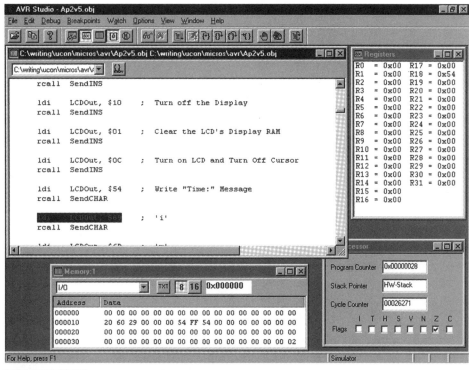

Figure 35.5 Atmel's AVRStudio screen.

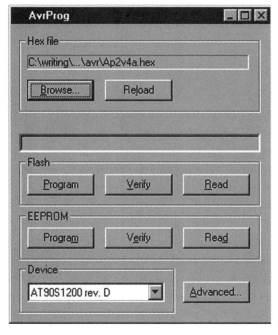

Figure 35.6 Atmel's starter kit
programmer control window.

This programmer window can be left active during execution of the assembler/simulator windows while updating the program. One aspect of the programmer I do not like is that there is no way to turn off power to the part being programmed. I found that when I used it, I had to unplug it from the power input to make sure I wasn't "hot plugging" the part while I was debugging an application in another circuit. The programming software worked without any problems with plugging and unplugging the programmer board.

AVR INSTRUCTION SET

CONTENTS AT A GLANCE

AVR Data Transfer Instructions

AVR Arithmetic and Logic Instructions

AVR Branch Instructions

AVR Bit and Bit-Test Instructions

The AVR has a very complete instruction set. As I have discussed in the other chapters of this section, the AVR is well suited to making compiler development simpler, which (in this case) also means that the AVR is quite easy to program with many instructions simplifying the task. Having many instructions is a two-edged sword. After you've read the documentation (and this section) and start to write your first application, you'll probably find that it is difficult to remember all the different instructions. Also, many are repeated, instructions either renamed, different bits explicitly set, or the input parameters modified. In the instructions presented in this chapter, I have reduced the instruction set to both save space in the book and group similar instructions together to make sure you can see the "big picture." This reduction is quite significant; in Atmel's AVR documentation, there are 121 instructions identified. I have been almost able to halve it.

Even without this reduction, the AVR instruction set is quite straightforward, although there are a number of things to watch out for when you use either Atmel's or my documentation for creating applications. The first thing to watch out for is the actual register address and data ranges available in the instruction. Many instructions can only access the most significant 16 GPRs (and not the least significant 16) or offsets, and constants may be quite restricted and not in the range that you expect. You will have to be cognizant of these limitations when planning which GPRs to use and what constant values you are using in data structures.

Atmel makes the claim for the 8515; "120 Powerful Instructions—Most Single Clock Cycle Exection" which implies that critical timing code in applications is easy to create (if all instructions require one cycle, timing becomes a lot easier). I, personally have a problem with this statement after looking at the instruction set. While it's true that most instructions execute in one cycle, many do not. To make matters worse, the actual timing for many instructions are not easily predictable (for example, the "CPSE" can execute in 1, 2, or 3 cycles). This is not to say that the AVR is a difficult architecture to time up for critical applications. For the most part, it isn't—but it's not as easy as you may expect when you first look at the documentation.

The last issue with the AVR instruction set that you should be aware of is the difference between the "full" AVR (i.e., the 8515) and the "low-end" AVR (i.e., the 1200). The "low-end" devices have a subset of the full AVR instruction set with only the "Z" index register available. While there aren't going to be instruction problems porting an application from the low-end devices to the full AVRs, there will probably be some problems going the other way.

Even with these caveats, I find the AVR to be an easy device to program because of the richness of the instruction set and the features designed into the device to make programming easier.

AVR Data Transfer Instructions

Moving data from one place to another in the AVR is quite easy with the large number of instructions available for the task. Many of the operations are obviously designed for implementing a high-level langauge (as discussed elsewhere in this section). In the full AVRs (i.e., the 8515), planning how data is to be stored and moved between the GPRs and SRAM is critical for creating a successful application. None of these instructions affect the SREG bits, which means that if a value is to be checked after the instruction, the "tst" instruction should be used to set the zero and negative flags of SREG appropriately.

The first instruction to be considered is the "mov" instruction (Instruction 36.1), which copies the value of one general-purpose register and puts it into another.

Along with "mov," the "ldi" instruction (Instruction 36.2) is used to load a register with a constant value and is another very basic instruction used to get a simple program running. "Ldi" loads one of the most significant 16 GPR addresses with a byte specified inside the instruction. The "ldi" instruction is used for loading arbitrary constants inside general-purpose registers.

To interface directly with the I/O register space, the "in" and "out" instructions (Instruction 36.3 and Instruction 36.4) are used. These instructions access the I/O registers starting at address zero of the I/O space (rather than address $1F, as the I/O register addresses in the AVR's "data space" are defined).

The previous instructions are basically everything the low-end AVR 1200 has available to it for data movement. The remaining instructions access the AVR's 64K data space (which is comprised of the GPRs, I/O registers, and SRAM) or control store, rather than as individual registers did in the previous instructions.

"Lds" and "Sts" are two word instructions that pass data directly between the GPRs and the data space (Instruction 36.5 and Instruction 36.6), while data can be loaded indirectly using the single word "ld(d)" and "st(d)" instructions (Instruction 36.7, Instruction 36.8, Instruction 36.9, Instruction 36.10, Instruction 36.11, Instruction 36.12, Instruction 36.13, and Instruction 36.14). In instructions 36.10 and 36.14, the data space address to be accessed is specified by the "X," "Y," or "Z" index registers.

When using the "ld" and "st" instructions, the index registers can be incremented or decremented as part of the instruction. The "pre-decrement" and "post-increment" allow these instructions to simulate a stack. The "ldd" and "std" instructions are very useful when the index is a pointer to a data structure. Elsewhere in this section, I detail how these instructions can be used in working with data structures and compiler-generated code.

The low-end AVR does have the most basic of the previous instructions to allow the "Z" index registers to access data within the general-purpose register space. This means that GPR tables can be created, although they do not have the flexibility and size of what the full AVR architecture is capable of.

The stack in the full AVR can be used to "push" and "pop" GPRs (Instruction 36.15 and Instruction 36.16). You might be surprised to discover that I would tend to stay away from using these instructions, instead using the "ld" and "st" instructions with the index register pre-decrement and post-increment functions because this more easily allows me access to the data (using the offset access commands). This leaves the AVR stack for just saving the program counter during subroutines or interrupt handler invocations.

The last data transfer instruction is the load from program memory ("lpm"—Instruction 36.17). This instruction is used for loading data from an instruction table. While it seems to be quite straightforward, there is one point that you should be aware of in how control store addressing is accomplished.

With this instruction, the LSB of the "Z" index register is used to specify the address of the byte to be read (high or low), while the remaining 14 bytes are used to specify the word address. (Figure 36.1.)

While most tables can be created to take advantage of the word operation (i.e., read low byte, increment Z, read high byte, etc.), there may be some cases where this is not possible. Also, if you have a table with an odd number of entries, care must be taken to ensure that the following instructions are placed starting on even addresses (otherwise, depending on the software used to create the object code, you may end up with instructions straddling the word boundaries).

AVR Arithmetic and Logic Instructions

Executing an arithmetic or logic instruction in the AVR is actually quite straightforward; if you're familiar with Intel microprocessor (8085 or 8086) assembly language programming, you won't have any problems with the AVR. In the instructions, the first

36

ATMEL AVR

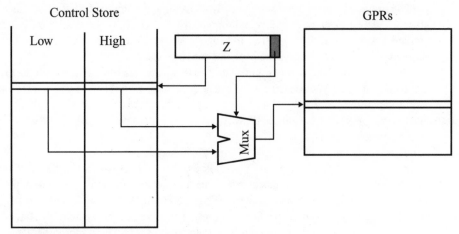

Figure 36.1 AVR "LPM" instruction operation.

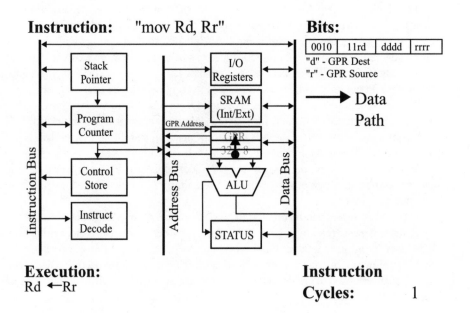

Instruction: "mov Rd, Rr"

Bits:

0010	11rd	dddd	rrrr

"d" - GPR Dest
"r" - GPR Source

➡️ Data
   Path

Execution:
Rd ←Rr

**Instruction
Cycles:**   1

Example: **MCUs:**   All AVRs
mov R0, R2   ;   R0 = R2

Instruction 36.1 AVR "mov Rd, Rr" instruction.

Instruction: "LDI Rd, Constant"

Bits:

| 1110 | kkkk | dddd | kkkk |

"d" - GPR Dest ($10 <= $1F)
"k" - Constant

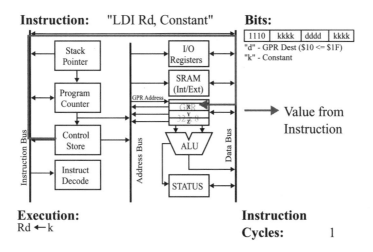

→ Value from
   Instruction

Execution:
Rd ← k

Instruction Cycles: 1

Example:
ldi   R20, $AA   ;   Load "R20" with a Test Value

MCUs: All AVRs

Instruction 36.2 AVR "ldi Rd, constant" instruction.

Instruction: "in Rd, Reg"

Bits:

| 1011 | 0rrd | dddd | rrrr |

"d" - GPR Dest
"r" - I/O Register

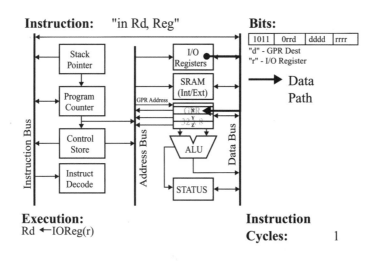

→ Data
   Path

Execution:
Rd ← IOReg(r)

Instruction Cycles: 1

Example:
in   R0, porta   ;   Read Contents of "porta" Reg

MCUs: All AVRs

Note: Register is $00 to $1F. "IOReg" is 0 to $3F

Instruction 36.3 AVR "in Rd, reg" instruction.

36

ATMEL AVR

Instruction: "out Reg, Rd"   **Bits:**

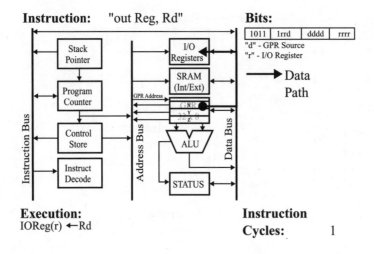

| 1011 | 1rrd | dddd | rrrr |

"d" - GPR Source
"r" - I/O Register

➤ Data Path

Execution:
IOReg(r) ← Rd

Instruction Cycles: 1

Example: **MCUs:** All AVRs
out porta, R0   ; Write New Value to "porta"

Note: Register is $00 to $1F. "IOReg" is 0 to $3F

Instruction 36.4 AVR "out Reg, Rd" instruction.

Instruction: "LDS Rd, Address   **Bits:**

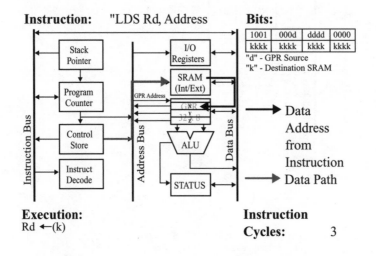

| 1001 | 000d | dddd | 0000 |
| kkkk | kkkk | kkkk | kkkk |

"d" - GPR Source
"k" - Destination SRAM

➤ Data Address from Instruction
➤ Data Path

Execution:
Rd ← (k)

Instruction Cycles: 3

Example: **MCUs:** Full AVRs
lds R0, $1235   ;   Get and Save Value in SRAM
sts $1234, R0

Instruction 36.5 AVR "lds Rd, addr" instruction.

Instruction: "STS Address, Rd"

Bits:

1001	001d	dddd	0000
kkkk	kkkk	kkkk	kkkk

"d" - GPR Source
"k" - Destination SRAM

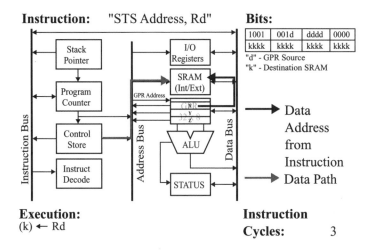

Data
Address
from
Instruction
Data Path

Execution:
(k) ← Rd

Instruction Cycles: 3

Example: **MCUs:**   Full AVRs
ldd R0, X+7   ;   Get and Save Value at "X"
sts $1234, R0   ;   Data Pointer

Instruction 36.6 AVR "sts addr, Rd" instruction.

Instruction: "LD Rd, Index"

Bits:

1001	000d	dddd	ii00

"d" - GPR Source
"i" - Index Register
     ("11" - "X")
     ("10" - "Y")
     ("00" - "Z")

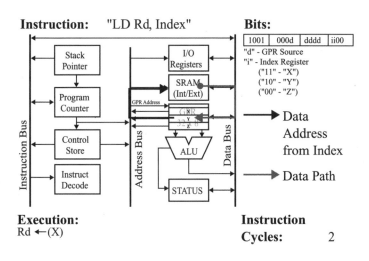

Data
Address
from Index

Data Path

Execution:
Rd ←(X)

Instruction Cycles: 2

Example: **MCUs:**   All AVRs*
ld   R0, X   ;   Use "X" and "Y" as Data
ld   R1, Y   ;   Pointers

Note: The Low-End AVRs (1200) can only use
the "Z" Index Register.

Instruction 36.7 AVR "ld Rd, index" instruction.

36

ATMEL AVR

Instruction: "LD Rd, Index+"   **Bits:**

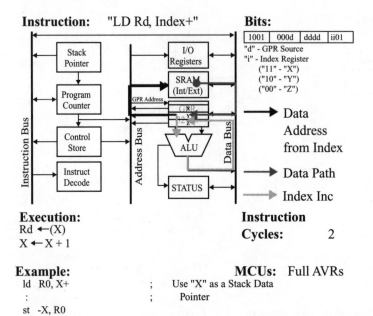

1001	000d	dddd	ii01

"d" - GPR Source
"i" - Index Register
   ("11" - "X")
   ("10" - "Y")
   ("00" - "Z")

➤ Data
Address
from Index

➤ Data Path

➤ Index Inc

Execution:
Rd ←(X)
X ← X + 1

**Instruction
Cycles:**   2

Example: **MCUs:**   Full AVRs
ld R0, X+   ;   Use "X" as a Stack Data
  :   ;   Pointer
st -X, R0

Instruction 36.8 AVR "ld Rd, index+" (post-increment) instruction.

Instruction: "LD Rd, -Index"   **Bits:**

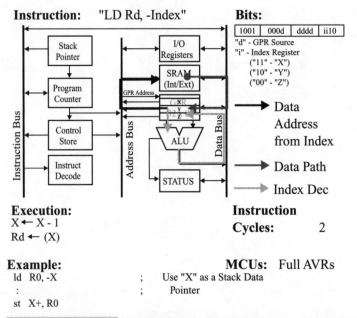

1001	000d	dddd	ii10

"d" - GPR Source
"i" - Index Register
   ("11" - "X")
   ("10" - "Y")
   ("00" - "Z")

➤ Data
Address
from Index

➤ Data Path

➤ Index Dec

Execution:
X ← X - 1
Rd ← (X)

**Instruction
Cycles:**   2

Example: **MCUs:**   Full AVRs
ld R0, -X   ;   Use "X" as a Stack Data
  :   ;   Pointer
st X+, R0

Instruction 36.9 AVR "ld Rd, -index" (pre-decrement) instruction.

Instruction: "LDD Rd, Index+Off" **Bits:**

10q0	qq0d	dddd	iqqq

"d" - GPR Source
"i" - Index Register
  ("1" - "Y")
  ("0" - "Z")
"q" - Index ($0 <= q <= 63$)

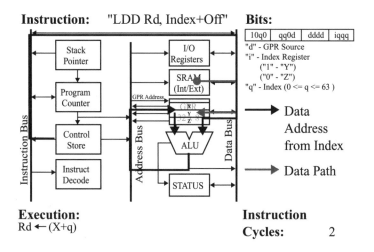

Data
Address
from Index

Data Path

Execution:
$Rd \leftarrow (X+q)$

Instruction Cycles: 2

Example:
ldd R0, X+7   ;   Use "X" and "Y" as Data
ld R1, Y   ;   Pointers

MCUs: Full AVRs

Instruction 36.10 AVR "ldd Rd, index+constant" instruction.

Instruction: "ST Index, Rd" **Bits:**

1001	001d	dddd	ii00

"d" - GPR Source
"i" - Index Register
  ("11" - "X")
  ("10" - "Y")
  ("00" - "Z")

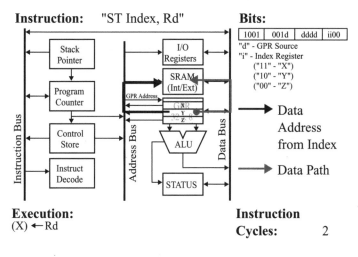

Data
Address
from Index

Data Path

Execution:
$(X) \leftarrow Rd$

Instruction Cycles: 2

Example:
ld R0, X   ;   Use "X" and "Y" as Data
st Y, R0   ;   Pointers

MCUs: All AVRs*

Note: The Low-End AVRs (1200) can only use the "Z" Index Register.

Instruction 36.11 AVR "st index, Rd" instruction.

36

ATMEL AVR

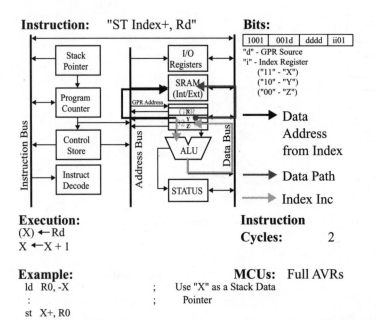

Instruction: "ST Index+, Rd"

Bits:

1001	001d	dddd	ii01

"d" - GPR Source
"i" - Index Register
 ("11" - "X")
 ("10" - "Y")
 ("00" - "Z")

→ Data Address from Index

→ Data Path

→ Index Inc

Execution:
(X) ← Rd
X ← X + 1

Instruction Cycles: 2

Example:

```
ld  R0, -X      ;   Use "X" as a Stack Data
:               ;       Pointer
st  X+, R0
```

MCUs: Full AVRs

Instruction 36.12 AVR "st index+, Rd" (post-increment) instruction.

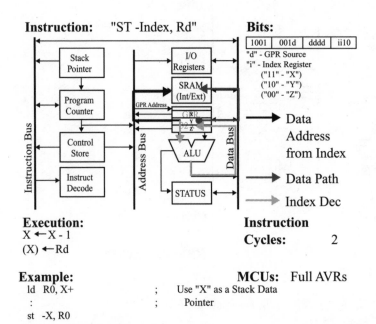

Instruction: "ST -Index, Rd"

Bits:

1001	001d	dddd	ii10

"d" - GPR Source
"i" - Index Register
 ("11" - "X")
 ("10" - "Y")
 ("00" - "Z")

→ Data Address from Index

→ Data Path

→ Index Dec

Execution:
X ← X - 1
(X) ← Rd

Instruction Cycles: 2

Example:

```
ld  R0, X+      ;   Use "X" as a Stack Data
:               ;       Pointer
st  -X, R0
```

MCUs: Full AVRs

Instruction 36.13 AVR "st -index, Rd" (pre-decrement) instruction.

Instruction: "STD Index+Off, Rd"   **Bits:**

10q0	qq1d	dddd	iqqq

"d" - GPR Source
"i" - Index Register
  ("1" - "Y")
  ("0" - "Z")
"q" - Index (0 <= q <= 63)

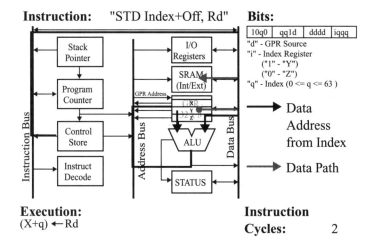

Data
Address
from Index

Data Path

Execution:
$(X+q) \leftarrow Rd$

Instruction
Cycles: 2

Example: **MCUs:**   Full AVRs
  ldd R0, X+7   ;   Use "X" and "Y" as Data
  std Y+5, R0   ;   Pointers

Instruction 36.14 AVR "std index+constant, Rd" instruction.

Instruction: "push Rd"   **Bits:**

1001	001d	dddd	1111

"d" - Source Register

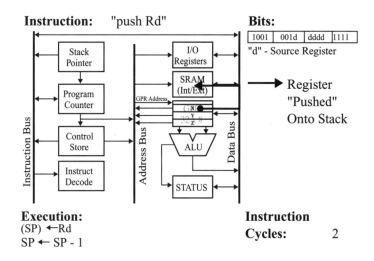

Register
"Pushed"
Onto Stack

Execution:
$(SP) \leftarrow Rd$
$SP \leftarrow SP - 1$

Instruction
Cycles: 2

Example: **MCUs:**   Full AVRs
  push R0   ;   Save "R0" during Operation
    :   ;   Operation Which Changed R0
  pop R0   ;   Restore "R0" after Operation

Instruction 36.15 AVR "push Rd" instruction.

36

ATMEL AVR

Instruction: "pop Rd"

Bits:

1001	000d	dddd	1111

"d" - Destination
Register

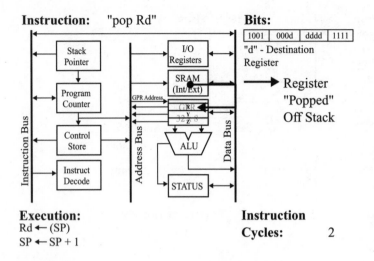

Register
"Popped"
Off Stack

Execution:
Rd ← (SP)
SP ← SP + 1

**Instruction
Cycles:**   2

Example: **MCUs:**   Full AVRs

```
push R0        ; Save "R0" during Operation
  :            ; Operation Which Changed R0
pop  R0        ; Restore "R0" after Operation
```

Instruction 36.16 AVR "pop Rd" instruction.

Instruction: "LPM"

Bits:

1001	0101	1100	1000

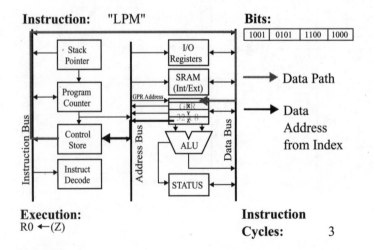

Data Path

Data
Address
from Index

Execution:
R0 ←(Z)

**Instruction
Cycles:**   3

Example: **MCUs:**   Full AVRs

```
ldi  R30, Table & $FF    ;   Read the Program Table
ldi  R31, Table >> 8
lpm
```

Instruction 36.17 AVR "lpm" instruction.

parameter is the first source and ultimate destination of the result. The second parameter of the instruction (which is optional) is the second parameter.

The basic arithmetic operations (Instruction 36.18, Instruction 36.19, Instruction 36.20, and Instruction 36.21) are addition and subtraction of two values. These instructions, for the most part, are quite straightforward.

Adding and subtracting registers is accomplished using the "add" and "sub" instructions. With the add/sub with carry instructions, variables stored in the general-purpose registers can be manipulated easily as 8- or 16-bit numbers.

The statement:

$$A = A - B$$

If "A" were R0 and R1 and "B" were R2 and R3, this could be implemented as the following AVR assembler code:

```
sub    R0, R2      ;  Subtract the lower 8 bits
sbc    R1, R3      ;  Now, the Higher 8 Bits
```

With these instructions, 24- and 32-bit signed numbers can be handled just as easily by using the add/sub with carry instructions.

Before going on with the different instructions, I just want to explain the operation of the negative, overflow, and sign bits because these bits are a little unusual and are a tad difficult to understand the first time you see them.

The "negative" flag is really just bit 7 of the result (which indicates whether or not the result is positive or negative). If you were going to execute the instruction:

```
sub    R4, R5
```

If R4 is greater than or equal to R5, the result will be positive and bit 7 will be reset. If R4 is less than R5, then bit 7 will be set, indicating that the result is a negative (really a two's complement negative) and the "N" flag of "SREG" will be set as well.

The overflow ("V") SREG bit will probably be somewhat confusing to you. This bit indicates when there has been a two's complement overflow after an addition or subtraction.

For example, after:

```
add    R1, R2
```

The "V" flag will be set if the values in R1 and R2 are both positive and the result is greater than 127 or if both are negative and the result is less than -128. This may seem quite confusing to you, but if you look at the actual values of the first overflow case, it should make more sense to you:

```
ldi    R1, 100     ;  Put in 0b001100100 into R1 and R2
ldi    R2, 100
add    R1, R2       ;  R1 = R1 + R2
                    ;      = 100 + 100
                    ;      = 200
                    ;      = $C8 = 0b011001000
```

Two-hundred decimal requires bit 7 of the result to be set, which indicates that it is actually a negative number (and the "N" SREG bit will be set after the "add" instruction). But, in this case, along with setting the "N" flag, the "V" flag will be set, indicating that the result is a two's complement overflow. If R1 and R2 were both equal to −100, the sum would be −200 or $38, which is actually positive. In this case, the negative flag would be reset and the "V" flag would be set indicating that the result isn't correct.

In the previous paragraph, you're probably wondering if the "N" and "V" flags can be used to determine the actual polarity of the result. This is exactly what the sign ("S") flag of the status register does. As you look through the instructions, you'll see

$$S = N \wedge V$$

quite a bit. The "S" bit actually turns the result into a 9-bit two's complement number with the most significant (or sign bit) actually being the "S" bit. In explaining the "V" flag, I noted that it would be set if bit 7 of the result were inappropriately (with respect to being a two's complement number polarity flag) changed. XORing this with the actual bit 7 value (which is stored in the "N" bit) will give you the actual polarity of the result. In the first example (100 + 100), the result sets the overflow flag and the "N" flag; "S" from this would be equal to Zero (1 ^ 1 = 0). In the second example (−100 + −100), the "N" flag will be reset and the "V" flag will be set, resulting in the "S" flag being set, indicating the result is negative.

The "S" flag should only be used with the most significant byte of a number. In cases where 16-, 24-, or 32-bit numbers are used, the "S" flag value should only be considered after the final operation on the most significant byte. For the lower significance bytes, the "carry" flag should be used as you would normally use it in addition and subtraction.

Going back to the addition and subtraction instructions, along with the register and add/subtract with optional carry, there are a number of other instructions you should be aware of because they will make your life developing software easier. The first is the subtract immediate (Instruction 36.22 and Instruction 36.23). These instructions will subtract a constant from a register, leaving the result in the register (there are no analogous "add" instructions).

There is one very important point to be aware of with the instructions which has an immediate value for the second parameter, and that's they can only access the top 16 GPRs (although a full 8-bit value can be subtracted from these values).

"Subi" and "sbci" can be combined to allow you to subtract a 16-bit value from a GPR register pair. Subtracting a 16-bit constant from the "X" index register could be carried out by:

```
subi   R26, Constant & $FF   ;   Subtract from Low Byte
sbci   R27, Constant >> 8    ;   Subtract from High Byte w/ Carry
```

When I introduced the "SUBI" and "SBCI" instructions, I said that there isn't any analogous "add" immediate instructions. Well, that's not quite true. You can simulate an add immediate by subtracting the negative, as is done in this macro:

```
MACRO addi Register, Value
   subi   Register, 0-Value
ENDMACRO
```

In this case, zero minus the value will return the two's complement negative of the value, and subtracting a negative will turn into adding a positive. This cannot be done with adding an immediate value with the carry flag because in the "sbci" instruction, the carry is taken away from the result.

After the previous example, I should point out that there is an easier way to add/subtract values from the index registers. This is to use the "adiw" and "sbiw" instructions (Instruction 36.24 and Instruction 36.25). These instructions allow adding and subtracting constant values from the upper four pairs of registers (which include the "X," "Y," and "Z" index registers). While these instructions only require one word, the constant to be added/subtracted can only be a maximum of 63. These two instructions are well suited to compiled code, where the index registers are used for pointers to data stacks and structures.

Incrementing and decrementing instructions (Instruction 36.26 and Instruction 36.27) are another form of explicit adding and subtracting. In either case, the value added/subtracted is one. Like most increment and decrement instructions used in other microcontrollers and processors, the carry flag is not affected (although it is in the "adiw" and "sbiw" instructions). Like in other processors, while 16-bit increment instructions can be implemented quite simply:

```
inc    A              ;  Increment Low Byte of 16 Bit Value
sbic   SREG, Z        ;    Increment High Byte if Result is equal to 0
 inc   A+1
```

Decrementing a 16-bit value, while taking the same number of instructions, is not as simple:

```
subi   A, 1           ;  Subtract 1 from the Low Byte
sbic   SREG, C        ;    Decrement High Byte if Result is Less than 0
 dec   A+1
```

This example could be further simplified to a single "sbiw" instruction, but I wanted to show that a 16-bit (and other multibyte values) would have to subtract 1 rather than decrement to execute properly. I should point out that the decrement example above will only work if the value is in the high 16 GPRs.

Negating the contents of a register can simply be accomplished by using the "neg" instruction (Instruction 36.28). This instruction simply subtracts the contents of the register from zero and stores the result back in the original register.

Getting the negative of a 16-bit (or larger) value is somewhat more complex and will require using the subtraction instructions and an unused (available) register.

```
neg    A              ;  Negate the First Value
clr    Rn             ;  Do a "sbc" with Zero for the High Byte
sbc    Rn, A+1        ;  "Rn" can be any GPR
mov    A+1, Rn
```

The complement instruction ("com"—Instruction 36.29) inverts the bits of a given GPR. "Com" does not negate a value; instead it is the same XORing a GPR with $0FF. This inversion is known as "one's complement."

A nice feature of the instruction set is being able to compare two registers (or a register and a constant) without having to put the result in an unused register (Instruction 36.30, Instruction 36.31, and Instruction 36.32). The "CP" (compare) instructions essentially perform a subtraction without saving the result in the first parameter. "CP" executes on two registers, while "CPC" executes on the two registers after taking the carry flag into account. "CPI" compares a register to a constant value.

The "TST" Instruction (Instruction 36.33) essentially ORs the value in the specified register with 0 and sets the zero and negative status bits in the SREG register. When you

36

look at the TST instruction, you'll be surprised to find out that the overflow flag is reset. This is done to make sure the correct value is placed in the "sign" bit ($S = N \char94 V$). By resetting the "V" bit, the value of the "N" bit will be passed directly to the "S" flag without being modified incorrectly by "V."

The last arithmetic instruction is the multiply ("Mul"—Instruction 36.34). This instruction multiplies two 8-bit numbers and produces a 16-bit result. Multiply operates on unsigned values only.

The "logic instructions" are what I would call "bitwise" instructions because they change the values of individual bits. To lessen confusion, I have grouped the instructions and reference them in the same way as Atmel has, but I want to point out they are what I would consider as not logic, but "bitwise."

"ANDing" the contents of a register (Instruction 36.35 and Instruction 36.36) holds no surprises and works exactly as you would expect. There is one thing to watch for, and that's the "CBR" instruction.

"CBR" is actually an "ANDI" instruction with the constant value inverted (XORed by $FF) before it is ANDed with the values in the first parameter's GPR. The purpose of this instruction is to clear the specified bits rather than keep the bits as is done in a "typical" AND instruction.

"ORing" bit instructions (Instruction 36.37 and Instruction 36.38) are handled exactly the same way in the AVR as ANDing. This is also true for the "SBR" instruction, which is analogous to "ORI" the same way as the "CBR" instruction is to "ANDI." This means that the contents of the register are not inverted as in the case of "CBR" because "SBR" is designed to set bits, where "CBR" is designed to clear them.

The "EOR" instruction (Instruction 36.39) will XOR the bits of two registers. Unfortunately, there isn't an "EORI" instruction which would allow individual bits to be flipped specifically by one instruction.

The EOR instruction can be used to swap the contents of two registers without having to use a third for temporary storage:

```
eor    A, B       ;  A = A ^ B,      B = B
eor    B, A       ;  A = A ^ B,      B = B ^ ( A ^ B )
                  ;                    = B ^ B ^ A
                  ;                    = A
eor    A, B       ;  A = A ^ B ^ A, B = A
                  ;  A = B,          B = A
```

The truly amazing aspect of this little snippet of code is that it actually uses the same amount of code as using an intermediate register:

```
mov    Rn, A
mov    A, B
mov    B, Rn
```

To be perfectly honest, I took this trick from the PIC.

The last two instructions ("clr" and "ser"—Instruction 36.40 and Instruction 36.41) are used to either reset or set, respectively, all the bits in a GPR register. "Clr" you're probably already familiar with and have found it useful in the past, but "ser" may seem less useful at first glance.

Actually, "ser" is very useful as setting a register to -1 ($FF is equal to -1 decimal). I often use -1 as an initial value to indicate that a variable hasn't been written to.

Instruction: "add Rd, Rr"

Bits:

0000	11rd	dddd	rrrr

"d" - GPR Source/Dest
"r" - GPR Source

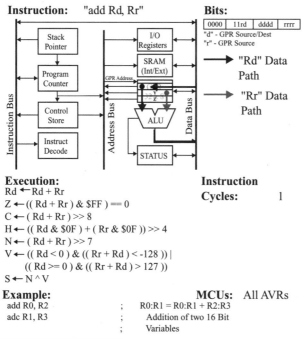

➤ "Rd" Data
    Path

➤ "Rr" Data
    Path

Execution:
Rd ← Rd + Rr
Z ← ((Rd + Rr) & $FF) == 0
C ← (Rd + Rr) >> 8
H ← ((Rd & $0F) + (Rr & $0F)) >> 4
N ← (Rd + Rr) >> 7
V ← ((Rd < 0) & ((Rr + Rd) < -128)) |
    ((Rd >= 0) & ((Rr + Rd) > 127))
S ← N ^ V

**Instruction
Cycles:**   1

Example: **MCUs:** All AVRs
  add R0, R2   ;   R0:R1 = R0:R1 + R2:R3
  adc R1, R3   ;   Addition of two 16 Bit
                       ;   Variables

Instruction 36.18 AVR "add Rd, Rr" instruction.

Instruction: "adc Rd, Rr"

Bits:

0001	11rd	dddd	rrrr

"d" - GPR Source/Dest
"r" - GPR Source

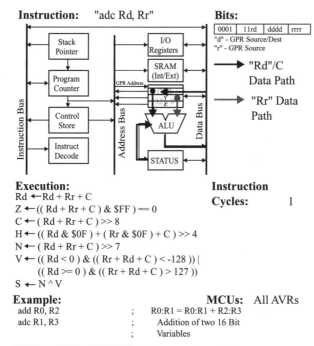

➤ "Rd"/C
    Data Path

➤ "Rr" Data
    Path

Execution:
Rd ← Rd + Rr + C
Z ← ((Rd + Rr + C) & $FF) == 0
C ← (Rd + Rr + C) >> 8
H ← ((Rd & $0F) + (Rr & $0F) + C) >> 4
N ← (Rd + Rr + C) >> 7
V ← ((Rd < 0) & ((Rr + Rd + C) < -128)) |
    ((Rd >= 0) & ((Rr + Rd + C) > 127))
S ← N ^ V

**Instruction
Cycles:**   1

Example: **MCUs:** All AVRs
  add R0, R2   ;   R0:R1 = R0:R1 + R2:R3
  adc R1, R3   ;   Addition of two 16 Bit
                       ;   Variables

Instruction 36.19 AVR "adc Rd, Rr" instruction.

36

ATMEL AVR

Instruction: "sub Rd, Rr"

Bits:

0001	10rd	dddd	rrrr

"d" - GPR Source/Dest
"r" - GPR Source

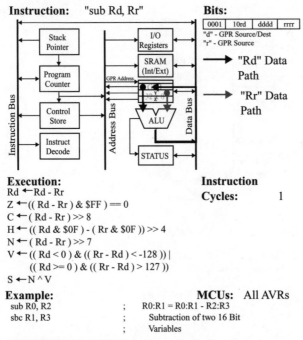

→ "Rd" Data Path

→ "Rr" Data Path

Execution:
$Rd \leftarrow Rd - Rr$
$Z \leftarrow ((\ Rd - Rr\ )\ \&\ \$FF\ ) == 0$
$C \leftarrow (\ Rd - Rr\ ) \gg 8$
$H \leftarrow ((\ Rd\ \&\ \$0F\ ) - (\ Rr\ \&\ \$0F\ )) \gg 4$
$N \leftarrow (\ Rd - Rr\ ) \gg 7$
$V \leftarrow ((\ Rd < 0\ )\ \&\ ((\ Rr - Rd\ ) < -128\ ))\ |$
$\quad ((\ Rd >= 0\ )\ \&\ ((\ Rr - Rd\ ) > 127\ ))$
$S \leftarrow N \wedge V$

Instruction Cycles: 1

Example: **MCUs:**   All AVRs
  sub R0, R2   ;   R0:R1 = R0:R1 - R2:R3
  sbc R1, R3   ;   Subtraction of two 16 Bit
                      ;   Variables

Instruction 36.20 AVR "sub Rd, Rr" instruction.

Instruction: "sbc Rd, Rr"

Bits:

0000	10rd	dddd	rrrr

"d" - GPR Source/Dest
"r" - GPR Source

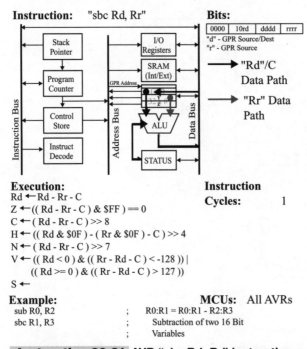

→ "Rd"/C Data Path

→ "Rr" Data Path

Execution:
$Rd \leftarrow Rd - Rr - C$
$Z \leftarrow ((\ Rd - Rr - C\ )\ \&\ \$FF\ ) == 0$
$C \leftarrow (\ Rd - Rr - C\ ) \gg 8$
$H \leftarrow ((\ Rd\ \&\ \$0F\ ) - (\ Rr\ \&\ \$0F\ ) - C\ ) \gg 4$
$N \leftarrow (\ Rd - Rr - C\ ) \gg 7$
$V \leftarrow ((\ Rd < 0\ )\ \&\ ((\ Rr - Rd - C\ ) < -128\ ))\ |$
$\quad ((\ Rd >= 0\ )\ \&\ ((\ Rr - Rd - C\ ) > 127\ ))$
$S \leftarrow$

Instruction Cycles: 1

Example: **MCUs:**   All AVRs
  sub R0, R2   ;   R0:R1 = R0:R1 - R2:R3
  sbc R1, R3   ;   Subtraction of two 16 Bit
                      ;   Variables

Instruction 36.21 AVR "sbc Rd, Rr" instruction.

Instruction: "subi Rd, k"

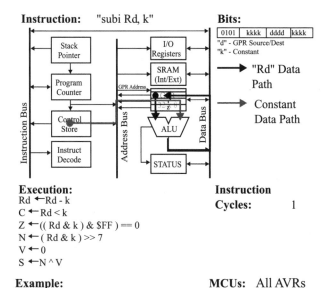

Bits:

| 0101 | kkkk | dddd | kkkk |

"d" - GPR Source/Dest
"k" - Constant

→ "Rd" Data
   Path

→ Constant
   Data Path

Execution:
Rd ← Rd - k
C ← Rd < k
Z ← ((Rd & k) & $FF) == 0
N ← (Rd & k) >> 7
V ← 0
S ← N ^ V

**Instruction
Cycles:**   1

Example: **MCUs:** All AVRs
  subi R20, 4   ;   Subtract 4 from Register

Note: Register is $10 to $1F.

Instruction 36.22 AVR "subi Rd, constant" instruction.

Instruction: "sbci Rd, k"

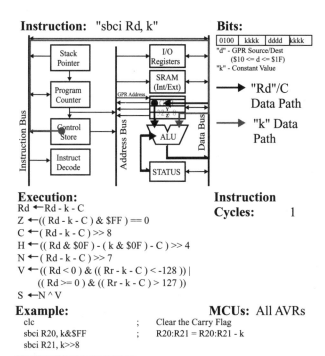

Bits:

| 0100 | kkkk | dddd | kkkk |

"d" - GPR Source/Dest
    ($10 <= d <= $1F)
"k" - Constant Value

→ "Rd"/C
   Data Path

→ "k" Data
   Path

Execution:
Rd ← Rd - k - C
Z ← ((Rd - k - C) & $FF) == 0
C ← (Rd - k - C) >> 8
H ← ((Rd & $0F) - (k & $0F) - C) >> 4
N ← (Rd - k - C) >> 7
V ← ((Rd < 0) & ((Rr - k - C) < -128)) |
     ((Rd >= 0) & ((Rr - k - C) > 127))
S ← N ^ V

**Instruction
Cycles:**   1

Example: **MCUs:** All AVRs
  clc   ;   Clear the Carry Flag
  sbci R20, k&$FF   ;   R20:R21 = R20:R21 - k
  sbci R21, k>>8

Instruction 36.23 AVR "sbci Rd, constant" instruction.

36

ATMEL AVR

Instruction: "adiw Rd, Const"

Bits:

1001	0110	kkdd	kkkk

"d" - GPR Source/Dest
(24, 26, 28, 30)
"k" - Constant (0 - 63)

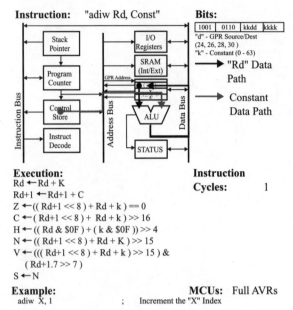

→ "Rd" Data Path

→ Constant Data Path

Execution:

$Rd \leftarrow Rd + K$

$Rd+1 \leftarrow Rd+1 + C$

$Z \leftarrow ((Rd+1 << 8) + Rd + k) == 0$

$C \leftarrow (Rd+1 << 8) + Rd + k) >> 16$

$H \leftarrow ((Rd \& \$0F) + (k \& \$0F)) >> 4$

$N \leftarrow ((Rd+1 << 8) + Rd + K) >> 15$

$V \leftarrow (((Rd+1 << 8) + Rd + k) >> 15) \&$
$(Rd+1.7 >> 7)$

$S \leftarrow N$

Instruction Cycles: 1

Example:

adiw X, 1   ;   Increment the "X" Index

MCUs: Full AVRs

Note: "Rd" can be 24, 26, 28 or 30 and "K" can be 0 to 63.

Instruction 36.24 AVR "adiw Rd, const" instruction.

Instruction: "sbiw Rd, Const"

Bits:

1001	0111	kkdd	kkkk

"d" - GPR Source/Dest
(24, 26, 28, 30)
"k" - Constant (0 - 63)

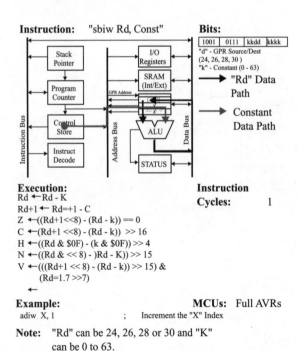

→ "Rd" Data Path

→ Constant Data Path

Execution:

$Rd \leftarrow Rd - K$

$Rd+1 \leftarrow Rd=+1 - C$

$Z \leftarrow ((Rd+1<<8) - (Rd - k)) == 0$

$C \leftarrow (Rd+1 <<8) - (Rd - k)) >> 16$

$H \leftarrow ((Rd \& \$0F) - (k \& \$0F)) >> 4$

$N \leftarrow ((Rd \& << 8) -)Rd - K)) >> 15$

$V \leftarrow (((Rd+1 << 8) - (Rd - k)) >> 15) \&$
$(Rd=1.7 >>7)$

$\leftarrow$

Instruction Cycles: 1

Example:

adiw X, 1   ;   Increment the "X" Index

MCUs: Full AVRs

Note: "Rd" can be 24, 26, 28 or 30 and "K" can be 0 to 63.

Instruction 36.25 AVR "sbiw Rd, const" instruction.

Instruction: "inc Rd"

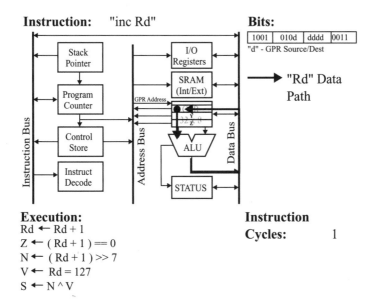

Bits:

1001	010d	dddd	0011

"d" - GPR Source/Dest

➡ "Rd" Data Path

Execution:
Rd ← Rd + 1
Z ← (Rd + 1) == 0
N ← (Rd + 1) >> 7
V ← Rd = 127
S ← N ^ V

Instruction Cycles: 1

Example:
inc R0   ;   Increment the Register

MCUs: All AVRs

Instruction 36.26 AVR "inc Rd" instruction.

Instruction: "dec Rd"

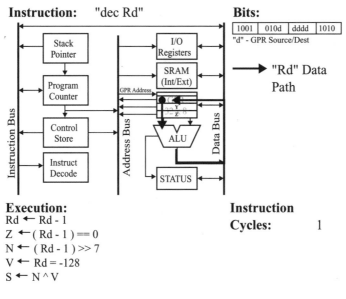

Bits:

1001	010d	dddd	1010

"d" - GPR Source/Dest

➡ "Rd" Data Path

Execution:
Rd ← Rd - 1
Z ← (Rd - 1) == 0
N ← (Rd - 1) >> 7
V ← Rd = -128
S ← N ^ V

Instruction Cycles: 1

Example:
dec R0   ;   Decrement the Register

MCUs: All AVRs

Instruction 36.27 AVR "dec Rd" instruction.

36

ATMEL AVR

Instruction: "neg Rd"

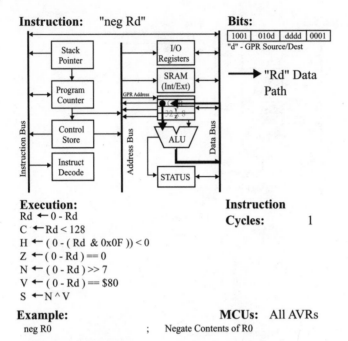

Bits:

1001	010d	dddd	0001

"d" - GPR Source/Dest

▶ "Rd" Data Path

Execution:

Rd ← 0 - Rd

C ← Rd < 128

H ← (0 - (Rd & 0x0F)) < 0

Z ← (0 - Rd) == 0

N ← (0 - Rd) >> 7

V ← (0 - Rd) == $80

S ← N ^ V

Instruction Cycles: 1

Example: **MCUs:** All AVRs

neg R0   ;   Negate Contents of R0

Instruction 36.28 AVR "neg Rd" instruction.

Instruction: "com Rd"

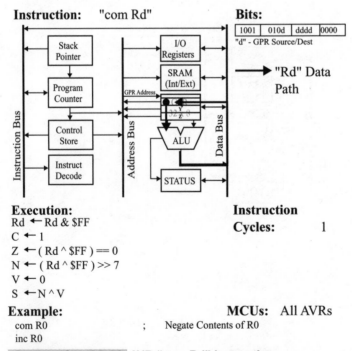

Bits:

1001	010d	dddd	0000

"d" - GPR Source/Dest

▶ "Rd" Data Path

Execution:

Rd ← Rd & $FF

C ← 1

Z ← (Rd ^ $FF) == 0

N ← (Rd ^ $FF) >> 7

V ← 0

S ← N ^ V

Instruction Cycles: 1

Example: **MCUs:** All AVRs

com R0   ;   Negate Contents of R0

inc R0

Instruction 36.29 AVR "com Rd" instruction.

Instruction: "cp Rd, Rr"

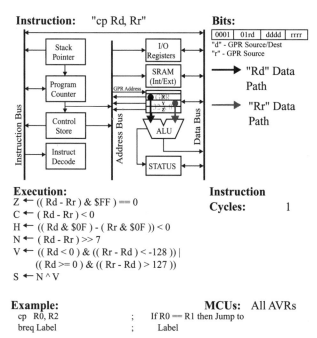

Bits:

0001	01rd	dddd	rrrr

"d" - GPR Source/Dest
"r" - GPR Source

➤ "Rd" Data Path

➤ "Rr" Data Path

Execution:

$Z \leftarrow ((Rd - Rr) \& \$FF) == 0$
$C \leftarrow (Rd - Rr) < 0$
$H \leftarrow ((Rd \& \$0F) - (Rr \& \$0F)) < 0$
$N \leftarrow (Rd - Rr) >> 7$
$V \leftarrow ((Rd < 0) \& ((Rr - Rd) < -128)) \,|\,$
$\quad ((Rd >= 0) \& ((Rr - Rd) > 127))$
$S \leftarrow N \wedge V$

Instruction Cycles: 1

Example:

```
cp   R0, R2          ;   If R0 == R1 then Jump to
breq Label           ;   Label
```

MCUs: All AVRs

Instruction 36.30 AVR "cp Rd, Rr" instruction.

Instruction: "cpc Rd, Rr"

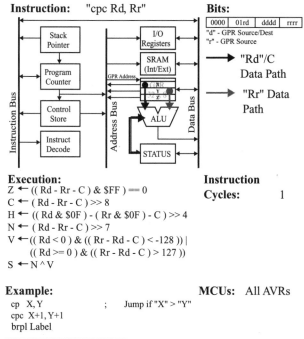

Bits:

0000	01rd	dddd	rrrr

"d" - GPR Source/Dest
"r" - GPR Source

➤ "Rd"/C Data Path

➤ "Rr" Data Path

Execution:

$Z \leftarrow ((Rd - Rr - C) \& \$FF) == 0$
$C \leftarrow (Rd - Rr - C) >> 8$
$H \leftarrow ((Rd \& \$0F) - (Rr \& \$0F) - C) >> 4$
$N \leftarrow (Rd - Rr - C) >> 7$
$V \leftarrow ((Rd < 0) \& ((Rr - Rd - C) < -128)) \,|\,$
$\quad ((Rd >= 0) \& ((Rr - Rd - C) > 127))$
$S \leftarrow N \wedge V$

Instruction Cycles: 1

Example:

```
cp   X, Y            ;   Jump if "X" > "Y"
cpc  X+1, Y+1
brpl Label
```

MCUs: All AVRs

Instruction 36.31 AVR "cpc Rd, Rr" instruction.

36

ATMEL AVR

Instruction: "cpi Rd, k"

Bits:

0011	kkkk	dddd	kkkk

"d" - GPR Source/Dest
"k" - Constant

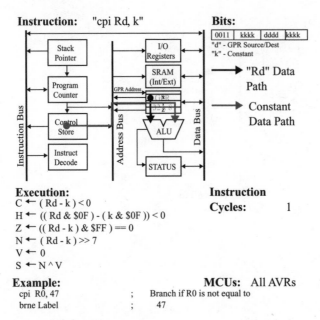

"Rd" Data
Path

Constant
Data Path

Execution:

$C \leftarrow (Rd - k) < 0$

$H \leftarrow ((Rd \ \& \ \$0F) - (k \ \& \ \$0F)) < 0$

$Z \leftarrow ((Rd - k) \ \& \ \$FF) == 0$

$N \leftarrow (Rd - k) >> 7$

$V \leftarrow 0$

$S \leftarrow N \wedge V$

Instruction Cycles: 1

Example:

```
cpi  R0, 47     ;     Branch if R0 is not equal to
brne Label      ;          47
```

MCUs: All AVRs

Note: Register is $10 to $1F.

Instruction 36.32 AVR "cpi Rd, const" instruction.

Instruction: "tst Rd"

Bits:

0010	00dd	dddd	dddd

"d" - GPR Source

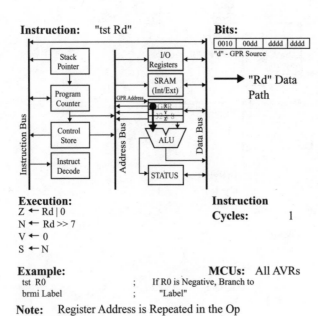

"Rd" Data
Path

Execution:

$Z \leftarrow Rd \ | \ 0$

$N \leftarrow Rd >> 7$

$V \leftarrow 0$

$S \leftarrow N$

Instruction Cycles: 1

Example:

```
tst  R0         ;     If R0 is Negative, Branch to
brmi Label      ;          "Label"
```

MCUs: All AVRs

Note: Register Address is Repeated in the Op
Codes

Instruction 36.33 AVR "tst Rd" instruction.

Instruction: "mul Rd, Rr"

Bits:

1001	11rd	dddd	rrrr

"d" - GPR Source/Dest
"r" - GPR Source

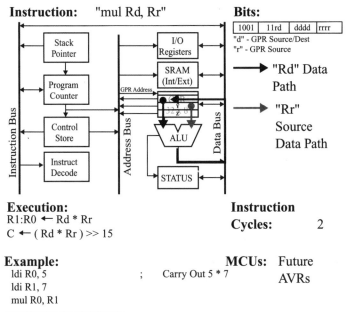

➤ "Rd" Data Path

➤ "Rr" Source Data Path

Execution:
R1:R0 ← Rd * Rr
C ← (Rd * Rr) >> 15

Instruction Cycles: 2

Example:
```
ldi R0, 5          ;   Carry Out 5 * 7
ldi R1, 7
mul R0, R1
```

MCUs: Future AVRs

Instruction 36.34 AVR "mul Rd, Rr" instruction.

Instruction: "and Rd, Rr"

Bits:

0010	00rd	dddd	rrrr

"d" - GPR Source/Dest
"r" - GPR Source

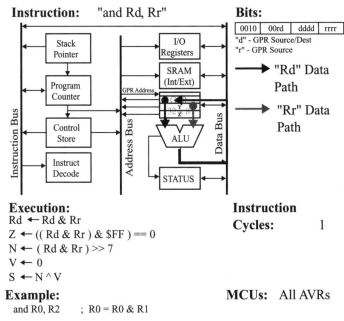

➤ "Rd" Data Path

➤ "Rr" Data Path

Execution:
Rd ← Rd & Rr
Z ← ((Rd & Rr) & $FF) == 0
N ← (Rd & Rr) >> 7
V ← 0
S ← N ^ V

Instruction Cycles: 1

Example:
```
and R0, R2     ;  R0 = R0 & R1
```

MCUs: All AVRs

Instruction 36.35 AVR "and Rd, Rr" instruction.

36

ATMEL AVR

Instruction: "andi Rd, k"

Bits:

0111	kkkk	dddd	kkkk

"d" - GPR Source/Dest
"k" - Constant

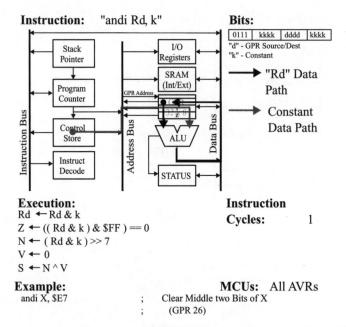

→ "Rd" Data
    Path

→ Constant
    Data Path

Execution:
Rd ← Rd & k
Z ← ((Rd & k) & $FF) == 0
N ← (Rd & k) >> 7
V ← 0
S ← N ^ V

**Instruction
Cycles:**   1

Example: **MCUs:** All AVRs
andi X, $E7   ;   Clear Middle two Bits of X
                     ;   (GPR 26)

Note: Register is $10 to $1F. "CBR" uses "ANDI"
          Instruction, but complements "k".

Instruction 36.36 AVR "andi Rd, const" instruction.

Instruction: "or Rd, Rr"

Bits:

0010	10rd	dddd	rrrr

"d" - GPR Source/Dest
"r" - GPR Source

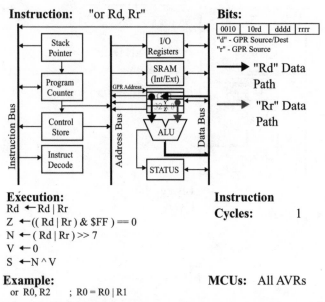

→ "Rd" Data
    Path

→ "Rr" Data
    Path

Execution:
Rd ← Rd | Rr
Z ← ((Rd | Rr) & $FF) == 0
N ← (Rd | Rr) >> 7
V ← 0
S ← N ^ V

**Instruction
Cycles:**   1

Example: **MCUs:** All AVRs
or R0, R2   ; R0 = R0 | R1

Instruction 36.37 AVR "or Rd, Rr" instruction.

Instruction: "ori Rd, k"

Bits:

0110	kkkk	dddd	kkkk

"d" - GPR Source/Dest
"k" - Constant

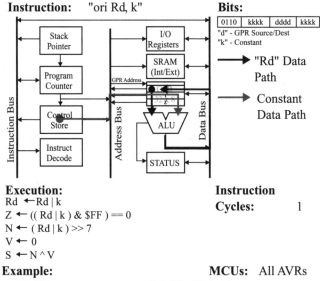

→ "Rd" Data
    Path

→ Constant
    Data Path

Execution:
Rd ← Rd | k
Z ← ((Rd | k) & $FF) == 0
N ← (Rd | k) >> 7
V ← 0
S ← N ^ V

Instruction Cycles: 1

Example:

ori X, $E7   ;   Set all the Bits but the
                ;   Middle Two Bits of X
                ;   (GPR 26)

MCUs: All AVRs

Note: Register is $10 to $1F. "SBR" is the ORI
Instruction, Specified to Set Specific Bits.

Instruction 36.38 AVR "ori Rd, const" instruction.

Instruction: "eor Rd, Rr"

Bits:

0010	01rd	dddd	rrrr

"d" - GPR Source/Dest
"r" - GPR Source

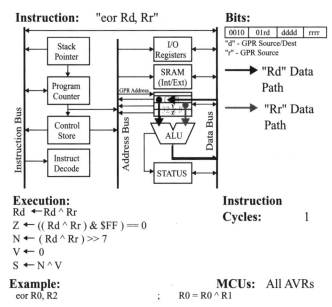

→ "Rd" Data
    Path

→ "Rr" Data
    Path

Execution:
Rd ← Rd ^ Rr
Z ← ((Rd ^ Rr) & $FF) == 0
N ← (Rd ^ Rr) >> 7
V ← 0
S ← N ^ V

Instruction Cycles: 1

Example:
eor R0, R2   ;   R0 = R0 ^ R1

MCUs: All AVRs

Instruction 36.39 AVR "eor Rd, Rr" instruction.

36

ATMEL AVR

Instruction: "clr Rd"

Bits:

0010	01dd	dddd	dddd

"d" - GPR Source/Dest

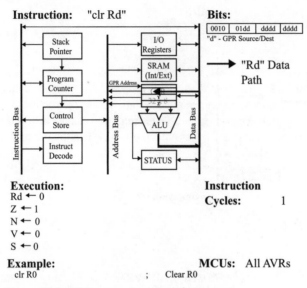

→ "Rd" Data Path

Execution:

Rd ← 0

Z ← 1

N ← 0

V ← 0

S ← 0

Instruction Cycles: 1

Example:

clr R0   ;   Clear R0

MCUs: All AVRs

Note: In the Bit Pattern, the address is repeated with the high order bit of the address repeated in the second nybble and the third and fourth nybbles contain the least significant four bits of the address.

Instruction 36.40 AVR "clr Rd" instruction.

Instruction: "ser Rd"

Bits:

1110	1111	dddd	1111

"d" - GPR Source/Dest minus 16

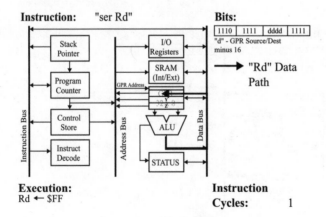

→ "Rd" Data Path

Execution:

Rd ← $FF

Instruction Cycles: 1

Example:

ser R20   ;   Set all Bits in R20

MCUs: All AVRs

Note: The Register Address is from $10 (16 Dec.) to $1F (31 Dec.).

Instruction 36.41 AVR "ser Rd" instruction.

AVR Branch Instructions

The AVR architecture allows for a very wide range of options for execution change. To take full advantage of the AVR's execution change capabilities, you really have to have a good understanding of the different ways the architecture can change the program counter.

The relative jump and call instructions (Instruction 36.42 and Instruction 36.43) are what I would consider the most basic units of the AVR's execution change instructions. The change of the program counter is actually done with an offset, where the offset is the least significant 12 bits of the instruction.

In this method of changing the program counter to start executing a subroutine (for the case of the "rcall" instruction), the old program counter is saved on the stack before it is updated with the new address. This allows the AVR to "find" its way back to the original caller, no matter where in the program execution it is currently taking place.

The offset is $+/-2K$, which means that these relative jump and call instructions can access any location in memory from anywhere else in the AVR 1200. This capability has meant that full "jmp"s and "call"s (described below) are not required for the AVR 1200.

One thing I haven't mentioned before about the AVR is how address and control store is set up. When Atmel specifies the amount of memory in the AVR, usually the number of bytes is given. Each instruction word takes up two or four bytes, so the actual number of instructions is one-half (or less if many four-byte instructions are used in the code) of the advertised control store size.

Now, all this may be familiar to you if you've worked with something like an 8086 (which uses a 16-bit word) or even the 68HC05 (where each instruction and addressing mode can take a different number of bytes). In many microprocessors (like the 8086), each byte has its own address (and each word starts at an even byte address). Each word of the AVR is on an incrementing address. As I went through the "LPM" instruction in the previous subchapter, understanding this will be very important.

Following the "RJMP" and "RCALL" instructions are the "JMP" and "CALL" (Instruction 36.44 and Instruction 36.45). These two instructions are designed for changing execution anywhere in a 4-MByte memory space. The 8515 has 4K words of EEPROM available for control store, which means that Atmel has some big plans for the AVR. While I don't see the need for a 4-meg word control store microcontroller, it's actually nice to see a company preparing for the future. (I remember when the first 64K Apple IIs became available and a lot of people thought that was the ultimate in personal computing.)

"JMP" and "CALL" are actually two-word (four-byte) instructions. This has a few implications on how the programs execute. The first is on how many cycles are required for the instructions to execute. Both the "JMP" and "CALL" instructions take one cycle more than the "RJMP" and "RCALL" (which require two and three cycles, respectively). As you'll see below, this also has an impact on the execution of other instructions.

36

ATMEL AVR

Figure 36.2 AVR "RJMP" and "RCALL" program counter update.

The last two jump and call instructions to be discussed are the indexed (using the "Z" registers) "IJMP" and "ICALL" (Instruction 36.46 and Instruction 36.47). These instructions are also only available in the full AVRs and update the PC as:

With the indexed jump and call, a state machine or table execution constructs can be easily implemented. These instructions are not available in the low-end (1200) AVRs, which means that indexed or table jumps and calls cannot be carried out (also, the "LPM" instruction is not available).

As I mentioned above, if any one of the "call" instructions is executed in the AVR, the full return address is saved on the stack (even if it is a short relative branch to the subroutine address). To return from the subroutine, the "RET" instruction is used (Instruction 36.48).

The "RETI" instruction (Instruction 36.49) behaves exactly the same as the "ret" instruction except that interrupts are enabled upon return. Later in this section, I will discuss interrupts further, but I did want to point out one novel use for the "reti" instruction, and that is in the case of timing critical subroutines. If you had a subroutine that was critically timed (i.e., for the DS1820) and you didn't want an interrupt to screw up the timing, you'd mask the interrupts before returning from this subroutine. You could execute an "SEI" instruction to re-enable interrupts and then a "ret"—or you could just execute a "reti."

The AVR is capable of branching on a condition in the status register (Instruction 36.50 and Instruction 36.51). Because the bit and its polarity has to be specified in the instruction, the offset range is reduced to +/−63 word addresses from the current address. This means that branching on "condition" is quite limited, although this problem could be mitigated the same way as in the case of the 8051 and 68HC05 by negatively branching around an instruction capable of jumping further.

For example, a branch on the zero flag set to "label" could be implemented as:

```
brne    Skip        ;  Skip over the Branch to "Label
  rjmp    Label
Skip
```

This would give you a branch address range of +/−2K word addresses rather than the +/−63 addresses of the branch instruction.

In the instruction set description, Atmel has provided a number (18 in total) of instructions that are based on "BRBC" and "BRBS." I have listed them in the instruction descriptions rather than make up a page for each one.

While I'm on the subject of branching, I wanted to point out that the compare and branch instructions can be used to represent very simple "if" statements for the GPR registers.

For example,

```
if ( A == B )       //  Compare GPR Variable "A" to GPR Variable "B"
  goto Label;       //   and Jump to "Label" if they're equal
```

could be compiled into:

```
cp    A, B
  breq    Label
```

PC ⟵ Z

Figure 36.3 AVR "IJMP"/"ICALL" program counter update.

which is a very simple conversion (compilation) of the two source statements. Less than or greater than can also be implemented with a few moments of thought. The AVR assembly code for:

```
if ( A < B )          // Compare GPR Variable "A" to GPR Variable "B"
  goto Label;         //   and Jump to "Label" if A < B
```

is simply:

```
cp     A, B
brlt   Label
```

But what about?

```
if ( A > B )          // Compare GPR Variable "A" to GPR Variable "B"
  goto Label;         //   and Jump to "Label" if A > B
```

If you look at the list of "pseudobranch" instructions, you won't see any instructions that will do the job.

In this case, you have to reverse the order of comparing to make the operation work with the tools we have. So the resulting assembler code is:

```
cp     B, A
brlt   Label
```

Which is easily generated by reversing the "if" statement to:

```
if ( B < A )
```

Using the same techniques, "less than or equal to" or "greater than or equal to" can also be implemented:

```
if ( A >= B )         // Compare GPR Variable "A" to GPR Variable "B"
  goto Label;         //   and Jump to "Label" if A >= B
```

is

```
cp     A, B
brge   Label
```

And:

```
if ( A <= B )         // Compare GPR Variable "A" to GPR Variable "B"
  goto Label;         //   and Jump to "Label" if A <= B
```

is equivalent to:

```
if ( B >= A )         // Compare GPR Variable "A" to GPR Variable "B"
  goto Label;         //   and Jump to "Label" if A <= B
```

which becomes:

```
cp     B, A
brge   Label
```

I use "brge" (branch on greater than or equal to), rather than "brpl" (branch on plus) because "brge" uses the "S" flag of SREG into account, and as I showed you in the previous subchapter, the "S" flag takes overflows of 8-bit two's complement subtraction into account. "Brpl" just takes the negative flag into account, which could be set incorrectly if bit 7 of the result is reflecting a change in polarity (i.e., a two's complement overflow).

36

ATMEL AVR

The last class of branch or execution change instructions is the "skip" instructions. These instructions, after checking for a specified condition, either execute the next instruction or skip over it.

When you look at the instruction summaries, you'll probably be surprised to see that the skip instructions can take one, two, or three cycles to execute. Like me, when you first saw this, you probably thought that somebody made a mistake.

Actually, they didn't. The skip instructions work as follows:

1. If the condition isn't met, then the next instruction is executed, which only takes one cycle.
2. If the condition is met and the next instruction isn't "JMP" or "CALL," then the instruction is skipped and the two cycles are required for execution.
3. If the condition is met and the next instruction is "JMP" or "CALL," then both words of the instruction are skipped, taking three cycles to execute.

Now, in the "SBIC" and "SBIS" instructions (Instruction 36.52 and Instruction 36.53), which skip the next instruction if the bit in the I/O register is set, you have to be careful because they can only reference the first 32 addresses in the I/O space. You would probably not think this is a problem, except when you look at the "SREG" and see that it's at address $3F of the I/O register space.

This can be worked around by using the branch on status instructions ("BRBC" and "BRBS"). When using these instructions, you will probably use them like this:

```
BRBS   Bit, $+2        ;  Skip Over Next Instruction if Bit = 1
  Instruction
```

With this format, there is a problem, and that's what if the "instruction" is a "jmp," "call," "lds," or "sts" (all of which require two words for storage)? Execution would jump to the address portion of the instruction and try to execute that as a separate instruction (which is going to lead to all kinds of trouble). To avoid this, you should really branch to a label rather than a relative address.

You can also skip the next instruction based on the value of a bit in a GPR byte. The instructions "SBRC" and "SBRS" (Instruction 36.54 and Instruction 36.55) will skip over the next instruction based on the condition of a bit in a GPR register.

The last branch instruction is the compare and skip if equal ("CPSE"—Instruction 36.56). This instruction is probably best suited for looking for end conditions in loops, as is shown below:

```
Loop
   :
   :
   cpse    A, B             ;  Stop if condition is true
     rjmp    Loop
```

AVR Bit and Bit-Test Instructions

When you first look at the instructions for this group, you're probably wondering where Atmel got the name for them. There are a number of "true" bit instructions, but this group seems more focussed on providing a grab-bag of the left-over instructions (especially after the shift and rotate instructions have been taken into account).

Instruction: "rjmp Label"   **Bits:**

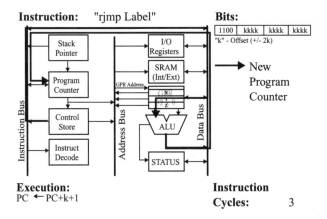

| 1100 | kkkk | kkkk | kkkk |

"k" - Offset (+/- 2k)

→ New
Program
Counter

Execution:
PC ← PC+k+1

**Instruction
Cycles:**   3

Example: **MCUs:** All AVRs
  rjmp Label   ;   Jump to the Label
  :
  Label

Note: Label can be up to -2048 to 2047 from the
      "rcall" Instruction.

Instruction 36.42 AVR "rjmp Label" instruction.

Instruction: "rcall Label"   **Bits:**

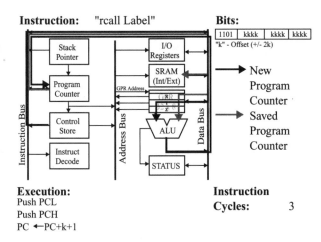

| 1101 | kkkk | kkkk | kkkk |

"k" - Offset (+/- 2k)

→ New
Program
Counter
→ Saved
Program
Counter

Execution:
Push PCL
Push PCH
PC ← PC+k+1

**Instruction
Cycles:**   3

Example: **MCUs:** All AVRs
  rcall Label   ;   Jump to the Subroutine
  :
  Label

Note: Label can be up to -2048 to 2047 from the
      "rcall" Instruction.

Instruction 36.43 AVR "rcall Label" instruction.

36

ATMEL AVR

Instruction: "jmp Label"

Bits:

1001	010k	kkkk	110k
kkkk	kkkk	kkkk	kkkk

"k" - Label Address

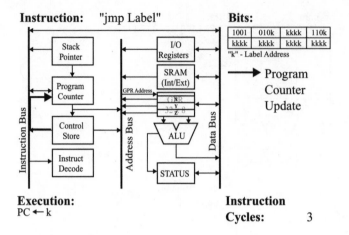

➤ Program
Counter
Update

Execution:
PC ← k

Instruction Cycles: 3

Example: **MCUs:** Full AVRs
jmp Label   ;   Jump (goto) Label
:
Label

Instruction 36.44 AVR "jmp label" instruction.

Instruction: "call Label"

Bits:

1001	010k	kkkk	111k
kkkk	kkkk	kkkk	kkkk

"k" - Subroutine Address

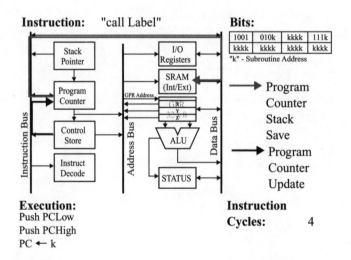

Program
Counter
Stack
Save
➤ Program
Counter
Update

Execution:
Push PCLow
Push PCHigh
PC ← k

Instruction Cycles: 4

Example: **MCUs:** Full AVRs
call Label   ;   Call Subroutine
:
Label

Instruction 36.45 AVR "call Label" instruction.

Instruction: "ijmp"

Bits:

| 1001 | 0100 | 0000 | 1001 |

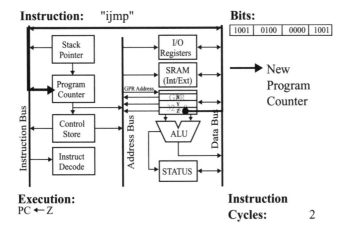

New
Program
Counter

Execution:
PC ← Z

**Instruction
Cycles:**   2

Example:
ldi R30, Label & $FF
ldi R31, Label / 256
ijmp   ;   Jump to (goto) "Label"

MCUs: Full AVRs

Instruction 36.46 AVR "ijmp" instruction.

Instruction: "icall"

Bits:

| 1001 | 0101 | 0000 | 1001 |

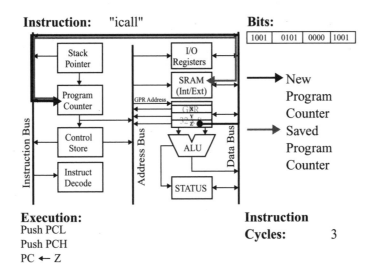

New
Program
Counter
Saved
Program
Counter

Execution:
Push PCL
Push PCH
PC ← Z

**Instruction
Cycles:**   3

Example:
ldi R30, Label & $FF
ldi R31, Label / 256
icall   ;   Call "Label"

MCUs: Full AVRs

Instruction 36.47 AVR "icall" instruction.

Instruction: "ret"

Bits:

1001	0101	0000	1000

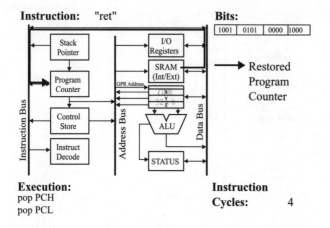

Restored
Program
Counter

Execution:
pop PCH
pop PCL

**Instruction
Cycles:**   4

Example: **MCUs:** All AVRs

call Label	;	Call "Label"
:		
Label	;	"Label" Subroutine
:		
ret	;	Return to Caller

Instruction 36.48 AVR "ret" instruction.

Instruction: "reti"

Bits:

1001	0101	0001	1000

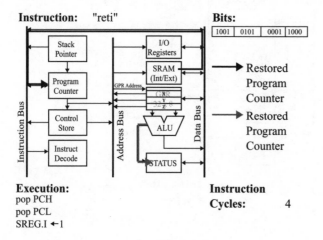

Restored
Program
Counter

Restored
Program
Counter

Execution:
pop PCH
pop PCL
SREG.I ←1

**Instruction
Cycles:**   4

Example: **MCUs:** All AVRs

:	;	Program Mainline
:		
Interupt	;	Interrupt Handler
:		
reti	;	Return to Mainline

Instruction 36.49 AVR "reti" instruction.

Instruction: "brbc bit, Label"

Bits:

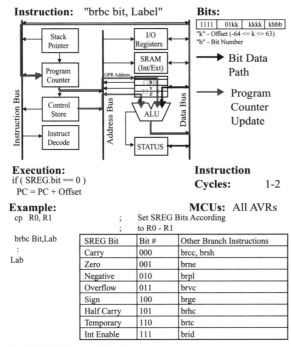

| 1111 | 01kk | kkkk | kbbb |

"k" - Offset (-64 <= k <= 63)
"b" - Bit Number

→ Bit Data Path

→ Program Counter Update

Execution:
if (SREG.bit == 0)
   PC = PC + Offset

Instruction Cycles: 1-2

Example:
cp   R0, R1   ;   Set SREG Bits According
                           ;   to R0 - R1
brbc Bit,Lab
  :
Lab

MCUs: All AVRs

SREG Bit	Bit #	Other Branch Instructions
Carry	000	brcc, brsh
Zero	001	brne
Negative	010	brpl
Overflow	011	brvc
Sign	100	brge
Half Carry	101	brhc
Temporary	110	brtc
Int Enable	111	brid

Instruction 36.50 AVR "brbc bit, Label" instruction.

Instruction: "brbs bit, Label"

Bits:

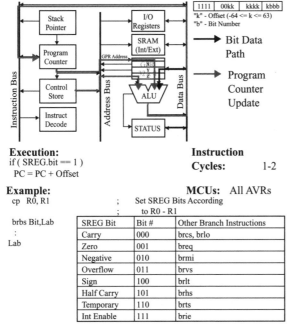

| 1111 | 00kk | kkkk | kbbb |

"k" - Offset (-64 <= k <= 63)
"b" - Bit Number

→ Bit Data Path

→ Program Counter Update

Execution:
if (SREG.bit == 1)
   PC = PC + Offset

Instruction Cycles: 1-2

Example:
cp   R0, R1   ;   Set SREG Bits According
                           ;   to R0 - R1
brbs Bit,Lab
  :
Lab

MCUs: All AVRs

SREG Bit	Bit #	Other Branch Instructions
Carry	000	brcs, brlo
Zero	001	breq
Negative	010	brmi
Overflow	011	brvs
Sign	100	brlt
Half Carry	101	brhs
Temporary	110	brts
Int Enable	111	brie

Instruction 36.51 AVR "brbs bit, Label" instruction.

36

Instruction: "sbic Reg, bit"

Bits:

1001	1001	rrrr	rbbb

"r" - Register (0 <= r <= 31)
"b" - Bit Number

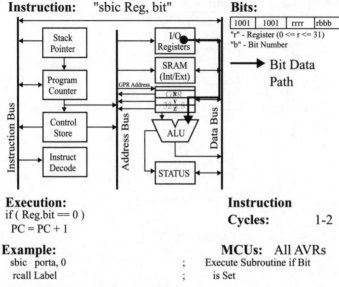

→ Bit Data Path

Execution:
if (Reg.bit == 0)
  PC = PC + 1

Instruction Cycles: 1-2

Example:

sbic porta, 0	;	Execute Subroutine if Bit
rcall Label	;	is Set

MCUs: All AVRs

Instruction 36.52 AVR "sbic Reg, bit" instruction.

Instruction: "sbis Reg, bit"

Bits:

1001	1011	rrrr	rbbb

"r" - Register (0 <= r <= 31)
"b" - Bit Number

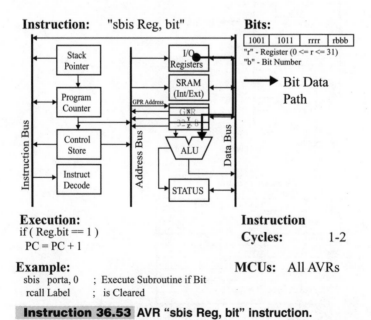

→ Bit Data Path

Execution:
if (Reg.bit == 1)
  PC = PC + 1

Instruction Cycles: 1-2

Example:

sbis porta, 0 ; Execute Subroutine if Bit
rcall Label   ; is Cleared

MCUs: All AVRs

Instruction 36.53 AVR "sbis Reg, bit" instruction.

Instruction: "sbrc Reg, bit"

Bits:

| 1111 | 110r | rrrr | 0bbb |

"r" - Register (0 <= r <= 31)
"b" - Bit Number

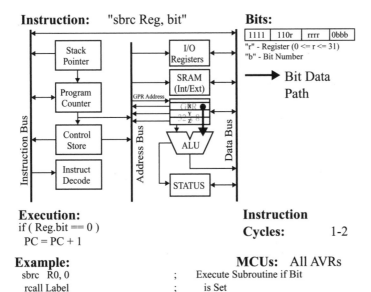

→ Bit Data
Path

Execution:
if (Reg.bit == 0)
　PC = PC + 1

**Instruction
Cycles:**　　1-2

Example:
sbrc   R0, 0　　　　　　；　Execute Subroutine if Bit
rcall Label　　　　　　；　　is Set

MCUs:　All AVRs

Instruction 36.54 AVR "sbrc Reg, bit" instruction.

Instruction: "sbrs Reg, bit"

Bits:

| 1111 | 111r | rrrr | 0bbb |

"r" - Register (0 <= r <= 31)
"b" - Bit Number

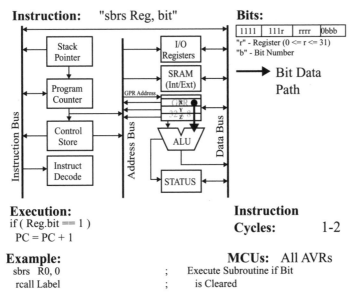

→ Bit Data
Path

Execution:
if (Reg.bit == 1)
　PC = PC + 1

**Instruction
Cycles:**　　1-2

Example:
sbrs   R0, 0　　　　　　；　Execute Subroutine if Bit
rcall Label　　　　　　；　　is Cleared

MCUs:　All AVRs

Instruction 36.55 AVR "sbrs Reg, bit" instruction.

36

ATMEL AVR

Instruction: "cpse Rd, Rr"

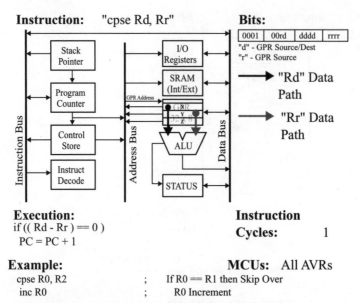

Bits:

| 0001 | 00rd | dddd | rrrr |

"d" - GPR Source/Dest
"r" - GPR Source

→ "Rd" Data Path

→ "Rr" Data Path

Execution:
if ((Rd - Rr) == 0)
   PC = PC + 1

Instruction Cycles: 1

Example:

| cpse R0, R2 | ; | If R0 == R1 then Skip Over |
| inc R0 | ; | R0 Increment |

MCUs: All AVRs

Instruction 36.56 AVR "cpse Rd, Rr" instruction.

The bit reset (clear) and set instructions (Instruction 36.57, Instruction 36.58, Instruction 36.59, and Instruction 36.60) are designed for modifying the contents of the I/O registers. When you look at the "BCLR," "BSET," "CBI," and "SBI" instructions, you'll see that they can only access a fraction of the I/O space ("BCLR" and "BSET" will modify a bit in the status register, and "CBI" and "SBI" will only access the first 32 I/O register addresses). This means that for many of the I/O registers, you will have to load them into the GPR space, modify the values, and then write them back into the I/O register space. For this case, you might want to create a macro like:

```
MACRO IOCBI Port, Bit   ; Clear the IO Bit Specified in the Port
  in    Temp, Port      ; Load Rn ($10 <= n <= $1F) with the Port Bit
  cbr   Temp, 1 << Bit  ; Clear the Specified Bit
                        ;   ( CBR Temp,1<<Bit == ANDI Temp,$FF^(1<<Bit)
  out   Port, Temp      ; Store the Result
ENDMACRO
```

You could replicate this macro to clear bits in the GPR space as well. Note that you have to make sure the "Temp" GPR is R16 to R31.

The "BSET" and "BCLR" instructions also have a number of "pseudoinstructions" that will make it easy to remember how to change a single SREG bit. These pseudoinstructions are listed in the instruction descriptions below.

It's funny, but as customers, little things tend to impress us. One of the really nice features that I really like about the AVR is the "BST" and "BLD" instructions (Instruction 36.61 and Instruction 36.62). These two instructions allow simple transference of bits between registers without affecting any registers critical to the operation of the software (i.e., carry).

What's so great about these instructions?

I always tend to get into situations where I have to transfer a single bit from one register or variable to another.

```
A.2 = B.5                    ; Move Bit 5 of "B" into Bit 2 of "A"
```

I would have to do something like this for the PIC:

```
rrf     B, w                 ; Move "B" down one Bit
movwf   Temp                 ; Save in a Temporary Register
rrf     Temp                 ; Bit 5 is now Bit 3
rrf     Temp                 ; Bit 5 is now Bit 2
movlw   B'00000100'          ; Now, Clear everything but Bit 2
andwf   Temp
movf    A                    ; Get "A"
andlw   B'11111011'          ; Clear Bit 2
iorwf   Temp,w               ; Add B.5
movwf   A                    ; Store "A" with Bit2 taken from B5
```

In the AVR, this could be accomplished simply by:

```
bst     B, 5                 ; Put B.5 into the "T" SREG bit
bld     A, 2                 ; Store "T" SREG Bit into A.2
```

The thing I like most about this is the lack of thinking that's required. In the PIC example above, I have to figure out the shortest path for the bits and what are the dependent bits (i.e., maybe I don't have to do the ANDing) to make sure that nothing can be inadvertently affected. Now, the PIC example is a generic set of instructions for moving a bit. In a real-life program, I would probably do things that would make moving a bit a lot simpler.

The "swap" instruction (Instruction 36.63) will exchange the nybbles of a GPR. This instruction is useful when you are using a GPR to store two digits (and not an 8-bit number). To output them to an LCD, you could use the following code:

```
mov     Temp, Value          ; Store the Value so it can be changed
swap    Temp                 ; Put the High Digit in the Low Position
andi    Temp, $0F            ; Clear Everything But the Display Digit
subi    Temp, 0-$30          ; Convert it to an ASCII Character
call    SendCHAR             ; Send the Character to the LCD
mov     Temp, Value          ; Now, Send the Low Nybble Value
andi    Temp, $0F
subi    Temp, 0-$30          ; Convert it to ASCII
call    SendCHAR
```

The shift and rotate instructions ("lsl," "lsr," "rol," "ror," and "asr"—Instruction 36.64, Instruction 36.65, Instruction 36.66, Instruction 36.67, and Instruction 36.68) are useful for either shifting data in or out, testing each bit in a GPR without having to create 8 separate bit tests (shifting through will allow you to check each bit individually at a set point in the byte).

If you're wondering what is the difference between shift and rotate, I tend to think of "rotate" as being a series of blocks (each containing a bit) on a wheel. The wheel can be turned to any position and now data is lost (in Figure 36.4 this is shown with the "carry flag" being one position on the wheel). The rotate instructions move a bit into and take a bit from the carry flag, which really means that the "carry" flag is one position in a 9-bit wheel.

The shift instructions are like having bits in a row by a ledge (Figure 36.4). As you shift the blocks, one of them falls off the ledge and is lost. You can shift in the opposite direction,

36

ATMEL AVR

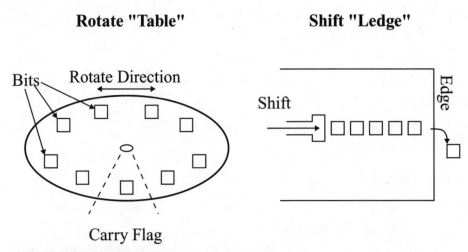

Figure 36.4 AVR Shift/Rotate instructions.

but the data is lost. This is in contrast to the "rotate" instructions in which no matter how often you rotate the value and in what direction, data is never lost.

In the shift, how the empty bits are filled is what differentiates the different types of shifts. In "logical" shifts, the fill is always zero. The "arithmetic" shift right retains the high bit (bit 7), which makes it useful for dividing two's complement numbers by powers of two.

The last three instructions in this group are really processor control instructions and should be very familiar to you because they are available in all microcontrollers (and many microprocessors). The first is the "nop" instruction (Instruction 36.69) which, in keeping with in the spirit of its operation, the less said about it the better.

The "WDR" instruction (Instruction 36.70) will reset the watchdog timer before it has a chance to reset the AVR. Elsewhere in this section, I explain the operation of the AVR's watchdog timer.

"Sleep" (Instruction 36.71) will put the AVR into a state of suspended animation (or low power) in which the microcontroller is stopped waiting for an interrupt or reset to "awaken" it. If the "SM" bit of the "MCU control register" ("MCUCR") is reset, the external clock continues to run, so timer and watchdog timer interrupts/resets can "wake" it up as well as external interrupts. If you look at the AVR documentation, you'll see that the "sleep" instruction is listed as taking three cycles. These three cycles are for executing the "sleep" instruction and then loading and executing the following instruction.

If the "SM" bit is set, then the oscillator will be stopped when "sleep" is executed. In this case, only an external interrupt (i.e., pin change) can wake up the AVR because the timers cannot run with the oscillator stopped. When using this "sleep" mode, you must plan for waiting 16 msec for the AVR's oscillator to restart and stabilize (this delay is built into the AVR).

Instruction: "bclr bit"

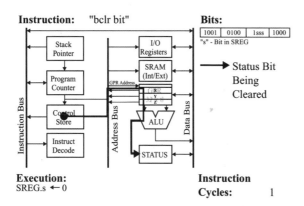

Bits:

1001	0100	1sss	1000

"s" - Bit in SREG

→ Status Bit Being Cleared

Execution:
SREG.s ← 0

Instruction Cycles: 1

"s" Definitions: **MCUs:**   All AVRs

"s"	SREG Bit	"CLx" Instruction
000	Carry Flag	CLC
001	Zero Flag	CLZ
010	Negative Flag	CLN
011	Overflow Flag	CLV
100	Sign Bit	CLS
101	Half Carry Flag	CLH
110	Temporary Bit	CLT
111	Global Interrupt Enable	CLI

Instruction 36.57 AVR "bclr bit" instruction.

Instruction: "bset bit"

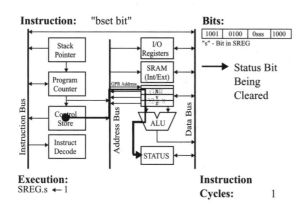

Bits:

1001	0100	0sss	1000

"s" - Bit in SREG

→ Status Bit Being Cleared

Execution:
SREG.s ← 1

Instruction Cycles: 1

"s" Definitions: **MCUs:**   All AVRs

"s"	SREG Bit	"SEx" Instruction
000	Carry Flag	SEC
001	Zero Flag	SEZ
010	Negative Flag	SEN
011	Overflow Flag	SEV
100	Sign Bit	SES
101	Half Carry Flag	SEH
110	Temporary Bit	SET
111	Global Interrupt Enable	SEI

Instruction 36.58 AVR "bset bit" instruction.

36

ATMEL AVR

Instruction: "cbi IOReg, bit"

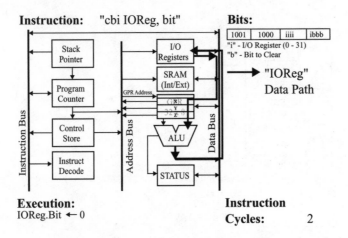

Bits:

| 1001 | 1000 | iiii | ibbb |

"i" - I/O Register (0 - 31)
"b" - Bit to Clear

"IOReg"
Data Path

Execution:
IOReg.Bit ← 0

**Instruction
Cycles:**   2

Example: **MCUs:** All AVRs
  cbi porta, 0   ;   Clear Bit 0 of PortA

Note: Only the Lower 32 Bits of the I/O Registers
            can be accessed.

Instruction 36.59 AVR "cbi IOReg, bit" instruction.

Instruction: "sbi IOReg, bit"

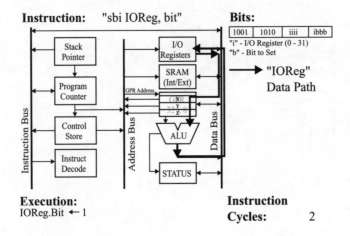

Bits:

| 1001 | 1010 | iiii | ibbb |

"i" - I/O Register (0 - 31)
"b" - Bit to Set

"IOReg"
Data Path

Execution:
IOReg.Bit ← 1

**Instruction
Cycles:**   2

Example: **MCUs:** All AVRs
  sbi porta, 0   ;   Set Bit 0 of PortA

Note: Only the Lower 32 Bits of the I/O Registers
            can be accessed.

Instruction 36.60 AVR "sbi IOReg, bit" instruction.

Instruction: "bst Rd, Bit"

Bits:

1111	101d	dddd	0bbb

"d" - GPR Source/Dest
"b" - Bit Number

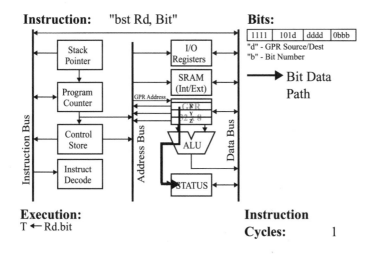

Bit Data
Path

Execution:
T ← Rd.bit

**Instruction
Cycles:**   1

Example:
bst R0, 2   ;   R1.4 = R0.2
bld R1, 4

MCUs: All AVRs

Instruction 36.61 AVR "bst Rd, Bit" instruction.

Instruction: "bld Rd, Bit"

Bits:

1111	100d	dddd	0bbb

"d" - GPR Source/Dest
"b" - Bit Number

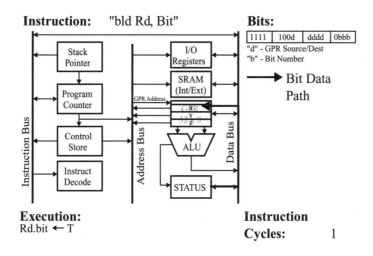

Bit Data
Path

Execution:
Rd.bit ← T

**Instruction
Cycles:**   1

Example:
bst R0, 2   ;   R1.4 = R0.2
bld R1, 4

MCUs: All AVRs

Instruction 36.62 AVR "bld Rd, Bit" instruction.

36

ATMEL AVR

Instruction: "swap Rd"

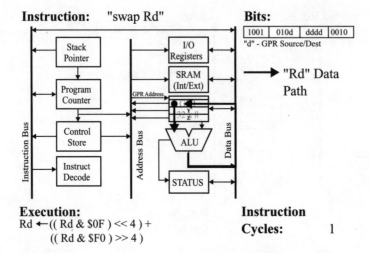

Bits:

1001	010d	dddd	0010

"d" - GPR Source/Dest

"Rd" Data Path

Execution:
Rd ◂─((Rd & $0F) << 4) +
((Rd & $F0) >> 4)

Instruction Cycles: 1

Example: **MCUs:** All AVRs
swap R0   ;   Swap the Nybbles of R0

Instruction 36.63 AVR "swap Rd" instruction.

Instruction: "lsl Rd"

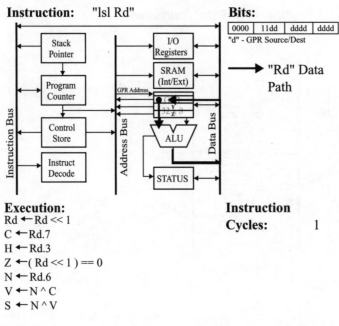

Bits:

0000	11dd	dddd	dddd

"d" - GPR Source/Dest

"Rd" Data Path

Execution:
Rd ◂─ Rd << 1
C ◂─ Rd.7
H ◂─ Rd.3
Z ◂─ (Rd << 1) == 0
N ◂─ Rd.6
V ◂─ N ^ C
S ◂─ N ^ V

Instruction Cycles: 1

Example: **MCUs:** All AVRs
lsl R0   ;   Multiply R0 by Two

Note: The Address of "Rd" is repeated in the
Op-Codes.

Instruction 36.64 AVR "lsl Rd" instruction.

Instruction: "lsr Rd"

Bits:

| 1001 | 010d | dddd | 0110 |

"d" - GPR Source/Dest

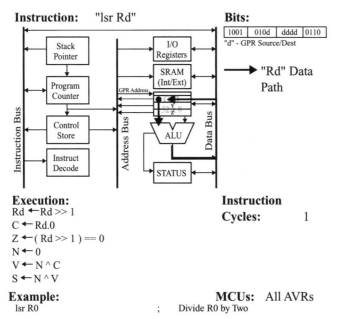

➤ "Rd" Data Path

Execution:
Rd ← Rd >> 1
C ← Rd.0
Z ← (Rd >> 1) == 0
N ← 0
V ← N ^ C
S ← N ^ V

Instruction Cycles: 1

Example: **MCUs:**   All AVRs
  lsr R0   ;   Divide R0 by Two

Instruction 36.65 AVR "lsr Rd" instruction.

Instruction: "rol Rd"

Bits:

| 0001 | 11dd | dddd | dddd |

"d" - GPR Source/Dest

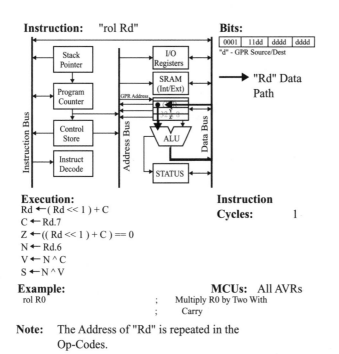

➤ "Rd" Data Path

Execution:
Rd ← (Rd << 1) + C
C ← Rd.7
Z ← ((Rd << 1) + C) == 0
N ← Rd.6
V ← N ^ C
S ← N ^ V

Instruction Cycles: 1

Example: **MCUs:**   All AVRs
  rol R0   ;   Multiply R0 by Two With
                                              ;   Carry

Note: The Address of "Rd" is repeated in the
           Op-Codes.

Instruction 36.66 AVR "rol Rd" instruction.

36

ATMEL AVR

Instruction: "ror Rd"

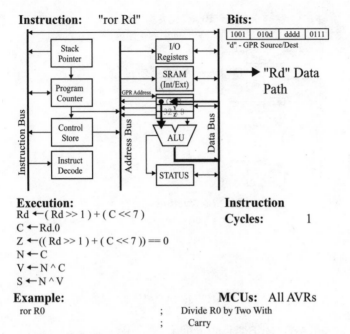

Bits:

1001	010d	dddd	0111

"d" - GPR Source/Dest

➤ **"Rd" Data Path**

Execution:

$Rd \leftarrow (Rd \gg 1) + (C \ll 7)$

$C \leftarrow Rd.0$

$Z \leftarrow ((Rd \gg 1) + (C \ll 7)) == 0$

$N \leftarrow C$

$V \leftarrow N \wedge C$

$S \leftarrow N \wedge V$

Instruction Cycles: 1

Example:

ror R0   ;   Divide R0 by Two With
                          ;   Carry

MCUs: All AVRs

Instruction 36.67 AVR "ror Rd" instruction.

Instruction: "asr Rd"

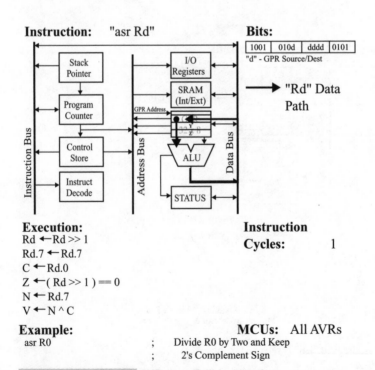

Bits:

1001	010d	dddd	0101

"d" - GPR Source/Dest

➤ **"Rd" Data Path**

Execution:

$Rd \leftarrow Rd \gg 1$

$Rd.7 \leftarrow Rd.7$

$C \leftarrow Rd.0$

$Z \leftarrow (Rd \gg 1) == 0$

$N \leftarrow Rd.7$

$V \leftarrow N \wedge C$

Instruction Cycles: 1

Example:

asr R0   ;   Divide R0 by Two and Keep
                          ;   2's Complement Sign

MCUs: All AVRs

Instruction 36.68 AVR "asr Rd" instruction.

Instruction: "nop"

Bits:

0000	0000	0000	0000

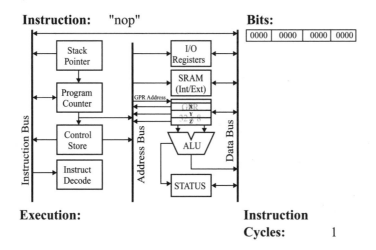

Execution:

**Instruction
Cycles:**   1

Example: **MCUs:**   All AVRs

nop   ;   Do Nothing for 1 Cycle

Instruction 36.69 AVR "nop" instruction.

Instruction: "wdr"

Bits:

1001	0101	1010	1000

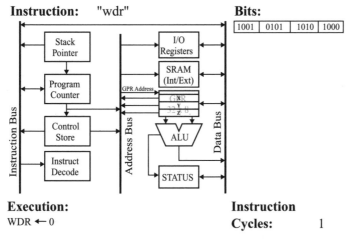

Execution:

WDR ← 0

**Instruction
Cycles:**   1

Example: **MCUs:**   All AVRs

wdr   ;   Reset WDR to Prevent TimeOut
                                 ;   and Reset

Instruction 36.70 AVR "wdr" instruction.

36

ATMEL AVR

Instruction: "AVRSLEEP"

Bits:

| 1001 | 0101 | 1000 | 1000 |

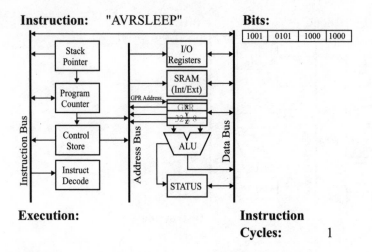

Execution:

Instruction Cycles: 1

Example:
sleep   ;   Do Nothing Until Interrupt
                                                ;   Request

MCUs: All AVRs

Instruction 36.71 AVR "sleep" instruction.

AVR EXAMPLE APPLICATIONS

CONTENTS AT A GLANCE

For all of the AVR example applications, I used the 1200 (low-end devices). This was probably a pretty good experience for me because it helped me get used to working with the GPR scheme of the AVR and its instruction set. These were the first applications that I wrote, and I would probably have liked to work through a series of experiments to understand how the devices worked better, rather than jumping right into the applications.

While the problems I had weren't serious (I created the first two applications in a few hours one evening, along with learning how to use the Atmel AT89/90 starter kit), but the difficulties were really indicative of my inexperience with the AVR architecture. Compounding the problems, I initially used an AVR chip that reset itself repeatedly without any warning, which caused some problems with debugging the second application. All the other devices presented in this book have a specific accumulator for carrying out arithmetic operations, which meant I had to shift mental gears somewhat for the applications.

First Application

If you have gone through the previous three microcontrollers, you should be an expert on implementing the two LED and button applications. The AVR will not pose any concerns for you.

The circuit used for the application will not hold any surprises. (Figure 37.1.) The only part of the circuit you should note is that I used a 10K resistor pull up on the "_Reset" pin. This isn't necessary (it could be left unconnected or floating), and I really did it out of habit more than anything else. Along with this, you should notice that I use PortD.5's internal pull up instead of an external pull up on the button.

I was able to write, simulate, and test this application in under an hour (and it was my first application for the AVR) and had it run first time. I was quite pleased with this because the application uses an interrupt handler (for the timer interrupt) and does not use any GPRs except for initializing the I/O registers.

```
;   AP1 - Flash the LED and Wait for the Button
;
;
;   This is AP1 for the AVR - Flash an LED on PB7 and, using a switch on
;    PD5, Flash an LED on PB0.
;
;   Myke Predko
;   97.11.06
;
;   Hardware Notes:
;    AVR1200 Running at 1 MHz (using an External Crystal)
;    PB7 - Connected to an LED and a Current Limiting Resistor
;    PB0 - Connected to an LED and a Current Limiting Resistor
;    PD5 - Connected to a Momentary On Switch Connected to Ground.

.include "c:\avrtools\appnotes\1200def.inc"
```

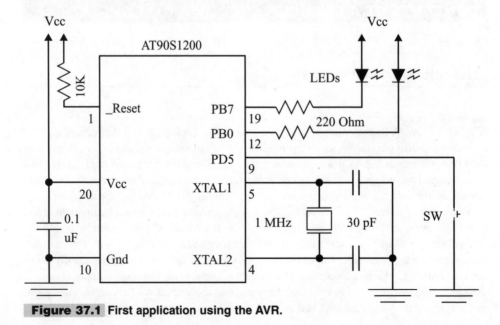

Figure 37.1 First application using the AVR.

```
        rjmp        Start            ;  MCU Reset Vector
        nop                          ;  Skip Over the "IRQ0" Interrupt
        rjmp        TmrInt           ;  Timer Interrupt Handler

TmrInt:                              ;  Timer Interrupt Handler - Toggle the
                                     ;  "Flashing" LED at PB7

        in          R0, SREG         ;  Save the Status Registers

;  NOTE - the T0V0 Flag is Automatically Reset when Vector is entered

        in          R16, PORTB       ;  Get the Current PortB value
        ldi         R17, $80         ;   Value to XOR it with
        eor         R16, R17
        out         PORTB, R16

        out         SREG, R0

        reti                         ;  Finished - Return to the Mainline


Start:                               ;  Start of Mainline

        ldi         R18, $81         ;  Enable the Bit Outputs
        out         DDRB, R18

        clr         R18
        out         PORTB, R18

        clr         R18              ;  Make All of PortD Input
        out         DDRD, R18

        ldi         R18, $20         ;  Turn on PortD.5's Internal Pull Up
        out         PORTD, R18

        ldi         R18, 5           ;  Start the Timer with 1024 Cycle Delay
        out         TCCR0, R18
        ldi         R18, 2           ;  Disable the Timer Interrupt Mask
        out         TIMSK, R18

        SEI                          ;  Enable Interrupts

Loop:                                ;  Loop Around Forever

        sbic        PIND, 5          ;  Skip If PORTD.5 is Low
        rjmp        PORTB0_Hi        ;   Else, it should be High

        cbi         PORTB, 0         ;  If the Bit is Low, Make LED Low as well

        rjmp   Loop

PORTB0_Hi:                           ;  Make the PortB.0 LED High

        sbi         PORTB, 0

        rjmp   Loop
```

   The only issue I had when I first powered up the application was that the timer LED flashed very quickly (much more than the expected two times per second). Like my using an explicit pull up resistor on "_Reset" out of habit, I was used to multiplying the timer cycles (from instruction cycles) to four clock cycles each to account for the instruction cycle clock driving the timer. The clock prescaler was increased four times (from 256 to 1024) and the application ran without any problems.

As a note on the AT89/90 starter kit, the programmer board also has eight LEDs and eight pushbutton switches that a part connected to the programmer can access (through the use of a cable and IDC connectors that come with the kit). This application can be implemented on the board very simply without doing anything other than connecting the cables (although the board's frequency is 4 MHz, rather than the 1 MHz used on the application, which means the LED will flash very quickly).

Real-Time Clock and Thermometer

Like the two-LED/button application, the digital clock thermometer design should be pretty old hat to you by now. With no surprises, the only thing to note is that I don't use a pull up on the time setting switch and do use one on the DS1820 serial communications line. (Figure 37.2.) This is done to avoid any issues with the internal CMOS pull-up.

The differences in how this application is implemented in the AVR compared to the other microcontrollers is the lack of being able to implement a table stored in control store. Instead, the "Time:" and "Temp:" headers have to be hard-coded into the source code as is shown below:

```
ldi     LCDOut, $54   ;  Write "Time:" Message
rcall   SendCHAR

ldi     LCDOut, $69   ;  'i'
rcall   SendCHAR

ldi     LCDOut, $6D   ;  'm'
rcall   SendCHAR

ldi     LCDOut, $65   ;  'e'
rcall   SendCHAR

ldi     LCDOut, $3A   ;  ':'
rcall   SendCHAR
```

With this application, a few of the shortcomings of the AVR assembler/simulator became very apparent. The first is the lack of ability to define constants as ASCII characters. Typically, in writing applications, I like to use the most appropriate data type for the application. Not having characters as a constant data type turned out to be something of a problem (I can never find a chart of ASCII codes when I'm creating an application). The AVR's simulator was also quite disappointing because it cannot display I/O registers (just the GPR and some processor registers). To be fair, these are just nits and to be honest, I never had a problem with any of the software I used and I'm sure later versions of the code will be updated to correct these deficiencies.

The big problem I had with implementing this application was keeping subroutine levels straight. As I mentioned at the beginning of the chapter, I had a problem with reliability on some parts, but this was made worse by my unfamiliarity of working with a processor that only has a three-deep stack. As you go through my source code, you'll notice that I have written the code initially with subroutines (mostly for delays, for decimal character

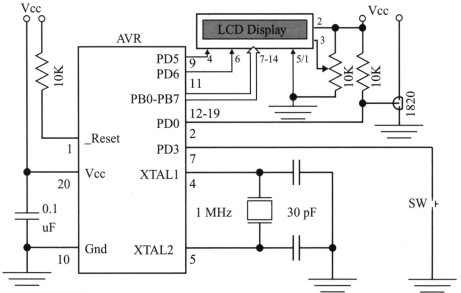

Figure 37.2 AVR-based digital clock/thermometer.

output). When I first ran the code, I found it to be very "buggy," with invalid characters being written on the LCD in invalid places.

As I looked through the code, I realized that I was probably blowing the stack. To fix this, all the subroutines were changed to stop them from calling other subroutines. This change did fix all of the problems with the invalid characters and positions.

But it did not fix the problem with the spurious resets. This was fixed by simply trying another AVR 1200. The 1200 parts that I have are very early production parts, so problems like these shouldn't be too surprising.

In the course of developing the application, I did come up with an interesting 16-bit delay routine for the AVR:

```
ldi     Count, lowValue       ;  ( Initial_Count ) & $FF
ldi     Counthi, HighValue    ;  ( Initial_Count >> 8 ) + 1
Loop:
dec     Count                 ;  Decrement the Low 8 Bits
brbc    1, Skip               ;  Skip the Next if Zero is Clear
dec     Counthi               ;  Decrement the High 8 Bits
Skip:
brne    Loop                  ;  Loop if the Zero Flag Isn't Set
```

In this case, "Count" and "Counthi" are GPR registers at address $10 to $1F. This snippet of code will provide a very large range of delays for the AVR that is much simpler to time than on the PIC. Each iteration of "loop" will take five cycles, no whether the high byte is incremented or not.

So, to get a specific delay, the formula:

```
Delay = ( Initial_Value * 5 ) / frequency
```

is used. To get the "Initial_Value" from the delay, the formula can be rearranged to:

```
Initial_Value = ( Delay * frequency ) / 5
```

Implementing the value from this formula only has one trick, and that's how to load in the "Count" and "Counthi" GPRs. "Count" is pretty straightforward, with the lower 8 bits of the value being loaded in directly, but "Counthi" must be loaded with the upper 8 bits of the delay plus one to make sure that the code runs through the correct number of times. This is shown in the comments of the example code above comments.

AVR Video Output with Pot Position

One of the things I talked about at the start of the book was interfacing microcontrollers to analog signals (both analog in and analog out). I briefly mentioned that a simple potentiometer and capacitor could be used for analog input and a resistor "ladder" used for analog output. I wanted to create an application which showed how this was done, and the best way I could come up with was creating a simple application that took an analog input and used it as a "paddle" value on a video screen. I wanted to do this on the AVR because the AVR's fast speed and single instruction cycle would be an advantage for the precise timings used by video. (Figure 37.3.)

The circuit itself will output NTSC composite video with the software provided with the application. The circuit itself is surprisingly simple (Figure 37.4).

I built my prototype on a "SimmStick" with the circuit plugged into a "DT003" power supply/backplane and the composite video output run through bus line "A15" to a video modulator attached to a SimmStick prototype card. This method of prototyping really was very easy and effective. (Figure 37.5.)

Figure 37.3 AVR video output SimmStick cards used (prototype card with video modulator, DT003 bus card/power supply and DT104 AVR processor SimmStick with composite video output resistor ladders, clockwise from top right).

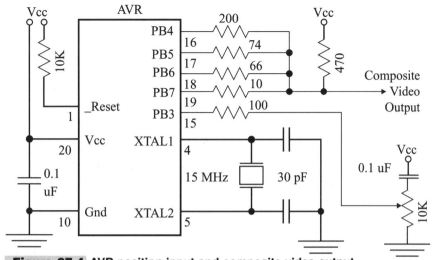

Figure 37.4 AVR position input and composite video output.

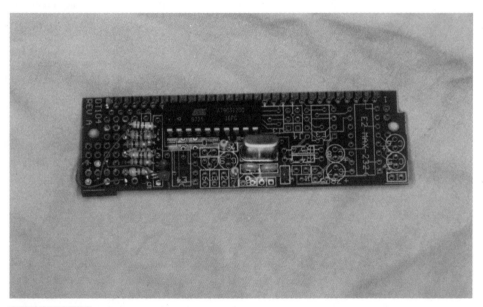

Figure 37.5 SimmStick DT104 card with AVR and composite video output resistor ladders.

As Figure 37.4 shows, I put all the components in the schematic on the SimmStick itself. This violates some of my philosophies about how I want to keep the peripheral interfaces seperate on the SimmStick, but I was able to connect the output resistors directly to output pins and wired to the pull-up resistor. The cap and potentiometer was attached to the AVR's SimmStick reversed (the devices on the "component" side), so I could change the potentiometer's position with the modulator's SimmStick "in front" of the AVR's SimmStick for easier packaging.

When I first started running the application, I had one problem and that was there was quite a bit of noise on the output pins. When I looked at it with an oscilloscope, I found that there was a 60-MHz, 200-mV "noise" on the pins. At the low-voltage-level output by this device, this was a problem. As I looked at the SimmStick itself, the AVR's decoupling capacitor was actually quite far away from the device. The noise was reduced to a much more reasonable 50 mV peak-to-peak by placing a 0.1-uF capacitor directly across the AVR's Vcc and Gnd pins.

The analog output voltages are actually formed by a voltage divider with the 470-ohm value being the "top" value. When you first looked at the circuit, you were probably wondering where I found 74-and 66-ohm resistors. These resistances were formed by using resistors in parallel (74 or 75 ohms is two 150-ohm resistors in parallel, and 66 ohms is created using three 200-ohm resistors in parallel). To output a specific voltage, the appropriate pin is pulled down to ground, which makes a voltage divider of the 470-ohm resistor and the resistor on the appropriate I/O pin.

This is not a circuit that I would really want to go into production with because it assumes that when power is applied, the microcontroller will always be active and running the software correctly. If all the I/O pins are in input mode or the output value is set high, then the output will be +4.5 volts or greater, which will be a problem with the modulator/TV the circuit is hooked up to.

If I was going to do this again, I would convert the resistor networks to drive a secondary voltage divider, which would take higher voltages down to the correct ranges (i.e., 5 volts would become 1.5 volts for "white").

The video modulator I used was bought at a local surplus store for $1.50. The voltage required was +12 V to run the modulator. To keep the application wiring simple, I ran the modulator from +13 V "Wall Wart" power output (connecting the modulator to the "PWR" pin of the SimmStick bus). The video modulator should be encased in a metal package to make sure a minimum of noise is broadcast during the device's operation.

Before I go much further, I should make some important comments, the first being that I did not have a copy of the NTSC composite video specification in front of me when I created this application. I actually used a "TycoVideoCam" that I bought at "Toys 'R Us," scoped out the composite video output, and applied what I saw on this application. The application runs great on a 12-inch black-and white TV I bought for $10 at a garage sale.

I would not recommend trying this application on your $3,000 home theatre. There is no reason why this circuit could damage a TV or monitor, but I wouldn't be willing to use my equipment for the experiment. Like all the applications presented in this book, many of the parts are from surplus stores and my junkbox, so certain specifications may be violated or a wiring error may cause a current flow between the TV and your application.

If you do decide that you want to see this application running on the family TV, I'm not responsible for your family's wrath if something goes wrong.

Another thing to note is that this circuit runs at a very high frequency; using an improperly shielded or grounded video modulator may result in interference with radios and TVs (yours and your neighbors). This is not an FCC-approved device and is only appropriate for experimentation. Having gotten the legal indemnification out of the way, let's get on with understanding the application.

The composite video output was set up to output four specific voltages for the video output. This can be shown in the horizontal synch pulse definition. (Figure 37.6.)

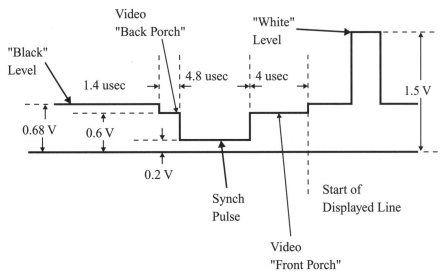

Figure 37.6 AVR composite video horizontal synch pulse.

Each of these voltages is produced by enabling one of the four I/O pins as output with a value of "0" (minimum voltage output possible). This creates a voltage divider that has more than 100-uA drive capability without affecting the voltage level significantly.

Note that there are actually three parts to each horizontal synch pulse. The first 0.6-volt part of the pulse is the "Video Backporch," followed by the 0.2-volt horizontal synch and then another 0.6-volt "Video Frontporch" (which is where the colour-burst information would go if this were a colour signal output). When I refer to a horizontal synch, I am really referring to these three features that must be present before the beginning of the video scan line data.

This horizontal synch pulse is part of the total "scan" line, which looks like Figure 37.7. After each horizontal synch pulse, there are 53 usecs available for video output. In Figure 37.7, I show varying shades of grey, but in this application, I only used "black" and "white."

Outputting the data in this 53 usecs is one of the areas where the AVR really shines. The fast clock speed and the single clock cycle per instruction cycle means that you can execute up to 795 instructions. This was important because the original purpose of this application was to be used as a video "pong" game (and actually, it still could be). Using a different micro would drastically reduce the number of instructions that could be executed because of the longer instruction cycles.

The application outputs 268 and then 267 scan lines of data (525 lines in total) for each of the two "fields." At the end of each field, six or seven short lines are output, followed by six vertical synch pulses, five or six short lines, and then ten or eleven "long" lines with the scan data following. This is repeated twice for each full "frame," the difference in the short pulses allowing data to be a half line different between each field, filling in the screen that the previous output missed.

In Figure 37.8, I have included the waveform at the potentiometer. During the start of the "field," I charge the capacitor and during the data scan out, I change the operation of the pin to input and wait for the capacitor to discharge. The idea behind this was to put the "paddle" on the screen at the point where the cap had discharged.

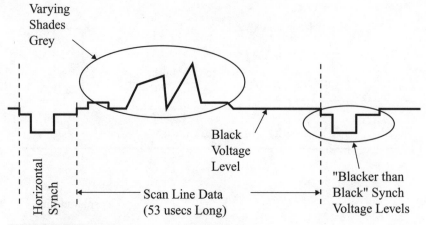

Figure 37.7 AVR composite video output line.

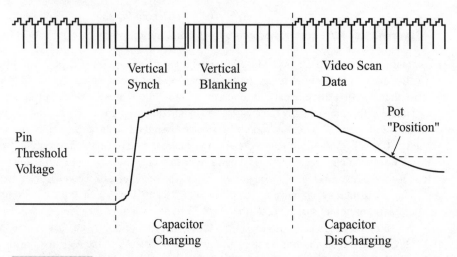

Figure 37.8 AVR composite video vertical synch with integral potentiometer position read.

This really didn't work out as planned. In the application, I found that the longest discharge I could get from the capacitor was about a sixth of the way through the scan lines. This was compensated for in software by multiplying the delay value by six before the next field output. During the field's scan output, this new value was checked and the paddle was put starting at this location. This is obviously suboptimal, and if I redo this application, I would change the capacitor and potentiometer values to make sure the discharge cycle would take place over the full length of the field (and simplify the software).

On the CD-ROM, you'll notice that there are three software programs for this application. The first is used to check the analog output levels before attempting to come up with the composite video waveforms. The second program ("Ap3v2.ASM") displays a white bar in the middle of the TV screen, and the final program ("Ap3v3.ASM") displays a bar down the right side of the screen and displays a "paddle" that can be moved by turning the potentiometer.

The final application uses 179 words of control store (versus 512 available), so it could be easily upgraded to implementing the "pong" game. The reason why I didn't go ahead with doing the pong game was that I wasn't comfortable with the hardware as it stands. The actual voltage outputs aren't quite what I want them to be (a bit on the high side)—although the application works fine on my cheap TV. The other major concern is with the operation of the capacitor/potentiometer network used for the input. I would like to respecify the components to have the maximum discharge to be greater than the length of time for a field output. To help this, I may put a 10K resistor between the potentiometer and ground to help extend this and clean up the waveform a bit when the potentiometer is set to minimal resistance to ground.

Actually, as I was proofreading this (just before sending the manuscript in to the publisher), I noticed that I connected the potentiometer incorrectly. The potentiometer terminal connected to ground should be left floating.

Having said this, this was the one application I did for this book that really made me sit back and make me feel like I had accomplished something. I wish I had been able to find a good specification for NTSC composite video, as it was quite labour intensive scoping the output from the "TycoVideoCam" and applying it to the application. I have spent many more hours than I probably should have looking at it operate and twiddling the pot. As I get more time, I probably will enhance the application, but in the meantime, I'm satisfied pointing to the simple screen and showing the kids what their dad did.

AVR SUMMARY

CONTENTS AT A GLANCE

AVR Resources
WEB SITES
LISTSERVER
COMPANIES

In the short time the AVR has been on the market, it has made a tremendous impact on the microcontroller world. As I write this, actual AVR parts have been available for less than six months and I am very surprised at the interest that the AVR has generated.

Each manufacturer presented here has a different business model. Atmel's marketing of devices that only have "flash" control store is interesting because it is different from all the other manufacturers presented here. Personally, I like it and from my manufacturing experiences, I always prefer Flash devices for storing firmware with ISP capabilities, rather than using OTP EPROM or Mask ROM.

I am looking forward to getting more experience with the AVR and trying out new applications (including experimenting with data structures). While I have presented the 32 general-purpose registers as a limitation, with the applications I have created for this book, I can see where I will be able be able to balance between the device's GPRs and RAM.

Looking back over what I have written, I guess I should have presented the architecture differences between the "full" AVR and what I call the "low-end" (i.e, the 1200). While the 1200 will run many of the instructions of the full architecture, the lack of external (to the GPRs) memory and the three element stack does change the way applications are implemented.

During 1998, Atmel is planning to release a number of new parts to be released. These new AVR parts will have additional peripheral features and memory options which should "flesh" out the AVR line.

AVR Resources

As one of the newest microcontroller devices to become available (the first product was available in the middle of 1997), the AVR understandably has the fewest resources in the devices available for your use. I expect this case to become better in the future and I wouldn't be surprised if the information in this chapter is out-of-date by the end of 1998.

WEB SITES

I expect AVR Web sites to become very prevalant over the next while. These initial sites should give you some good basic information about the AVR as well as different programmer designs.

http://www.dontronics.com/

- SimmStick site with AVR interfaces.
- AVR programmer designs.

http://www.ipc.o.za/people/kalle/atmel.htm

- Links to microcontroller and AVR sites.
- Home of the AVR listserver.

http://www.sistudio.com

- AVR programmers.
- Some third-party AVR FAQs and APNotes.

LISTSERVER

Interface Products has made an Atmel listserver available. At the time of writing, this list server has about five to ten messages per day on average.

To subscribe, send a note to:

atmel-request@pic.co.za

With the word "JOIN" in the body of the message.

COMPANIES

Atmel
Atmel Corporation
2325 Orchard Parkway
San Jose, California
95131
Tel: 408-441-0311
http://www.atmel.com

38

ATMEL AVR

PARALLAX: BASIC STAMP

PARALLAX BASIC STAMP

CONTENTS AT A GLANCE

The Parallax BASIC Stamp is truly an innovative product. Programmed and controlled by a PC host while it is in the application circuit with no extra hardware required to run it really is an amazing concept and an excellent tool for beginners in electronics, programming or microcontrollers. It has also found a niche in providing control solutions for various applications. There is also an unparallel wealth of information available for it, from "PBASIC" (the BASIC Stamp's programming language) programming and interfacing tutorials to example applications. The name "Stamp" came from the original design, which was a full computer system that took up the same area as a postage stamp.

Currently, there are two devices available from Parallax, Inc., as shown in Figure 39.1. The "BS1" (BASIC Stamp I) comes in a 14-pin single inline package ("SIP") which allows the Stamp to take up the smallest amount of board area possible. The "BS2" (BASIC Stamp II) is designed to take up the same amount of space as a 24-pin 0.600" dual inline package ("DIP") and offers significantly more performance and features than the BS1C.

The Stamps are not embedded microcontrollers per the definition given earlier in the book (because they consist of multiple active chips making up a system). However, the Stamp can run a user-defined program like a microcontroller, but without the support circuitry required to provide reset, system clock, or ISP that an embedded device would. The downloaded application programs are stored in EEPROM, so they will not be lost even if power has been turned off and the host PC has been disconnected.

While the performance of the Stamps would be rated as "modest" when compared to embedded microcontrollers, they do offer a much simpler programming interface and ease of use that the embedded microcontrollers can't match. If you receive a Stamp and its programming kit on Friday, you'll be able to develop your own applications by Monday. This ease of use can make the Stamp a very attractive first microcontroller development tool.

In this section of the book, I refer to both Stamps collectively, but I point out differences between the two devices where appropriate.

To give you an idea of the two Stamp's capabilities, I have reproduced the chart below from Parallax:

FEATURES	STAMP 1 (BS1C)	STAMP 2 (BS2C)
I/O Lines	8	16, plus 2 RS-232 I/Os
EEPROM	256 Bytes	2048 Bytes
RAM (Variables)	7 Word Registers	16 Word Registers
Maximum EEPROM Program Size	~ 80 Instructions	~ 500 Instructions
Clock Speed	4 MHz	20 MHz
Execution Speed	~ 2000 Instruct/s	~ 4000 Instruct/s
Running I Req'd	2 mA	7 mA
Sleep I Req'd	20 uA	50 uA
Serial I/O Speed	300-2400 bps	300-50000 bps
		0-19200 bps w/ Flow Control
Package	14 Pin SIP	24 Pin DIP
Programming I/F	PC Parallel Port	RS-232 Port

As you can see, the BS2 has somewhat more capabilities than the BS1, but these extra capabilities come at a higher cost as well as requiring more space and power than the BS1. Also, the BS2 offers more BASIC functions, which will make interfacing to external devices easier.

Figure 39.1 BS1 and BS2 alongside a dime to show relative sizes.

Stamp Hardware

The Stamps consist of a PICMicro microcontroller connected to a serial EEPROM and a host PC interface. The PIC has been preprogrammed with boot code, EEPROM interface, and a token program executor. Also on the Stamp board is a power regulator, voltage brownout sensor for reset, and a ceramic resonator to provide the system clock.

The BASIC Stamp 1C ("BS1") has the following circuit and is arranged as a "SIP" with the pinout shown in Figure 39.2.

The BASIC Stamp 2C ("BS2") offers considerably more I/O capabilities and takes up the same footprint as a 24-pin 0.600" DIP package. (Figure 39.3.)

THE STAMP PROCESSOR

Rather than cop out and say that the Stamp is built around the PICMicro and say the architecture is simply the same, I want to introduce the Stamp as having its own, self-contained processor architecture. (Figure 39.4.)

The Stamp itself uses a low-end PICMicro which does not have interrupts or any hardware that will run concurrently with the main program. The special features of the ALU and I/O pins are all handled in software, which gives much more flexibility than a specific microcontroller. It also makes the Stamp slower to execute special functions than a microcontroller with hardware built in.

The BASIC Stamp 2 has a similar architecture, but with one important difference. The program counter has a four-entry stack for saving the return address for subroutines (which allows up to three nested subroutines; see Figure 39.5).

39

PARALLAX: BASIC STAMP

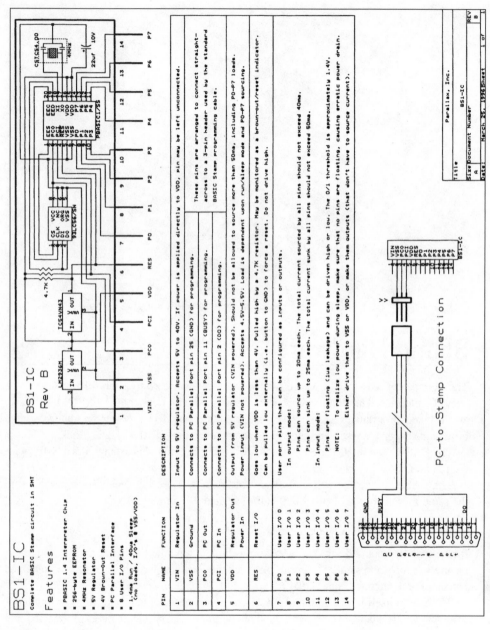

Figure 39.2 BS1-IC: Complete BASIC stamp circuit in SMT.

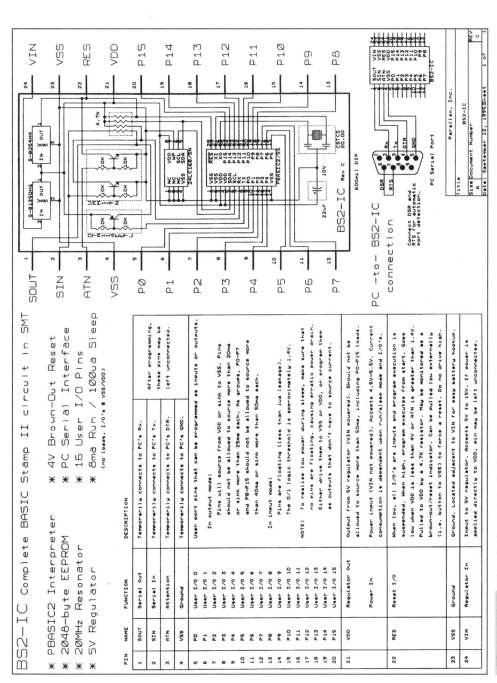

Figure 39.3 BS2-IC: Complete BASIC stamp circuit in SMT.

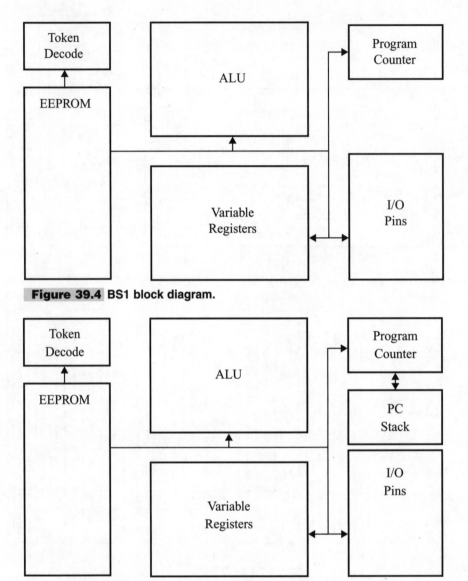

Figure 39.4 BS1 block diagram.

Figure 39.5 BS2 block diagram.

PROGRAM "TOKENS"

One of the important points to realize with the Stamp is that it executes "Tokens" out of the EEPROM, rather than actual instructions. These tokens are small commands that are generated from the source code.

Tokens are usually two or three bytes in length and are retrieved serially from the EEPROM. This serial data transfer is the primary reason for the poor performance of the Stamp, compared to an embedded microcontroller. You will have probably noticed that the BS2's PICMicro runs five times faster than the BS1, but the quoted instruction speed is only two times better. This is because the BS2 relies on longer tokens to carry out the instructions (which takes longer to load from the EEPROM).

Once the instruction is loaded in, it is executed by calling the appropriate function. These functions could be arithmetic operations, data transfers, condition checks, pin-specific operations, or serial communications with a host system/user interface. Because of the differences in token length and differences in possible token execution times, it is very difficult to determine what is the actual program execution time without determining the execution period empirically (i.e., timing the application).

The "ALU" itself operates 16-bit integer "words" (shown in the "Stamp PBASIC Programming" chapter, there are a number of "words," which can be broken up into bits, nybbles, and bytes).

I/O PINS

If you were to categorize the BASIC Stamp 1's I/O capabilities, they could be listed as:

- Input/output with output enabling.
- Serial I/O.
- Pulse generation/pulse width determination.
- Button debounce.
- Sound (frequency) generation.
- PWM I/O.

The Stamp 2 expands this list with:

- Synchronous shift in/out.
- Cycle counters.
- X-10 (home automation) interface.

This is quite an impressive list. No other microcontroller described in this book (and no other that I know of) is capable of carrying out this number of diverse functions as the Stamp (especially considering that each I/O pin is capable of these functions). You are probably confused as to how the Stamps can do all these things; the I/O pins are part of a standard PICMicro (and a "low-end" device at that).

All of these functions are provided in software (not hardware). Later in this section, I go through each of the different functions available to the Stamp PBASIC Language, but I just wanted to point out that the Stamps are really limited to what the internal PIC is capable of (and that's 20 mA sourced and 25 mA sinked). These built-in functions provide a great deal of flexibility in the BASIC Stamps but cannot be carried out concurently with other program execution. This limits the complexity of the applications that can be written.

SERIAL EEPROM

Once the program has been compiled into tokens, it will be downloaded from the host PC into the Stamp, which, in turn, downloads it into the integral serial EEPROM. The serial EEPROM is not only used for program storage, but can also be used for variable storage. Using the EEPROM for variable storage has the advantage that data stored in the EEPROM will remain even after power to the Stamp is taken away.

In both Stamps, the program start is placed at the end of the EEPROM, and successive addresses are placed in descending addresses (the EEPROM is programmed with negative increment; see Figure 39.6).

Anywhere in the EEPROM can be written to/from. This means that care must be taken to ensure that the tokenized source code is not overwritten.

Figuring out where the data can go is not a trivial task and can result in several program iterations until sufficient space is available and correctly addressed. In the BASIC Stamp II, after program compilation (executing "Alt-R"), the amount of EEPROM used as both "data" (using the "EEPROM" programming statement) and program tokens can be checked by pressing the key sequence "Alt-M."

The BASIC Stamp I is not quite this simple. As the program is downloaded into the Stamp, a window with a bargraph appears to show how much EEPROM has been used.

In Figure 39.7, there are 32 characters which represent the 256 EEPROM bytes available (for 8 bytes per character). There are seven characters marked, which means that 200 bytes are available for use in the Serial EEPROM for data storage.

The EEPROMs are wired to the PICMicros as standard Serial EEPROM devices. The BASIC Stamp 1 uses a Microchip 93LC56, which is a Microwire interface device. The BASIC Stamp 2 uses a Microchip 24LC16B, which is an I2C device. Both EEPROMS cannot be substituted for larger memory devices. But this does not preclude serial EEPROMs being connected to the I/O pins and used for additional storage.

The amount of EEPROM can be read as the last byte (address $FF) in the BS1. This value is the last program address of the program and can be converted to bytes by:

```
Read 255, Last      ' Read address 255 ($FF) of the EEPROM
Size = 255 - Last   ' "Size" is the Size of the Program in Bytes
```

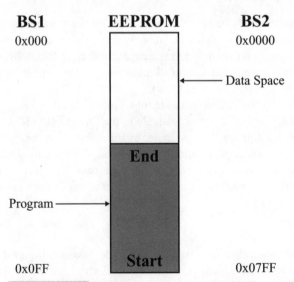

Figure 39.6 BASIC Stamp serial EEPROM organization.

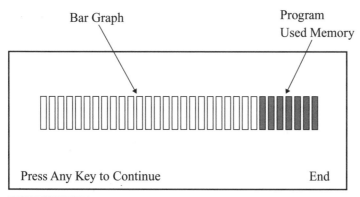

Figure 39.7 BS1 download bar graph.

This feature is not available in the BS2, but the "Alt-M" command listed above can be used to find the size of the program, and then you can change the source code to note the end of the program.

PROGRAMMING INTERFACES

The Stamps have in-system programming interfaces. Both types of Stamp have a bidirectional serial interface that is used for programming the Serial EEPROMs as well as sending "DEBUG" data back to the host PC during execution.

The Stamp I uses a PC parallel (printer) port for data transfers. (Figure 39.8.)

This interface takes input data from the "D0" bit of the parallel port and sends data through the "BUSY" bit of the parallel port. One nice feature about this method of transferring data is, the parallel port doesn't have to be specified when the editor/development systems is initiated. This is because in a typical parallel port application, data is clocked out by the "_STROBE" pin. Just wiggling the "D0" bit will only affect a BASIC Stamp1 attached to the port.

Because this interface is so simple, I always put in three pins for programming in the application. This will eliminate the need for buying a Stamp carrier board to use to program the Stamp outside the application circuit.

The Stamp II uses a serial port for sending and receiving data. (See Figure 39.9.)

The serial port programming/interface hardware is quite a bit more complex than the Stamp 1 programming interface. This interface can be used for serial data transmission/reception with the host PC. Because the serial port can have other devices on it, the port to be used has to be specified when starting the editor/development system.

To initiate the Stamp II editor/development system, the command line instruction:

```
stamp2 /n
```

must be entered where "n" is the "COM" port to be used (1-4).

If the application uses the programming interface as a serial port (which can be done by specifying pin "16" in the "SERIN" and "SEROUT" instructions), the "DTR" connection must be disconnected may have to be disabled if you are using a PC terminal program to

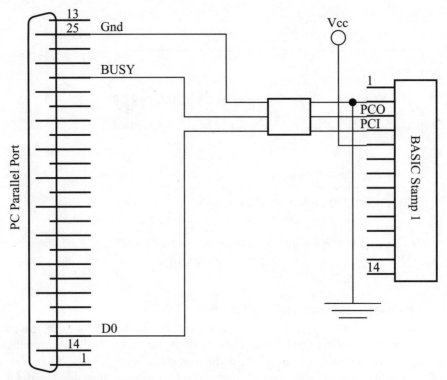

Figure 39.8 BS1 programming interface.

interface with the application. The BS2 uses the "ATN" bit to reset itself and come up and look for the "stamp2.exe" program trying to download to it. If the serial port isn't being controlled by "stamp2.exe," then it will wait until it is or execute the program in the EEP-ROM.

The easiest way to get around this is to disconnect the "ATN" connection between the PC and the BS2 (I usually put in two pins 0.100" apart and jumper them when I want to program them).

This use of the serial port makes the BS2 ISP and eliminates the need to buy a Stamp II carrier board.

In fact, if you properly design your application (and this includes circuit prototypes on breadboards), you will never need to buy Stamp carrier boards (which are primarily used for programming the Stamps outside of the circuit). Or, if your PC's communication software writes directly to the serial transmit/receive registers, you can probably ignore this because "DSR" (what "ATN" is connected to) will probably continuously output a "0" (or positive voltage).

When you first start working with the Stamps, you may want to program them outside the circuit or build circuits around them with their own power. Parallax does have two programming/prototyping boards for your use (see Figures 39.10 and 39.11).

Both of these boards have sockets for the Stamps, a programming interface to connect to the PC, and a 9-volt radio battery connector for simplified interfacing.

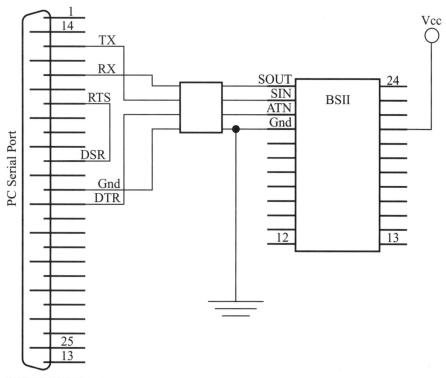

Figure 39.9 BS2 programming interface.

Figure 39.10 BS1 programming interface and circuit prototype board.

Figure 39.11 BS2 programming interface and circuit prototype board.

STAMP PBASIC PROGRAMMING

Through the use of the "PBASIC" (what I will often refer to as "Stamp BASIC") Language, the Stamp really is very easy to program. Working only in a high level language eliminates the need to understand how individual bits and bytes flow through a processor. However, there are some tricks, non-standard language constructs and general strangeness that you will have to understand before you are able to begin programming your own applications.

Interface

Both Stamps use a full-screen editor which is executed from an MS-DOS command line. This editor allows creation of software, downloading it into a stamp, as well as a limited amount of application debug support.

The editor will run on a variety of MS-DOS emulators (if you are not working with an IBM-compatible PC). The editor itself may seem a bit awkward, especially if you are used to working with a GUI editor that requires a mouse. But, for the most part, the control key sequences used in the Stamp editors are what you would use in a standard Microsoft Windows editor.

KEY SEQUENCE	FUNCTION
Enter	Start a New Line
Tab	Move over to the Next 8 Character Boundary
Backspace	Move one character to the left and delete that character
Delete	Delete the current character or marked text
Shift-Delete	Delete to the End of the Line
Left Arrow	Move the Cursor to the Left one Column
Right Arrow	Move the Cursor to the Right one Column
Up Arrow	Move the Cursor up a Line
Home	Move to the Start of the Line
End	Move to the End of the Line
Ctrl-Left Arrow	Jump to the Start of the Current Word, or if at Blank or Start of Word, Jump to Start of the Previous Word
Ctrl-Right Arrow	Jump to the Start of the Next Word
Shift-Home	Jump to the Start of the File
Shift-End	Jump to the End of the File
Shift-Arrow Key	Move Cursor as described above and mark text from starting point to cursor destination
Shift-Insert	Mark the Current Word

ESC	Turn off Text Marking
Alt-X	Delete Marked Text and Place in the Clipboard
Alt-C	Place Marked Text in the Clipboard
Alt-V	Place Clipboard Text at the Current Cursor

The basic editing functions that you will have to know are:
File operations include:

Alt-L	Load a File
Alt-S	Save the Current File
Alt-Q	Quit and Return to the Command Line Prompt

When the program has been completed, it can be compiled into tokens and run in a connected Stamp by using the "Alt-R" command. Any syntax errors will be identified before the Stamp is to be programmed and begins to execute the program.

To help with determining the actual range a potentiometer will use in the BASIC Stamp I editor, "Alt-P" can be be executed. This will download a special program and display a window which will display (with prompts) how the pot works both in terms of ranges and the specified scale. The results from this can be used in the program's "POT" instruction to "tune" the program to the actual potentiometer and capacitor wired to the application.

The "Alt-M" command is only available in the BASIC Stamp II and is used to show how much of the EEPROM has been used for both the application program and data storage. This feature isn't available in the BASIC Stamp I, instead, as is described in the "Stamp Hardware" chapter, the download window will show you how much EEPROM is used by the program.

Stamp PBASIC Language

If you've worked at all with a high level language, you shouldn't have any problems with the stamp's "PBASIC." There are a few deviations from standards that you should be aware of. This subchapter is devoted to identifying deviations to more traditional BASICs and other high-level languages.

BS2 I/O DATA TYPES

When sending serial data to external devices from the BS2 (either through the "DEBUG" or "SEROUT" commands) the data has to be formatted into a type. These types are also used by the "SERIN" command to format incoming data. These type commands eliminate the need to convert values in variables to ASCII, HEX, or Decimal and will allow transmission of strings of data.

The output data types (or "prefixes" in PBASIC) are:

PREFIX	PARAMETERS	DESCRIPTION
ASC	bytevar	Send ASCII Value
STR	bytevar[\n]	Output byte array until 0 encountered or "n" values sent
REP	value\n	Send the character "n" times
[S]DEC[n]	value	Send the value as [Signed] Decimal "n" characters long
[I][S]HEX[n]	value	Send the value as [Signed] Hex "n" characters long. If "I" specified, first send "$"
[I][S]BIN[n]	value	Send the value as [Signed] Binary "n" characters long. If "I" specified, first send "%"

If a variable is specified for "value" and a "?" is at the end of the prefix, the variable name will be sent along with the value.

For example:

```
DEBUG dec X
```

will output (if X = 42):

```
42
```

But,

```
Debug dec? X
```

will output:

```
X = 42
```

The "?" is available on all prefixes except for "REP."

For "SERIN," the prefixes are used to filter the incoming data and convert incoming ASCII strings to binary data that can be put directly into variables and used. This allows quite complex input processing without requiring the user to write explicit "if" statements to process the data.

The "WAIT" and "SKIP" commands are used to filter the incoming stream.

The "SERIN" Wait and Skip prefixes are as follows:

PREFIX	PARAMETERS	DESCRIPTION
SKIP	n	Ignore "n" Bytes
WAITSTR	byteArray[\L]	Wait for the [Sub]String to be Received
WAIT	(Value[, value...])	Wait for the up to 6 byte Sequence
STR	byteArray\n[\E]	Input "n" bytes and stop if the "E" character is received.

All the other DEBUG/SEROUT commands except for "REP" are available for use in "SERIN" to change the incoming data.

There are also a number of predefined ASCII control codes preprogrammed in the BS2:

LABEL	VALUE	DESCRIPTION
CLS	0	Clear the Screen and homes the cursor (not available in all ASCII devices)
HOME	1	Returns the Cursor to Home
BELL	7	Beep the device's speaker
BKSP	8	Back up the Cursor and Delete the previous character
TAB	9	Advance to the next 8th column
CR	13	Carriage Return

The only ASCII character that should also be included in this list is the "LF" or "LineFeed" (0x00A) character.

But, this can be defined as a constant with:

```
LF con  10
```

BS1 VARIABLES AND "SYMBOLS"

In discussing how variables are accessed in the BASIC Stamp, I broke this section up into BASIC Stamp 1 and BASIC Stamp 2 sections because there are some significant differences between the two devices.

Variables in the Stamp 1 PBASIC probably work differently than any other high-level programming language you've been exposed to because the variables are totally predefined in function, location, and name.

The BASIC Stamp 1s variable memory is defined as eight sixteen bit "words." Each word can be accessed simply by specifying the word identifier (ie "W0") in PBASIC.

WORD	BYTE NAMES	DESCRIPTION	
Port	Pins, Dirs	I/O Pins and Dir ("TRIS")	Read/Write
W0	B0, B1	Bit Addressable GP Word	Read/Write
W1	B2, B3	GP Word	Read/Write
W2	B4, B5	GP Word	Read/Write
W3	B6, B7	GP Word	Read/Write
W4	B8, B9	GP Word	Read/Write
W5	B10, B11	GP Word	Read/Write
W6	B12, B13	Changed by "Gosub" Function	Read/Write

The bytes in these words can be accessed directly as "B#," instead of "W#." As well, in the first two words, all the bits can be accessed individually.

The eight I/O bits are accessed and output controlled in the first word ("PORT"). These pins work similarly to most other microcontrollers (being PICMicro based would probably account for this). It is important to note that on power up, all eight bits have output disabled.

The six general-purpose data variable words are all initialized to zero on power up.

When developing a program, the various bits, bytes, and words are accessed directly. This allows data to be transferred inside the Stamp very efficiently.

A good example is given in the "First Stamp Application" later in the book. In it, I want to transfer a single bit input (on Pin 7) to an output bit (Pin 4).

In a typical microcontroller and "C" language, this would be done as:

```
if (( PORT & 0x080 ) != 0 )
PORT = PORT | 0x010;
else
PORT = PORT & 0x0EF;
```

or

```
PORT = ( PORT & 0x0EF ) | (( PORT & 0x080 ) >> 3 );
```

But in the Stamp 1 BASIC language (and the Stamp 2 BASIC Language), this statement can be accomplished by the single line:

```
PIN4 = PIN7
```

This example can be made even easier to read and understand by the use of "symbols." "Symbols" are really simple macros which can be used to define the different memory locations with meaningful labels. Symbols can also be used to define constants.

For the example above, if the pins were defined by symbols as:

```
symbol LED2 = PIN4
symbol SW = PIN7
```

which gives me identifiers I can relate to more easily than pin numbers. The final line which takes the input from a pin and outputs it on another becomes:

```
LED2 = SW
```

There is one serious (in my opinion) deficiency in the Stamp 1 variables capabilities; this is the lack of array variables.

If array functions are required, the EEPROM can be used to save and retrieve data according to an address (array index). "LOOKUP" table instructions can be created to provide output for read-only arrays.

BS2 VARIABLES

The BS2 variables differ from the BS1s in one very important area; the variables are resources that are allocated by the compiler—and not the user (as is done by in the BS1).

The BS2 variable area is defined similarly to the BS1's, with each word 16-bits long.

WORD	DESCRIPTION	
$0	Pin Input States	Read Only

$2	Pin Output Enable	Read/Write
$3	Variable Space	Read/Write
$4	Variable Space	Read/Write
$5	Variable Space	Read/Write
$6	Variable Space	Read/Write
$7	Variable Space	Read/Write
$8	Variable Space	Read/Write
$9	Variable Space	Read/Write
$A	Variable Space	Read/Write
$B	Variable Space	Read/Write
$C	Variable Space	Read/Write
$D	Variable Space	Read/Write
$E	Variable Space	Read/Write

The I/O pins are not definable and are known as "IN," "OUT," and "DIR." These pins carry out the same function as in the BS1. Like the BS1, these pins can be accessed in different groupings according to the ending applied to the variable.

For example, to access the "IN" bits:

INS	All 16 I/P Pins as a Word
INL	Input Pins 0 - 7
INH	Input Pins 8 - 15
INA	Input Pins 0 - 3
INB	Input Pins 4 - 7
INC	Input Pins 8 - 11
IND	Input Pins 12 - 15
IN0	Input Pin 0
IN1	Input Pin 1
IN2	Input Pin 2
:	
IN15	Input Pin 15

The same endings apply to "OUT" and "DIR."

To maintain a level of compatibility with the BS1, the registers in the BS2 can be accessed as "W0" to "W12" or "B0" to "B25," but the recommended method to use registers is to declare them using the "var" statement which takes the form:

```
Symbol var size(array)
```

where size is:

word	16 bits
byte	8 bits
nib	4 bits
bit	1 bit

Array declaration is optional and can be declared on any size type.

Variable names for I/O pins can also be defined similarly. For example, the low eight I/O bits could be defined as:

```
LCDOut var     INL
```

Variables can be broken up into smaller variables using "variable modifiers" (a simple form of data structures). The variable modifiers are:

HIGHBYTE	High Byte (Byte 1) of the Word
BYTE1	High Byte of the Word
LOWBYTE	Low Byte (Byte 0) of the Word
BYTE0	Low Byte of the Word
HIGHNIB	High Nybble of a Word or Byte
NIB3	High Nybble of a Word
NIB1	High Nybble of a Byte or Nybble 1 of a Word
LOWNIB	Low Nybble of a Word or Byte
NIB2	Nybble 2 of a Word
NIB0	Low Nybble of a Word or Byte
HIGHBIT	High Bit of a Word, Byte or Nybble
LOWBIT	Low Bit of a Word, Byte or Nybble
BIT0	Bit 0 of a Word, Byte or Nybble
BIT1	Bit 1 of a Word, Byte or Nybble
:	
BIT7	Bit 7 of a Word or High Bit of a Byte
:	
BIT15	High Bit of a Word

An example of this would be defining a PICMicro 14-bit immediate instruction. First, the instruction would be defined:

```
PICInstruct var word
```

Next, the various parts would be defined:

```
PICInstruction var PICInstruct.HIGHBYTE
```

Followed by the immediate data:

```
PIC Immediate var PICInstruct.LOWBYTE
```

Arrays are handled similarly to most other high-level languages, although it's important to note two things about arrays in the Stamp II. The first is that the Array index is not checked; going outside of the range will not cause an error but may affect how the Stamp operates. The second thing to note is that arrays take up space and with only 26 bytes of program RAM available, large arrays (greater than ten bytes) can use up this RAM very quickly.

OPERATOR EXPRESSIONS

I consider "Operator Expression" to be the arithmetic formula placed at the right of the equals sign ("=") in an assignment statement or to the right of the "if" in a conditional execution statement. While it appears to be similar to the format used in other languages you may be familiar with, there is one major wrinkle that can cause problems when you develop code for the Stamp.

This "wrinkle" is in how the statements are evaluated (and ultimately converted into tokens). In the Stamp, they are evaluated from left to right with no regard for "order of operations" (carrying out arithmetic operations in an priority sequence, i.e., multiplication is executed before addition or subtraction, but not before comparisons). This has been improved somewhat in the BS2, but even when creating BS2 code, making sure the operations are carried out in the correct order requires some care.

For example, if we had to execute the assignment:

```
A = A * B + C * D
in most languages, this would be processed as:
```

1. A * B
2. C * D
3. Result of 1. + Result of 2.
4. Store 3. in "A"

Because the BASIC Stamp 1 does everything from left to right, the assignment statement would be processed as:

1. A * B
2. (A * B) + C
3. ((A * B) + C) * D
4. Store 3. in "A"

If you know something about "reverse Polish notation" (aka "RPN"—the method of operating and programming HP calculators), you might be tempted to put arithmetic expressions in this format. To some extent, this can be done, but complex expressions (like the example above) cannot be accomplished because intermediate values cannot be stored in the BASIC Stamp 1.

The example statement can be converted into two BASIC Stamp 1 statements:

```
Temp = C * D
A = A * B + Temp
```

The algorithm that I use for developing complex operation expressions in the BASIC Stamp 1 is to put all the high-priority operations on separate lines and then add or subtract them on the final line to "glue" the operations together. Sometimes, such as in the example shown here, it is possible to move one of the high-order operations to the actual assignment lines.

If, in the BASIC Stamp 2, the two multiplication operations were placed inside parenthesis:

```
A = ( A * B ) + ( C * D )
```

the "normal" order of operations would be executed. The BASIC Stamp 2 can handle up to eight levels of parenthesis, which should allow you to program in "expected" order of operations at all times.

There is one additional complication with the BASIC Stamp 2 and that's the execution of "unary" operations (operations which only have one input parameter) like "NOT" and "binary" operations like "AND" take place before the "binary operators" (like "+", "*", and "/"). The easiest way to remember the order of operations in the BASIC Stamp 2 is to remember that operations which are spelled out have a higher priority than those which use arithmetic characters.

After any complex operator expression, I recommend that during application development the "DEBUG" BASIC command be used to print out the result of the expression until you are comfortable with the way the Stamp BASIC evaluates expressions. (And, if you're like me, you'll always use "DEBUG" after every complex expression for application debug because years of working with more traditional languages causes me to "slip" back into writing equations the "normal" way).

Remember that the same concerns are present for the comparison (which is a type of operator expression) as in the assignment statement. For this reason, I never have any more than one comparison in an "if" statement (for example, "IF A > B" is as complex as I ever get).

SUBROUTINES

If you are familiar with the "GOSUB" and "RETURN" statements in regular BASIC, the PBASIC counterparts will seem to work similarly. But, there are a few differences to "standard" BASIC implementations you should be aware of when using them in the BASIC Stamps.

In the BS1, subroutines will probably seem quite restrictive because of the maximum of 16 "GOSUB" statements (subroutine calls) and the use of a single word ("W6") for storing the return address. Actually, the maximum of 16 calls is not a significant concern in a device where only 256 bytes are available for program storage. (In fact, just making 16 calls will use up a very significant percentage of the control store.)

What is of more consequence is the lack of a program counter stack. If you are in a subroutine and you call another one from within it ("nesting" the second subroutine) you will discover that it's impossible to return to the location where the original subroutine was called. There is no program counter stack and no way to read or save the address of the "call" statement. You may wish to modify your coding style to put more code in line and avoid subroutines if at all possible. While this may seem to be sacrilegious to people who have been trained in structured coding techniques, it is quite advantageous in the BS1 in terms of space required and doesn't affect the readability of the code that much.

In the BS2, up to 255 "GOSUB" statements can be placed in the source along with up to four nesting levels and no variable registers are affected or used for storing the program counter. This means that traditional coding techniques can be used in the BS2 without really having to worry about how the program will operate.

PBASIC Source Formatting

The PBASIC Language differs from many other languages, I find it quite a challenge to write readable code in PBASIC. This is because PBASIC, along with most other BASICs, is in the "grey" zone between assembly code and high-level languages. With the different BASICs available, the color of grey ranges from dirty white to charcoal. PBASIC is somewhere in the middle ("battleship" grey).

My typical coding style has variables and constants declared at the start of each function. Global variables and constants are declared at the start of the program followed by include files, subroutines, and then the mainline.

I put the subroutines before the mainline because many languages ("C" most notably) and some assemblers cannot reference labels below the current location without explicit references at the start of the program. Rather than repeat the references (which may have problems when code is updated in one place and not another), I put the subroutines at the top of the source and only declare them once.

In most languages, the beginning of the code (or the location where the code begins) is explicitly defined. In PBASIC, the programs begins at the first line of code. This means that in PBASIC, I put subroutines after the mainline code.

At the start of the PBASIC program, I put all the variable and constant declarations right after the heading comments to allow me to monitor the resources (i.e., RAM words) required for the program.

Declaring the variables as I normally would (which in PBASIC would look like):

```
'  Start of Program


    :

SubRtn1:              '  The first Subroutine

Symbol i = W2         '  Declare a "Local" Variable


    :

SubRtn2:              '  The second Subroutine

Symbol j = W3         '  Declare a "Local" Variable
```

is clearly asking for trouble in the form of variables that are repeated or, in the case of the BS2, having more variables declared than are available.

Making sure that all variables are defined in one place may cut down on the readability of the code (as defined by structured techniques) but it will avoid difficult-to-debug variable problems later.

Other factors that I feel limits the readability of the code is the inability to include files and the lack of a listing file with conditional compiling and listing options (i.e., the ability to turn on and off listing and forcing page breaks).

PBASIC, like other BASICs, allows multiple statements on a single line. For example, if you wanted to clear a line (or row) on an LCD, you would use the code:

```
OutChar = " "
for i = 0 to 20
gosub SendCHAR                    ' Send the Blank to the LCD
next
```

This may be written as:

```
OutChar = " ": for i = 0 to 20: gosub SendCHAR: next ' Blank LCD Row
```

The number of tokens produced for either example will be exactly the same number of bytes because the same code is used to produce the function, except that it's the format of the source code. I recommend against doing this with conditional code (i.e., "ifs") because the operation will not be all that clear and will be difficult to debug (because the execution path may be difficult to understand).

With everything I've written here, you'll probably feel that PBASIC is not very conducive to allowing readable code to be written. Making sure that white space is used to separate blocks of code does help as does making sure that all the code and comments are put into specific columns will help in creating source that can be searched easily (which is what "readability" is all about).

Debugging

One big disadvantage of how the Stamp and its development tools are designed is the difficulty to "get inside" the application and its software as it's executing and see what's actually happening. I always thought that a simulator/emulator was really needed (which is why I designed one of my own and present it in the example applications).

Traditional Stamp debugging involves placing "DEBUG" statements throughout the code to send status information from certain points in the code. Doing this efficiently (because the debug statements take up EEPROM space) is important.

This subsection presents a few rules that have worked for me. The first is, don't use messages in the debug statements or keep them very short. Using a debug statement like:

```
DEBUG "Button Pressed, Count =", Count
```

Will use up all the available EEPROM space much faster than:

```
DEBUG "A", Count
```

This means that you'll have to print out a copy of the PBASIC source to keep track of where the program is executing (which is not necessarily a bad thing).

The next rule I use when debugging Stamp applications is, only activate the debug statements that are critical to the current task at hand. To "deactivate" a debug statement, simply comment out the line by placing a "/" at the first column.

Thus, the line:

```
' DEBUG "A", Count
```

won't compile (and be put into the EEPROM) until it's needed and the comment identifier "/" is taken out and the program recompiled. This will also make the task at hand easier because there won't be any extraneous messages being transmitted.

The last trick I've found to make debugging easier is the one I presented in the first section of the book and that is to debug individual I/O functions and then integrate them into the final application. With most other development systems, this is a relatively easy task, but with the Stamp editor/development system editing multiple files or including files is not possible.

This means that some of the development is done offline in a MS-DOS or Windows editor. I realize that this may be an issue for some people who are not very PC-literate.

It's unfortunate that the Stamps do not offer interactive debugging capabilities, but by planning the application development and debug process, getting a working application can be achieved quite quickly. This is one of the goals the third example application (the "BS1 Emulator") is designed to address.

STAMP APPLICATION DESIGN

CONTENTS AT A GLANCE

Packaging

Power Input

Reset

The Stamp has very few application-specific options compared to the other microcontrollers presented in this book. This is due to the on-board oscillator and reset. The Stamp is more susceptible than other microcontrollers to damage (both physical and electrical) due to its design and manufacture.

Packaging

A typical microcontroller is encased in an epoxy encapsulant. This is not the case with the Stamps. The Stamps themselves are SMT components soldered to an "FR4" (standard printed circuit board fibreglass raw card) carrier. This means they are somewhat fragile and the components could be damaged by repeated insertions/pulls from a socket.

This damage is caused by the raw card flexing (and breaking solder joints) and finger pressure cracking solder joints and raw card traces. At no time should pliers be used to pull a Stamp out of a circuit, which would increase the liklihood of damage to either the components, solder joints, or raw card.

Instead, when I design a Stamp application, I make sure the three (for the BS1) and four (for BS2) programming pins are always available to allow a PC to program the Stamp without having it pulled from the circuit. For the BS1 this means that a 3-pin 0.100" spaced header is put on the board. For the BS2, I go to the extent of wiring a 9-pin D-shell female connector into the circuit. This eliminates any requirements to remove the Stamp from the circuit when developing an application.

The Stamps are not well suited for applications where they will be exposed to high humidity or chemical fumes. This is because of the exposed solder joints on the components and raw card carrier. If the Stamp application is going to be placed in an environment that can be potentially damaging to the solder joints, then I recommend hermetically sealing the Stamp from the environment. (Water can cause corrosion, shorting, or metal migration between pins, and chemicals can accelerate metal migration or corrode metal,) Hermetic sealing can be done by placing the Stamp in an airtight box or encasing the Stamp and the circuitry it's connected to in epoxy or plastic (such as the "dip" used for tools, to replace grips that have worn out or fallen off).

I would also be concerned about the reliability of the connection of the BS1 into the circuit in a high-vibration environment (such as in a radio control car or airplane). The BS1 is designed to be plugged into a card carrier. In a high-vibration environment, the BS1 is basically a weight at the end of a stick; eventually the connection to the board, the connection to the BS1, or the pins will break due to mechanical fatigue.

To prevent this from happening, the BS1 should be rigidly fastened to the board it's plugged into (there are right-angle supports or connectors available for this purpose) so there is no opportunity for the Stamp to move relative to the board it's connected to. If this is not possible, you may want to buy a Stamp PICMicro chip from Parallax and solder it and an EEPROM directly to the board. Another option would be using the PBASIC compiler that comes with the development kit and program a 16C58 with the application once it's debugged.

Power Input

The Stamps will take a wide variety of power from different sources due to their built-in voltage regulators. The most common voltage source I've seen for the Stamps is a 9-volt radio battery.

This is not to say there aren't some considerations regarding the power input to the Stamp. The biggest is the maximum amount of current drawn through the voltage regulator. The voltage regulators not only have enough current-sourcing capabilities for the Stamps themselves, but some external parts as well. The parts used on the Stamps (an LM2946 on the BS1 and a S-0135 on the BS2) are very easy to burn out if too much curent is drawn through them by external devices.

The BS1 draws one to two mA of current, allowing the voltage regulator to provide the excess currents for external devices for the following input voltages:

INPUT VOLTAGE	EXCESS CURRENT
5-9 Volts	50 mA
10-15 Volts	25 mA
16-25 Volts	10 mA
25-35 Volts	5 mA
35+ Volts	0 mA

Drawing more than this current (even for an instant) can burn out the voltage regulator.

The BS2 uses a somewhat more robust voltage regulator and can normally accept 5 to 15 volts and source 50 mA to external devices. Care must still be taken with the amount of current.

When I list current for external devices, I should note that the current sourced by the Stamp (i.e., for driving LEDs) will take away from the current available to external devices.

One thing that you will see commonly done is that the voltage regulators on board the Stamps are replaced with 78L05s. These devices can source up to 100 mA and will shut down if the output current is exceeded.

Having said all this about the regulators on the Stamps, I must confess that I very rarely use them and normally bypass them by supplying 5 volts to the circuit the Stamp is mounted on and then providing power to the Stamp through the Vdd pins. This eliminates having to worry about the Stamp's regulator (especially during application debug when an I/O pin may inadvertently be shorted to Vcc or ground).

Reset

In both the BS1 and BS2, there are built-in "brownout" circuits controlling reset. These circuits will pull the reset line (which is pulled up by a 4.7K resistor) low if the input voltage ever goes below 4.5 volts. The reset lines on the Stamps can also be pulled low externally by open collector (open drain) drivers or a momentary on switch pulling the signal to ground.

STAMP PBASIC FUNCTIONS

The built-in functions of the Stamp's PBASIC language are really quite easy to understand. I have broken up the functions according to operation type to make understanding how they relate to the hardware easier. "PBASIC" is not standard across both devices, and for this reason I have tried to note the differences between the BS1 and BS2.

There is one important thing to note in these descriptions, and that is I haven't included a time/cycle count for the functions. This is because of the number of different factors (data size, data speed, number of parameters, etc.) that will make the time required for an operation unpredictable. Because of this and the lack of an internal hardware timer, to understand how long a program or section of code takes to run, you're really going to have to time it manually.

When I review the functions, there is one thing that you should be aware of. In PBASIC, functions can be referenced in mixed case. In the text below and the sheets explaining the instructions, I have mixed the cases deliberately to show that the case doesn't matter. Even though the case doesn't matter for functions, it does matter for labels and variable names.

BS1 Mathematical Operators

The mathematical operators used in "PBASIC" are similar both in format and execution to analogous operators in other high-level languages. As I present in this chapter, the major difference is that there is no order of operations, everything is executed from right to left.

The BS1, as would be expected, has the fewest number and most restricted operators. I will try to group operators together to help explain their functions.

Unlike the PBASIC used for the BS2 (and in most high-level languages), these operators cannot be used in "if" statement conditions (the error "Expected an Operator" will be encountered). This means that statements like:

```
if ( W1 + W2 ) > 77 then Greater Than
```

cannot be used in the BS1. Instead, the addition would have to be done before the "if" statement, like:

```
Temp = W1 + W2          ' Get the Value for "if"
if Temp > 77 then Greater Than
```

Addition ("+") and subtraction ("-") work as would be expected on 8- and 16-bit values. Before I continue, I should probably explain what I mean when I say these operators "work as would be expected."

The best way to explain what I expect is to say that addition and subtraction (along with all other operators) produce a 16-bit (one-word) result. If the destination of an assignment is 16 bits long, the result will be passed unchanged.

If the destination is something less than a word, then the high-order bits will be lost from the result.

The following example will show this:

```
Symbol   A = W2          '  16 Bit Source
Symbol   B = B6          '  8 Bit Source

Symbol   DestBit = Bit3
Symbol   DestByte = B7
Symbol   DestWord = W4

  A = $1234              '  Initialize Variables
  B = $EF
```

```
DestWord = A + B        '  $1323 in Destination
DestByte = A + B        '  $23 in Destination
DestBit  = A + B        '  1 (LSB) in Destination
```

Subtraction of a higher number from a smaller will result in a "two's complement" negative number.

For the previous example, if the line:

```
DestWord = B - A        '  Subtract a Larger from a Smaller
```

the result put in "DestWord" will be $EEBB, which is not a negative number, but actually a two's complement representation of one. But to check to see if this is negative, you just have to check to see if the most significant bit is set. This means you effectively have a numeric range of -32768 to +32767 or 0 to 65535 if negative numbers are not to be used.

Multiplication ("*" and "**") is quite straightforward—multiplication of two 16-bit numbers and potentially getting a 32 result. Executing a single "splat" (as I prefer to call asterisks) returns the lower word or 16 bits of the result. The double splat operation returns the high 16 bits.

This can be shown as the program:

```
Symbol A = W2            '  Everything is 16 Bits
Symbol B = W3
Symbol C = W4

Symbol Dest = W5

  A = $4                 '  Some Values for Multiplication
  B = $1234
  C = $10

  Dest = A * B           '  Dest = $48D0
  Dest = A ** B          '  Dest = $0000

  Dest = B * C           '  Dest = $2340
  Dest = B ** C          '  Dest = $0001
```

Handling a negative number in multiplication can be tricky.
For example:

```
Symbol  A = B2           '  This Variable is 8 Bits
Symbol  B = W2           '  The rest are 16 Bits
Symbol  C = W3

Symbol  Dest = W4

  A = -5                 '  Setup Test Values
  B = -5
  C = 7

  Dest = A * C           '  Result is $0699

  Dest = B * C           '  Result is $FFDD
```

This is again because negative numbers are not really recognized in the Stamp's PBASIC (or pretty much all other 8-bit microcontroller languages). To get the "correct" answer ($FFDD), the line:

```
Dest = A * C
```

would change to:

```
Dest = A & $80                        ' Get Bit 7 to see if Number is Neg
 if Dest <> 0 then NegSkip            ' If Negative, then Handle As Neg
   Dest = A * C                       '  Else, Positive
   goto MulSkip
NegSkip:                              ' Get Negative Result.
   Dest = A - 1 ^ $FF * C ^ $FFFF + 1
MulSkip:
```

At "NegSkip," the value in "A" is made into a positive number, multiplied by "C" and then made into a two's complement 16-bit negative number. The reason for the "if" statement is to handle a positive value correctly as well as the negative. This code would account for "A" being positive or negative. This code would not change if "C" were negative because "C" is already a full word.

Earlier in this section, I mentioned that I put in a "debug" statement after every complex assignment statement I create in PBASIC.

The assignment:

```
Dest = A - 1 ^ $FF * C ^ $FFFF + 1
```

certainly qualifies as this, and when I was writing this section, I debugged this snippet of code using a BS1 and lots of "debug" statements.

Division ("/") follows in multiplication but differs in that the dividend and divisor can be a maximum of 16 bits. Division of (potentially) negative numbers will require this PBASIC code:

```
ActDividend = Dividend
Quotient = ActDividend & MSBDividend
if Quotient = 0 then DividendDone  ' Most Sig Bit = 0, + Dividend
  ActDividend = -Dividend          ' Make Sure Dividend Used is Pos
DividendDone:
ActDivisor = Divisor
Quotient = ActDivisor & MSBDivisor
if Quotient = 0 then DivisorDone   ' Most Sig Bit = 0, +Divisor
  ActDivisor = -Divisor            ' Make Sure Divisor Used is Pos
DivisorDone:                       ' Get the Actual Value
 Quotient = ActDividend / ActDivisor
 if Divisor > 0 AND Dividend > 0 OR Divisor < 0 AND Dividend < 0 then
DivideDone
   Quotient = -Quotient
DivideDone:                        ' Quotient Has Correct Value
```

Which is really more trouble than it's worth. If at all possible, division of negative numbers should be avoided.

The modulo ("//") operator is a nice feature to have. In most languages, to get the integer remainder for division, the following algorithm must be used:

```
modulo = Dividend - (( Dividend / Divisor ) * Divisor )
```

This "fools" the compiler to integer divide by the divisor, which looses the remainder or fractional part of the quotient. Multiplying this value by the divisor will restore the dividend minus the modulo, which can be found be subtracting this value from the original dividend.

I should note that in some compilers, the statement above will be optimized to:

```
modulo = 0
```

This is because the compiler recognizes that "/ Divisor * Divisor" equals 1 and the value operated on does not change and is then subtracted from itself, giving the result of zero.

This means that another way will have to be used to calculate the modulo of a dividend for a divisor, but, in PBASIC, this can be done by simply using the "//" operator.

The "Min" and "Max" operators (which don't use any special characters and are just represented by the labels) return the minimum and maximum, respectively, of the values presented to them.

```
Dest = 5 max 7          '  Dest = 7
```

Like the previous operations, negative numbers have to be considered. Because negative numbers don't really exist in PBASIC, they will be handled as numbers with their most significant bits set, which will cause PBASIC to think that a large positive number is actually being checked, which will throw off the expected result.

The last operators in BS1 PBASIC are the bitwise operators: AND ("&"), OR ("¦"), and XOR ("^"). In the BS1 literature, these operators are identified as "logical" operators. "AND" and "OR" are the "if" statement logical AND and OR operations and, like the comparison operators ("=," ">," etc.), cannot be used in the BS1 PBASIC assignment statements. The single character versions of these operators ("&" and "¦") perform bitwise operations on the individual bits of the two values.

As is shown above, if you want to isolate bit 7 of a byte and save it for later use (i.e., checking to see if the value is two's complement negative), the following statement is used:

```
Dest  = A & $80         '  Isolate Bit 7
```

These bitwise operations work as you'd probably expect bitwise operations to work in a microcontroller.

BS2 Mathematical Operators

Many of the concepts I just discussed for the BS1's PBASIC apply to the BS2s, but the BS2 also has many other mathematical operators available. In this subchapter, I will only address the different mathematical operators available on the BS2.

One of the first differences that should be identified is how parameters work for the different functions. In the BS2, each parameter is a value that can be created by using mathematical operators. This makes creating parameters simpler and more logical. Like in the BS1, logical operators (such as "=," ">," "AND," etc.) cannot be used in expressions except in the "if" statement (or in the instructions that allow it).

The first set of operators are the BS2 "unary" operators. These operators take precedence over all the other mathematical operations.

This "precedence" means that the single operand to the right of an unary operator will be used by the unary operation:

```
SQR 4 + 5
```

Will return "7," as many other compilers would return (which is the square root taken of 4 and then added to 5).

I learned years ago that complex expressions should have major blocks in parentheses to ensure there is no confusion, either by me or the language compiler. This should be done in the BS2's PBASIC unary operators to make sure there is never any ambiguity in what is being done. In the example above, I would prefer it to be written as:

OPERATOR	DESCRIPTION
SQR	Return the square root of the unsigned value
-	Sixteen bit two's complement of a number
~	Complement bits in 16-bit number
ABS	Absolute value of a 16-bit number
DCD	Decode 4-bit number to 16-bit output
NCD	Priority encoder of 16-bit number
SIN	Sine of 8-bit number
COS	Cosine of 8-bit number

```
SQR( 4 ) + 5
```

Which makes the unary operator appear as a function, but how the expression is to be executed looks much more obvious. Actually, for most of the unary operators, I treat them like functions with parentheses around the input parameter.

In engineering mathematics (if I called this "pure" mathematics, I'm sure somebody would complain), doing the square root ("SQR") on a negative number will result in a complex result (i.e., "i" or "j"). In the BS2, a two's complement negative number will be processed by the SQR operator as if it were a 16-bit number, and the result will be the square root of this 16-bit number.

```
A var nib
B var byte
C var word
D var word

Dest var word

  A = -4                ' Actually $C
  B = -4                ' Actually $FC
  C = -4                ' Actually $FFFC
  D = 4                 ' Actually $0004

  Dest = SQR( A )       ' Dest = SQR( $C ) = 3
  Dest = SQR( B )       ' Dest = SQR( $FC ) = 15
  Dest = SQR( C )       ' Dest = SQR( $FFFC ) = 255
  Dest = SQR( D )       ' Dest = SQR( $0004 ) = 2
```

So, you'll agree that to get the correct square root of a number, it's important that only positive numbers are passed to "SQR."

I'm a bit surprised that "-" is regarded as an unary operator because it is available in the BS1's PBASIC with the implication that the parameter is negated:

```
B = -A
```

This will put the 16-bit two's complement negated number for "A" in "B."

If we look back to the BS1 discussion, operating on a 4- or 8-bit negative number in a 16-bit operation will result in some strange results.

If we had the example:

```
A var byte                ' Define Variables
B var word

Dest var word

  A = -5                  ' Initialize Variables
  B = 7

  Dest = A + B            ' Dest = $102

  Dest = A               ' Dest = $FB

  Dest = -A              ' Dest = $FF05
```

Note that "-" cannot be used to convert "A" into a positive value for adding properly to "B." Instead, to get a valid "A + B" (with an expected result of "2"), the expression would have to be:

```
  Dest = -(( A ^ $FF ) + 1 ) + B
```

The "~" operator is the same as XORing the value with 16 ones. To write this out mathematically:

```
  ~A = A ^ $FFFF
```

This is not an operation I use a lot of simply because it is not a symbol that is immediately recognizable (although it is easy to confuse with a two's complement negation ("-")). And if "A" is defined as a byte (as in the examples above), the result will be 16 bits (and not 8 bits, as expected).

The absolute value ("ABS") operator simply returns the absolute value of a 16-bit number. The important thing to note is that it is for a 16-bit number.

So, in the square root example, if ABS were used, we'd have the following results:

```
A var nib
B var byte
C var word
D var word

  A = -4                  ' Actually $C
  B = -4                  ' Actually $FC
  C = -4                  ' Actually $FFFC
  D = 4                   ' Actually $0004

  Dest = ABS( A )         ' Dest = ABS( $000C ) = $C
  Dest = ABS( B )         ' Dest = ABS( $00FC ) = $FC
  Dest = ABS( C )         ' Dest = ABS( $FFFC ) = 4
  Dest = ABS( D )         ' Dest = ABS( $0004 ) = 4
```

Like all 16-bit operators, ABS will not work properly (and as expected) unless it has a 16-bit operand.

Next, the decoder/encoder operands ("DCD" and "NCD," respectively) can be used as demultiplexing/multiplexing functions. The NCD operator returns the number of the most active bit plus one (or 0 if nothing is set) of a 16-bit word. This is a bit different than what the BS2 documentation says, but it can be checked empirically using the code:

```
A var word
```

```
Dest var word

  A = 1234              '   Some Random Value

  Dest = NCD( A )       '   Dest = 11 (most significant bit)
```

The value for "A" can be changed to see what happens for different values.

"DCD" can be thought of as an operator which provides the power of two:

```
A var word
Dest var word
  A = 4
  Dest = DCD( A )       '   Dest = 16 = ( 2 ^ 4 )
```

This power of two can be used for providing a demultiplexer output for controlling individual circuits one at a time.

The last two unary operators are the trig functions "sine" and "cosine" ("SIN" and "COS," respectively). These functions (I don't really think that they can be called "operators") return an 8-bit value, from -127 to 127, which is the trig value for a 256-point circle that is 127 units in radius. (Figure 42.1.)

Each quadrant of the circle is broken up into 64 "degrees," rather than the 90 degrees of a "standard" circle. The output value can be calculated as a fraction of 127 to get the actual trig value. Later in this subchapter, I will show you how to get a fraction in the BS2.

"Fractional multiplication" ("*/") is a really interesting feature of the BS2's PBASIC. When you multiply two 16-bit numbers together, you can get up to a 32-bit result. The "*/" operator returns the middle two bytes of a product, ignoring the most and least significant bytes. This makes it very useful for finding fractional values.

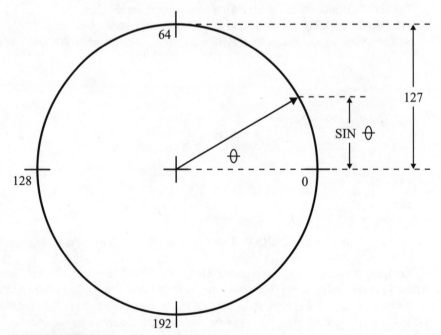

Figure 42.1 Stamp sine/cosine circle.

Let's say you have a stick that is 36 inches long and is being held at a 50-degree angle. The top of the stick could be found by the formula:

$$\text{Height} = \text{Stick\_Length} * \text{Sin(Angle)}$$
$$= 36 * \text{Sin(50) inches}$$

In the BS2 PBASIC, this would be coded as:

```
Height = ( Stick_Length * 2 * sin(( Angle * 64 ) / 90 )) */ 1
```

The "(Angle * 64) / 90" calculation is to get the correct angle in PBASIC's 256-degree circle. Each degree is different from "standard" degrees by the fraction 64/90. By putting "Angle" and 64 in the same parentheses, I make sure that a number is produced that is greater than 90 (if it's not when a value is divided by 90, the result will always be 0, and 0 multiplied by any value is always 0) and I get a valid angle from the calculation.

The sine of the angle is multiplied by two so that the effective radius of the circle is 256 (instead of 127 as defaulted by the function).

This leaves the fractional multiplication by 1 to get the result (which, by the way is correct at 27 inches). The sine has a maximum value of 256 (actually 254, resulting in less than 1% error under all circumstances), so I'm using the "*/" operator to take the 32-bit result and convert it to a 16-bit result, with the fractional result (the first 8 bits) taken off.

This operation could also be done by using the bit shift ("<<" for left shift and ">>" for right shift) operators.

```
Temp   = ( 36 ** Sin(( Angle * 64 ) / 90 )) << 9
Height = ( 36 * Sin(( Angle * 64 )/ 90 )) >> 7
Height = Height + Temp
```

In this example, the 16 bits of the height is shifted 9 bits up (or multiplied by 512), and then the lower product is shifted downwards by 7 bits (divided by 128) to get a product of the stick length and the sine of the angle with a circle radius of 128 divided by $2 \wedge 7$, which is 1.

The shift operators can be used in the example above to shift the two 16-bit halves of the 32-bit product to get a value at a certain point (i.e., cutting off the fractional bits) or to rotate data to test bits.

For example, if you wanted to find the most significant bit in a byte (and not use "NCD"), you could use the code:

```
A var byte
Bit var byte

  A = Something          '   Some Value to Test
  Bit = 7

Loop:                    '   Loop Around until MSB is Set
  if (( A & $80 ) <> 0 ) OR ( B = 0 ) then Stop

    A = A << 1           '   Shift up the value in "A"

    Bit = Bit - 1

    goto Loop

Stop:                    '   Have Bit or have tested them all
```

Each time through "Loop," the number is shifted upwards (putting a lower bit into bit 7, which is tested) and decrementing the bit counter. "Stop" is encountered when either bit 7 of "A" is set or each bit has been tested.

"DIG" is useful in returning a specific digit of a decimal number. A possible application of this operator is to output a number to a seven-segment LED:

```
A = 1234                    ' Define the Number to Output
Digit = 2                   ' Want to Output "3" or Digit 2
Lookup A Dig Digit,[Pat0, Pat1, ... Pat9], Pat
```

After the "Lookup" instruction, "Pat" will have the bit pattern required to display the specific digit on the LCD.

The last BS2 unique binary operator is "REV," which reverses the bit order of a value for a certain number of bits.

```
A = %10010110
B = A Rev 8                 '  B = %01101001
```

This operator is useful in those cases where you wire up your hardware backwards (I'm not being very facetious in this; I've wired up serial to parallel convertors wrong a number of times and wished this operator was available, rather than having to code it for a microcontroller as I'm debugging the program) or work with multiple external bus devices that require data least significant bit first and most significant bit first.

This and the previous subchapter are a reasonably complete explanation of how the Stamps process data in assignments and functions. While it is certainly possible to write Stamp programs without understanding these operations backwards and forwards, I highly recommend studying what I've written here and trying out the example code before writing applications that have complex operations.

Branching/Looping

Now that you understand how mathematical operators work, we can start discussing the PBASIC language's built-in functions.

The first PBASIC function to be considered is the "goto label." The label used must start in the first column of the source and end with a colon (":"). To visually separate code and labels (and follow the convention used for other languages), I put all other code starting in a column other than the first one (although the first one will work fine). The PBASIC "Goto" instruction for both the BS1 and BS2 is shown in Instruction 42.1.

Calling a subroutine in the BS1 (using the "Gosub" instruction shown in Instruction 42.2) will change contents of "W6" and then jump the specified label. As noted earlier, W6 should not be used for any other purpose, and subroutines must not be called from within other subroutines. Only 16 "gosubs" can be placed in a BS1 PBASIC program.

In reading the Parallax documentation, you might be wondering if the BS1 PBASIC "return" instruction could be used as a "computed goto":

```
W6 = Label       ' Get the Address to Jump to
return
   :
Label:
```

This will not work because "W6" is not loaded with the return address for a subroutine. A much better method of providing computed gotos is to use the "Branch" instruction (explained in the next subchapter).

The "gosub" and "return" statements (shown in Instruction 42.4 and Instruction 42.5, respectively) in the BS2 work more like a "traditional" high-level language; the return value is placed on a program counter stack and is not available to the executing program.

Conditional Branches

Conditional program execution is one of the defining features of a processor architecture (without them, all you really have is a programmable calculator/I/O controller—maybe). PBASIC has a number of functions which are used to control the operation of the program.

The "if...then" function is fundamental to all high-level programming languages. (Instruction 42.6.) Unlike many other language "if"s, in the PBASIC if function, when the condition specified is valid, then a jump is specified. This may be confusing if you are used to structured languages where code is executed if a condition is true. In PBASIC you are jumping over code if a condition is true (esentially negative logic).

In "C" you may have the statements:

```
if ( A > B )
   i = i + 1;
```

Instruction: "Goto"   **Bits:** N/A

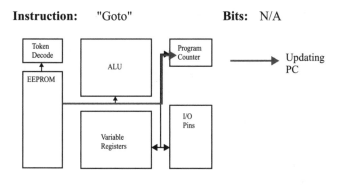

Execution: PC → Label   **Instruction Cycles:**   N/A

Example: goto Label   **MCUs:** BS1/BS2
⋮
Label:

Comments: The "Label" can be anywhere in the PBASIC Source.

Instruction 42.1 BS1/BS2 "goto label" instruction.

Instruction: "Gosub"   **Bits:** N/A

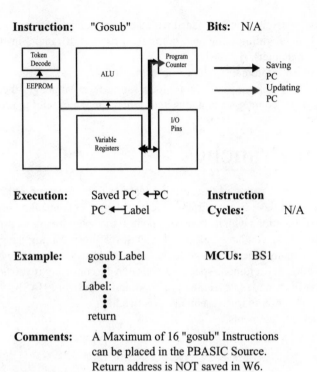

Execution: Saved PC ← PC   **Instruction**
              PC ← Label   **Cycles:** N/A

Example: gosub Label   **MCUs:** BS1
            ⋮
            Label:
            ⋮
            return

Comments: A Maximum of 16 "gosub" Instructions
             can be placed in the PBASIC Source.
             Return address is NOT saved in W6.

Instruction 42.2 BS1 "gosub label" instruction.

Instruction: "Return"   **Bits:** N/A

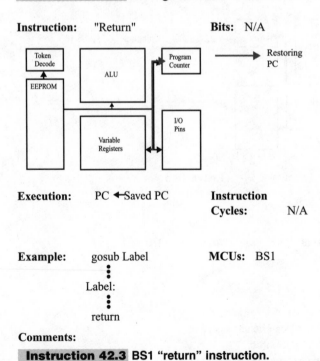

Execution: PC ← Saved PC   **Instruction**
                                     Cycles: N/A

Example: gosub Label   **MCUs:** BS1
            ⋮
            Label:
            ⋮
            return

Comments:

Instruction 42.3 BS1 "return" instruction.

Instruction: Gosub   **Bits:** N/A

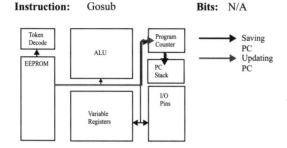

Execution: Stack ◄─Next Ins.   **Instruction**
                 PC ◄─ Label   **Cycles:**   N/A

Example: gosub Label   **MCUs:** BS2
                ⋮
                Label:
                ⋮
                return

Comments: Up to 255 "Gosub" Instructions can
                be placed in the Source. Up to 4
                Levels of Subroutine Nesting.

Instruction 42.4 BS2 "gosub label" instruction.

Instruction: Gosub   **Bits:** N/A

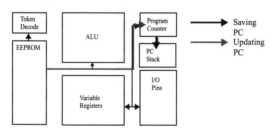

Execution: Stack ◄─Next Ins.   **Instruction**
                 PC ◄─ Label   **Cycles:**   N/A

Example: gosub Label   **MCUs:** BS2
                ⋮
                Label:
                ⋮
                return

Comments: Up to 255 "Gosub" Instructions can
                be placed in the Source. Up to 4
                Levels of Subroutine Nesting.

Instruction 42.5 BS2 "return" instruction.

In PBASIC the same operation would be executed by:

```
  if A <= B then Skip
    i = i + 1
Skip:
```

Both the BS1 and BS2 are capable of executing compound conditions in the "if" statement using "AND," "OR," and, in the BS2, "NOT." This allows more complex conditions for the "if" statement. In the Stamps, these statements are at a higher priority than the comparisons (i.e., they execute after the comparisons) while in the BS1, they are at the same priority level.

In the previous example, if "i" was to be incremented if "A" was greater than "B" AND "C" was equal to "D," it would be written as:

```
  if  A <= B OR C <> D then Skip
    i = i + 1
Skip:
```

Notice that the logic has been again reversed to how you would normally think about it in a structured language.

A very useful programming construct is the "for" loop. (Instruction 42.7.) This is used to execute code a set number of times. For example, the BS2 code:

```
  debug str "%"
  for i = 0 to 8
   debug dec ( Data & $80 ) >> 7
   Data = Data << 1
  next
```

will display "Data" as an 8-bit binary number. The "next" statement defines the end of the "for" statement and returns execution to the appropriate "for" statement. (Up to 8 "for" statements can be nested in the BS1 and up to 16 in the BS2.)

As shown in Instruction 42.7, there is the "step" parameter, which is used to specify the incrementing value. This value can be any negative or positive value. For example, if you wanted to output a countdown message, the code below could be used:

```
  debug str "Counting down...", cr
  for i = 10 to 0 step -1
   pause 1000          '  Delay 1 Second between messages
   debug dec i, cr
  next
  debug str "Liftoff!!", cr
```

Using the "step" parameter may lead to some problems where the count variable never reaches the final value. An example of this is:

```
  for i = 0 to 3 step 2
   '  Do something
  next
```

This will never stop because "i" will never equal 3 if it starts at 0 and is incremented by 2.

Normally, the count variable should never be modified. But if the variable is set to the ending value minus the step (because the "next" adds the step increment before checking for a match), then you can "break" from the loop.

In the next example, a check for execution running amok (i.e., "i" becoming greater than "3" in the code above) can be easily put in:

```
  for i = 0 to 3 step 2
```

```
     '  Do something
     if i < 3 then Skip        '  Check for i Valid
      i = 3 - 2                 '  Invalid Value - Stop the Looping
Skip:
  next
```

The last conditional execution function is the "Branch." (Instruction 42.8.) This function allows the program to jump to a label based on an offset value. This instruction allows easy implementation of software state machines. A classic example of this is controlling traffic lights.

In this example, the stamp can control three LEDs for two directions each (for a total of six). The LEDs are grouped in two different displays (red, yellow, green).

There are five "states" to be defined:

1. Both red.
2. N/S yellow and E/W red.
3. N/S green and E/W red.
4. E/W yellow and N/S red.
5. E/W green and N/S red.

For the north/south ("N/S" above) display, the least significant three bits are used to drive the LEDs. For the east/west display, the most significant three bits are used. For the code, I will just use two 8-bit variables for keeping track of the state.

```
'  Traffic Lights program

Symbol NSRed = pin0          '  Define the Lights
Symbol NSYel = pin1
Symbol NSGrn = Pin2
Symbol EWRed = Pin7
Symbol EWYel = Pin6
Symbol EWGrn = Pin5

Symbol State = b0            '  State Variable
Symbol Direct = b1          '  Current "on" direction

State = 0                   '  Initialize to Both Red
Direct = 0                  '  North South to Execute First

Loop:                       '  Return Here to Change Lights

  branch State, ( State1, State2, State3 )

State1:
  pins = 0                  '  Turn off all lights
  NSRed = 1                 '  Turn on Red Lights
  EWRed = 1

  pause 2000                '  Both Red for two seconds

  State = State + 1         '  Go to the Next State

  goto Loop


State2:                     '  Turn on Green Light for 20 Seconds

  if Direct = 0 then State2NS  '  Handle North/South Condition
```

42

PARALLAX: BASIC STAMP

```
     EWRed = 0
     EWGrn = 1
     goto State2Skip
State2NS:
  NSRed = 0
  NSGrn = 1
State2Skip:

  Pause 30000                    ' Leave Green Light for thirty Seconds

  State = State + 1


State3:                          ' Put on Yellow Lights

  if Direct = 0 then State3NS
  EWGrn = 0
  EWYel = 1
  goto State3Skip
State3NS:   NSGrn = 0
  EWYel = 1
State3Skip:

  Pause 5000                     ' Yellow for five Seconds

  State = 0                      ' Reset the State
  Direct = Direct ^ 1            ' Change the Direction

  goto State1                    ' Start all over again
```

Reading through this code, you're probably wondering what the big deal is. This is a simple example, but where the power is in fixing problems and adding enhancements. You could probably write this application in line quite easily (and save a few bytes in the EEP-ROM doing it), but how would you add a check to see if somebody is pressing a button requesting the lights to change? In a conventional program, this could be quite difficult, with a lot of changes. In the state machine above, the state routines are simply changed (and, as written, changing for one direction will change for them both).

"Branch" will also simplify multiple "if's" when used with the "lookdown" instruction explained in "Data Tables" later in this chapter.

Digital I/O

Digital input/output in the Stamp is similar to digital I/O of other devices. The primary method that I use to read and write the I/O pins in PBASIC is to write directly to the registers that access the pins. But there are a number of PBASIC functions that can be used to access the I/O pins directly.

As I explained earlier in this section, both Stamp's digital I/O pins are mapped as the first register (variable) addresses in the Stamp's data space.

For the BS1, there are 8 I/O pins, the first byte ("B0") is the data pins and the second byte ("B1") is the direction pins (or the "TRIS" bits as known in the PIC). In both the BS1 and BS2, the "Dir" bits are reversed from the PICMicro's "TRIS" convention. (In the Stamps, if a direction register bit is reset ("0"), the pin is an input, which is reversed to what the PICMicro's TRIS bit is set as).

Instruction: "if Cond then Label" **Bits:** N/A

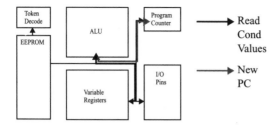

Read
Cond
Values

New
PC

Execution: If Cond != 0   **Instruction**
PC ← Label   **Cycles:**   N/A

Example: **MCUs:** BS1/BS2

  if A > B then Label
   ' Conditional Code
Label:

Comments: "AND", "OR", "NOT" and "XOR" (the
latter two only available in the BS2)
are used to enhance the "Cond".

Instruction 42.6 BS1/BS2 "if Cond then label" instruction.

Instruction: "For Var = Strt to End" **Bits:** N/A

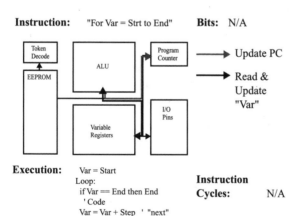

Update PC

Read &
Update
"Var"

42

Execution: Var = Start
       Loop: **Instruction**
         if Var == End then End   **Cycles:**   N/A
          ' Code
         Var = Var + Step   ' "next"
         goto Loop
        End   **MCUs:** BS1/BS2

Example:
For i = 0 to 10 step 21
    ' Code
next

Comments: "step" parameter is used to specify
the incrementing of "Var" through
each loop.

Instruction 42.7 BS1/BS2 "for var = start to end" instruction.

Instruction: "Branch Var, (Label,..."   **Bits:** N/A

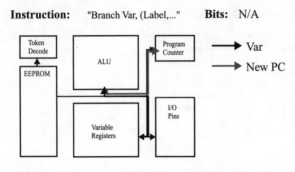

Execution: **Instruction**
PC ← LabelTable[Var]   **Cycles:**   N/A

Example: **MCUs:** BS1/BS2

Branch i, (Label1, Label2)
Label1:
Label2:

Comments:

Instruction 42.8 BS1/BS2 "branch var,(label, .." instruction.

In the BS2, the first three 16-bit words are devoted to the 16 input/output pins. "W0" is used to read the current state of the I/O pins, while "W1" is the value to be output (which, as noted in the PIC I/O pin description can be completely different from "W0"). "W2" is the pin direction ("TRIS") register.

In both the BS1 and BS2, the I/O pins are all set to input on powerup or reset (as would be expected from the behaviour of the PICMicro and other microcontrollers discussed in this book). So, if you had a circuit that was designed to use the least-significant 6 bits as output on a BS1, the easiest way to set the direction word ("W2") is:

```
Dir = %00111111        '  Set the LS 6 Bits to Output
```

Or using the "Output" function, which sets individual bits as output:

```
output 0
output 1
 :
output 5
```

Along with "output," there are also the "input" and "reverse" functions in PBASIC. (Instruction 42.9, Instruction 42.10, and Instruction 42.11.) "Input" will make an individual pin an input and "reverse" will change an input pin to an output (and visa-versa).

Reading and writing data out on the pins is done exactly the same way as the "direction" control. Instead of reading and writing the registers directly, the "low," "high," and "toggle" functions (Instruction 42.12, Instruction 42.13, and Instruction 42.14) can be used to access the bits individually.

In most of my programming, I access the I/O registers directly instead of using these instructions. I have written some applications where only these instructions have been used. Ideally, a good balance between accessing these registers and using the bit instructions has to be made.

For example, what I would think of the following routine for writing to an LCD in 4-bit mode (with the least significant 4 I/O pins being used as the data pins).

```
SendChar                    '  Send the Character in "OutChar" to the LCD

  Pins = OutChar / 16       '  Start with the high 4 Bits

  High RS                   '  RS = 1 for Character Write

  Pulsout E, 1              '  Pulse "E" for 2 - 10 usec

  Pins = OutChar // 16      '  Repeat Sequence for the low 4 Bits

  High RS

  Pulsout E, 1

  return                    '  Return to the caller
```

At first glance, this code is actually a pretty good balance betwen writing to registers as opposed to the I/O port pins, but there is one concern that I would have; the code above will not allow the I/O ports to control any other external hardware (unless the I/O pins were normally "low") because even though we only want writing the lower 4 bits of the "Pins" variable, we are also writing to the higher 4 bits inadvertently as well. In a real application, writing to the "Pins" port would be accomplished by:

```
Pins = Pins & $F0           '  Clear the Lower 4 Bits
Pins = OutChar / 16 | Pins  '  Write the Appropriate 4 Bits
```

The above code is, however, an excellent introduction to "Pulsout" and "Pulsin." (Instruction 42.15 and Instruction 42.16.)

The "Pulsout" function toggles a pin from its original state, waits a set amount of time (in 10-usec increments for the BS1 and in 2-usec increments for the BS2) and then returns the pin to its original state. This is really useful for applications like the one above, where it simplifies the code.

Like many other functions with timing precision, I do not feel that using pulsout will make the Stamp into a tool that should be used in any applications requiring any degree of precision. The reason for this isn't that the pulsout instruction isn't precise; it's because the code around it isn't precise (i.e., a pulse is not usually sent in conjunction with other signals; these signals cannot be timed with any degree of precision relative to the pulse).

"Pulsin" is used to measure the width of a pulse on an input pin (in usecs). If a pulse is not received within a preset interval (65535 times the timing interval), then the function times out and returns "0" as the pulse width.

For both pulsout and pulsin, the timing interval is different for the BS1 and BS2. For the BS1, this value is 10 usecs, and for the BS2 it is 2 usecs. The differences in these intervals affects the maximum pulse size as well as the time-out interval.

As I've shown in this book (and probably scared you off from ever attempting to implement it on your own), debouncing a button can be a pain. To make this operation easier, the PBASIC designers came up with the "button" function, which allows you to wait for a button to be pressed and debounced, while executing code in the background. The parameters for debouncing the button press will affect how the code executes. The button function behaves more complexly than any other built-in function, and I will spend some time going through it. (Instruction 42.17.)

Don't worry if you don't understand how "button" works the first few times you look at it. I do recommend experimenting with it and looking at how it's described in the Stamp manual as well as applications.

The most important measure used is the counter of the number of times "button" is invoked. This count is used to determine whether or not the count is adequately debounced and whether or not the auto-repeat function is to be used. This means that "button" should be placed within a polling loop with a specific delay.

```
b0 = 0                         '  Reset Button Timer
Loop
   button 0,0,10,125,b0,1,Press  '  Wait for Button on Pin 0 to go
   goto Loop                   '    down for 20 msec
Press                          '  Button has been pressed
```

This example will loop 20 times with the button pressed (pin 0 in the down state) before jumping to "press." To roughly time this code, I have assumed that each statement will take 1 msec to execute. With this assumption, each "loop" will take 2 msec, and for the button to be debounced in 20 msec, the "button" function will have to execute 10 times (which is the third parameter to the "button" function).

The first two parameters specify the pin and the "downstate" (when the button is pressed). In the example above, I am using pin 0, and it is normally high (pulled up with a resistor, and the button pulls the line to ground when pressed).

The third parameter is the "delay," and while you may be more comfortable with the idea that it is measured in terms of time, this is not how it's measured in PBASIC. As noted above, it is measured by the number of times "button" is invoked (and, indirectly the code surrounding "button"). There are two special values that you should be aware of. A delay of zero will act on the button state without any debounce (it just jumps to the "address" if the downstate is active). A delay of 255 will preform debounce (albeit a relatively long one) and no autorepeat.

Next, the "rate" parameter is used to specify the delay (again measured in number of times the "button" function is invoked) that the button has to be pressed down before another button press is registered. This is really the "auto-repeat" function. For the example above, I have used "125," which means that every 125 invocations of "button" (which happen 2 msecs apart) with the button in the downstate, the code will jump to "press." This delay of 125 translates to roughly 250 msecs, or an auto-repeat button "press" will be registered approximately four times a second.

The "bytevariable" parameter ("b0" in the example above) is an 8-bit value for recording the current number of "button" invocations (basically the "delay" counter). Before the button is invoked for the first time, this value should be reset so the timer is starting from "scratch." This value can be modified (i.e., to restart the process or to modify the auto-repeat interval), but I would recommend against this. Once an 8-bit variable has been assigned to the button, this should not be changed or accessed in any way. Changing this variable may cause unpredictable behavior in the Stamp—which is another way of saying you might get button down conditions unexpectedly or not at all.

The "targetstate" parameter (the sixth one of "button") is used to specify when the branch on a button condition should be made. "1" indicates the button check is happening on the "downstate" (which can either be a "0" or a "1") and a "0" indicates that the check is happening on the "upstate." Normally, this parameter would be set to a "1," but if you want to wait for a switch to be released (debounce the switch release), a "0" can be used.

The last parameter is the "address" or label the code is to jump to when there has been a valid button press (i.e., debounced first press or auto-repeat). In the example above, when a valid button press has been recorded, execution jumps to "press" or otherwise keeps looping.

Now, with the last two parameters, you might think that the example above can be simplified to:

```
  b0 = 0                       '  Reset Button Timer
Loop
  button 0,0,10,125,b0,0,Loop  '  Wait for Button on Pin 0
Press                          '  Button has been pressed
```

But this code will not work as you will want it to. When it is first invoked, execution will continue to "press" until "button" has been invoked ten times (which is the button debounce). Then, after the single jump back to loop, "press" will execute until 125 debounce "button" invocations, at which time it will jump back to "loop" once again (and then wait 125 times to go back to "loop" and so on). So, in no time at all, the program will have executed as if several thousand buttons have been pressed (which is what happens when "press" is executed), rather than as if there were none at all (as is the actual case).

"Button" really is a very complex function and, as I said above, don't get frustrated if you don't understand how it works after reading through this subchapter once (or even twice). I highly recommend experimenting with the "button" function until you understand it well.

The "count" function allows the BS2 to behave as a tachometer, counting events per unit time. (Instruction 42.18.) The function has three input parameters: the pin which will receive the input signal, the 16-bit period in milliseconds, and a 16-bit variable to store the count value. The input signal must stay at the same state (either high or low) for at least 4 usecs for a valid read (this means the maximum input signal is 125 kHz with a 50% duty cycle).

This function makes some applications dead easy. For example, if you were an airplane modeler and you wanted to send the current propeller speed to your PC for logging, the code could be:

```
'  Two Bladed Propeller Tach Application

RPM var word           '  Count of the Speed of the Propeller

Loop

  count 0, 1000, RPM   '  Count the number of revolutions
                       '    per second

  serout 16,84+$8000,0,("Current Speed is", dec RPM * 60 / 2, cr)

  goto Loop
```

In this program, the number of times the propeller goes by the sensor in a second will be recorded by "count" and put into "RPM." The data is sent to the PC as "Revolutions per minute," which means that I multiply the per-second rate by 60 and divide by the number of blades on the propeller.

Instruction: "Output Pin"   **Bits:**   N/A

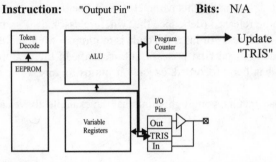

Execution:
TRIS.Pin ← 1

Instruction Cycles: N/A

MCUs: BS1/BS2

Example:
Pins = 0
Output 4   ' Output "0" on Pin 4

Comments:

Instruction 42.9 BS1/BS2 "output pin" instruction.

Instruction: "Input Pin"   **Bits:**   N/A

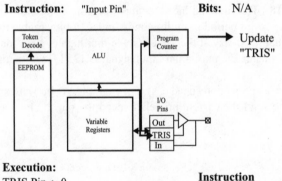

Execution:
TRIS.Pin ← 0

Instruction Cycles: N/A

MCUs: BS1/BS2

Example:
Pins = 0
Dirs = $FF   ' Everything is an Output
Input 7   ' Pin 7 is an Input

Comments:

Instruction 42.10 BS1/BS2 "input pin" instruction.

Instruction: "Reverse Pin"   **Bits:**   N/A

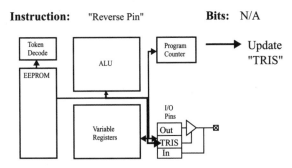

Update
"TRIS"

Execution:
TRIS.Pin ←TRIS.Pin ^ 1

**Instruction
Cycles:**   N/A

MCUs: BS1/BS2

Example:
Pins = 0
Dirs = $FF   ' Everything is an Output
Reverse 7   ' Pin 7 is an Input

Comments:

Instruction 42.11 BS1/BS2 "reverse pin" instruction.

Instruction: "High Pin"   **Bits:**   N/A

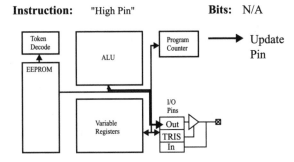

Update
Pin

Execution:
Pin ←1

**Instruction
Cycles:**   N/A

MCUs: BS1/BS2

Example:
Pins = 0
Dirs = $FF   ' Everything is an Output
High 5   ' Pin 5 is Outputting a "1"

Comments:

Instruction 42.12 BS1/BS2 "high pin" instruction.

Instruction: "Low Pin"   **Bits:**   N/A

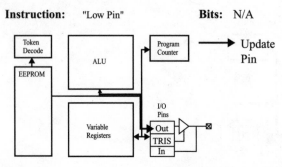

Execution:

Pin $\leftarrow$ 0

Instruction Cycles: N/A

MCUs: BS1/BS2

Example:

```
Pins = 0
Dirs = $FF      ' Everything is an Output
High 5          ' Pin 5 is Outputting a "1"
Low 3           ' Pin 3 is Outputting a "0"
```

Comments:

Instruction 42.13 BS1/BS2 "low pin" instruction.

Instruction: "Toggle Pin"   **Bits:**   N/A

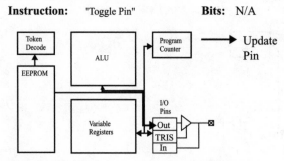

Execution:

Pin $\leftarrow$ Pin $^\wedge$ 1

Instruction Cycles: N/A

MCUs: BS1/BS2

Example:

```
Pins = 0
Dirs = $FF      ' Everything is an Output
Toggle 5        ' Pin 5 is Outputting a "1"
```

Comments:

Instruction 42.14 BS1/BS2 "toggle pin" instruction.

Instruction: "Pulsin Pin, state, var"   **Bits:**   N/A

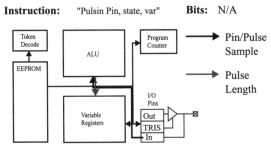

Execution:
var = 0
while Pin != State
while Pin == State
 var = var + 1

**Instruction
Cycles:**   N/A

Example:
Pulsin 4, 1, W2
debug "Pulse Width is", W2

MCUs: BS1/BS2

Comments: For BS1, Timing Granularity is 10 us.
         For BS2, Timing Granularity is 2 us.
         Timeout in 65535x Granularity.

Instruction 42.15 BS1/BS2 "pulsin pin, state, var" instruction.

Instruction: "Pulsout Pin time"   **Bits:**   N/A

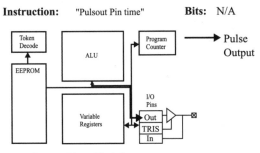

Execution: Pin = Pin ^ 1
         Dlay = 0
         while Dlay < time
          Dlay = Dlay + 1
          Pin = Pin ^ 1

**Instruction
Cycles:**   N/A

MCUs: BS1/BS2

Example:
Loop   ' Output RC Servo Control
 Pulseout 4, Pos   ' Variable "Pos" has Servo
 pause 18000   ' Position
 goto Loop
Comments: For BS1, Timing Granularity is 10 us.
         For BS2, Timing Granularity is 2 us.

Instruction 42.16 BS1/BS2 "puslout pin, time" instruction.

42

PARALLAX: BASIC STAMP

Instruction: "Button Pin,down,delay, rate,bytevar,target,label"   **Bits:** N/A

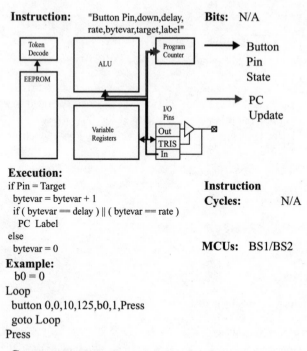

Button
Pin
State

PC
Update

Execution:
if Pin = Target
  bytevar = bytevar + 1
  if (bytevar == delay) || (bytevar == rate)
    PC Label
else
  bytevar = 0

**Instruction
Cycles:**   N/A

MCUs: BS1/BS2

Example:
  b0 = 0
Loop
  button 0,0,10,125,b0,1,Press
  goto Loop
Press

Comments:

Instruction 42.17 BS1/BS2 "button" instruction.

Instruction: "count, pin, period, var"   **Bits:** N/A

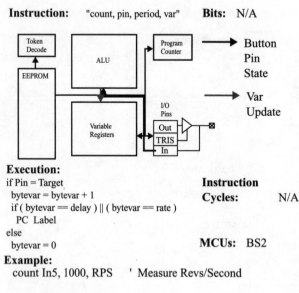

Button
Pin
State

Var
Update

Execution:
if Pin = Target
  bytevar = bytevar + 1
  if (bytevar == delay) || (bytevar == rate)
    PC Label
else
  bytevar = 0

**Instruction
Cycles:**   N/A

MCUs: BS2

Example:
  count In5, 1000, RPS   ' Measure Revs/Second

Comments:

Instruction 42.18 BS2 "count pin, period, var" instruction.

Serial I/O

Being able to communicate with other devices is very critical for all computers. The Stamps have a number of built-in functions that will make serial communications (both asynchronous and synchronous) much easier to implement. At the end of this subchapter, I will present a simple application showing how these commands can be used to allow two Stamps to communicate with one another.

The primary method of serial communication for the Stamps is asynchronous data transfer (typically 8 bits long in "8-N-1" format) using the "Serin" and "Serout" commands (Instruction 42.19, Instruction 42.20, Instruction 42.21, and Instruction 42.22).

For the BS1, the data speeds (known as "mode" or "baudmode") are explicitly specified as either a symbol or a number, as shown in the table below:

NUM	SYMBOL	DATA RATE	SERIN	SEROUT	POLARITY AND OUTPUT MODE
0	T2400	2400 bps	X	X	Positive and CMOS Driven
1	T1200	1200	X	X	Positive and CMOS Driven
2	T600	600	X	X	Positive and CMOS Driven
3	T300	300	X	X	Positive and CMOS Driven
4	N2400	2400	X	X	Negative and CMOS Driven
5	N1200	1200	X	X	Negative and CMOS Driven
6	N600	600	X	X	Negative and CMOS Driven
7	N300	300	X	X	Negative and CMOS Driven
8	OT2400	2400		X	Positive and Open-Collector
9	OT1200	1200		X	Positive and Open-Collector
10	OT600	600		X	Positive and Open-Collector
11	OT300	300		X	Positive and Open-Collector
12	ON2400	2400		X	Negative and Open-Collector
13	ON1200	1200		X	Negative and Open-Collector
14	ON600	600		X	Negative and Open-Collector
15	ON300	300		X	Negative and Open-Collector

Note that data can be transmitted as either CMOS logic or open-collector (actually open-drain). This means that multiple devices can be put onto a pulled-up net as "Dotted AND" logic. Also, data can be received with either positive or negative polarity. Both of these features are really nice to have to allow an informal local network or interface with RS-232 levels directly.

For the BS2, the data rate "mode" specification not only specifies the data speed but also the operating mode of the serial port as a 16-bit value. The bits are defined as:

BIT(S)	FUNCTION	COMMENTS
0-12	Data Rate	See Formula below for calculating the Data Speed
13	Packet Size	"0" - 8 Bits no parity, "1" - 7 Bits with Parity
14	Data State	"0" - Positive Logic, "1" - Negative Logic
15	Output Driver	"Serout" Only: "0" - CMOS, "1" - Open Collector

The data speed value is calculated using the equation:

```
Bits 0-12 = ( 10^6 / Data Rate ) - 20
```

This means that a wide variety of speeds up to 76,800 bps can be implemented with very little data rate error (for 38,400 bps, the error is 0.16%). For example, if you wanted to implement a 1200-bps negative data, 8-bit open collector serial transmission, the instruction below would be used:

```
serout  Bit, 813 + $C000, ["Watch me Transmit!"]
```

With the BS2 "serout" command, a wait value between characters can be specified (the default is to send a character as soon as the stop bit of the previous has been transmitted). Also, a timeout value can be specified.

If you are going to interface with RS-232 directly, make sure there is a current-limiting resistor on both the Rx and Tx lines between the Stamp and the device you are communi-

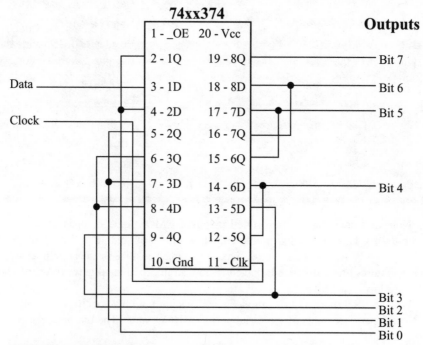

Figure 42.2 374 Wired as a serial-to-parallel converter.

cating with. As I've discussed elsewhere in the book, simply transmitting an inverted $+5V$ string to a "true" RS-232 receiver may not work.

Along with asynchronous communications, the BS2 has the capability of simple synchronous communications (Instruction 42.23 and Instruction 42.24). While these functions can be used to interface with SPI and microwire devices, I prefer to think of them as I/O pin "multipliers."

In Figure 42.2, two pins can be used to create eight output pins where only two were before:

I use this circuit a lot for converting serial data to parallel data. In Figure 42.2 I do not show output enable ("_OE") connected to anything. For a shift-out register, this should be tied to the ground pin (pin 10). For a shift-in register, to load 8 bits, "8Q" should be connected to "1D," and the "_OE" pin should be held high when the parallel data is loaded in and then pulled down to allow shifting out of the data.

For "Shiftin," the "mode" parameter determines the order of when the data is sampled and in what order (most or least significant bit sent first). The table below outlines the value and what these predefined symbols mean:

SYMBOL	VALUE	COMMENTS
MSBPRE	0	Receive MSB First, sample before clock
LSBPRE	1	Receive LSB First, sample before clock
MSBPOST	2	Receive MSB First, sample after clock
LSBPOST	3	Receive LSB First, sample after clock

For "Shiftout," data can be sent most significant bit first (which has a value of 1 and a symbol of "MSBFIRST") or the least significant bit first ("LSBFIRST" with a value of 0). In Figure 42.2, "MSBFIRST" would be specified to load the bits in the correct order.

In the other microcontroller sections, I have saved the applications for the specific chapter, but to give you an idea of how the serial interface functions worked, I wanted to create a small application. This application consists two BASIC Stamps (a BS1 and a BS2), which send data back and forth to each other.

The BS1 circuit shown in Figure 42.3 uses all eight I/O pins to control an LCD and provide serial input and output lines. The program initially writes "Waiting" to the LCD, and then when serial data is received from the BS2 (at 1200 bps), it is displayed, the character incremented, and sent back to the BS2.

The BS1 PBASIC code for this application is:

```
'   BS1STEST - Serial Test/Demo for Basic Stamp 1
'
'   This program Puts on an Initial Message and then waits for another
'     Stamp to send data to it serially at 1200 bps. When the Data is
'     Received, it is displayed and then resent on, incremented at 1200
'     bps
'
'   Myke Predko
'
'   97.09.07

symbol E    = 3              '  LCD Control Bits
```

42

PARALLAX: BASIC STAMP

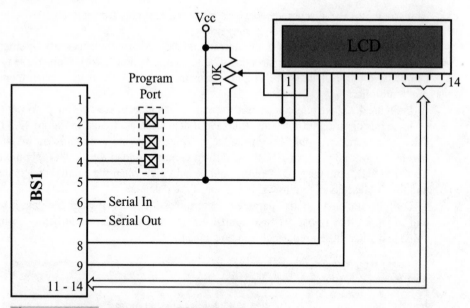

Figure 42.3 Circuit used for BS1 serial test.

```
symbol RS    = 2

symbol SIn   = 0            ' Serial Input
symbol SOut  = 1            ' Serial Output

symbol i     = b0          ' Counters
symbol j     = b1
symbol k     = b2
symbol n     = b3


' Initialize the I/O Ports

   Pins = $02               ' Make Sure everything is low Except
                            '   Serial Output
   Dirs = $FE               ' Just Bit0 is an Input

   j = 0                    ' Use "J" for RS

'  Initialize the LCD

   pause 200                ' Wait 15 msec for LCD to Initialize

   Pins = $30               ' Initialize the LCD
   pulsout E, 1
   pause 10
   PulsOut E, 1
   pause 10
   PulsOut E, 1
   pause 10

   Pins = $20               ' Enable 4 Bit Mode
   PulsOut E, 1
   PulsOut E, 1
```

```
    PulsOut E, 1

    i = $28                         '   "Set Interface Length"
    gosub LCDOut

    i = $0C
    gosub LCDOut
    i = $01
    gosub LCDOut

    i = $06
    gosub LCDOut

'   Display Initial Message

    j = $04                         '   Now, Sending Characters
    for n = 0 to 6
      lookup n, ("Waiting"), i
      gosub LCDOut
    next

Loop:

    Serin SIn, T1200, n

    j = 0                           '   Output in a Clear Screen
    i = 1
    gosub LCDOut
    pause 10

    j = $04                         '   Output the Character
    i = n
    gosub LCDOut

    n = n + 1
    Serout SOut, T1200, ( n )

    goto Loop


'   Subroutines

LCDOut:                             '   Send an Instruction

    Pins = i & $F0 + 2 + j
    k = 0
    pulsout E, 1

    Pins = i * 16 & $F0 + 2 + j
    k = 0
    pulsout E, 1

    return
```

The BS2 is very similar, but different in one important respect; the "serin" command has a timeout value (one second) which will put a "waiting" message on the LCD if nothing is received from the BS1 and then send an "A" character, which will start the incrementing and resending process. When the two circuits are hooked up, the BS2 will initiate the data transmission and continually "Ping" the BS1 if the connection is broken.

The circuit is shown in Figure 42.4.

And the code is:

```
'   BS2STEST - Serial Test/Demo for Basic Stamp 2
'
'   This program Puts on an Initial Message and then waits for another
'     Stamp to send data to it serially at 1200 bps. When the Data is
'     Received, it is displayed and then resent on, incremented at 1200
'     bps
'
'   This Program Differs from "BS1STest" by using "SHIFTOUT" to
'     Communicate with the LCD and that it uses the BS2 PBASIC to Timeout
'     on the "SERIN" and if "SERIN" times out, then a "Waiting" message is
'     put on the LCD and a "A" is sent out.
'
'   Myke Predko
'
'   97.09.07

E           con 6           '   LCD Control Bits
RS          con 7
DataOut     con 1           '   LCD Data Shifting
Clock       con 0

SeIn        con 3           '   Serial I/O Bits
SeOut       con 2

i           var byte        '   Counters
j           var byte
k           var byte
n           var byte

'   #### - Repeat what was done with the BS1

' Initialize the I/O Ports

    Out1 = 0                '   Make Sure everything is low
    Dir1 = %11000111        '   Pins 0,1,6,7,2 for Output

    j = 0                   '   Use "J" for RS

'   Initialize the LCD

    pause 200               '   Wait 15 msec for LCD to Initialize

    Shiftout DataOut, Clock, 1, [$30]
    pulsout E, 1
    pause 10
    PulsOut E, 1
    pause 10
    PulsOut E, 1
    pause 10

    Shiftout DataOut, Clock, 1, [$38]       '   "Set Interface Length"
    pulsout E, 1

    Shiftout DataOut, Clock, 1, [$0C]   pulsout E, 1

    Shiftout DataOut, Clock, 1, [$01]
    pulsout E, 1

    Shiftout DataOut, Clock, 1, [$06]
    Pulsout E, 1
```

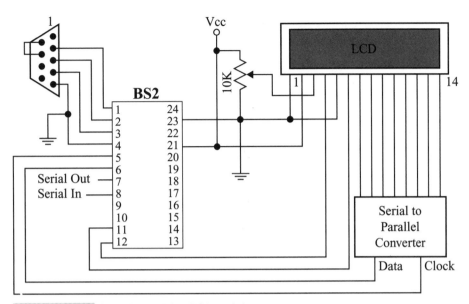

Figure 42.4 Circuit used for BS2 serial test.

```
'  Display Initial Message

NothingLoop:                ' Come Here when Nothing Coming In

  Low RS                    ' Clear the Screen
  Shiftout DataOut, Clock, 1, [1]
  Pulsout E, 1
  pause 10

  High RS                   ' Output Data Characters
  for n = 0 to 6
    lookup n, ["Waiting"], i
    Shiftout DataOut, Clock, 1, [i]
    Pulsout E, 1
  next

  j = "A"                   ' Send a New Output
  SerOut SeOut, 813, [j]

Loop:

  SerIn SeIn, 813, 1000, NothingLoop, [j]

  Low RS
  Shiftout DataOut, Clock, 1, [1]
  Pulsout E, 1
  pause 10                  ' Reset/Clear the Screen

  High RS
  ShiftOut DataOut, Clock, 1, [j]
  Pulsout E, 1

  SerOut SeOut, 813, [j + 1]

  goto Loop
```

Instruction: "Serin Bit,mode,{(Qual,...)},{#}Var,..."

Bits: N/A

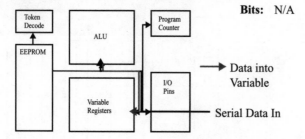

Data into Variable

Serial Data In

Execution:
```
do
  Var = RX( Pin, Mode)
  while Var != Qual
if "#Var"
  do
    Var = ( Var * 10 ) + RX( Pin, Mode )
    while '0' < Var < '9'
else
  Var = RX( Pin, Mode )
```

Instruction Cycles: N/A

MCUs: BS1

Example:

Serin Bit, N2400, i   ' Get a Character

Comments: In the Book's Text, the "mode" Parameter is defined.

Instruction 42.19 BS1 "serin pin, mode, {data.}" instruction.

Instruction: "Serout Bit,mode,({#}Data,...)"

Bits: N/A

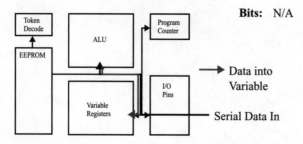

Data into Variable

Serial Data In

Execution:
```
for Count = 0 to varCount
  TX( Bit, mode, var[ count ])
```

Instruction Cycles: N/A

MCUs: BS1

Example:

Serout Bit, OT1200, "Data = ", i, $0D
       ' Send String with "i" on OC Bus

Comments: In the Book's Text, the "mode" Parameter is defined.

Instruction 42.20 BS1 "serout pin, mode, {data.}" instruction.

Instruction: "Serin Bit,mode,{to,tolabel,}[Parms]"

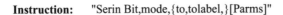

Bits: N/A

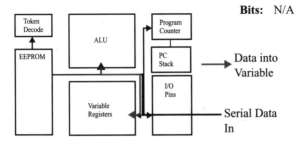

Data into
Variable

Serial Data
In

Execution:

do
  Var = RX(Pin, mode)
  while Var != "WaitParms"
do
  Var = RX(Pin, mode)

**Instruction
Cycles:**   N/A

MCUs: BS2

Example:

Serin Bit, 813 + $4000, 1000, TOLabel, [i, j]
  ' wait 1 sec to Rx two bytes at 1200 bps

Comments: In the Book's Text, the "mode"
            Parameter is defined.

Instruction 42.21 BS2 "serin pin, mode, {label}, [data.]" instruction.

Instruction: "Serout Bit,mode,{pace,}[Parms]"

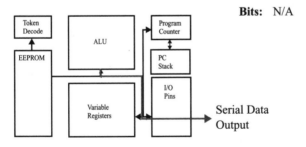

Bits: N/A

Serial Data
Output

Execution:

for Count = 0 to varCount
  TX(Bit, mode, Var[Count])
  if pace
    Dlay pace msecs
next

**Instruction
Cycles:**   N/A

MCUs: BS2

Example:

Serout Bit, 813 + $4000, 100, [i, j, cr]
  ' Send two bytes at 1200 bps with 0.1 sec
  ' between characters and follow with a $0D

Comments: In the Book's Text, the "mode"
            Parameter is defined.

Instruction 42.22 BS2 "serout pin, mode, [data.]" instruction.

42

PARALLAX: BASIC STAMP

Instruction: "Shiftin dBit,cBit,mode,[Parms]"

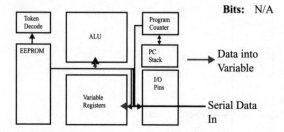

Bits: N/A

Data into
Variable

Serial Data
In

Execution:

    for Count = 0 to Bits
       while Clock == 0
       Var = (Var << 1) + dBit
       while Clock != 0
    next

**Instruction
Cycles:**   N/A

MCUs: BS2

Example:

Shiftin dBit, cBit, MSBPRE, [Var]
    ' Get 8 Bits, sample when Clock is Low

Comments: In the Book's Text, the "mode"
Parameter is defined. The Number
of Bits to Shift in are Specified in
"Parms"

Instruction 42.23 BS2 "shiftin dpin, cpin, mode, [data.]" instruction.

Instruction: "Shiftout dBit,cBit,mode,[Parms]"

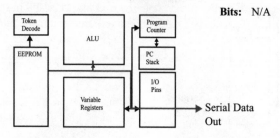

Bits: N/A

Serial Data
Out

Execution:

    for Count = 0 to Bits
       dBit = Var & 1
       CBit = 1
       CBit = 0
       Var = Var >> 1
    next

**Instruction
Cycles:**   N/A

MCUs: BS2

Example:

Shiftout dBit, cBit, MSBFIRST, [Var]
    ' Output 8 Bits, MSB First

Comments: In the Book's Text, the "mode"
Parameter is defined. The Number
of Bits to Shift in are Specified in
"Parms"

Instruction 42.24 BS2 "shiftout dpin, cpin, mode, [data.]" instruction.

There are a couple of things to note about both applications. The first is, I built in programming ports as part of the applications. This is important because it allowed me to change the applications during debug.

The second thing to notice about the applications is that I don't use the "End" function in either Stamp's source code. This is because both are in endless loops; there is no way for the code to extend beyond the current program location.

Analog I/O

You're probably wondering what kind of analog I/O capabilities the Stamp has, especially considering that it is based on the low-end PICMicros, which have no analog I/O capabilities at all. Actually, the Stamp's built-in analog I/O capabilities are quite limited but can offer some useful features. For input, the Stamp is able to determine a potentiometer's position and can output an analog voltage level through the use of a PWM and a low-pass filter.

Reading a potentiometer can be done quite simply in both the BS1 and the BS2 (Instruction 42.25 and Instruction 42.26). In the BS1, a capacitor is charged by an output pin set "high" and then changed to a low, and the amount of time for the capacitor to discharge through the potentiometer is measured.

In the BS1's "Pot" command, the amount of time the Stamp waits for the capacitor to discharge is the "scale" parameter. At full value, the internal delay will count up to 65,536 and return the count when the cap has discharged below the input threshold (1.4 volts approximately in the PIC). The "scale" parameter will allow you to tailor the POT command to be able to detect a full swing of the pot, irregardless of the actual values of the pot and capacitor combination and their tolerances.

Determining the best value for "scale" can be done by pressing "Ctrl-P" in the Stamp development system ("Stamp.Exe") with the Stamp and potentiometer attached to the programming PC. Once this is done, a window will pop up and ask you to select a pin, and then the scale value can be modified and the actual pot value will be displayed. Note that to do this, a special program is loaded into the Stamp, so after executing this and determining the appropriate value for "scale," you will have to reload the application program.

The BS2 works somewhat differently, as can be seen from Instruction 42.26. The capacitor is charged by the Stamp, and then the discharge cycle is monitored by the Stamp's PIC. The advantage of this method is that the nonlinearities of the PIC's pins do not affect the discharge cycle of the RC network. The 100-ohm resistor between the RC network and the Stamp is to ensure that short-circuit currents don't damage the I/O pin.

"RCTime" measures the discharge cycle in terms of 2-usec increments to a maximum of 65536 (and a "scale" parameter is not used). This means that the RC values must be chosen to ensure that the count isn't exceeded (if it is, i.e., more than 130 msec have gone by without the cap discharging below 1.4 volts, a zero is returned).

Looking over these two functions, you should notice one very large concern for applications that use the Stamps and are going to be built in production; each unit will have to be separately "tuned" according to the actual resistor/capacitor pairs that are connected to the Stamp. This is an unreasonable amount of effort; instead, the application should be redesigned so that it doesn't require a potentiometer for input or use a separate ADC that can be controlled by the Stamp.

Outputting analog voltages using the Stamp is carried out by using the "PWM" function. The PWM function outputs a number of digital pulses with a specified duty cycle (Instruction 42.27 and Instruction 42.28). The primary purpose of these functions is to output an analog voltage, but these instructions can be used for different applications, which require digital PWM signals.

It is important to note that the period of the PWM signal changes with the specified duty cycle, to ensure that the duty cycle is valid for different cases. This is different than in most other microcontrollers, where the period stays constant. This should not drastically affect the usefulness of the PWM function.

The most obvious nonanalog voltage output application is for driving the position of a radio control servo. The BS1's "PWM" command can be used to output 1- to 20-msec pulses (which would require "duty" to be 50 to 100 to get a full swing of the servo) with a 15-msec delay to the next pulse output. Even though it is very hard to get a precise 20-msec period between pulses in the Stamp, most servos are quite forgiving and will take varying periods. Interestingly enough, the BS2, with its 1-msec PWM period cannot control servos (although the "pulse" function can).

The PWM signal could also be used to control motors, although I don't recommend it. The low pulse frequency could set up an audible whine in the motors (to avoid this, PWM signals should be above 20 kHz).

As I was investigating the "PWM" command for this section, I wrote the following program:

```
'   PWMTest - Demonstrate how the PWM works
'
'   Simple program to try and send a PWM Signal to an LED to dim it.
'
'   Myke Predko
'   97.09.02

symbol i=b0                 ' Use "i" as a counter

  output 0                  ' LED That "fades" on and off

  output 4                  ' LED full on at all times

  low 0

  low 4

Loop:                       ' Loop Around Here for PWM

  for i = 0 to 255 step 1
  PWM 0, i, 1               ' Send out a bunch of PWM signals
  next

  for i = 255 to 0 step -1
  PWM 0, i, 1
  next

  goto Loop

  end
```

Instruction: "POT Bit, Scale, Dest"   **Bits:** N/A

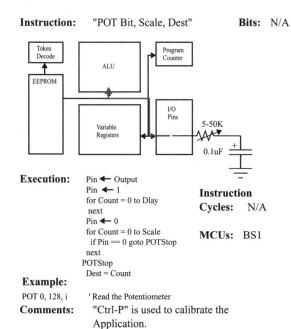

Execution: Pin ← Output
                  Pin ← 1
                  for Count = 0 to Dlay
                    next
                  Pin ← 0
                  for Count = 0 to Scale
                    if Pin == 0 goto POTStop
                    next
                  POTStop
                    Dest = Count

Instruction Cycles: N/A

MCUs: BS1

Example:

POT 0, 128, i   ' Read the Potentiometer

Comments: "Ctrl-P" is used to calibrate the
                 Application.

Instruction 42.25 BS1 "pot pin, scale, dest" instruction.

Instruction: "RCTIME Pin, state, Dest"   **Bits:** N/A

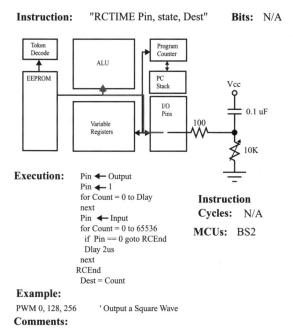

Execution: Pin ← Output
                  Pin ← 1
                  for Count = 0 to Dlay
                    next
                  Pin ← Input
                  for Count = 0 to 65536
                    if Pin == 0 goto RCEnd
                    Dlay 2us
                    next
                  RCEnd
                    Dest = Count

Instruction Cycles: N/A

MCUs: BS2

Example:

PWM 0, 128, 256   ' Output a Square Wave

Comments:

Instruction 42.26 BS2 "rctime pin, state, dest" instruction.

Instruction: "PWM Bit, duty, Cycles"   **Bits:** N/A

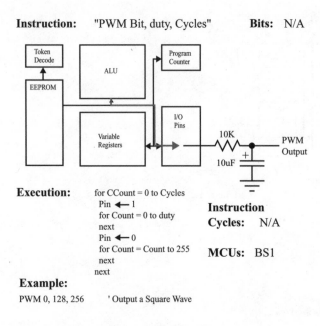

Execution: for CCount = 0 to Cycles
                   Pin ← 1
                   for Count = 0 to duty
                   next
                   Pin ← 0
                   for Count = Count to 255
                   next
                   next

**Instruction
Cycles:**   N/A

MCUs: BS1

Example:

PWM 0, 128, 256   ' Output a Square Wave

Comments: In the BS1, the PWM period is 5
                  msec.

Instruction 42.27 BS1 "pwm pin, duty, cycles" instruction.

Instruction: "PWM Pin, Duty, Cycles"   **Bits:** N/A

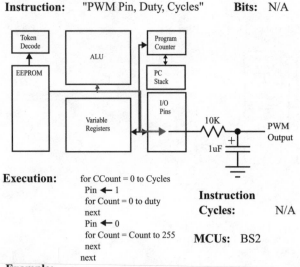

Execution: for CCount = 0 to Cycles
                   Pin ← 1
                   for Count = 0 to duty
                   next
                   Pin ← 0
                   for Count = Count to 255
                   next
                   next

**Instruction
Cycles:**   N/A

MCUs: BS2

Example:

PWM 0, 128, 256   ' Output a Square Wave

Comments: In the BS2, the PWM period is 1
                  msec.

Instruction 42.28 BS2 "pwm pin, duty, cycles" instruction.

This program has two LEDs lit, with one fading on and off due to the changing PWM duty cycles. The "fading" LED does so very smoothly and attractively. This capability of the Stamp and the PWM function could lead to some very pleasing applications.

As I said at the start of this subchapter, the analog I/O capabilities of the Stamp are quite limited and, more importantly, device-parameter specific. If you are looking at using the Stamp for any kind of volume production, and analog I/O is required, then I highly recommend using external ADCs and DACs.

Sound

The Stamp is capable of outputting sounds in a variety of different ways. While in some ways you may think that the BS1 is more flexible than the BS2 in outputting different sounds, I'm sure you'll come to the conclusion that the BS1 is actually quite limited in its ability to accurately reproduce specific notes.

When investigating the sound capabilities of the Stamps, I used the circuit shown in Figure 42.5 to hear what was actually coming out.

This circuit uses a common piezo-speaker and a cap to filter the signal. Any relatively high-impedance (15 ohms or more) speaker could be used. This circuit can also be used with other devices for outputting sound.

The BS1 "sound" function (Instruction 42.29) can be used to output a number of tones sequentially (i.e., as a tune). "Time" is given in 12-msec increments (i.e., a value of 42 will

NOTE	FREQUENCY	SOUND "NOTE" VALUE	ACTUAL FREQUENCY	ERROR
A	440 Hz	101	443.85 Hz	0.9%
A#	466	102	460.83	1.1%
B	494	104	499.00	1.0%
C	523	105	520.56	0.5%
C#	554	106	544.07	1.8%
D	587	108	598.09	1.9%
D#	622	109	629.33	1.2%
E	659	110	664.01	0.8%
F	698	111	702.74	0.7%
F#	740	112	746.27	0.8%
G	784	113	795.54	1.5%
G#	831	114	851.79	2.5%
A(H)	880	115	916.59	4.2%

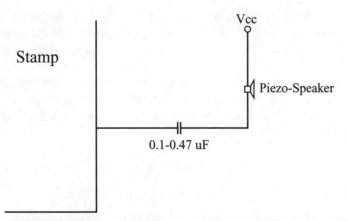

Figure 42.5 BASIC Stamp piezo-speaker output.

sound the note for approximately 500 msec, or a half second). To determine the frequency value (the "note" parameter), the following formula is used:

```
note = 127 - ((( 1 / frequency ) - 95(10^-6)) / 83(10^-6))
```

To save you the hassle of figuring out the notes for a musical tune (and then calculating the frequencies into a BS1 "sound" note value), I have created the following table of the octave around "middle" C:

At first glance, you might think that the BS1 is well designed for handling different notes (most of them are only one value different from the next one). But there will be a bit of error (especially with the tolerance of the Stamp's ceramic resonator) that may make the notes seem somewhat out of tune. In some cases, it may be hard to discern the actual tune (even though the error seems quite small) because some notes may encroach on the adjacent ones (for the "108" for D has an error of 1.9% to the target frequency, but it has an error of 3.8% to D#), especially as the notes go higher. I realize that the errors seem small, but they really are quite significant if you are trying to implement a recognizable tune.

The BS2 "Freqout" function (Instruction 42.30) will allow one or two frequencies to be output simultaneously. The frequency is specified without having to be "massaged" by a formula to get an actual counting value.

The BS2 can be used to control devices connected to DTMF decoders using the "DTMFOut" function (Instruction 42.31). When I experiemented with it, I found that the DTMF output was very faint and destructively filtered by the cap/piezo-speaker circuit shown in Figure 42.5. This means that the output should be properly filtered and amplified before using it to control external DTMF devices.

Data Tables

PBASIC has a few functions that make processing data quite easy and efficient. These functions process a byte and return specific values based on the byte. Along with these functions, there is a randomize function that can be used to provide a pseudorandom value for a given "seed." The "random" function is included in this list because it can be thought of as

Instruction: "Sound Bit, (Note, Time {,...})"

Bits: N/A

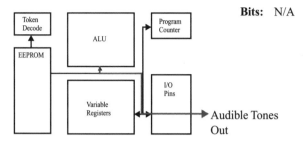

➤ Audible Tones Out

Execution:

```
for Count = 0 to NoteCount
  if Note[ Count ] == 0
    pause Time[ Count ]
  else
    for DCount = 0 to Time
      Pin ← Note[ Count ]
    next
next
```

Instruction Cycles: N/A

MCUs: BS1

Example:

Sound 7, (A, 20, B, 20, C, 20)
   ' Output a Series of Ascending Tones

Comments:

Instruction 42.29 BS1 "sound pin, (note, time {,..})" instruction.

Instruction: "FREQout Bit,Time, freq{,freq2}"

Bits: N/A

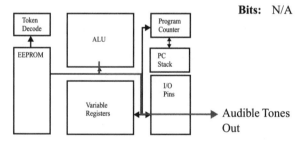

➤ Audible Tones Out

Execution:

```
for Count = 0 to Time
  Bit ← freq { + freq2 }
next
```

Instruction Cycles: N/A

Example:

FREQout 7, 500, 1000
   ' Output a 1 KHz Signal for 1/2 Second

MCUs: BS2

Comments: When Two frequencies are output
at the same time, use an amplifier
and filter for output signal.

Instruction 42.30 BS2 "freqout pin, time, freq{, freq})" instruction.

Instruction: "DTMFout Bit,{on,off,}[key,...]"

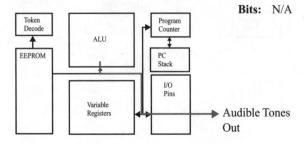

Bits: N/A

Audible Tones Out

Execution:

```
for Count = 0 to KeyCount
   Bit ← Key[Count].Freqs
next
```

Instruction Cycles: N/A

Example:

DTMFout 7, 500, 100, [1,2,1,2,5,5,5,1,2,1,2]
 ' call New York City's Directory Assistance

MCUs: BS2

Comments: Two frequencies are sent at the same time which means an amplifier and are required for the output value.

Instruction 42.31 BS2 "dtmf pin, {on, off,}[key]" instruction.

a table operation; a single value is returned for a specific value. In the Parallax PBASIC manuals, the table operations and "random" function are known as "numeric" functions.

The "lookdown" function (Instruction 42.32 and Instruction 42.33) will match a value with a table of values. This is a function I would like to have in every language (for some reason, I always end up having to write this function manually because I am trying to respond to an ASCII character). In the BS1 function example, I show how a single ASCII character can be used to specify a branch address in only two instructions.

"Lookdown" has been enhanced in the BS2 to include different types of comparisons. This actually makes it quite useful to do some funky things. In Instruction 42.33, I have commented the example as 'Find Range "i" is in'—but do you really see what is happening?

In this example, "i" is being divided by 5 and the result is being put into "j."

The "lookup" functions (Instruction 42.34 and Instruction 42.35) return a value for a given value. In the BS1 example code, I use it to simulate a read-only array (getting the offset to the values is the same as reading an array (as I've shown under "execution").

The last "data table" instruction will probably seem misplaced. The purpose of the "random" function (Instruction 42.36) is to to return a random number.

The "random" function does return a "pseudorandom" number, which means that it returns a number that is algorithmically generated from "seed" value. Actually, the "random" function takes the seed value, calculates a 16-bit number from it, and then stores it back into "seed." To explain why "random" is in this subchapter, "random" can be thought of as accessing a very large array that returns a value for a given offset into the table (which is really the "seed" value).

For the BS2 "lookup" instruction graphic (Instruction 42.35), I have shown how a random number generator can be implemented with a "lookup" table (which is the same as a single dimensional array) which takes an offset and returns a random value.

Instruction: "Lookdown Source,(value,...),Dest"

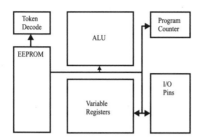

Bits: N/A

Execution:
```
for Count = 0 to ValueSize
  if Source == Value[ Count ]
    Dest = Count
    Count = ValueSize
next
```

Instruction Cycles: N/A

MCUs: BS1

Example:
```
gosub GetCommand          ' Get a Command

lookdown S, ("RST"), C     ' Translate it to an
branch C, (Run, Stop, Step) ' Address
```

Comments:

Instruction 42.32 BS1 "lookdown source, (value,..), dest" instruction.

Instruction: "lookdown Src, Cond, (value..), Dst"

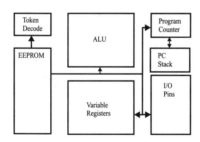

Bits: N/A

Execution:
```
for Count = 0 to ValueSize
  if Src Cond Value[ Count ]
    Dest = Count
    Count = ValueSize
next
```

Instruction Cycles: N/A

MCUs: BS2

Example:
```
lookdown i, <, ( 5, 10, 15 ), j   ' Find Range
                                  '  "i" is in
```

Comments: "Cond" can be: "+", "<>", ">", "<",
"<=", "=>" with "=" being the
default.

Instruction 42.33 BS2 "lookdown source, condition, (value,..), dest" instruction.

Instruction: "Lookup Offset,(value,...),Dest"

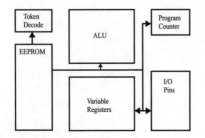

Bits: N/A

Execution:

Dest ← Value[Offset]

Instruction Cycles: N/A

MCUs: BS1

Example:

```
for i = 0 to 5      ' Output a Message
  lookup i, ("Hello"), j
  gosub Output
next
```

Comments:

Instruction 42.34 BS1 "lookup offset,(value,..), dest" instruction.

Instruction: "lookup Offset, (value,...), Dest"

Bits: N/A

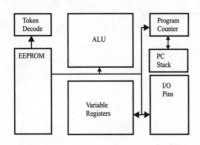

Execution:

Dest ← Value[Offset]

Instruction Cycles: N/A

MCUs: BS2

Example:

```
for i = 0 to 7
  lookup i, ( 5, 7, 2, 3, 1, 6, 4 ), j
  gosub Output         ' Output a pseudo
next                   ' Random Number
```

Comments:

Instruction 42.35 BS2 "lookup offset,(value,..), dest" instruction.

Instruction: "Random Seed"

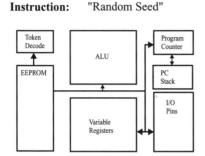

Bits: N/A

Execution:

Seed ← Random[Seed]

Instruction Cycles: N/A

MCUs: BS1/BS2

Example:

```
Loop                ' Get a Random Seed
  Seed = Seed + 1
  if Bit0 == 1 then Loop

Random Seed        'Randomize the Seed
```

Comments:

Instruction 42.36 BS1/BS2 "random seed" instruction.

However, the random number is generated from the "seed," or "offset" is really immaterial. The problem with creating random numbers in the Stamp (and all digital systems) is finding a random "seed" value. To get a random value, the "seed" also has to be random to some extent. This means that the seed value will have to be created from external sources.

An "external source" could be asking the user to input a random number, it may count the noise on a reverse-biased diode in a given amount of time, or it may use some other external event that will provide a random value. There are a lot of different methods of doing this, the point being that if you want "random" to provide truly random values all the time, the seed value will have to be generated from an external source that is nondeterministic (i.e., it can't be predicted).

EEPROM Access

One of the nice features of the Stamp is the ability to store data in the EEPROM. Not only can the EEPROM be used as extra RAM (which, as a bonus is nonvolatile and can be used as an array), it can be also be used to store messages and tables directly from the source file. Using the EEPROM can make your program much more efficient.

Before discussing how the EEPROM instructions work, I should introduce a few concepts about how data and programs are stored on the Stamp. The EEPROM in the Stamp is broken up into two pieces with an "unused" area in between. Starting at address 0 and working its way down is the data area of the EEPROM. Starting at the end of the EEPROM and working its way up, program tokens are stored. There is one very important concept to understand with the Stamp's EEPROM implementation, and that is the amount EEPROM

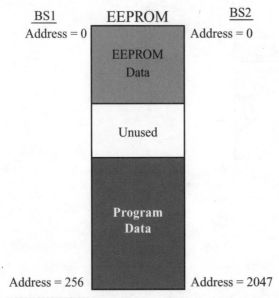

Figure 42.6 BASIC Stamp EEPROM organization.

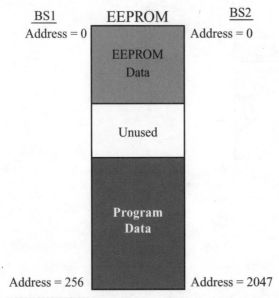

Figure 42.7 BASIC Stamp 1 download screen.

available for data is dependent on the size of the program (i.e., the larger the program, the less space that is available for data).

Determining how much space is available is not extremely hard, but it is not intuitive. For the BS1, there is only one way to find out how much space is available in the EEPROM, and that's when the program is being downloaded into the EEPROM. In the screen snapshot below, the download window is shown for the BS1. (Figure 42.7.)

When the program is being downloaded into the Stamp, a window with 32 bars appears. Once the download has completed, a number of the bars will be red in colour. In the diagram above, this is a screen shot taken from Windows/95 after "Alt-R" has been pressed, and of the 32 bars that come up in the download window, four are coloured red. This indicates that 32 bytes of the EEPROM have been used by the program and there are 224 bytes available for data storage.

In the BS2, after "Alt-R" has been pressed and source code compiled and tokens downloaded into the Stamp, "Alt-M" can be pressed, which brings up a new screen that will show you the EEPROM and RAM usage.

After determining how much EEPROM is available for data use, you can start putting things in there. As you would expect, balancing program and data is an iterative process. The most basic method of using the EEPROM is to access it as if you were accessing an array.

This is done by using the "read" and "write" (Instruction 42.37, Instruction 42.38) functions. Both of these instructions access the EEPROM using an arithmetic address (which can be generated arithmetically).

For example, if you wanted to measure the acceleration of a rocket using a BS1 and its built-in EEPROM to store the data, the following program could be used:

```
LaunchLoop               '  Wait for signal indicating Launch Start
  if bit0 = 0 then LaunchLoop

BlastOff                 '  Bit0 = 1, Launch has started
  for i = 0 to 20        '  Measure accel. for the first 2 secs of flight
    gosub AccMeasure     '  Get the current Acceleration
    write i, A           '  Save current Acceleration in EEPROM
    pause 90             '  Pause 100 msec to sample 1x every 0.1 secs
  next                   '   (this assumes that "for", "gosub", "write" &
                         '      "next" takes 10 msec)

DumpWait                 '  Flight finished, now Wait to Dump Data
  if bit1 = 1 then DumpWait

Dump                     '  Dump the contents of the EEPROM
  for i = 0 to 20
    read i, A            '  Get the Contents of EEPROM
    gosub SendData       '  Send it Out
  next
```

In the BS1, the "EEPROM" function (Instruction 42.39) is used to store multiple bytes of data at a specific location in EEPROM. The "EEPROM" function is somewhat more efficient than using multiple "write" statements. This is because a single token is used to store multiple bytes in the Stamp's EEPROM.

The BS2's "data" function (Instruction 42.40) is an extremely flexible compile time EEPROM data definition. "Data" is very similar to the "Var" statement in that resources are allocated by the compiler or can be specified by the programmer.

Instruction: "Read Addr, Variable"   **Bits:** N/A

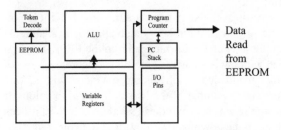

Execution: Variable ← EEPROM.Addr

Instruction Cycles: N/A

MCUs: BS2

Example:
```
for i = 0 to 4        ' Output Contents of
  read Addr + i, A    '   EEPROM
  gosub LCDOut
next
```

Comments: The maximum EEPROM Address
for "Read" in the BS1 is 255. For
the BS2, the Maximum EEPROM
Address is 2047. Note how to
determine valid EEPROM Addresses

Instruction 42.37 BS1/BS2 "read addr, variable" instruction.

Instruction: "write Addr, Variable"   **Bits:** N/A

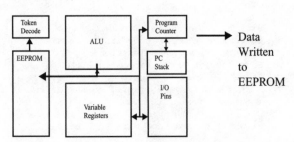

Execution: EEPROM.Addr ← Variable

Instruction Cycles: N/A

MCUs: BS2

Example:
```
gosub Sample       ' Store Sample Value in
write Addr + i, A  '   EEPROM
```

Comments: The maximum EEPROM Address
for "Write" in the BS1 is 255. For
the BS2, the Maximum EEPROM
Address is 2047. Note how to
determine valid EEPROM Addresses

Instruction 42.38 BS1/BS2 "write addr, variable" instruction.

Instruction: "EEPROM Addr, (Byte[,Byte...])"

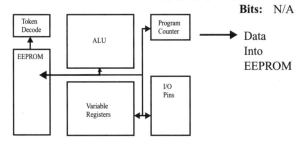

Bits: N/A

Data
Into
EEPROM

Execution:

```
for Count = 0 to #Bytes
    EEPROM.Addr+Count ⟵ Byte[ Count ]
next
```

Instruction Cycles: N/A

MCUs: BS1

Example:

EEPROM 0, ("myke")   ' Put my Name in EEPROM

Comments:

Instruction 42.39 BS1 "EEROM addr, (data..)" instruction.

Instruction: "(Label) DATA Data[,...]"   **Bits:** N/A

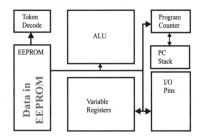

Execution: N/A

Instruction Cycles: N/A

MCUs: BS2

Example:

My_Name data "myke"   ' Store my Name in EEPROM

Comments: The BS2 Considers the "Data" Statement NOT to be a language Function, instead bytes that are set up in the Source.

Instruction 42.40 BS2 "{label} data value{, value..}" instruction.

The typical format of the "data" function is:

```
Label Data "Something to be Stored"
```

where, "Label" will be a constant assigned by the compiler which identifies the starting address where "Something to be Stored" is put into EEPROM.

The compiler's EEPROM data placement can be overruled by placing an address preceeded by an "@" character. This makes the label optional. So, if I wanted to put "Something to be Stored" at address 10 in the EEPROM, I would use the statement:

```
Data
@10, "Something to be Stored"
```

Delay

The "pause" command is used to put in a specific time delay (measured in milliseconds) into the execution of a PBASIC program. (Instruction 42.49.) When the delay has passed, execution continues with the next instruction.

If you read the Stamp documentation, you will see that Parallax indicates that the pause (and "sleep") functions are quite accurate (to " +/- 1 percent"). This is something that I would be very reluctant to count on because of the great variablity of the instructions around the pause instruction (i.e., different instructions and different parameters take different lengths of time to execute). This means that to get precise timings from the Stamp, you will have to first time the code with a nominal delay value for pause, and then by changing this value (and nothing else) you will be able to get a repeatable timing.

The "sleep" function (Instruction 42.42) will allow much larger delays (up to 65535 seconds or up to about 18 and a half hours). The "sleep" intervals are 2.3 seconds in length (the time required for the Stamp's PICMicro to be woken up by the watchdog timer) even though the delays are specified in one-second increments. The advantage of using the PICMicro "sleep" instruction for the pause in execution is the drastically reduced power requirements.

Because the PICMicro's "sleep" instruction is used with the WDT, there will be approximately 18 msecs every 2.3 seconds where the output pins are put into a tristate condition (because the WDT resets the PICMicro and disables all the outputs). This means that when you develop your application, you may have to place pull ups or pull downs on pins used for outputs to make sure the external devices don't change state during the 18-msec period of high impedance on the I/O pins.

Power/Execution Control

An extension to the delay functions are the "power/execution control" functions. Actually, the line between delay and power/execution control is quite blurred, and the functions I have identified as "delay" could be considered "power/execution" and visa-versa. For the power/execution control instructions, the Stamp (and its constituent PICMicro) are put in sleep mode.

Instruction: "Pause millseconds" **Bits:** N/A

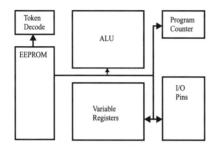

Execution: **Instruction Cycles:** N/A

Example: **MCUs:** BS1/BS2

Pause 1000 ' Delay 1 Second

Comments:

Instruction 42.41 BS1/BS2 "pause delay" instruction.

Instruction: "Sleep seconds" **Bits:** N/A

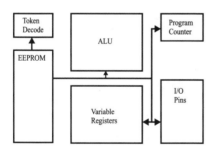

Execution: **Instruction Cycles:** N/A

Example: **MCUs:** BS1/BS2

Sleep 60 ' Delay 1 Minute

Comments: Granularity of the Instruction is 2.3 Seconds with an 18 msec interval of High-Z after each 2.3 Second Interval.

Instruction 42.42 BS1/BS2 "sleep delay" instruction.

To fully understand what happens in these instructions, you may want to go back and review what I have written about the PICMicro's "sleep" instruction and the watchdog timer. Except for "pause," all the Stamp delay and power/execution control instructions actually put the Stamp's PICMicro into "sleep" mode, which is controlled by the PICMicro's watchdog timer. When the WDT timer times out and wakes the Stamp's PICMicro out of sleep, there is a period of approximately 18 msecs in which the I/O pin outputs are disabled and the PICMicro's clock is starting up again. As noted in the previous subchapter, any critical output pins should have pull ups and pull downs on them to make sure the state doesn't change during these intervals.

The "nap" instruction (Instruction 42.43) puts the Stamp's PICMicro to sleep for a variable period of time, which is specified in the watchdog timer's prescaler. This variable period of time is provided by the "OPTION" register in the Stamp. The delay works out to be a 18 msecs times a power of two specified by the least significant three bits of the OPTION register. The delays are:

NAP VALUE	NAP TIME
0	18 msec
1	36 msec
2	72 msec
3	144 msec
4	288 msec
5	576 msec
6	1.15 sec
7	2.3 sec

While "nap" is active, all the Stamp pins stay at the same state until the period has expired, and then for 18 msec the output pins are in input (high-impedance) mode until the clock has restarted and the state has been re-established. This means that a "Nap 0" instruction will actually take 36 msec (and "Nap 1" will actually take 54 msec, and so on) because the instruction takes the sleep period plus 18 msec to restart the Stamp's PICMicro.

"End" should be used in applications where the Stamp doesn't execute in an endless loop. "End" puts the Stamp's PICMicro into "sleep" mode, to be "woken up" by the WDT once every 2.3 seconds (at which time the PICMicro is put back to sleep). "End" can only be terminated by cycling the Stamp's reset line.

The reason why an "end" (Instruction 42.44) should be put at the end of a program is because the following instructions in the Stamp's EEPROM are unknown. If you've taken the Stamp from another application, which uses more instructions, once the new application ends, it will encounter the instructions left in the EEPROM (and not end automatically). This means that the Stamp may continue executing without your understanding exactly what is happening.

Instruction: "Nap Value"   **Bits:** N/A

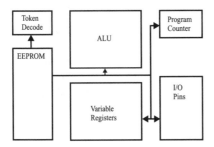

Execution:
PIC.OPTION ← Value
PIC ← Sleep

Instruction
Cycles: N/A

Example: **MCUs:** BS1/BS2

Nap 6   ' Delay Approx 1 Second

Comments: Nap Time is 18 msec * 2 ** Value

Instruction 42.43 BS1/BS2 "nap delay" instruction.

Instruction: "End"   **Bits:** N/A

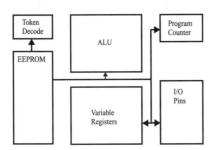

Execution:
PIC.OPTION ← 7
PIC ← Sleep

Instruction
Cycles: N/A

Example: **MCUs:** BS1/BS2

End   ' Program End Here

Comments: Stamp Outputs turn to Inputs every
2.3 msec (approx) for 18 msec

Instruction 42.44 BS1/BS2 "end" instruction.

42

PARALLAX: BASIC STAMP

Debug

The "debug" function of the Stamp is a method of displaying data on the host PC during program execution. "Debug" allows simple messages and variable contents to be displayed on the PC's screen (in a "debug window" that pops up when a debug statement is executed and the Stamp is connected to the host PC). Despite the apparent ease of use, this function has a few points to fully understand before you can use it to display data as you expect it.

The BS1 "debug" function (Instruction 42.45) has a few quirks that you should be aware of. "Debug" takes the form:

```
debug data[, data ... ]
```

Which means that information such as:

```
debug "Last A = ", #A
```

will output the message, followed by the value of the register referenced by "A." The leading "#" turns off the debug statement from printing " A =." So, if the line above didn't have the "#" before "A." The output would be (if "A" contained 37):

```
Last A = A = 37
```

There are other modifiers that will specify how the data is to be output. "$" will output the data as hex, "%" will output the data as binary, and "@" will output the data as an ASCII character. The "cr" and "cls" values will start a new line and clear the debug window, respectively.

Instruction: Debug var[,var...]   **Bits:**   N/A

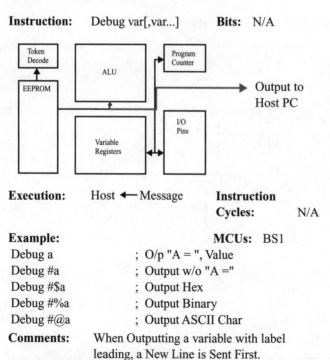

Execution: Host ◄─ Message   **Instruction Cycles:**   N/A

Example: **MCUs:**   BS1
Debug a   ; O/p "A = ", Value
Debug #a   ; Output w/o "A ="
Debug #$a   ; Output Hex
Debug #%a   ; Output Binary
Debug #@a   ; Output ASCII Char
Comments: When Outputting a variable with label
                 leading, a New Line is Sent First.

Instruction 42.45 BS1 "debug var[, var..]" instruction.

If "#" is not specified, a new line (carriage return and line feed) is sent to the "debug window" of the host PC before the variable name, value. This can lead to some unexpected formatting of the window. No new line command is sent after the value is output, except if the "cr" value is sent explicitly.

The "BS1 Emulator" I created in the "Example Stamp Applications" chapter does execute the BS1 PBASIC "debug" function properly. You may want to play around with that to see how "debug" works under different circumstances.

"Debug" in the BS2 (Instruction 42.46) works similarly to the BS1, but the output data is specified differently (due to the differences in how the memory is organized and accessed). Instead of the simple prefixes of the BS1 "debug" function, the BS2 uses descriptive prefixes before the variable name:

PREFIX	PARM	DESCRIPTION
asc?	byte	Show ASCII of Variable with Variable Name
str	byte[\n]	Output String to Zero or "n" characters
rep	value\n	Output value "n" times
dec[1-5]	value	Output Decimal or specific Decimal Digit
sdec[1-5]	value	Output Signed Decimal or specific Digit
hex[1-5]	value	Print Value in Hex, or Digit
shex[1-5]	value	Print Signed Hex or Digit
i[s]hex[1-5]	value	Print "$" before Hex or Digit
bin[1-4]	value	Print Binary Value or Specific Digit
sbin[1-16]	value	Print Signed Value in Binary or Digit
i[s]bin[1-16]	value	Print "%" before Binary or Digit

If the "?" character is put after the prefix, the variable name will be included (if applicable). The BS2 "debug" statement will accept operator expressions (i.e., "a + b / c") instead of straight variables, which can make the output data more meaningful.

The BS2 "debug" statement also has the following special control characters:

STRING	VALUE	DESCRIPTION
cls	0	Clear the Debug Window
home	1	Return Cursor to Home Position
bell	7	Beep the Host Speaker
bksp	8	Backspace
tab	9	Advances to the Next 8 column
cr	13	New Line

Instruction: debug data[, data...]   **Bits:** N/A

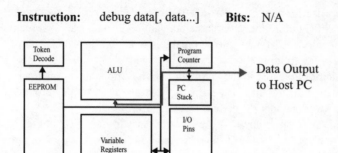

Execution: Host Message   **Instruction**
                                      Cycles: N/A

Example: **MCUs:** BS2
Debug dec? a   ; "A = " Value
Debug "A = ", Hex a   ; "A = " $Value

Comments:

Instruction 42.46 BS2 "debug var[, var..]" instruction.

"Debug" is not a method for communicating with a PC (or other type of terminal) during application execution. There is no way of sending data to the executing Stamp, and the incoming data can only be read by the editor/compiler/downloader. If the Stamp is to communicate with the host device, the "Serin" and "Serout" commands should be used.

EXAMPLE STAMP APPLICATIONS

CONTENTS AT A GLANCE

To develop the BASIC Stamp applications shown in this book, the "BASIC Stamp Programming Package" (Parallax P/N 27200) was used (Figure 43.1). This package consists of a BS1C programming cable, BS2C serial programming cable, and a diskette containing BS1 (Version 2.0) and BS2 (Version 2.1) programming software (along with software for programming a PIC 16C58 with PBASIC). To facillitate programming, I purchased the BS1-IC carrier board and BS2-IC carrier board.

First Stamp Application

Like the other microcontrollers, the first application I tried was to flash an LED on and off. This was easily done with a BS1 and the Stamp BASIC program:

```
'  myke's First Stamp Program
'
'  97.05.10 - Flash an LED
'
   Dirs = %00000001      '  Just Have Bit 0 as Output

Loop:                    '  Come Back here each second

   Pins = 1

   PAUSE 500             '  Wait another 1/2 Second Before Turning On

   Pins = 0

   PAUSE 500             '  Wait 1/2 Second Before Turning off the LED

   goto Loop             '  Loop forever
```

This software is obviously very simple and could be improved quite a bit, but it was a good start. The code turns off the LED, waits a half second (PAUSE 500), turns on the LED, and waits another half second before looping around and repeating the process. +5 volts was applied to pin 5 (bypassing the built in regulator) and ground connected to pin 2. A 220-ohm resistor and LED combination was attached to bit 0 (pin 7) and Vcc.

One of the first things I noticed was that by putting in a three-pin 0.100" header into the prototype circuit connected to pins 2, 3, and 4, I could dispense with the carrier board altogether. Looking over the BS2 programming specification, I would do the same thing as well with a D-9F shell hand wired. As I have said, you can really do without the Stamp prototype cards in most applications if you put in the three-pin IDC connector for the BS1 and the nine-pin "D-Shell" connector for the BS2 on the application circuit. By putting in these

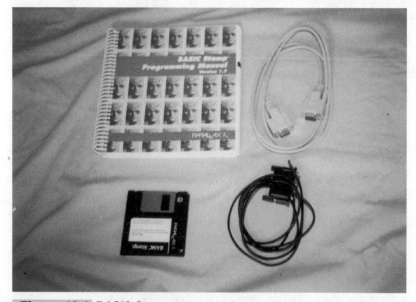

Figure 43.1 BASIC Stamp programming package.

connectors, you can program your Stamps in circuit and avoid plugging and replugging into the prototype cards.

With this program running, I then went on to do the "First MCU Application," which is an LED flashing on and off once per second (half second on and half second off). The circuit used is shown in Figure 43.2.

In Figure 43.2, the placement of the LEDs and switch are only for convenience. Placing each of the three components as far away from each other made the circuit easier to prototype.

In the other microcontrollers, the half-second delay for the LED is created within an interrupt handler. Because the STAMP doesn't have any interrupts, a variable counter and the knowledge that each line takes approximately 0.5 msec of time was used. This meant that for a half second, 1000 lines would have to be executed. With this background, I was able to write the program:

```
'  myke's Second Stamp Program
'
'  97.05.10 - Flash an LED, but Don't use Pause Instruction
'           - Poll Switch and Use to Light Second LED


  Dirs = %00010001       '  Bit 0 & Bit 4 as Outputs

symbol LED1 = Pin0       '  Just Work with the Single Bit
symbol LED2 = Pin4
symbol SW = Pin7         '  Input Switch

symbol i =  W1           '  Define the Counter

  i = 0
```

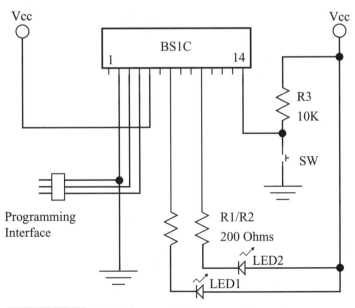

Figure 43.2 BASIC Stamp 1 first application schematic.

```
Loop:                       '  Come Back here each second

  LED2 = SW                 '  Pass the Switch Value to LED

  i = i + 1                 '  Increment the Count

  IF i < 333 THEN Loop      '  Loop Until 1/2 Second Up

  LED1 = LED1 ^ 1           '  After Waiting a 1/2 Second, Flip LED

  i = 0                     '  Reset Counter

  goto Loop                 '  Loop forever
```

In the basic "Loop:" there are three instructions. So 333 loops have to be executed before, to get the number of loops before "flipping" the LED1 bit. Please note that I have not accurately timed this; it just seemed like a good looping delay when I first tried it out.

In the circuit, when the button is pressed, the input pin (pin 7) is pulled to ground, which is passed to LED2 directly. This is a very simple method of passing input to an output bit (if the bit had to be inverted, the line "LED2 = SW ^ 1" could have been used).

Clock/Thermometer Application

Implementing the digital clock/thermometer with the hardware that I have specified (namely the LCD and DS1820) is actually very difficult in the BASIC Stamp (both the BS1 and BS2). While I was not able to complete this application, I will detail what the problems were and some ideas for solving them. I should point out that my original goal was to create this application for the BS1. I was not able to come up with a way of actually completing the application, although I was able to get the different pieces working.

The biggest problem with this application was communicating with the DS1820 digital thermometer. The DS1820's single wire interface causes several problems with trying to wire a Stamp (both BS1 and BS2) up to it. This is due to the relatively high-speed data transfers required.

To send a "1," a pulse less than 15 usecs is required, and sending a "0" requires a pulse about 30 usecs long. Neither of these pulse lengths is a problem when the Stamp is communicating to the DS1820. (The "pulsout" function in the BS1 can output a pulse as short as 10 usecs and as long as 65 seconds.)

The problem appears when the Stamp is going to read back the value from the DS1820. There is no pulse and read command (and doing it as separate instructions cannot be accomplished in less than 10 usecs, which is what would be required with the DS1820), but I did get the interface to work with the circuit shown in Figure 43.3.

When this circuit is set up, "PinOut" is set as an output pin, outputting a "0," and "PinIn" is simply left as an input pin.

In this circuit, after a 10-usec pulse is output, the "'D' Flip Flop" is latched with the value on the line 20 usecs later. So, if this line is being held low by the DS1820, then it will be latched into the "'D' Flip Flop." The 20-usec delay was made up of six 74HC04 inverter gates wired in series to delay the signal coming out of the Stamp.

To output data, I created the following subroutine:

```
DSSend:                          '  Send a Byte to the DS1820

  Count = 8                      '  Send 8 Bits
DSS_Loop:                        '  Loop Here for Each Bit
  Temp = A & 1                   '  Get the LSB
  A = A / 2                      '  Divide "A" by 2 to Get the Next Bit
  if Temp = 0 then DSS_Zero      '  If zero, Send Zero
    pulsout PinOut, 10           '  1 - Send out a 10 usec Pulse
    goto DSS_Skip
DSS_Zero:                        '  Send a Zero Bit
    pulsout PinOut, 30           '  0 - Send out a 30 usec Pulse
DSS_Skip:
  Count = Count - 1
  if Count > 0 then DSS_Loop     '  Loop Around 8 Times
  return                         '  Return to Caller
```

To read a byte, similar code (although simpler) is used:

```
DSRead:                          '  Read 8 Bits from the DS1820

  Count = 8                      '  Read 8 Bits
```

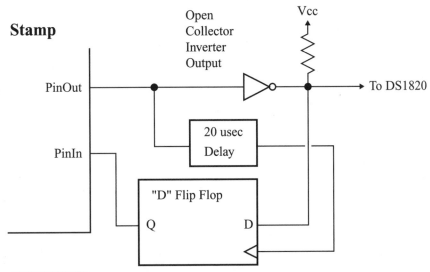

Figure 43.3 Stamp/DS1820 interface wiring.

```
A = 0                         '  Clear the Return Register

DSR_Loop:                     '  Return Here for Each Bit

 A = A / 2                    '  Move the Bits Down

 puslout PinOut, 10           '  Initiate the Bit Read

 A = PinIn * $80 + A          '  Store the Bit Read Back as the High Bit

 Count = Count - 1

 if Count > 0 then DSR_Loop   '  Read 8 Bits

 return                       '  Return to Caller
```

This code takes advantage of PBASIC's order of operations (where everything goes to the right). In "DSRead," when reading back a bit in other languages, I would probably use the statement:

$$A = A + (\text{PinIn} * \$80)$$

Because it's easier for me to understand when I first see it.

This line takes the "PinIn" bit and moves it to bit 7 before adding it to the read in variable.

The 500-usec reset pulse can be simply implemented in this hardware by executing the statement:

```
pulsout PinOut, 500
```

This code leads to the problem in the BS1 of using a number of the subroutine "gosubs" (of which only 16 are available). In the basic operation, at least six "gosubs" will be used for reading the temperature (sending $CC $44 and then $CC $BE before reading back the SP0 and SP1 registers). If you look around a bit, there are other DS1820 interfaces for the Stamps available on the Internet.

The next problem to be overcome centers around interfacing to an LCD. While I could do a 3-, 6-, or 10-pin interface (the 10-pin interface would require a BS2), I would probably go with a serial-LCD interface of which there are a lot on the market and only require one I/O pin from the Stamp. (Check the Wirz Electronics "SLI" at http://www.wirz.com—this is one of the cheapest and most full-functioned ones available on the market.)

With this out of the way, the last problem was being able to tell the time. As I have repeatedly said in this section, the BASIC Stamp cannot be used for accurate time delays. This means that an external real-time clock has to be connected to the device (I played around with a DS1307).

With the problems identified and sample code written, why didn't I do the application? The honest reason why was, I couldn't get it to all work together in a BS1 and then I couldn't get the port to work on the BS2.

Even though I did not get the application running, I was able to gain a new perspective on the Stamp and that is it's not a toy or a learning tool. It can be used very effectively as a "what if" tool. If you are trying out a new application or want to interface to a new device, I highly recommend using the BASIC Stamp. The ease of programming and fast compilation and downloading really is a bonus. If you are going to use the Stamp as a "what if" tool, always remember to include the programming interface as part of the application to allow easy updating (without having to pull the device out of the application every time you want to try new code).

BS1 Emulator

For me, one of the most interesting projects for a microcontroller is to come up with an emulator for it. (Figure 43.4.) I was able to create one for the PIC, and I wanted to do something like that for this book. As I was going through the BASIC Stamp write up, I realized that the BS1 would be an excellent device to create an emulator for; there were a few aspects of the BS1 I wanted to understand better, and this seemed to be an excellent way to do it.

As the emulating device, I choose the BS2 and created the circuit shown in Figure 43.5 for the emulator:

This circuit provides an RS-232 programming/operating interface to a host PC. Actually, this was a nice way to do it because the BS2 used as the emulator could be reprogrammed in the emulator circuit without having to remove it. The LED was designed to flash if the emulator was not in contact with the host program. When I built this circuit, I designed a simple raw card to be used with it (see Figure 43.4). This circuit could also be simply wired to a "veroboard" for your prototyping.

The host PC runs the emulator software (under a DOS command line) and downloads I/O commands to the BS2 in the emulator circuit. Along with displaying the code and giving you a window into the register contents, the current "debug" function output can be displayed. Right now, the "BSEMU.EXE" program only supports single stepping. (Figure 43.6.)

The "BSEMU" emulator supports assignment statements which do not access pin bits (although byte I/O works well), along with the full BS1 "debug," "end," "goto," "gosub," "return," "if," "branch," "for," and "next" PBASIC functions. Actually, I used the emulator as a way for me to learn how these functions worked. (Once I had

Figure 43.4 BS1 emulator circuit board (with BS2 on the card).

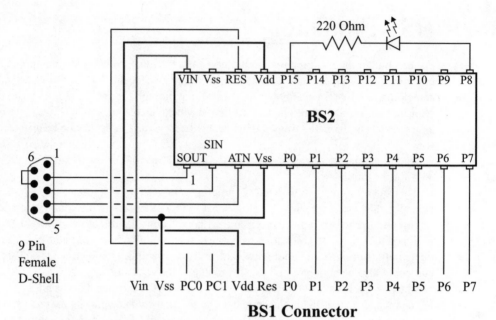

Figure 43.5 BASIC Stamp 1 emulator circuit.

an understanding of the basic functions, it was pretty smooth sailing to understand how the others worked.)

What I have described here is really a PBASIC simulator with a hardware I/O interface. This hardware interface is similar to how the 68HC05J1A "J1CS" pod works. The interesting aspects of the application are in regards to interfacing the PC host to the BS2. I wanted to have as fast and as robust an interface as possible with no connects detected and reconnects allowing "BSEMU" to continue to operate. For the most part, I have achieved this goal (although if you start up "BSEMU.EXE" without a BS2 with the proper software loaded into it, you won't be able to get into the emulator, and on some PCs running under Windows/95, the code locks up if the emulator isn't present at start up).

The PC-to-BS2 interface is what I consider to be the real "magic" of the application. Going back in this section and looking at the BS2 schematic page, you'll see that it uses a single-transistor/two-resistor RS-232 interface where the negative voltage of the signal coming in is used for the negative voltage of the signal going out. In this circuit, anything sent by the PC will be echoed back to the PC.

When I "ping" the BS2, I send a $0FF character at 9,600 bps to the BS2 and look at what is returned (if anything). If the BS2 is operating properly, it will be polling its pin 16 (the serial port) at 76,800 bps, and when a character comes through, the BS2 replies by "pulling" down the signal to a "0," which changes the echo going back to the PC. (Figure 43.7.)

This is similar to using the PC host's serial receiver like a "dotted AND" bus. If the BS2 is on the bus and running properly, then the host PC will receive a different character than it sent out. This allows the PC host to detect whether or not the BS2 is attached to the serial line and whether or not the BS2 is power up and running.

```
MS-DOS Prompt - BSEMU                                                    _ B X
            Step(F8)   reseT   rEgs(F2)                    Debug   Quit(F3)  ↑
'   TEST3,BAS - Program to TePort Pins  $00 abilities of the BSEMU
'                                Dirs  $00
'   Myke Predko                W0  B0  $00
'   97.07.07 - Next Version,        B1  $00 nd "for"
'                               W1  B2  $00
                                    B3  $00
symbol a=b0                    ' FW2 B4  $00 ust works with DEBUG Statement
symbol b=b1                         B5  $00
symbol c=b2                    W3  B6  $00
                                    B7  $00
a = 7                          ' DW4 B8  $00 h Values
                                    B9  $00
b = a * 2                      W5  B10 $00
                                    B11 $00
goto PrintHere                 ' SW6 B12 $00 ast Check
                                    B13 $00
SetupC:                        '   Now, Setup "C"

c = a * 3 + b * 7

goto  HaveC

PrintHere:
```

Figure 43.6 BSEMU screen.

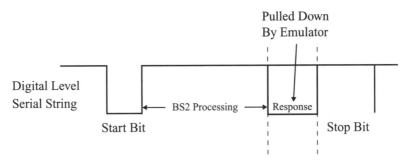

Figure 43.7 BASIC Stamp 1 emulator ping.

In this application, I "ping" the BS2 once every 18.2 msecs using the PC's real-time clock interrupt. The BS2 code is continually waiting for data to come over the serial port and responds by pulling the line down. If the host software doesn't detect this, it puts a red "X" in the top right-hand corner of the screen. If everything is working properly, then a white upward-pointing arrow is displayed.

With this protocol, I can read and write to the BS2 in roughly 5 msecs, which is a bit slower than what the BS1 is capable of running at, but probably not enough to matter for most applications (the high speed of the PC when it executes code will more than make up for this delay).

The file "SERIAL.ASM" in the "\Stamp\BSEMU" subdirectory of the CD-ROM is the 8086 assembler code used to provide the PC host's communication with the BS2. This is my *typical* 8086 assembler programming, and I apologize if it's hard to understand. In the I/O read and write, I had to put in some delays (as measured by sending a character in the serial port's "loop" mode to make sure the BS2 has time to execute the information neccesary to execute the instruction).

The current state of the software is pretty primitive; as I said, this application was really used to help me understand and characterize how PBASIC functions work in the BS1. While I don't have any plans to enhance it from the current state, if there are requests for me to do it, I will be happy to upgrade the emulator's functionality.

The "BSEMU" has the following "todo" list of things to look at:

1. Look at replacing the BS2 with a PIC. As well as making the emulator cheaper, some BS1 I/O functions (most notably the "pot" function), which may not work with the BS2, will be guaranteed to work.
2. Find the reason why the PC host "BSEMU" code locks up under the Windows 95 DOS command line if the BS2 is not present.
3. Upgrade the PC host "BSEMU" code to allow applications to run at full speed and provide breakpoints.

STAMP SUMMARY

CONTENTS AT A GLANCE

The Parallax BASIC Stamps are excellent devices to first get into microcontrollers. With the device's simple programming language and ease of use, I wouldn't hesitate to recommend it for use in teaching high-school-level students the fundamentals of programming and logic interfacing. Also, the plethora of applications and support available for the Stamp provide a good range of ideas and example code for your use.

The three most serious downsides to the Stamp for complex applications are the nondeterministic instruction timing, nonorder of operations programming, and lack of interrupts. As shown in the examples, the instruction timing can be approximated to 2,000 lines per second for the Stamp 1 and 4,000 lines per second for the Stamp 2, but, as the saying goes, your mileage may vary. The nonorder of operations programming can be a problem if you've been programming traditional languages (which compile operations in a predefined order). Neither of these issues are serious, but will make the back-end work more complex, requiring more in-depth debug and "tuning" of the application.

The programming language can be considered to be quite primitive (lacking in the array data type for the BS1, primarily evaluating expressions from left to right and not having symbolic debugging or single-stepping), but is a good introduction to programming and microcontroller application development. The simplicity of the language is a definite plus because it allows you to develop and test ideas very easily and quickly.

There are some significant advantages to the Stamp in terms of application development. Stamps are in-system programmable by design and only require a single +5-volt supply (which can be provided by a battery), which means they can be built into an application very simply. One thing I have not mentioned is the speed of the PBASIC compiler software and download speed. You will definitely not feel like trying something out because you have to wait a long time for the Stamp to be loaded; the Parallax development software runs very quickly and programs the Stamp in very short order.

While the Stamp does have some deficiencies relative to the other devices presented in this book in terms of speed and I/O capabilities, it is not a toy. I am amazed at the wealth of serious projects that have been implemented on the Stamp that really validate its use as a "what if" tool. If you are inclined to dismiss it as a toy or learning tool, take a look at the "List of Stamp Applications" (L.O.S.A.) and see what people have been doing with the BASIC Stamp; I think you'll be surprised at what it can do.

BASIC Stamp Resources

Along with my traditional sources of Stamp information, you might want to check out *Nuts and Volts* magazine's "Stamp Applications" column every month (actually, the Stamp is the only microcontroller that has a monthly column devoted to it). The Stamp manuals, which have many application notes showing how to interface the Stamp to a variety of different devices, is also another excellent source of applications and interface ideas that you can use.

WEB SITES
http://www.paralaxinc.com

- Stamp manuals and development software.
- Pointers to distributors and other links.

http://www.radioshack.com/sw/swb

- Radio Shack's BASIC Stamp page.
- Example applications.
- Some Q & As.

http://www.hth.com/losa.com

- The "List of Stamp Applications."
- Look at what other people have done with the STAMP (with addresses to contact them with).

- Tell other people what you have done.

http://www.albany.net/~pjmac/stamp.

- List of searchable Stamp applications.

LISTSERVERS

Parallax provides a very active listserver for the BASIC Stamp. To subscribe, go to Parallax's Web site (http://www.parallaxinc.com), go to "links," and follow the information for subscribing to the list.

COMPANIES

Parallax, Inc.
3805 Atherton Road, Suite 102
Rocklin, CA 967651(888)512-1024 or (916)624-8333
Fax: (916)624-8003
email: infor
@parallaxinc.com
//www.parallaxinc.com

IN CLOSING

FINAL WORDS

I hope that this book can be used as a tool for deciding which is the "best" microcontroller for a given application. I have tried to describe the important features (both hardware and processor architecture) and point out any advantages or problems of each microcontroller. I have also tried to provide you with a reasonable amount of resources to help you with developing your applications.

When I first started this book, I thought it would be interesting to write about what I thought was the perfect 8-bit microcontroller (and it would give me a standard with which to compare the other devices presented in this book). I knew that I would be reviewing five radically different processor architectures with a variety of peripheral I/O features, and I wanted to see if there was an architecture that most closely matched my "ideal." I actually spent a few weeks and came up with some interesting ideas.

What I was hoping to do was create a device that would be easy to program in assembly and a high-level language, be simple, and have fast memory and peripheral register I/O. But at the end of the three weeks, I discovered that I had to make some trade-offs in various areas to fit in different features. The result was 30 pages outlining a device that had features allowing certain applications to run well but did not hit a "home run" by any stretch of the imagination.

Some of the concepts I wanted to put forward included: a "do-everything timer" that could run in several different modes without significant processor overhead, an idea where a single instruction bit could be devoted to masking interrupts, a processor where all instructions execute in one instruction cycle regardless of the path taken, and an array of stacks used to provide a method of fast task switching for Harvard architectures. All are very worthwhile ideas, but the limiting factor was the lack of a processor architecture that would allow fast and consistent access to peripheral registers, data memory, and control store under all circumstances.

At the end of writing this book, I was able to go back with quite a bit of newfound wisdom and knowledge and examine what I had done and compare it to the other devices to see if I could improve on the design. In each device, the problems that I was trying to tackle were dealt with in different ways, allowing some specific applications to run very quickly and be easy to code, while other applications would be less efficient.

This validated the assertion made throughout this book; there is not one microcontroller or architecture that is "best" for all applications. In the various example applications and code you will see many different sections of code that are incredibly efficient in some microcontrollers and are slow and difficult to implement in others.

In my PIC book (*Programming and Customizing the PIC Microcontroller,* also published by McGraw-Hill), I asked for questions and comments to be directed toward me on the PIC listserver. For this book, if you have any questions or comments, also direct them through the appropriate listserver. The questions you ask may help others.

I look forward to hearing from you and seeing what you come up with when developing your own microcontroller applications.

Myke Predko

APPENDIX A

Appendix A Microcontroller Comparison Chart

DEVICE	FAMILY	MANUFACTURER	CONTROL STORE/RAM	SPEED RANGE	I/O PINS	ADDITIONAL FEATURES
8OC31	8051	Intel	0 KB/128	0.5-12 MHz	14	Int/Tmr/Ser/Ext
8OC51	8051	Intel	4 KB/128	3.5-20 MHz	32	Int/Tmr/Ser/Ext
AT89S2051	8051	Atmel	2 KB/128	0-24 MHz	15	Int/Tmr/Ser/Cmp/Fla
DS80C310	8051/HSM	Dal. Semi.	0 KB/256	0-33 MHz	14	Int/Tmr/Ser/Ext
DS87C520	8051/HSM	Dal. Semi.	16 KB/256	0-33 MHz	32	Int/Tmr/Ser/Ext
DS5000	8051/Secure	Dal. Semi.	0 KB/256	0-16 MHz	32	Int/Tmr/Ser/Ext
68HC05BD	68HC05	Motorola	3.75 KB/128-256	0-4 MHz	24	Int/Tmr/Ser/Syn
68HC05Cx	68HC05	Motorola	0-16 KB/176-512	0-4 MHz	18-29	Int/Tmr/Ser
68HC05CC	68HC05	Motorola	16KB-31.5KB/544-928	0-4 MHz	31	Int/Tmr/Ser/CC/Syn
68HC05E	68HC05	Motorola	4KB-16KB/128-368	0-4 MHz	20-47	Int/Tmr/Ser/PLL
68HC05G	68HC05	Motorola	8K-32K/176-1024	0-4 MHz	40-48	Int/Tmr/Ser/PWM
68HC05J	68HC05	Motorola	0.5K-2K/32-128	0-4 MHz	10-14	Int/Tmr
68HC05L	68HC05	Motorola	4K-16K/128-512	0-4 MHz	34-39	Int/Tmr/LCD
68HC05MC	68HC05	Motorola	3.5K/176	0-4 MHz	22	Int/Tmr/PWM
12C5xx	PIC/Low	Microchip	512-1024 Words/25-41	0-4 MHz	3-6	Tmr/ISP/Brn
16C5x	PIC/Low	Microchip	384-2K Words/25-73	0-20 MHz	12-20	Tmr
16C55x	PIC/Mid	Microchip	5I2-2K Words/80-128	0-20 MHz	13	Tmr/Int/ISP

16C62x	PIC/Mid	Microchip	5l2-2K Words/80-128	0-20 MHz	13	Tmr/Int/ISP/Cmp
16C6x	PIC/Mid	Microchip	2K-8K Words/128-368	0-20 MHz	22-33	Tmr/Int/ISP/Ser/Brn
16C7x	PIC/Mid	Microchip	512-8K Words/128-368	0-20 MHz	13-33	Tmr/Int/ISP/Ser/Brn/ADC
16F84	PIC/Mid	Microchip	1K Words/68	0-20 MHz	13	Tmr/Int/ISP/Fla
16C9xx	PIC/Mid	Microchip	4K Words/ 176	0-8 MHz	52	Tmr/Int/ISP/Ser/LCD
17Cxx	PIC/High	Microchip	2K-16K Words/	0-33 MHz	33	Tmr/Int/Ex
1200	AVR/Low	Atmel	512 Words/ 32	0-16 MHz	15	Tmr/Int/Ser/Cmp/ISP/Fla
8515	AVR/Full	Atmel	4K Words/544	0-16 MHz	32	Tmr/Int/Ser/Cmp/ISP/Ext/Fla
BS1	BASIC Stamp	Parallax	256 Bytes/12	N/A	8	Tmr/Ser/ADC/ISP

Legend:

ADC - Analog to Digital Converter
Brn - Brown Out Protection
Cmp - Analog Voltage Comparator
Ext - External Memory Interface
Fla - Flash Control Store/Data
Int - Interrupts
ISP - InSystem Programing
LCD - LCD Controller
PLL - Phased Locked Loop Clock Synthesizor
PWM - Pulse Width Modulated Output
Ser - Serial I/O
Syn - Video Synch Pulse Interface
Tmr - Timer

RESOURCES

Throughout the book, I have provided you with my favorite Web sites for different products as well as the contact information for the various device manufacturers. Before ending the book, I wanted to leave you with a number of other sites, resources, and companies that are available to help you out.

Please note that these addresses (mail, e-mail, and Web) may change without notice.

Contacting the Author

I can be contacted by sending a note to "emailme@myke.com," or visit my Web site at:
http://www.myke.com

But, as I've said elsewhere, for technical questions or suggestions, contact me through the appropriate listserver so that the information can be made available to a much larger audience.

Periodicals

Here are a number of magazines that do give a lot of information and projects on microcontrollers. Every month, each magazine has a better than 90% chance of presenting at least one microcontroller application.

Circuit Cellar Ink
Subscriptions:
P.O. Box 698
Holmes, PA
19043-9613
1(800)269-6301
Web site: http://www.circellar.com/
BBS: (860)871-1988

GERNSBACK PUBLICATIONS

*Electr*onics Now
Popular Electronics
Subscriptions:
Subscription Department
P.O. Box 55115
Boulder, CO
1(800)999-7139
Web site: http://www.gernsback.com

Microcontroller Journal
Web site: http://www.mcjournal.com/
This is published on the Web.
Nuts & Volts
Subscriptions:
430 Princeland Court
Corona, CA 91719
1(800) 783-4624
Web site: http://www.nutsvolts.com

Everyday Practical Electronics
Subscriptions:
EPE Subscriptions Dept.

Allen House, East Borough
Wimborne, Dorset,
BH21 1PF
United Kingdom
144 (0)1202 881749
Web site: http://www.epemag.wimborne.co.uk

Web Sites and Suppliers of Interest

While very few of these are microcontroller specific, they are a good source of ideas, information, and products which will make working with the microcontrollers a bit easier and interesting.

HOWARD H. SAMS AND COMPANY INTERNET GUIDE TO THE ELECTRONICS INDUSTRY

Web site: http://pobox.com/~electronics/

Basic primer on the Internet as it relates to electronics as well as a directory to electronics-related URLs (PICs included).

SEATTLE ROBOTICS SOCIETY

Web site: http://www.hhhh.org/srs/

The Seattle Robotics Society has lots of information on interfacing digital devices to such "real world" devices as motors, sensors, and servos. They also do a lot of neat things.

ADOBE PDF VIEWERS

Web site: http://www.adobe.com

Adobe .pdf file format is used for Microchip, Parallax, and most other datasheets and application notes.

"PKZIP" and "PKUNZIP"

Web site: http://www.pkware.com

PKWare's "zip" file compression format is a "standard" for combining and compressing files for transfer.

HARDWARE FAQs

Web site: http:paranoia.com/~filipg/HTML/LINK/LINK_IN.html

A set of FAQs (frequently asked questions) about the PC and other hardware platforms that will be useful when interfacing a microcontroller to a host PC.

HTTP://WWW.INNOVATUS.COM

Innovatus has made available "PICBots," an interesting PICMicro simulator which allows programs to be written for virtual robots which will fight amongst themselves.

TOWER HOBBIES

Excellent source for servos and R/C parts useful in homebuilt robots.

Tower Hobbies
P.O. Box 9078
Champaign, IL 61826-9078
Toll-free ordering in the United States and Canada: 1(800)637-4989
Toll-free fax in the United States and Canada: 1(800)637-7303
Toll-free support in the United States and Canada: 1(800)637-6050
Phone: (217)398-3636
Fax: (217)356-6608
E-mail: orders@towerhobbies.com
http://www.towerhobbies.com/

MONDO-TRONICS ROBOTICS STORE

"The world's biggest collection of miniature robots and supplies." This is a great source for servos, tracked vehicles, and robot arms.

Order Desk
Mondo-tronics Inc.
524 San Anselmo Ave #107-13
San Anselmo, CA 94960
Toll-free in the United States and Canada: 1(800)374-5764
Fax: (415)455-9333
http://www.robotstore.com/

Consultants and Product Suppliers

Here are a number of companies which sell microcontroller products and provide consulting services. While I haven't broken up the products and services, I have tried to outline what each company's specialities are. Many of these companies are active on the listservers.

I think you'll be surprised at how widespread the companies are; the world really has become smaller.

AWC

AWC provides solderless breadboards specifically designed for Basic Stamp, PIC, and other microcontrollers. No more soldering or wire wrapping! Coming soon: hands-on microcontroller training and microcontroller programmers that interface with breadboards.

310 Ivy Glen Court
League City, TX 77573
(281)334-4341
Fax: (281)334-4341
E-Mail: stamps@al-williams.com
http://www.al-williams.com/awce.htm

BYTE CRAFT LIMITED

Byte Craft produces application code development products for 8-bit embedded systems. Byte Craft is noted for its excellence in design and product performance on diverse architectures and for providing innovative solutions to developers, manufacturers, and consultants. Byte Craft's products include assemblers, C compilers, and fuzzy logic preprocessors.

421 King Street North
Waterloo, Ontario, Canada
N2J 4E4
Phone: (519)888-6911
Fax: (519)746-6751
E-mail: info@bytecraft.com
http://www.bytecraft.com

BROUHAHA COMPUTER MERCENARY SERVICES

Embedded System Design Consulting. A few PIC project designs available free from their Web page.

142 North Milpitas Boulevard, Suite 379
Milpitas, CA 95035
Phone: (408)263-3894
http://www.brouhaha.com/~eric/pic/

CINEMATRONICS

Consultant specializing in the design and fabrication of electronic devices for the film/video and entertainment industry. Custom design of lighting controllers, motion control devices, and remote control electronics. Cinematronics also designs PIC-based electronic devices for consumer electronics.

344 Dupont St., Suite 304
Toronto, Ontario, Canada
M5R 1V9
Phone: (416)927-7679
Fax: (416)927-7679
E-mail: cinetron@passport.ca

DECADE ENGINEERING

(Contact: Mike Hardwick.) Decade Engineering offers low-cost video character overlay (genlock) boards, image processing boards, and consulting on small systems. PIC, AVR, and 8051 families are actively supported, using Assembly, Forth, BASIC, and C. Analog & digital hardware design, programming, PCB design, and prototype construction are performed in-house.

5504 ValView Dr. SE
Turner, OR 97392-9517
(503)743 3194
Fax: (503)743 2095
E-mail: decade@worldnet.att.net
http://www.decadenet.com

DONTRONICS

DIY PCB kits including Microchip Technology PIC based micro products, FED and MEL PIC Basic Compilers, FED PIC Basic interpreters, CCS C compilers, Square 1 Electronics EasyPIC'n Beginners Guide, Newfound PIC Programmers DonTronics DT.001 Programmers, *Nuts and Volts* magazine, Scott Edward's *PIC Sourcebook* and disk, SiStudio SimmStick, and Wirz Electronics SLI-LCD Interface and Emu PIC 18-Pin Emulator.

P.O. Box 595
Tullamarine 3043 Australia
Phone: 61319338-6286
Fax: 61319338-2935
E-mail: don@dontronics.com
http://www.dontronics.com

ENGENHARIA MESTRA DE SISTEMAS

Products: Phone line communicators, from alarm models in the market to custom designs. They also represent Linear Corporation for Brazil.

- STX—Alarm monitoring system (alarm panel and receiver for 10,000 panels).
- STI—Fire monitoring system (same as above).
- SSD—Communicator for Linear's DF-16 panel to receiver described above.
- ALARMPHONE—Alarm monitoring system (panel and receiver for 1,000,000 panels).
- LGP—Communicator system for delivery companies.

Services: General consultation in microprocessor-based devices. Custom designs using Atmel and BASIC Stamps. Operational specification and documentation (access control, etc.).

Rua Guaiauna, 439 - Penha
Sao Paulo - SP - Brazil 04531-020
55-11-218.5008
Fax: 55-11-217.6610
E-mail: pdrummond@ibm.net

FAST FORWARD ENGINEERING

Contract design of PIC-based products, specializing in RF systems, high-volume consumer electronics, automotive electronics, and remote telemetry and control. Software-only services are available, as well as start-to-finish handling of the entire design process. Consulting/training services are also available.

Certified by Microchip as one of their Microchip Technology Consultant Program Members. They support the PIC, Motorola 68HC05/HC08, and 8051/8031.

1984 Casablanca Court
Vista, CA 92083-5043
Phone: (760)598-0200
Fax: (760)598-2950
E-mail: fastfwd@ix.netcom.com
http://www.geocities.com/SiliconValley/2499

HTH

HTH distributes Parallax, Inc. products here in Scandinavia, among others. They will introduce a Power Line Modem suitable for electronic hobbyists and DIY-er's capable of sending and receiving serial data up to 2400 bps on the power line.

They also have a file library available for everyone that contains hundreds of code examples for the BASIC Stamp. (This is the "List of Stamp Applications" mentioned in Section 6.)

Asbogatan 29 C
Angelholm, Sweden S-262 51
+46 431-41 00 88
Fax: +46 431-41 00 88
E-mail: info@hth.com
http://www.hth.com

INNOVATUS

PICBots—a free simulation where you can program robots with different PIC programs and watch them battle to the death. They also provide contract development. For a proposal, e-mail your requirements to

proposals@innovatus.com
E-mail: ags@innovatus.com
http://www.innovatus.com

IAR SYSTEMS AB

Products: Integrated ANSI-C development tools (compilers, assemblers, debuggers, etc.): Embedded Workbench and C-SPY (Windows based) ANSI-C cross compilers

Publication: *PROgramming MICROS*
P.O. Box 23051
Uppsala, Sweden S-75023
+46 18 16 78 00
Fax: +46 18 16 78 38
E-mail: info@//www.iar.se

INTERFACE PRODUCTS (PTY) LTD.

Supplier of microcontroller development tools, custom electronic design and manufacturing, remote automation, monitoring and control across commodity networks, positioning support for GPS-assisted airborne remote sensing, stocklist of Garmin equipment, business-level Internet services for engineering professionals, distributor for DonTronics, Silicon Studio, and Wirz Electronics microcontroller products.

2nd Floor, Quinor Court, 81 Beit Street
New Doorfontein, Gauteng, South Africa
P.O. Box 15775, DOORNFONTEIN, 2028 South Africa
Phone: +27 (11) 402-7750
Fax: +27 (11) 402-7751
E-mail: info@ip.co.za
http://www.ip.co.za

KROEKER BUILT ELECTRONICS

They deal with programmers for Atmel microcontrollers. Currently, they have programmers for all of Atmels 8-bit micros as well as a production gang programmer for Atmel 20-pin micros. Their product line is continually expanding to include new types of micros. They also design custom programmers to suit the customer's needs.

1219 SW 26th #2
Corvallis, OR, 97333
(541)766-8722
E-mail: tech@kroekerbuilt.com
http://www.kroekerbuilt.com

DR. CLAUS KUEHNEL CONSULTING & DISTRIBUTION

Microcontroller and DSP applications, distribution of hw and sw, technical publications (for more, see Web site).

Schlyffistrasse 14
CH-8806 Baech / SZ Switzerland
+41-1-7850238
Fax: +41-1-7850275
E-mail: ckuehnel@access.ch
http://www.access.ch/ckuehnel

MANDENO GRANVILLE ELECTRONICS LTD.

Manufacturer of (distributors wanted):

- IceP2051—The only full ICE 1 programmer for the ATMEL 89C2051, 89C1051, and 89C4451 advanced, full, windowed debugger (DbgX51), and IDE, 24-MHz capable.
- Trice-52—Bondout ICE for 89C51 and 52.55
  24-MHz Capable, Universal C51 ICE, DbgX51
- Asm51—Macro assembler for x51 cores
- Mod51—Professional, structured text, type safe, optimizing compiler. For serious projects, where C error rates cannot be tolerated. Ideal for 89C1051 and up.
- OptoPGM—Optoisolated (safe) ISP cable for AVR, 89S, AT24x, and AT17X serial programable devices. Designed for FAST development/production operation.
- CAN tools: CANPort (PC Dongle) 1 Emul517C emulation platform, for Siemens 80C517A 1 81C90 CAN controller.

128 Grange Rd
Mt Eden, Auckland, New Zealand
03
+64 9 6300 558
Fax: + 64 9 6301 720
E-mail: DesignTools@xtra.co.nz

MONTANA DESIGN

Montana Design provides custom electronic hardware, firmware, and PC-based application support for a variety of industries, including cable television (CATV, SMATV), radio control hobby products, process monitoring and control, and communications (RF and hardwired).

Their products are in use worldwide, with volume manufacturing associates in Taiwan, China, and the Untied States. They design to meet the user's needs, whether they be to minimize development cost or to minimize manufacturing, and can provide full support services from concept to mass production.

Support for:
- Microchip PICmicro 12Cxx, 14000, 16Cxxx
- Intel 8051 (and TI, Atmel, etc. variants)
- Motorola 6805
- Zilog Z-80, Z-180 (and Hitachi variants)
- Western Design 65C02

409 S. Sixth Street
Phillipsburg, NJ 08865-1925
(908)454-4611
Fax: (908)454-7882
E-mail: montana@//www.users.fast.net/~montana/root.html
http://wwww.montanadesign.com

NELSON RESEARCH

Expert in Microchip PICMicro microprocessors and embedded systems design, design and coding of assembly language software for embedded systems, design of analog systems and subsystems, including low-level instrumentation, troubleshooting and failure analysis of systems and processes, creation and presentation of custom training courses and seminars.

In addition to the above, they support Intel 8051 family processors and Parallax products and are listed with Z-World as a consultant for their products.

130 School Street, P.O. Box 416
Webster, MA
01570-0416
Phone: (508)943-1075
Fax: (508)949-2914
E-mail: L.Nelson@ieee.org
http://www.ultranet.com/~NR

ORMIX LTD.

Low-cost development programmers COMPIC-1 and COMPIC-5X for Microchip MCUs and serial EEPROMs, connected to the serial port. COMPIC-1 works without an external power supply; COMPIC-5X has two ZIF sockets and excellent software flexibility. New devices can be added to the text configuration file by the end user. Very simple and friendly user interface, built-in HEX editor, serialization of parts possible. Low price.

Kr.Barona, 136
Riga, Latvia
LV-1012
Phone: (371)-7310660
Fax: (371)-2292823
E-mail: avlad@mail.ormix.riga.lv
http://www.ormix.riga.lv/eng/index.htm

PIPE-THOMPSON TECHNOLOGIES INC.

Pipe-Thompson is the Microchip Rep for the Toronto Area. Along with providing technical information to Microchip customers, Pipe-Thompson can provide technical guidance and support.

4 Robert Speck Pkwy
Suite 1170
Mississauga, Ontario, Canada
L4Z 1S1
Phone: (905)281-8281
Fax: (905)281-8550
E-mail: pipethom@idirect.com

PRACTICAL MICRO DESIGN, INC.

Practical Micro Design is an engineering services company specializing in systems utilizing microprocessors or digital control logic. The company was founded in April 1984. Their experience includes all phases of a project's life, from initial definition through design and prototyping, and on to full production utilizing subcontract assemblers. Their services include custom hardware and software development, circuit board layout, and mechanical packaging design. Sample listing of PIC-related projects: cable TV tuner, VCR controller and IR code translator, credit card reader, custom production in-circuit programmer for PIC 16C84/F84-based products. Sample listing of 8051-related projects: telephone line simulator with modem for credit card verification terminals, precision frequency generator, satellite communication radio control, industrial control (feeder system for plastic injection molding).

7432 Alban Station Blvd., A-105
Springfield, VA 22150-2321
Phone: (703)912-4991
Fax: (703)912-5849
E-mail: development@pmdinc.com
http://www.pmdinc.com

ROCHESTER MICROSYSTEMS, INC.

Rochester MicroSystems, Inc. provides electronic design services to research and industry. They develop specialty and custom products and instrumentation. They have applied PICMicro microcontrollers in many product areas, such as specialized test equipment for commercial imaging satellite development, instrumentation for medical research, computer input devices, consumer appliance control systems, equipment for military control systems research, and others. They have expertise in interfacing many sensor and circuit types to microcontrollers and standard bus interfaces, including high-speed analog and digital systems, TTL, ECL, CMOS, capacitive sensors, fiber optics, laser diodes, photodiodes and other optical sensors, programmable logic, DSP devices, and others.

200 Buell Road, Suite 9
Rochester, NY 14624
(716)328-5850
Fax: (716)328-1144
E-mail: rmi@//www.frontiernet.net/~rmi

RTN

RTN manufactures small stand-alone microcontroller modules using the BASIC Stamp and the 84/71 Microchip products. They also build custom boards for machine control applications, and they program Xilinx devices for high-speed data collection and easy interfacing, especially to the BASIC Stamp modules.

35 Woolart Street
Victoria, Australia 3041
(61)(3) 9338-3306
Fax: (61)(3)9338-3306
E-mail: nollet@mail.enternet.com.au
http://people.enternet.com.au/~nollet

SOLUTIONS CUBED

Solutions Cubed provides embedded systems design, specializing in Microchip Technology microcontrollers. In addition to full design services and capabilities, Solutions Cubed provides a product line of Mini Mods. These miniature engineering modules are ideal for the electronic hobbiest and can be easily interfaced to BASIC Stamps and their ilk.

3029 Esplanade #F
Chico, CA 95973
Phone: (916)891-8045
Fax: (916)891-1643
E-mail: solcubed@solutions-cubed.com
http://www.solutions-cubed.com

TELESYSTEMS

1. Production-quality programmer for MicroChip's product (PICMicro, Serial EEPROM, Parallel EEPROM, EPROM, Sequire Products). In the near future, support for Atmel's product (Serial EEPROM, MicroControllers). The programmer is connected to a PC via a printer port in transparent mode, allowing a printer to still be connected. Also supports the stand-alone mode of operation with a counter of programmed chips. The programmer supports flexible, user-selected, programming algorithms. Free program update available from their Web site.
2. Programming and developing of PICMicro-based projects upon request. They have much experience in this field, having developed more than 50 devices based on PICMicro, about 30 of them now in production.
3. They have published a book about applications of the PICMicro (Russian language). Now they are writing a book about modern microcontrollers (Russian language)—brief description, tools, applications.

P.O Box 232
Zelenograd
Moscow 103575
Russia
7-095-5310063

Fax: 7-095-5314840
E-mail: ts@aha.ru
http://www.ts.aha.ru

WIRZ ELECTRONICS

Wirz Electronics offers a wide range of products for microcontroller development and prototyping, including the SimmStick(TM) development system. In-circuit programmers, prototyping boards, books, compilers, and simulators are currently available for the Microchip PIC, 8051, and the Atmel AVR. Wirz is the US Distributor for Universal Microprocessor Program Simulator (UMPS) which supports all of the microcontrollers covered in this publication and many others.

Wirz carries several peripheral interface products such as DC and stepper motor controllers, relay and signal expansion boards, and the popular Serial LCD Interface (SLI). Just requiring one I/O line, SLI is a powerful debugging tool and display interface for the embedded microcontroller. Wirz specializes in offering the most competitive pricing by advertising and providing customer support via the Internet. Documentation and data sheets for the majority of their products are available on their Web page as well as many other resources.

P.O. Box 457
Littleton, MA 01460-0457 USA
Tel: 1-888-289-9479
E-mail: sales@wirz.com
http://wirz.com/

COMMON ASSEMBLER COMMANDS

In most assemblers, commands can be embedded in the source code to allow you to specify how the file is to be assembled or the results written to a listing file. This appendix will give you an idea of the commands that are available and how they are used.

As I go through each common command type, I want to point out that these commands may be syntactially different from the assembler you are currently using (although the function will probably be the same).

For example, the "list" command could be formatted as:

```
list              ;   "list" not in the First Column
   or

.list             ;   "dot" preceeding Command
   or

%list             ;   "%" used to indicate Assembler command.
```

Before using any commands, make sure you understand the syntax for the assembler you are using. This list should be used as a guide of what could be available (not all assemblers will have all these commands, or with some microcontroller architectures, the features specified are not appropriate).

list/nolist	The list/nolist instructions are used to enable/disable, respectively, the assmbler output to the listing file. I only use these commands when I have a block of information that is not critical to the operation of the application (i.e., defining registers) and takes up an unreasonable amount of space in the listing file.
title/subtitle	I always like to have a title at the top of each page so when I'm using a listing as a reference for another one, I don't have to go to the first page to see what each one is. A subtitle can be nice to identify subroutines/ interrupt handlers/variable definition areas/etc.
page	The "page" command is used to force a page break (new page) in the listing file. This command can be used to place complete routines on individual pages of the listing.
lines #	Sometimes, some printers are able to print more or less lines on a page than the assembler defaults to when creating the listing file. The "lines" command will allow you to change the maximum number of lines on each page. If you have to decrease the maximum number of lines on the page, then make sure that the first page (up to the first "page" command) which has the "lines" command is shorter than what the printer outputs because in many assemblers, the "lines" command is active on the page after the one with the "lines" command.
dseg/cseg	To define separate code/data areas in the control store of a microcontroller, the "dseg" and "cseg" commands are used. This command is usually only available in "Von Neumann" architectures.
org #	Code is placed starting at address "#".
db/dw	These commands are used to reserve space and optionally specify space for data in the control store. Using the "db" command is a very

common way to define tables in control store.

There is one thing to be aware of with this. If you've used this command in PC assembler in a data segment to define a variable with an initial value, you might accidentally try it with a microcontroller. The initialization will not work because there is nowhere to store the initial value (in the PC object file, it is stored in the portion of the file that will be loaded into the PC's RAM). If a variable is to be initialized, you will have to write to the memory explicitly at the start of the application.

equ/=	Constants are defined using the "equal" command. This is not to be confused with the "define" command. A label which has a matching "equate" constant will be replaced with the constant and nothing more.
define	Using this command will associate a string to a label. This is a very rudimentary form of macro processing. It is important to remember that a string replaces the label when "define" is used. For microcontrollers, I often use a defined string for identifying bits with a register (i.e., "Clock define porta, 3").

When working with Conditional Assembly Commands, the label that is "defined" does not have to have a string associated with it. In this case the conditional statement "ifdef operation" will return "true" if the label has been defined. |
undefine	The "undefine" command removes the defined label and replacement string from memory and if the defined label is encountered later in the code's assembly, an error will occur just as if the label was never defined in the first place.
device	Many assemblers are capable of handling more than one device in the same family (although the different devices probably have different memory capacities, registers and I/O options). The "device" command will specify to the assembler which device's characteristics are to be used when assembling the code.
error #	Stopping the program's assembly or outputting a message in the listing file is usually initiated by conditional assembly commands. Causing an error in the code usually is the result of some parameter in conditional code being incorrect. These commands usually stop assembly, output a string into the listing file (and, often, on the console), but can include

	warnings and messages which allow the assembly to continue.
expand/hide	These instructions are used to specify whether or not the code used for a macro is displayed in the listing file ("expanded") or is hidden.
$, *	This command is replaced by the current program counter during assembly. It is used within an assembler instruction. "$" and "*" are common symbols for this command.
high	Return the high byte of a 16-bit constant without making the programmer put in "(Constant AND 0x0FF00) >> 8".
low	Return the low byte of a 16-bit constant without making the programmer put in "Constant AND 0x0FF".

Conditional Assembly Commands

If you're new to assembly language programming or new to microcontroller assembly language programming, you might be surprised to see the occasional "if," "else," or "while" in the source code. These instructions will not be compiled and used in the application, instead they will be used by the assembler (and compiler if it can execute conditional commands) during the first pass read of the source code.

A pretty typical example of how conditional commands are used (in PIC assembly language) would be:

```
Dlay                            ;  Wait for Operation to Complete
 ifdef Debug                    ;  If in Debug Mode (Simulator)
  movlw         1               ;   Just Loop Once
 else                           ;  Else going to burn PIC
  movlw         250                ;    Put in the Full Delay
 endif
  movwf         Count
  decfsz        Count           ;  Delay Loop
   goto         $ - 1
  return                        ;  Return to caller
```

In this example if "Debug" has been defined (and, as pointed out above, it does not have to have a string associated with it) then the value of "1" will be moved into the "w" register. The purpose of this conditional statement is to keep a delay very short if the program is being debugged in a simulator and you are stepping through the code and don't want to single step through the "decfsz"/"goto" instructions 250 times.

The "ifdef" conditional command is used to test whether or not a label has been defined. Typically, there is also an "ifndef" command which is the complement (ie it's true if the label hasn't been defined).

When the "if" condition is true, the code following to either the "else" or "endif" (whichever is encountered first) is used as source. If it is not true then the code after the "if" is ignored to the "else" or "endif." If an "else" follows, then the code following the "else" is used as source.

In the example above, if "Debug" was not defined, then the code passed to the assembler will be:

```
Dlay                          ;   Wait for Operation to Complete
    movlw       250           ;    Put in the Full Delay
    movwf       Count
    decfsz      Count         ;   Delay Loop
    goto        $ - 1
    return                    ;   Return to caller
```

In many assemblers, the "while" conditional command is also allowed. In this case, everything within the "while" loop is repeated each time the "while" command is executed.

In the 8051, I told you that if any unused EPROM was left unprogrammed, somebody could figure out the encryption array values by reading out the EPROM contents. To prevent this, a non-repeating pattern should be put into the unused EPROM.

The following conditional code could be used:

```
ProgEnd EQU $              ;   Identify the End Address of the Code
 while ( $ < DEVEND )  ;   Repeat to the End Address of the Device   db  (
ProgEnd + (( $ - ProgEnd ) * 3 ) & 0FFh
 wend
```

If the code above was put at the end of an 8051's program, the remainder of control store memory, no matter how large or how small, would be filled with a pattern increasing by three for each byte and starting with the least significant byte of the address after the end of the program. A much more complex algorithm could be used, but this one will make it very difficult for a pirate to figure out what the contents of an 8051's encryption array are (without which, they will not be able to figure out what the contents of the EPROM are).

Macros

Macros are really the culmination of everything presented in this appendix up to now. The purpose of macros is to replace a label (and optional parameters) with a series of instructions, labels, and commands.

I could make a 16-bit addition macro for the AVR as:

```
Macro Add16      A, B        ;   A = A + B
    ld      R16, A           ;   Load "A"
    ld      R17, A+1
    ld      R18, B           ;   Load "B"
    ld      R19, B+1
    add     R16, R18         ;   A = A + B
    adc     R17, R19         ;   A+1 = A+1 + B+1 + (( A + B ) >> 8 )
    st      A, R16           ;   Store Result in "A"
    st      A+1, R17
EndMacro
```

This macro can be placed anywhere an addition of two 16-bit variables is required. It actually could be used as a pseudo-instruction to enhance the AVR's instruction set.

The parameters "A" and "B," like defines, copy in the string specified (and not a constant value). I should point out that the AVR macros do not use labels parameters, instead the parameters specified at the "Macro" definition line are ignored and the "@1" and "@2" strings are used for the first two Macro parameters, respectively.

One thing to be careful of in macros is labels. If a label is defined in the macro, you must determine whether or not the label is to be "local" to the macro. "Local" means that the label cannot be referenced by code outside of the macro.

Going back to the discussion above about conditional code, we had the PIC delay subroutine (which I've modified by adding a label to the start of the loop):

```
Dlay                            ;  Wait for Operation to Complete
  movlw          250            ;   Put in the Full Delay
  movwf          Count
  decfsz         Count          ;  Delay Loop
Dlay_Loop
   goto          Dlay_Loop
   return                       ;  Return to caller
```

Now, if I needed several of these subroutines with varying delay values, I could define the code as the macro:

```
Macro Dlay_Macro Delay          ;  Loop around "Delay" cycles
local Dlay_Loop
  movlw          Delay          ;   Put in the Full Delay
  movwf          Count
Dlay_Loop
  decfsz         Count          ;  Delay Loop
   goto          Dlay_Loop
   return                       ;  Return to caller
endm
```

To place the code inside of a subroutine, the code:

```
Dlay250                         ;  Dlay 250 Loops
  Dlay_Macro 250
```

could be used.

Look back at the macro and you'll see that I defined "Dlay_Loop as a "local" label. If I didn't do this, "Dlay_Loop" would be present in every invocation of "Dlay_Macro" and cause an error because of repeated labels.

Anytime you are using a macro, you should be asking yourself if the code should actually use a subroutine. This question should be asked because in many ways, macros replace subroutines, except that each time the code is invoked, more control store space is taken up. Times when macros should only be used include critically timed code that cannot afford the overhead of the call/return instructions, code that is repeated multiple times, or resource constraints (such as the stack constraints in "mykeRTOS") prevent the use of subroutines.

UMPS

In researching this book, I was lucky enough to discover a real treasure in the "UMPS" ("Universal Microprocessor Program Simulator") IDE. This program is able to handle the development for a startling number of different microcontrollers (basically everything presented in this book). Along with an editor and assembler, UMPS contains the ability to simulate devices with external hardware, which really sets UMPS apart from other tools and eliminates the need for stimulus files. This capability of connecting UMPS to virtual devices gives you a real "what if" capability in your application design. (Figure D.1.)

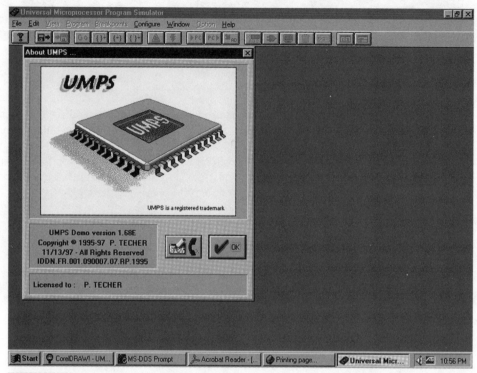

Figure D BS2-IC: The universal microprocessor program simulator Windows entry screen.

UMPS runs under Microsoft Windows (3.11, 95, and NT) PC operating systems. Along with its own internal assembler, UMPS can initiate·the operation of the Microchip PIC assembler ("MPASMWIN") as well as the Cosmic assembler and "C" compiler and use their symbolic output for the UMPS simulator.

The most powerful and useful feature of UMPS is its graphical "Resources" which can be "wired" to the device. At the time of writing, the following virtual hardware for the simulated microcontroller includes:

- LEDs
- Pushbuttons
- Logic functions (AND, OR, XOR, NOT)
- 7-segment LEDs
- Square wave generator
- Digital recorder/player
- D/A convertor
- A/D convertor
- A/D "slider"
- Serial receivers/transmitters
- I2C memory (RAM and EEPROM)
- I2C peripherals (LED displays, real-time clocks, etc.)
- HD44780 compatible LCDs
- Phase-locked loops

- PWM monitors
- PWM generators
- Pull-up resistors
- Serial A/D convertors
- 74LS138, 74LS139, 74LS373, 74LS374 TTL chip simulations
- CD4017 and CD4094 CMOS chip simulations

More simulations will be added as time goes on, but you should see that there really is a critical mass of different devices available which should make simulating many different applications possible. These simulated devices (which are known as "resources") are very full featured. I was able to simulate all of the 8051's first application as well as most of the second application (digital clock and thermometer) using UMPs just about exclusively and have it run with very few problems. When setting up the resources, you can move them around the resource window to arrange them as they make sense to you or how they will be laid out in the final application. You can also modify many of the I/O devices with different options (for example, the LCD display can be 1 or 2 rows and 8 to 20 columns or, along with the pull-up resistor, the I/O pins can be hard wired to Vcc or ground).

In the 8051 section, in the "Example Applications" chapter, I go through a simple tutorial on setting up UMPS with two LEDs and a button as well as monitoring specific registers. You may want to go back and look at this example application to see how UMPS works and get an idea of how it can help you with your application development.

UMPS currently supports the following devices (with more being added all the time):
- Microchip
  - PIC12C5xx
  - PIC16C5x
  - PIC16C84, PIC16F84, PIC16F83, PIC16C554, PIC16C556, PIC16C558
  - PIC16C671, PIC16C672
  - PIC16C71, PIC16C710, PIC16C711
- Motorola
  - 68HC705, 68HC705J1A, 68HC705P9, 68HC705B16, 68HC705B32 68HC11
- Intel
  - 8031, 8032
  - 8051
- Atmel
  - AT89C1051, AT89C2051
  - AT90C1200, AT90C8515
- Dallas Semiconductor
  - DS87C320
- SGS Thomson
  - ST6210, ST6215, ST6220, ST6225
  - ST6252, ST6253
  - ST6260, ST6262, ST6263, ST6265
- National Semiconductor
  - COP820C

This is actually quite a list, and by the time you've read this, the Atmel AVRs will be added to it as well.

The assembler and simulator available in UMPS are very fast (even when compared to the other devices available in this book). With the consistent interface, constant improvements, and additional microcontrollers and resources being added all the time, UMPS is an investment that you will use for a very long time.

The copy of "UMPS" on the CD-ROM included with this book is the latest demo version. This is a full version of UMPS that will run for three months after being installed, and the only restriction is that projects cannot be saved (which means that you will have to recreate your graphical simulator each time you use it).

Additional features include in this version of UMPs includes:

1. "Back trace" as you single step. You can go back up to 16 instructions to see what happened.
2. A register can be incremented or decremented by selecting it and using the "+" or " − " keys.
3. In the UMPS assembler source, a binary word can be written in the following formats:
   %010010110
   10010110B
   B'10010110'

To find out more about UMPS:

Virtual Micro Design
I.D.L.S
Technopole Izarbel
64210 Bidart
France
011-33(0)559.438.458
Fax: 011-33(0)559.438.401
E-mail: p.techer@idls.izarbel.tm.fr
http://idls.izarbel.tm.fr/entp/techer/index.htm

UMPS is available in North America from:Wirz Electronics
P.O.Box 457
Littleton, MA 01460-0457
E-mail: sales@wirz.com
http://www.wirz.com

SIMMSTICK

One of the most useful products to come along for developing fast microcontroller applications (either for hobbyists or industrial applications) is the SiStudio/Dontronics SimmStick cards and bus. This system of cards will provide you with a basis for electrically wiring a microcontroller into an application. When I used the SimmStick for my AVR video output application, I was able to solder the application onto a SimmStick, build a backplane, and wire a video modulator to the device in under an hour. (Figure E.1.)

Figure E-1 A variety of the SimmStick cards available.

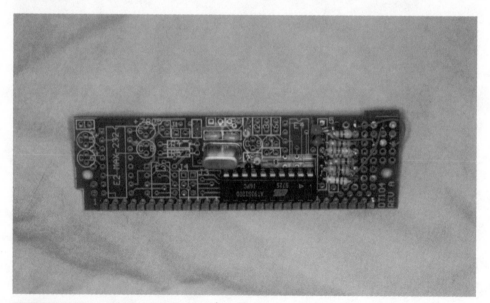

Figure E-2 SimmStick with AVR video generator circuit.

The SimmStick was originally built around the "PICStic" (by Micromint). This device, using a PIC16C84 could, functionally simulate a BASIC Stamp (using microEngineering Lab's PBASIC Compiler) or be used as an application unique to itself by deleting or adding components to the various boards. The original "PICStic" was just designed for the PIC16C84; the SimmSticks were originally designed to provide prototype cards for the full range of PICMicro products. Now, along with the PICMicros, the SimmSticks can also support the AVR as well. (Figure E.2.)

The SimmStick can be loaded into a standard 30-pin memory SIMM socket.
The SimmStick Bus consists of:

PIN	LABEL	DESCRIPTION/COMMENTS
1	A1/Tx	RS-232 Transmit Line from the SimmStick
2	A2/Rx	RS-232 Receive Line to the SimmStick
3	A3	Microcontroller General Purpose I/O
4	PWR	Unregulated Power In
5	CI	Line to Microcontroller's XTAL pins
6	CO	Line to Microcontroller's XTAL pins
7	+5V	Regulated +5 Volts
8	Reset	Microcontroller Negative Active Reset
9	Ground	System Ground
10	SCL	I2C Clock Line/Microcontroller General Purpose I/O
11	SDA	I2C Data Line/Microcontroller General Purpose I/O
12	SI	CMOS Logic Serial Line In/MCU General Purpose I/O
13	SO	CMOS Logic Serial Line Out/MCU General Purpose I/O
14	IO	Microcontroller General Purpose I/O and Timer In
15	D0	Microcontroller General Purpose I/O
16	D1	Microcontroller General Purpose I/O
17	D2	Microcontroller General Purpose I/O
18	D3	Microcontroller General Purpose I/O
19	D4	Microcontroller General Purpose I/O
20	D5	Microcontroller General Purpose I/O
21	D6	Microcontroller General Purpose I/O
22	D7	Microcontroller General Purpose I/O
23	D8	Microcontroller General Purpose I/O
24	D9	Microcontroller General Purpose I/O
25	D10	Microcontroller General Purpose I/O
26	D11	Microcontroller General Purpose I/O
27	D12	Microcontroller General Purpose I/O
28	D13	Microcontroller General Purpose I/O
29	D14	Microcontroller General Purpose I/O
30	D15	Microcontroller General Purpose I/O

I should discuss a few things about this bus, the first being the number of pins available for digital I/O. The 23 I/O pins were originally specified to provide I/O capabilities for a variety of microcontrollers. If the microcontroller that you are using does not have up to 23 I/O pins, then the extra pins can be used for other purposes (the AVR Video example places a voltage divider D/A convertor in the prototyping area to provide the composite video). For each microcontroller, you will have to understand how the I/O lines are wired to the SimmStick bus.

Serial data can be transmitted or received at TTL (CMOS) or RS-232 levels. The RS-232 interface uses a Maxim MAX-232 chip that has vias and connections built into the SimmStick card. These pins could also be used for digital signal I/O. The RS-232 communications feature should really be wired in such a way that the connector on a bus card or on a prototype card is used and the appropriate bus lines are used for transmitting the data.

Actually, this brings up a good point. I typically only use prototype cards for I/O with signals passed through the backplane. This method of wiring will allow the microcontroller to be reused for new applications while the prototype I/O card can be hacked to bits.

The SimmStick cards are capable of taking unregulated power, regulating it, and distributing it throughout the application. Personally, I don't like to do this; instead I use a SimmStick backplane (either the DT001 or DT003) for power (and RS-232 connections), eliminating the need to wire the backplane myself. (Figure E.3.)

The MCU's clock lines are also available on the bus. Either a crystal or ceramic resonator can be mounted on the SimmStick board with optional capacitors using the built-in

Figure E-3 SimmStick bus and power supply.

vias and traces. The XTAL lines can also be distributed using the bus (a clock is mounted on a single card and distributed to microcontroller SimmSticks on the bus).

I routinely cut the traces leading from the bus to the microcontroller on the SimmStick if I am using an onboard crystal. These traces will cause extra capacitances on the crystal lines and could cause application execution problems later. If the clock is to be distributed on the bus, I would recommend redriving the crystal signal on the SimmStick using a buffer redriving it on an unused pin or other devices on the bus.

Microcontroller reset is negative active only. On the DT104, if an Atmel 8051 20-pin microcontroller (which has the same pin out as the 20-pin AVR) is put on the card, a single transistor inverter can be wired in to provide the positive active reset the device requires.

The current range of SimmStick products includes bus and development platforms, microcontroller interface boards, and a number of add-on interface boards for the bus.

Backplanes and development Systems:	
Part Number	Features
DT001	PICMicro Programmer/SimmStick BackPlane
DT003	Backplane with integrated power and RS-232 Interface
Microcontroller Interface Boards:	
Part Number	Features
DT101	18 Pin PICMicro SimmStick board with full RS-232 and I2C/SPI EEPROM access and control
DT103	40 Pin AVR Atmel microcontroller SimmStick board with RS-232 access
DT104	20 Pin Atmel microcontroller SimmStick board with RS-232 access and I2C/SPI EEPROM access and control
Interface SimmStick Boards:	
Part Number	Features
DT203	24 LED, 4/8 Switch Interface Board
DT204	4 Slot Expansion Board for SimmStick Bus
DT205	4 Relay Control Card with 4 LED Outputs

Along with these boards, there are two prototype boards for the SimmStick bus. The DT001 is actually quite a complex board, as Figure E.4 shows.

Wtih the SimmStick, there is one advantage I wonder if you've noticed—the SimmStick product line, at the time of this writing, can support four of the microcontroller architectures presented in this book (the PICMicro, AVR, Atmel's 20-Pin 8051, and

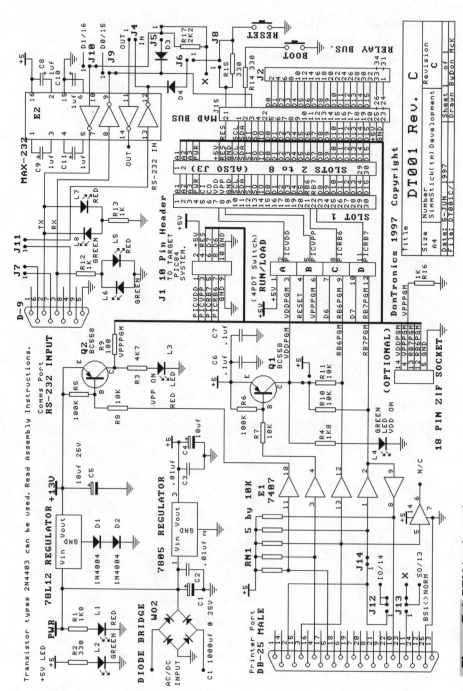

Figure E-4 DT001 schematic.

Parallax's BS1 design). This gives you an interesting amount of capabilities because the devices can be interchanged in a single application to evaluate the performance of the different devices. This is why I like to keep the I/O peripherals on a separate SimmStick card.

As I was proofreading this appendix, I found out that the information above is in error; the SimmStick can support five microcontroller architectures; the 18 pin Z8's can be put (backwards) into the 18-pin PICMicro platform!

What I have written here is really an introduction to the SimmStick. I highly recommend that you look at the DonTronics Website (http://www.dontronics.com) to see the options available for the SimmStick. Also go through the documentation to understand how the SimmStick can help you in your next application.

The SimmStick is available from:

DonTronics
P.O. Box 595
Tullamarine 3043, Australia
011 1(613)9338-6286
Fax: 011 1(613)9338-2935
E-mail: don@dontronics.com
http://www.dontronics.com

The SimmStick is available in North America from:

Wirz Electronics
P.O. Box 457
Littleton, MA 01460-0457
E-mail: sales@wirz.com
http://www.wirz.com

LISTSERVERS

In this book, I have given you a number of different Internet listservers to subscribe to. The purpose of the listserver is to provide an address that you can send a message to and have it relayed to other subscribers. This means that a large amount of mail can be sent and received in a short period of time (MIT's PIC Listserver typically processes 50 to 100 e-mails per day) to a large number of people (MIT's PIC Listserver has almost 1,500 subscribers as I write this).

Listservers are really wonderful things that make it possible to get answers to questions within literally minutes after posing them (although hours afterward is probably more typical). There are a great deal of very knowledgeable people who can answer questions on a variety of subjects (and have opinions on more than just the subject at hand).

Having a great deal of people available makes the list essentially a community. This is a worldwide community, and you have to try to be sensitive to different people's feelings and cultures. In thinking of this, I have created the following set of guidelines for listservers. The genesis of these guidelines came about after the PICList went through a period of time with problems with the same type of message coming through over and over.

I think these are pretty good guidelines for any listserver, and I suggest that you try to follow them as much as possible to avoid getting into embarrassing situations because you made a gaff.

1. Don't subscribe to a list and then immediately start sending questions to the list. Instead, wait a day or so to get the hang of how messages are sent and replied to on the list and get a "feel" for the best way of asking questions.

2. Some lists resend a note sent to it (while others do not). If you receive a copy of your first message, don't automatically think that it is a "bounce" (wrong address) and resend it. In this case, you might want to wait a day or so to see if any replies show up before trying to resend it. Once you've been on the list for a while, you should get an idea of how long it takes to show up on the list and how long it takes to get a reply.

3. If you don't get a reply to a request, don't get angry or frustrated and send off a reply demanding help. There's a good chance that nobody on the list knows exactly how to solve your problem. In this case, try to break down the problem and ask the question a different way.

4. I've talked about being able to get replies within minutes, but please don't feel that this is something you can count on. Nobody on any of the lists I've given in this book are paid to reply to your questions. The majority of people who reply are doing so to help others. Please respect that and don't badger, and help out in any way that you can.

5. If you are changing the "subject" line of a post, please reference the previous topic (i.e., put in "was: '...'"). This will help others keep track of the conversation.

6. When replying to a previous post, try to minimize how much of the previous note is copied in your note and maximize the relevance to your reply. This is not to say that none of the message should be copied or referenced. There is a very fine balance between having too much and too little. The sender of the note you are replying to should be referenced (with their name or ID). My rule of thumb is, if the original question is less than ten lines, I copy it all. If it is longer, then I cut it down (identifying what was cut out with a "SNIP" message), leaving just the question and any relevent information as quoted. Most mail programs will mark the quoted text with a ">" character. Please use this convention to make it easier for others to follow your reply.

7. If you have a program that doesn't work, please don't copy the entire source into a note and then post it to a list. As soon as I see a note like this, I just delete it and go on to the next one (and I suspect that I'm not the only one). Also, some lists may have a message size limit (anything above this limit is thrown out), and you will not receive any kind of confirmation. If you are going to post source code, keep it short. People on the list are more than happy and willing to answer specific questions, but simply copying the complete source code in the note and asking a question like "Why won't the LCD

display anything" really isn't useful for anybody. Instead, try to isolate the failing code and describe what is actually happening, along with what you want to happen. If you do this, chances are you will get a helpful answer quickly. Here's a good thing to remember when asking why something won't work: make sure you discuss the hardware that you are using. If you are asking about support hardware (i.e., a programmer or emulator), make sure you describe your PC (or workstation) setup. If your application isn't working as expected, describe the hardware that you are using and what you have observed (i.e., if the clock lines are wiggling, or the application works normally when you put a scope probe on a pin).

8. You may find a totally awesome and appropriate Web page and want to share it with the list. Please make it easier on the people in the list to cut and paste the URL by putting it on a line all by itself in the format:

   http://www.awesome-pic-page.com

9. If you have a new application, graphic, or whatever that takes up more than 1K you would like to share with everyone on the list, please don't send it as an attachment in a note to the list. Instead, either indicate you are have this amazing piece of work and tell people that you have it and where to request it (either to you directly or to a Web server address). If a large file is received, many listservers may automatically delete it (throw it into the "bit bucket"), and you may or may not get a message telling you what happened. If you don't have a Web page of your own or one you can access, requesting somebody to put it on their Web page or ftp server is cool.

10. Many of these listservers are made available, maintained, and/or moderated by the device's manufacturer. Keep this in mind if you are going to advertise your own product, and understand what the company's policy on this is before sending out an advertisement.

11. Putting job postings or employment requests may be appropriate for a list (like the previous point, check with the list's maintainer). However, I don't recommend that the rate of pay or conditions of employment be included in the note (unless you want to be characterized as cheap, greedy, unreasonable, or exploitive).

12. Spams are sent to every listserver occasionally. Please do not "reply" to the note even if the message says that to get off the spammer's mailing list just "reply." This will send a message to everyone in the list. If you must send a note detailing your disgust, send it to the spam orignator (although to their ISP will probably get better results). NOTE: There are a number of companies sending out bogus spams to collect the originating addresses of replying messages and sell them to other companies or distributors of addresses on CD-ROM. When receiving a spam, see if it has been sent to you personally or the list before replying, but be aware that if you are replying to the spam, you may be just sending your e-mail address for some company to resell to real spammers. I know it's frustrating and, like everyone else, I'm sure you would like to have all spammers eviscerated, but if you want to minimize how much you are bothered by spams in the future, you just have to ignore any spams that are sent to you.

13. Off-topic messages, while tolerated, will probably bring lots of abuse upon you. If you feel it is appropriate to send an off-topic message, some lists request that you put "[OT]" in the subject line. Some members of the list use mail filters, and this will allow them to ignore the off-topic posts automatically. Eventually a discussion (this usually happens with off-topic discussions) will get so strung out that there are only two people left arguing with each other. At this point, stop the discussion entirely or

go "private." You can obtain the other person's e-mail address from the header of the message. Send your message to him/her and not to the entire list. Everyone else on the list would have lost interest a long time ago and probably would like the discussion to just go away (so oblige them).

14. Posts referencing pirate sites and sources for "cracked" or "hacked" software is not appropriate in any case and may be illegal. If you are not sure if it is okay to post the latest software you've found on the 'Net, then DON'T until you have checked with the owners of the software and gotten their permission. It would also be a good idea to indicate in your post that you have the owner's permission to distribute cracked software. A variety of different microcontrollers are used in "smart cards" (such as used with cable and satellite scrambling) and asking how they work will probably result in abusive replies or having your questions ignored. If you have a legitimate reason for asking about smart cards, make sure you state it in your e-mail to the list.

15. When you first subscribe to a list, you will get a reply telling you how to unsubscribe from the list. DON'T LOSE THIS NOTE. In the past in some lists, people having trouble unsubscribing have sent questions to the list asking how and sometimes getting angry when their requests go unheeded. If you are trying to unsubscribe from a list and need help from others on the list, explain what you are trying to do and how you've tried to accomplish it.

16. If you're like me and just log on once or twice a day, read all the notes regarding a specific thread before replying. When replying to a question that has already been answered, look for what you can add to the discussion. Do not reiterate what's already been said.

17. Lastly, please try to be courteous to all on the list. Others may not have your knowledge and experience or they may be sensitive about different issues. There is a very high level of professionalism on all lists. Please help maintain it. Being insulting or rude will only get the same back and probably have your posts and legitimate questions ignored in the future by others on the list who don't want to have anything to do with you. To put this succinctly: "Don't be offensive or easily offended."

CD-ROM

CONTENTS AT A GLANCE

I am very pleased to be able to offer a CD-ROM with this book that includes the data sheets and development tools that I referenced for writing this book, along with the source files for the various applications presented in the book.

I have set up the CD-ROM with subdirectories for each device. In this appendix, I reference each device subdirectory with the subdirectories containing files below them.

To look at the datasheets (which end in ".pdf"), you will require an Adobe Reader (Version 3.0 or later) which can be downloaded at:

http://www.adobe.com

Many of the files have been "zipped" using PKWare's pkzip 2.04G. This tool (along with an "unzipper") is available at:

http://www.pkware.com

Please do not consider these files as the "ultimate" version. You may want to check with the manufacturer's Web sites to see if later versions of the data sheets and application programs are available.

"8051" Subdirectory

"DATASHT" SUBDIRECTORY

This subdirectory contains the data sheets for the devices presented in this book:

Doc0368.pdf - Atmel 20 Pin 2KByte Flash 8051
80C310.pdf - Dallas Semiconductor HSM Datasheets
80C320.pdf
80C520.pdf
5000PF.pdf - Dallas Semiconductor Secure Microcontroller Datasheets
5000.pdf

"DS87000" SUBDIRECTORY

The DS87000 runs from the MS-DOS command line.
DS87000.exe - DS87000 Programmer Software

"APPS" SUBDIRECTORY

51AP1.asm - First Application (Two Flashing LEDs)
51AP2.asm - Second Application (Digital Clock/Thermometer)
51AP2V2.asm
51AP2V3.asm
51AP2V4.asm
51AP3.ASM - Marya's Talking Keyboard Source Code
51AP3V2.ASM
51AP3V3.ASM

"68HC05" SUBDIRECTORY

"DATASHT" SUBDIRECTORY

05AGR3.pdf - 68HC05C8 Introduction and Datasheet
7J1AR2_1.pdf - 68HC705J1A Datasheet
P9A.pdf - 68HC05P9A Datasheet

"APPS" SUBDIRECTORY

AP1.asm - First Application (Two Flashing LEDs)
RTOS4.asm - Downlevel Version of "mykeRTOS"
MYKERTOS.asm - RTOS presented in this book
RTOSAP.asm - Digital Clock/Thermometer written for mykeRTOS
RTOSAPA.asm
RTOSAPB.asm
RTOSAPC.asm
RTOSAPD.asm
RTOSAPE.asm
RTOSAPF.asm

"RAPID" SUBDIRECTORY

RAPID runs from the MS-DOS command line.

RAPID.hlp - Help Files for Rapid, assembler and simulator
CASM5J1A.hlp
ICS05J1A.hlp
INST_DOC.exe - RAPID Installation help program
RAPID_DOC.exe - RAPID Documentation program
RAPID.exe - RAPID IDE
RINSTALL.exe - Installation program for RAPID
CASM5J1A.exe - 68HC705J1A Assembler
ICS05J1A.exe - 68HC705 Simulator/Programmer Software

"PICMicro" Subdirectory

"DATASHT" SUBDIRECTORY

40139A.pdf - PIC 12C5xx Datasheet
30015N.pdf - Low-End PICMicro Datasheet
30236C.pdf - Enhanced Low-End PICMicro Datasheet
40143A.pdf - Low-Function Mid-Range PICMicro Datasheet

30234D.pdf - PIC16C6x Datasheet
30390D.pdf - PIC16C7x (PICMicro with ADC) Datasheet
30445B.pdf - PIC16C84 Datasheet
30430B.pdf - PIC16F84 (PICMicro with Flash Control Store) Datasheet
30444D.pdf - PIC16C9xx (LCD Controller) Datasheet
30412C.pdf - High-End PICMicro Datasheet
30557B.pdf - 12C5xx Programming Specification
30190F.pdf - Low-End PICMicro Programming Specification
30228F.pdf - Mid-Range PICMicro Programming Specification
30262A.pdf - PIC16F84 Programming Specification
30139I.pdf - High-End PICMicro Programming Specification
30238A.pdf - Fuzzy Logic Handbook
51044A.pdf - KEELOQ HCS300 Evaluation Kit User's Guide

"MPLAB" SUBDIRECTORY

MPLAB runs under Windows 3.11, Windows/95, Windows/NT or Windows compatible emulators.

51025A.pdf - MPLAB User's Guide
33014E.pdf - MPASM Assembler User's Guide
51028A.pdf - PICStart Plus Development System User's Guide
MPL34000.zip - PKZipped version of MPLAB Version 3.40.09

"PICLite" Subdirectory

PICLITE.zip - PICLite Compiler Version 1.07a
THERMO5.pic - Digital Clock/Thermometer written in PICLite

"APPS" SUBDIRECTORY

PROG2.asm - First Application (Flashing LEDs)
2Thermo1.asm - Second Application (Digital Clock/Thermometer)
2Thermo2.asm
2Thermo3.asm
2Thermo4.asm
2Thermo5.asm

"AVR" Subdirectory

"DATASHT" SUBDIRECTORY

1200.pdf - AVR 1200 Datasheet
8515.pdf - AVR 8515 Datasheet
DOC0856.pdf - AVR Instruction Set

"APPS" SUBDIRECTORY

AP1.asm - Flashing LED Application
AP2.asm - Digital Clock/Thermometer Application
AP2V2.asm
AP2V3.asm
AP2V4.asm
AP2V4A.asm
AP2V5.asm
AP3.ASM - Composite Video ADC Test Code
AP3V2.ASM - Vertical Bar Composite Video Output
AP3V3.ASM - Potentiometer Control of "Paddle" on TV Screen

"AVRTOOLS" SUBDIRECTORY

The AVR software development tools run under Windows 3.11, Windows/95, Windows/NT or Windows compatible emulators.
AVR.exe - AVR Assembler and Simulator
ASTUDIO.exe - AVR Studio

"Stamp" Subdirectory

"MANUALS" SUBDIRECTORY

MANUAL.pdf - Version 1.8 of the BS1 and BS2 Manual with Example Applications.

"DEVTOOLS" SUBDIRECTORY

The BASIC Stamp development software runs from the MS-DOS command line.
STAMP.zip - Stamp Programming Development Tools

"APPS" SUBDIRECTORY

BASPGM1.bas - First Application Code (Flashing LEDs)
BASPGM2.bas
PWMTEST.BAS - "Fade" an LED
BS1STEST.bas - BASIC Stamp Serial Communications Example
BS2STEST.bs2

"BSEMU" SUBDIRECTORY

The BASIC Stamp 1 Emulator runs from the MS-DOS command line.
BSEMU.exe - BS1 Emulator Software
*.bas - Miscellaneous Test/Example PBASIC Programs for BSEMU

"UMPS" Subdirectory

UMPS runs under Windows 3.11, Windows/95, Windows/NT or Windows-compatible emulators.

INSTALL.exe - Run to Install UMPS
INSTMPS.$$$ - Data/Program Files
MPINST.000
MPINST.001
MPINST.002
MPINST.003

"Devices" Subdirectory

1820.pdf - DS1820 Digital Thermometer Datasheet
1307.pdf - DS1307 Real Time Clock Datasheet

GLOSSARY

If this book is your first experience with microcontrollers, I'm sure there are a lot of terms that are unfamiliar to you. I've tried to give a complete list of all the acronyms, terms, and expressions that may be unfamiliar to you. Acronyms are explained before they are described.

accumulator Register used as a temporary storage register for an operation's data source and destination.

active components Generally integrated circuits and transistors. Devices which require external power to operate.

ADC "Analog-to-Digital Converter." Hardware devoted to converting the value of a DC voltage into a digital representation. See "DAC."

address The location that a register, RAM byte, or instruction word is positioned at within its specific memory space.

Alt The "alternate" keys on your PC's keyboard. Usually located on either side of the "spacebar."

analog A quantity at a fractional value rather than a binary, one or zero. Analog voltages are the quantity most often measured.

ASCII "American Standard Character Interchange Interface." Bit-to-character representation standard most used in computer systems.

assembler A computer program that converts assembly language source to object code. See "cross assembler."

assembly language A set of word symbols used to represent the instructions of a processor. Along with a primary instruction, there are parameters that are used to specify values, registers, or addresses.

asynchronous serial Data sent serially to a receiver without clocking information. Instead, data synching information for the receiver is available inside the data packet or as part of each bit.

bare board See "raw card."

BCD Binary Code Decimal. Using four bits to represent a decimal number (zero to nine).

BGA Ball Grid Array. A Chip solder technology which provides connection from a chip to a bare board via a two dimensional grid of solder balls (typically 0.050" from center to center).

binary numbers Numbers represented as powers of two. Each digit is two raised to a specific power. For example, 37 decimal is $32 + 4 + 1 = 2 ** 4 + 2 ** 2 + 2 ** 0 = 00010101$ binary. Binary can be represented in the forms: 0b0nnnn, B'nnnn' or %nnnn where "nnnn" is a multidigit binary number comprised of 1s and 0s.

bipolar logic Logic circuits made from bipolar transistors (either discrete devices or integrated onto a chip).

bit mask A bit pattern that is ANDed with a value to turn off specific bits.

blues, the Good music to listen to while developing applications.

ceramic resonator A device used to provide timing signals to a microcontroller. More robust than a crystal but with poorer frequency accuracy.

character Series of bits used to represent an alphabetic, numeric, control, or other symbol or representation. See "ASCII."

chip package The method by which a chip is protected from the environment (usually either encased in ceramic or plastic) with wire interconnects to external circuitry (see "PTH" and "SMT").

CISC "Complex Instruction Set Computer." A type of computer architecture which uses a large number of very complete instructions rather than a few short instructions. See "RISC."

clock cycle The operation of a microcontroller's primary oscillator going from a low voltage to a high voltage and back again. This is normally referenced as the speed the device runs at. Multiple clock cycles may be used to make up one "instruction cycle."

CMOS logic Logic circuits made from "N-Channel" and "P-Channel" MOSFET ("Metal Oxide Silicon Field Effect Transistor") devices (either discrete devices or integrated onto a chip).

comparator A device used to compare two voltages and indicate through logic output if one is greater than the other.

compiler A program which takes a high-level language source file and converts it to either assembly language code or object code for a microcontroller.

control store See "program store."

constant Numeric value used as a parameter for an operation or instruction. This differs from a variable value which is stored in a "RAM" or register memory location.

cross assembler A program written to take assembly language code for one processor and convert it to object code while working on an unrelated processor and operating system. See "assembler."

crystal Device used for precisely timing the instructions of a microcontroller.

Ctrl The "control" keys on a PC keyboard. Usually located at the bottom left and right of the PC keyboard.

DAC "Digital to Analog Converter." Hardware designed to convert a digital representation of an analog DC voltage into that analog voltage. See "ADC."

decimal numbers Base 10 numbers used for constants. These values are normally converted into hex or binary numbers for the microcontroller.

digital A term used to describe a variety of logic families where values are either high ("1") or low ("0"). For most logic families, the voltage levels are either approximately 0 volts or approximately 5 volts with a switching level somewhere between 1.4 and 2.5 volts.

duty cycle In a pulse wave modulated digital signal, the "duty cycle" is the fraction of time the signal is high over the total time of the repeating signal.

edge triggered Logic that changes based on the change of a digital logic level. See "level sensitive."

EEPROM Electrically Eraseable Programmable Memory (a.k.a. "flash"). Nonvolatile memory that can be erased and reprogrammed electrically (i.e., it doesn't require the UV light of EPROM).

EPROM Eraseable Programmable Read Only Memory. Nonvolatile memory that can be electrically programmed and erased using ultraviolet light.

FIFO First In First Out. Memory that will retrieve data in the order in which it was stored.

flash A type of EEPROM. Memory that can be electrically erased in "blocks," instead of as individual memory locations. True "flash" is very unusual in microcontrollers, many manufacturers describe their devices as having "flash," when in actuality they use "EEPROM."

FR4 A type of fiberglass typically used for making "raw cards." Correctly identified as "G10FR4."

frequency The number of repetitions of a signal that can take place in a given period of time (typically one second). See "period" and "hertz."

FTP "File Transfer Protocol." A method of transferring files to/from the Internet.

fuzzy logic A branch of computer science in which decisions are made on partially "on" data rather than "on" or "off" data like digital logic uses. These decisions are often made for controlling physical and electronic systems. See "PID."

ground Common negative voltage to microcontroller/circuit. Also referred to as "Vss."

Harvard architecture Computer processor architecture which interfaces with two memory subsystems, one for instructions ("control store") memory and one for variable memory and I/O registers.

hertz A unit of measurement of frequency. One "hertz" (or "Hz") means that the incoming signal is oscillating once per second.

hex numbers A value from 0 to 15 that is represented using four bits or the numbers "0" through "9" and "A" through "F."

high-level language A set of English (or other human language) statements which have been formatted for use as instructions for a computer. Some popular high-level languages used for microcontrollers include "C," "BASIC," "Pascal" and "Forth."

hot plugging Connecting/disconnecting a circuit board or part into a powered connector. This is to be avoided to prevent damaging both the connector circuits as well as what's being plugged into it.

HTTP "HyperText Transfer Protocol." A method of providing the data in "Web pages" to your computer.

Hz Abbreviation for "hertz."

index register An 8- or 16-bit register that can have its contents used to point to a location in variable storage, control store, or the microcontroller's register space. See "stack pointer."

instruction cycle The minimum amount of time needed to execute a basic function in a microcontroller. One instruction cycle typically takes several clock cycles. See "clock cycles."

in-system programming The ability to program a microcontroller's control store while the device is in the final application's circuit without having to remove it.

IR light "Infrared light." Electromagnetic radiation at wavelengths longer than the human eye can see. Typically used for communication between devices (such as a remote control and TV).

I2C "Inter-InterComputer" communication. A synchronous serial network protocol allowing microcontrollers to communicate with peripheral devices and each other. Only common lines are required for the network.

kHz An abbreviation for measuring frequency in thousands of cycles per second.

label An identifier used within a program to denote the address location of a control store or register address. See "variable."

LCD "Liquid Crystal Display." A device used for outputting information from a microcontroller. Typically controlled by a Hitatchi 44780 controller, although some microcontrollers contain circuitry for interfacing to an LCD directly without an intermediate controller circuit.

LED "Light Emitting Diode." Diode (rectifier) device which will emit light of a specific frequency when current is passed through it. When used with microcontrollers, LEDs are usually wired with the "anode" (positive pin) connected to Vcc and the microcontroller I/O pin sinking current (using a series 200- to 270-ohm resistor) to allow the LED to turn on. In typical LEDs in hemispherical plastic packages, the flat side (which has the shorter lead) is the "cathode."

level sensitive Logic that changes based on the state of a digital logic signal. See "edge triggered."

LIFO Last In First Out. Type of memory in which the most recently stored data will be the first retrieved.

linker A software product which combines "object" files into a final program file that can be loaded into a microcontroller.

listserver An Internet device that takes mail sent to it and resends it to a number of E-mail addresses.

logic analyzer A tool that graphically shows the relationship of the waveforms of a number of different pins.

logic probe A simple device used to test a line for either being high, low, or transitioning.

macro A programming construct which replaces a string of characters (and parameters) into a previously specified block of code or information.

mask programmable ROM A method of programming a memory which takes place at final assembly of a microcontroller. When the aluminum traces of a chip are laid down, a special photographic mask is made to create wiring which will result in a specific program being read from a microcontroller's control store.

master In microcontroller and external device networking, a "master" is a device which initiates and optionally controls the transfer of data. See "multimaster" and "slave."

MCU Acronym/abbreviation for "microcontroller."

memory-mapped I/O A method of placing peripheral registers in the same memory space as RAM or variable registers.

MHz This is an abbreviation for measuring frequency in millions of cycles per second.

MIPS Millions of Instructions Per Second. This acronym should really be: "Misleading Indicator of Performance" and should not be a consideration when deciding which microcontroller to use for an application.

MPU Acronym/abbreviation for "microprocessor."

msec On thousandth of a second (0.001 seconds). See "nsec" and "usec."

multimaster A microcontroller networking philosophy which allows multiple "masters" on the network bus to initiate data transfers.

negative active logic A type of logic where the digital signal is said to be asserted if it is at a "low" ("0") value. See "positive active logic."

nesting Placing subroutine or interrupt execution within the execution of other subroutines or interrupts.

net A technical term for the connection of device pins in a circuit. Each "net" consists of all the connections of one circuit in an application.

net, the A colloquial term for the "Internet."

NiCad Abbreviation for "nickel-cadmium batteries." These batteries are rechargable, although typically provide 1.2 volts per cell output compared to 1.5 to 2.0 volts for standard "dry" or "alkaline" radio batteries.

NMOS logic Digital logic where only "N-Channel" MOSFET transistors are used.

nsec One billionth of a second (0.000000001 seconds). See "usec" and "msec."

object file After assembly or high-level language compilation, a file is produced with the hex values ("op codes") which make up a processor's instructions. An "object file" can either be loaded directly into a microcontroller, or multiple "object files" can be linked together to form an executable file that is loaded into a microcontroller's control store. See "linker."

octal numbers A method of representing numbers as the digits from "0" to "7." This method of representing numbers is not widely used, although some high-level languages, such as "C," have made it available to programmers.

offset The relative address from a specific point in memory.

one's complement The result of XORing a value with 0x0FF, which will invert each bit of a number. See "two's complement."

op codes The hex values which make up the processor instructions in an application.

oscillator A circuit used to provide a constant frequency repeating signal for a microcontroller. This circuit can consist of a crystal, ceramic resonator, or resistor-capacitor network for providing the delay between edge transitions. The term is also used for a device which can be wired to a microcontroller to provide clocking signals without having to provide a crystal, caps, and other components to the device.

oscilloscope An instrument which is used to observe the waveform of an electrical signal. The two primary types of oscilloscopes in use today are the "analog" oscilloscope, which "writes" the current signal onto the phosphers of a CRT. The other common type of oscilloscope is the "digital storage oscilloscope" and saves the analog values of an incoming signal in RAM for replaying on either a built-in CRT or a computer connected to the device.

OTP One Time Programamble. This term generally refers to a device with EPROM memory encased in a plastic package that does not allow the chip to be exposed to UV light. Note that EEPROM devices in a plastic package may also be described as "OTP" even though they can be electrically erased and reprogrammed.

parallel Passing data between devices with all the data bits being sent at the same time on multiple lines. This is typically much faster than sending data "serially."

parameter A user-specified value for a subroutine or macro. A "parameter" can be a numeric value, a string, or a pointer, depending on the application.

passive components Generally resistors, capacitors, inductors, and diodes. Components which do not require an external power source to operate.

PCA "Printed Circuit Assembly." A bare board with components (both active and passive) soldered onto it.

PCB "Printed Circuit Card." See "raw card."

.PDF files Files suitable for viewing with Adobe Postscript.

period The length of time that a repeating signal takes to go through one full cycle. The reciprocal of "frequency."

PIC Peripheral Interface Controller. Just in case you wondered.

PID "Parallel Integrating Differential." A classical method of controlling physical and electronic systems. See "fuzzy logic."

poll A programming technique in which a bit (or byte) is repeatedly checked until a specific value is found.

port Move an application from one device to another or across operating systems/environments.

positive active logic Logic which becomes active when a signal becomes high ("1"). See "negative active logic."

PPM Measurement of something in parts per million. An easy way of calculating the PPM of a value is to divide the value by the total number of samples or opportunities and multiplying by 1,000,000. 1% is equal to 10,000 PPM, 10% is equal to 100,000 PPM.

Princeton architecture Computer processor architecture which uses one memory subsystem for instructions ("control store") memory, variable memory, and I/O registers.

program counter A counter within a computer processor which keeps track of the current program execution location. This counter can be updated by the counter and have its contents saved/restored on a stack.

program store Or "program storage." Memory (usually nonvolatile) devoted to saving the application program for when the microcontroller is powered down. Also known as "control store."

PROM "Programmable Read Only Memory." Originally an array of "fuses" which were "blown" to load in a program. Now "PROM" can refer to EPROM memory in an "OTP" package.

PTH "Pin Through Hole." Technology in which the pins of a chip are inserted into holes drilled into a "FR4" printed circuit card before soldering.

pull up A resistor (typically 1K to 10K) which is wired between a microcontroller pin and Vcc. A switch pulling the signal at the microprocessor pin may be used to provide user input. See "pull down."

pull down A resistor (typically 100 to 500 ohms) which is wired between a microcontroller pin and ground. See "pull up."

PWB "Printed Wiring Board." See "raw card."

PWM "Pulse Width Modulation." A digital output technique where a single line is used to output analog information by varying the length of time a pulse is active on the line.

RAM "Random Access Memory." Memory which you can write to and read from. In microcontrollers, virtually all RAM is "static" RAM ("SRAM"), which means that data is stored within it as long as power is supplied to the circuit. "Dynamic" RAM ("DRAM") is very rarely used in microcontroller applications. "EEPROM" may be used for nonvolatile RAM storage.

raw card Fiberglass board with copper "traces" attached to it which allows components to be interconnected. Also known as "PCB," "PWA," and "bare board."

RC Resistor/capacitor network used to provide a specific delay for a built-in oscillator or reset circuit.

recursion A programming technique where a subroutine calls itself with modified parameters to carry out a task. This technique is not recommended for microcontrollers which may have a limited stack. An old joke about defining recursion in a glossary is: Recursion—See "recursion."

register A memory address devoted to saving a value (like "RAM") or providing a hardware interface for the processor.

relocatable Code written or compiled in such a way that it can be placed anywhere in the control store memory map after assembly and run without any problems.

resistor ladder A circuit which consists of a number of resistors which can be selected to provide varying voltage divider circuits and output differing analog voltages.

RISC "Reduced Instruction Set Computer." This is a philosophy in which the operation of a computer is sped up by reducing the operations performed by a processor to the absolute minimum for application execution and making all resources accessible by a consistent interface. The advantages of "RISC" include faster execution time and a smaller instruction set. See "CISC."

ROM "Read Only Memory." This type of memory is typically used for control store because it cannot be changed by a processor during the execution of an application.

"Mask programmable ROM" is specified by the chip manufacturer to build devices with specific software as part of the device and cannot be programmed "in the field."

rotate A method of moving bits within a single or multiple registers. No matter how many times a "rotate" operation or instruction is carried out, the data in the registers will not be lost. See "shift."

serial Passing multiple bits using a single serial line. See "parallel."

servo A device which converts an electrical signal into mechanical movement. Radio control modeler's servos are often interfaced to microcontrollers. In these devices, the position is specified by a 1- to 2-msec pulse every 20 msecs.

shift A method of moving bits within a single or multiple registers. After a "shift" operation, bits are lost. See "rotate."

slave In microcontroller networking, a device which does not initiate communications but does respond to the instructions of a "master."

SMT Surface Mount Technology (aka "SMD"). Technology in which the pins of a chip are soldered to the surface of a printed circuit card.

splat Asterisk ("*"). Easier to say and spell and is funnier than "asterisk."

stack "LIFO" Memory used to store program counter and other context register information.

stack pointer An index register available within a processor which is used for storing data and updating itself to allow the next operation to be carried out with the index pointing to a new location.

state analyzer A tool used to store and display state data on several lines. Rather than requiring a separate instrument, this is often an option available in many "logic analyzers."

state machine A programming technique which uses external conditions and "state variables" for determining how a program is to execute.

string Series of ASCII characters saved sequentially in memory. When ended with 0x000 to note the end of the string, known as an "ASCIIZ string."

synchronous serial Data transmitted serially along with a clocking signal which is used by the receiver to indicate when the incoming data is valid.

traces Electrical signal paths etched in copper in a printed circuit card.

two's complement A method for representing positive and negative numbers in a digital system. To convert a number to a two's complement negative, it is complemented (converted to "one's complement") and incremented.

usec One millionth of a second (0.000001 seconds). See "nsec" and "msec."

UART "Universal Asynchronous Receiver/Transmitter." Peripheral hardware inside a microcontroller used to asynchronously communicate with external devices. See "USART" and "asynchronous serial."

USART "Universal Synchronous/Asynchronous Receiver/Transmitter." Peripheral hardware inside a microcontroller used to synchronously (using a clock signal either produced by the microcontroller or provided externally) or asynchronously communicate with external devices. See "UART" and "synchronous serial."

UV light "Ultraviolet light." Light at shorter wavelengths than the human eye can see. UV Light sources are often used with windowed microcontrollers with EPROM control store for erasing the contents of the control store.

variable A "label" used in an application program which represents an address that contains the actual value to be used by the operation or instruction. "Variables" are normally located in RAM and can be read from or written to by a program.

Vcc Positive power voltage applied to a microcontroller/circuit. Generally 2.0V to 6.0V, depending on the application. Also known as "Vdd."

Vdd See "Vcc."

Vias Holes in a printed circuit card.

volatile RAM is considered to be "volatile" because when power is removed, the contents are lost. EPROM, EEPROM, and PROM are considered to be "nonvolatile" because the values stored in the memory are saved, even if power is removed.

Von Neumann See "Princeton architecture."

Vss See "ground."

watchdog timer Timer used to reset a microcontroller upon overflow. The purpose of the watchdog timer is to return the microcontroller to a known state if the program begins to run errantly (or "amok").

Web page Internet data locations used to provide information or products.

ZIF "Zero Insertion Force." "ZIF" sockets will allow the plugging/unplugging of devices without placing stress upon the device's pins.

.ZIP files Files combined and compressed into a single file using the "PKZIP" program by PKWARE, Inc.

INDEX

About the Author

Myke Predko is a new-product test engineer at Celestica in Toronto, Ontario, Canada, where he works with new electronic product designers. He has also served as a test engineer, product engineer, and manufacturing manager for some of the world's largest computer manufacturers. Mr. Predko has a number of patents pending regarding microcontroller architectures and peripherals. He is a graduate of the University of Waterloo in the field of electrical engineering.

DISK WARRANTY

This software is protected by both United States copyright law and international copyright treaty provision. You must treat this software just like a book, except that you may copy it into a computer in order to be used and you may make archival copies of the software for the sole purpose of backing up our software and protecting your investment from loss.

By saying "just like a book," McGraw-Hill means, for example, that this software may be used by any number of people and may be freely moved from one computer location to another, so long as there is no possibility of its being used at one location or on one computer while it also is being used at another. Just as a book cannot be read by two different people in two different places at the same time, neither can the software be used by two different people in two different places at the same time (unless, of course, McGraw-Hill's copyright is being violated).

LIMITED WARRANTY

McGraw-Hill takes great care to provide you with top-quality software, thoroughly checked to prevent virus infections. McGraw-Hill warrants the physical diskette(s) contained herein to be free of defects in materials and workmanship for a period of sixty days from the purchase date. If McGraw-Hill receives written notification within the warranty period of defects in materials or workmanship, and such notification is determined by McGraw-Hill to be correct, McGraw-Hill will replace the defective diskette(s). Send requests to:

McGraw-Hill, Inc.
Customer Services
P.O. Box 545
Blacklick, OH 43004-0545

The entire and exclusive liability and remedy for breach of this Limited Warranty shall be limited to replacement of defective diskette(s) and shall not include or extend to any claim for or right to cover any other damages, including but not limited to, loss of profit, data, or use of the software, or special, incidental, or consequential damages or other similar claims, even if McGraw-Hill has been specifically advised of the possibility of such damages. In no event will McGraw-Hill's liability for any damages to you or any other person ever exceed the lower of suggested list price or actual price paid for the license to use the software, regardless of any form of the claim.

McGRAW-HILL, INC. SPECIFICALLY DISCLAIMS ALL OTHER WARRANTIES, EXPRESS OR IMPLIED, INCLUDING, BUT NOT LIMITED TO, ANY IMPLIED WARRANTY OF MERCHANTABILITY OR FITNESS FOR A PARTICULAR PURPOSE.

Specifically, McGraw-Hill makes no representation or warranty that the software is fit for any particular purpose and any implied warranty of merchantability is limited to the sixty-day duration of the Limited Warranty covering the physical diskette(s) only (and not the software) and is otherwise expressly and specifically disclaimed.

This limited warranty gives you specific legal rights; you may have others which may vary from state to state. Some states do not allow the exclusion of incidental or consequential damages, or the limitation on how long an implied warranty lasts, so some of the above may not apply to you.